FRANK R. MIELE, MSEE

President, Pegasus Lectures Inc.

VOLUME II

ULTRASOUND PHYSICS & INSTRUMENTATION

4ᵀᴴ EDITION

2006

Miele Enterprises, LLC

The author and publisher of this book have used their best efforts in preparing this book. Their efforts include the development, research, and testing of the theories and problems to determine their effectiveness. The author and publisher shall not be liable in any event for incidental or consequential damages in connection with, or arise out of, the furnishing, performance or use of these programs.

A Cataloging In Publication Record is available from the Library of Congress

Printed in the United States of America

Last Digit is the print number: 9   8   7   6   5   4   3   2

ISBN: 978-1-933250-06-9 Volume 1
               978-1-933250-07-6 Volume 2
               978-1-933250-08-3 Set of Volume 1 and 2

Copyright 2006 by Miele Enterprises, LLC

P.O. Box 157
Forney, TX 75126
www.pegasuslectures.com

TABLE OF CONTENTS

VOLUME 1

CHAPTER 1 - Mathematics

Table of Contents

Table of Contents

CHAPTER 3 - Attenuation

CHAPTER 4 - Pulsed Wave Operation

CHAPTER 5 - Transducers

Table of Contents

Pegasus Lectures, Inc.

Table of Contents

Table of Contents

VOLUME 2

CHAPTER 7 - Doppler

Table of Contents

CHAPTER 9 - Bioeffects

Table of Contents

Table of Contents

APPENDIX B: Cardiovascular Principles

CHAPTER 7

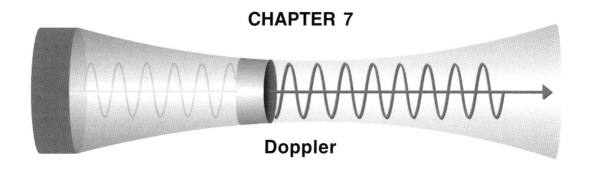

Doppler

Introduction

One of the principal requirements of diagnostic ultrasound is to measure the velocity and characteristics of blood flow. Doppler is actually a broad category which includes spectral Doppler, waveform Doppler, audio Doppler, and color flow imaging. It is important to realize that everything you have learned about waves, sound, transducers, etc., holds true for Doppler, with the addition of a new effect - a shift in frequency called the Doppler effect. The Doppler effect has been used for many years as the mechanism by which blood flow is detected, measured, and monitored non-invasively within the body.

Doppler is one of the most powerful techniques used in ultrasound, but also the tool most under-utilized and misinterpreted. A Doppler spectrum contains a wealth of information for the person who has learned the theory of Doppler, the practical application, and the relationship to the hemodynamic situations being assessed. This chapter focuses on the fundamentals of Doppler. By itself, the fundamentals of Doppler are less than half of the whole story. To fully appreciate the significance of Doppler and Doppler measurements, you must review the principles of fluid dynamics and hemodynamics. In essence, you should consider this chapter as part of a trilogy which concludes with Chapters 12 and 13.

Level 1 will discuss general Doppler theory, fundamental principles, and basics. Level 2 presumes the theory of Level 1 to develop an understanding of the Doppler system controls, functionality, limitations, and trade-offs. We will begin Level 1 by discussing the basic theory behind the Doppler effect.

1. The Doppler Effect

1.1 Change in Frequency

The Doppler effect is an apparent shift in frequency of an interrogating wave caused by relative motion between an observer and an object. This apparent frequency shift is actually the result of changes which occur to the wavelength because of the relative motion. In other words, if a wave (with a given wavelength) reflects from an object which is moving, the wavelength of the reflected wave will be different than the original wavelength. Specifically, if the object is moving toward the observer (wave source) then the wavelength will be shorter than the original wavelength; whereas, if the object is moving away from the observer, then the reflected wave will have a longer wavelength. Since a shorter wavelength represents a higher frequency, motion toward the observer produces a higher frequency than the original wave. Conversely, motion away from the observer produces a lower frequency than the frequency of the transmitted wave.

1.2 The Doppler Thought Experiment

To understand the Doppler effect we will use the classic example of a moving train blowing its whistle and two observers.

Scenario 1: **Stationary Train**

Let's begin by considering a stationary train blowing its whistle. There are two observers, observer A and observer B, on either side of the train. As the whistle blows, it produces a series of compressions and rarefactions at uniform time increments. The time increment between each compression (the period) is determined by the frequency of the whistle. Over time, the waves propagate radially away from the stationary train. For the figure below, the rings surrounding the train represent the propagating mechanical sound waves over time. The solid circles represent the peak wave compressions, and the light regions in between represent rarefactions. Also recall that the distance between these compressions is called the wavelength.

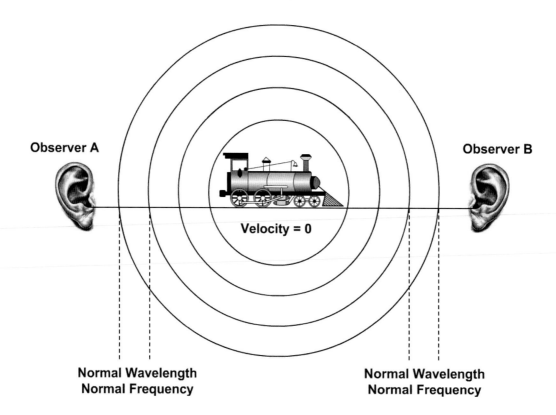

Fig. 1 **No Doppler Shift**

Eventually, the radiating wave reaches both observers. Since the wavelengths of the wave that reaches each observer is identical, both observers will hear the same pitch (frequency) whistle.

View Animation and Image Library CD

Pegasus Lectures, Inc.

Scenario 2: **Moving Train**

Now let's modify the situation such that the train is now traveling at a velocity (v) directly toward observer B, and directly away from observer A. Again we must imagine time and motion from our still drawing. When the train reaches the same location as in the scenario with the stationary train, it blows the same whistle. Again the whistle produces a series of compressions and rarefactions separated uniformly in time. However, between the time of emitting the first compression and the second compression, the train has moved some distance toward observer B. This movement results in the wavefronts in front of the train being closer than if the train had been stationary. Similarly, the wavefronts will be separated by a greater distance behind the train than if the train had been stationary.

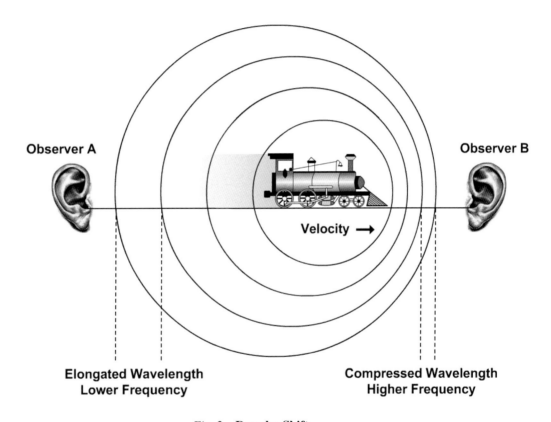

Observer A

Observer B

Velocity →

**Elongated Wavelength
Lower Frequency**

**Compressed Wavelength
Higher Frequency**

Fig. 2 **Doppler Shift**

Effectively, the wavelength was compressed toward observer B, and decompressed (elongated) relative to observer A. Since a shorter wavelength represents a higher frequency, observer B hears a higher pitch whistle than when the train was stationary. Conversely, since a longer wavelength implies a lower frequency, observer A hears a lower pitch whistle than when the train was stationary. This change in frequency for both observers is the Doppler effect.

View Animation and Image Library CD

Scenario 3: **Faster Train**

Now let's modify the situation by increasing the train's velocity. As in *Scenario 2*, when the train reaches the same location midway between the two observers, the train blows its whistle. In the time between compressions, the train is moving. Since the velocity of the train is higher than in *Scenario 2*, the distance traveled during the period will increase. The compression of the wavefront toward observer B will be greater than in *Scenario 2*. Similarly, the elongation (decompression) of the wavefront toward observer A will also be greater than in *Scenario 2*.

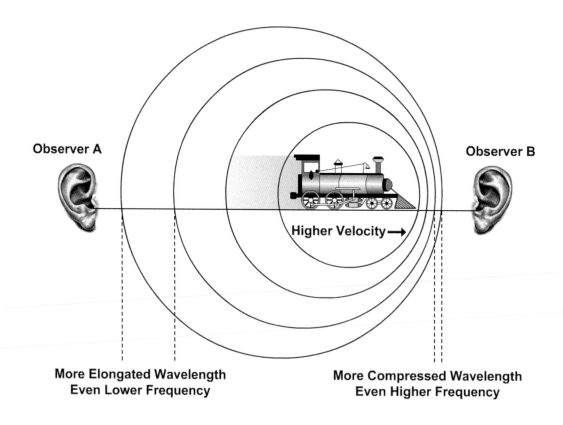

Observer A

Higher Velocity →

Observer B

More Elongated Wavelength
Even Lower Frequency

More Compressed Wavelength
Even Higher Frequency

Fig. 3   **Greater Doppler Shift**

Observer B hears an even higher pitched whistle, and observer A hears an even lower pitch whistle than in *Scenario 2*.

View Animation and Image Library CD

1.3 The Relationship Between Velocity (v) and the Doppler Shift

In essence, the train's motion as a percentage of the wavelength is greater when the train moves with a higher velocity than when it moves with a slower velocity. The result is a greater compression of the wavelength toward the observer and a greater decompression of the wavelength away from the observer. The greater the compression, the greater the apparent change in frequency, or equivalently, the greater the Doppler shift. Mathematically, we can write the relationship between the train's velocity (v) and the Doppler frequency shift f_{Dop} as:

$$f_{Dop} \propto v$$

1.4 Wavelength (λ) and the Doppler Effect

In our description of the Doppler effect, you should have noticed that the change in frequency resulted from a change in the wavelength caused by relative motion. Therefore, it should not be surprising that whatever parameters affect the wavelength, will also affect the Doppler shift. In Chapter 3 we derived the wavelength equation, which dictates the parameters which determine the wavelength, and hence, affect the Doppler shift. If you don't recall this equation, this might be a good time to review Chapter 3.

1.5 Relative Motion

In Chapter 1, a considerable effort was made to make clear the distinction between absolute and relative. In our definition of the Doppler effect, the fact that the motion is described as "relative" is no accident. One of Einstein's famous theorems was about the inability to determine absolute motion. Without a reference frame, it is not possible to determine whether the observer is moving or the train is moving.

Imagine if we changed our *Scenario 2* such that the train was stationary and the observers were moving instead. Observer B moves toward the train with velocity v and observer A moves away from the train with the same velocity v. For observer B, the distance between wavefronts will be compressed because of the decreasing distance between the train and the observer. Conversely, the wavefronts will be elongated for observer A because of the increasing distance between the train and the observer. Therefore, the exact same effect occurs as when the train was moving instead of the observers.

When the distance between the source and the observer is increasing, the relative motion is "away" and a decompression occurs. When the distance between the source and the observer is decreasing, the relative motion is "towards" and a compression occurs. Compression leads to a higher frequency, and hence, a positive frequency shift whereas decompression leads to a lower frequency and a negative frequency shift.

1.6 The Relative Shift

If there is one area that catches people, it is making the distinction between the word shift and the word frequency. The problem yet again comes down to paying attention to the difference between a relative term versus an absolute term. The term "shift" implies a relative relationship. A shift can be positive or negative. Like the word change, a greater shift does not tell direction, only amount. A faster velocity will result in a greater frequency shift. Note that there is no way of knowing whether the shift was positive or negative unless we know about the relative motion. If the relative motion is towards, then a greater shift implies an increasing higher frequency. If the relative motion is away then a greater shift implies an increasing lower frequency.

1.7 Determining the Relative Doppler Shift Numerically

The Doppler shift is the relative difference between the detected frequency and the transmitted frequency. Mathematically, this is expressed as:

$$f_{Dop} = f_{detected} - f_{transmitted} = \Delta f$$

Let's add some numbers to our previous train example to illustrate the relative nature of the Doppler effect. Imagine that the train's whistle was transmitted with a frequency of 2 MHz. Our observers will now have to be ultrasound listening devices since 2 MHz is well above human hearing.

In *Scenario 1*, the absolute frequency detected by both ultrasound observers is 2 MHz. The shift is the difference between the transmitted and received detected frequencies. In this case, the Doppler shift for both observer A and observer B is zero and there is no Doppler effect.

$$f_{Dop} = f_{detected} - f_{transmitted} = 2 \text{ MHz} - 2 \text{ MHz} = 0$$

In *Scenario 2*, suppose ultrasound observer A detected an absolute frequency of 1.98 MHz while observer B detected an absolute frequency of 2.02 MHz.

The Doppler shift for observer A is:

$$f_{Dop} = f_{detected} - f_{transmitted} = 1.98 \text{ MHz} - 2 \text{ MHz} = -0.02 \text{ MHz} = -20 \text{ kHz}.$$

The Doppler shift for observer B is:

$$f_{Dop} = f_{detected} - f_{transmitted} = 2.02 \text{ MHz} - 2 \text{ MHz} = +0.02 \text{ MHz} = +20 \text{ kHz}.$$

Note that both observer A and observer B detected the same frequency shift of 20 kHz. The difference is that observer A detected a negative frequency shift whereas observer B detected a positive frequency shift.

1.8 Exercises   Answers: Pg. 959

So far we have learned that the Doppler shift is proportional to the relative velocity. Let us now consider a few scenarios to test our understanding.

1. Police radar employs the Doppler effect to determine a car's velocity. Which of the following scenarios would have the greatest frequency shift?

    a) A stationary police car with a radar gun pointed at a car moving 60 mph directly toward the police car.
    b) A police car with a radar gun moving 60 mph directly toward a stationery car.
    c) A police car moving east at 30 mph with radar gun pointing at a car moving west at 30 mph.

2.	Which of the following scenarios would have the greatest frequency shift?

a) A stationary police car with a radar gun pointed at a car moving 60 mph directly toward the police car.
b) A stationary police car with a radar gun pointed at a car moving 60 mph directly away from the police car.
c) A police car moving east at 30 mph with a radar gun pointing at a car moving east at 30 mph

3.	Which of the following scenarios would have the greatest positive frequency shift?

a) A stationary police car with a radar gun pointed at a car moving 60 mph directly toward the police car.
b) A stationary police car with a radar gun pointed at a car moving 60 mph directly away from the police car.
c) A police car moving east at 30 mph with radar gun pointing at a car moving west at 30 mph.

4.	Which of the following scenarios would have the greatest negative frequency shift?

a) A stationary police car with a radar gun pointed at a car moving 60 mph directly toward the police car.
b) A stationary police car with a radar gun pointed at a car moving 60 mph directly away from the police car.
c) A police car moving east at 30 mph with radar gun pointing at the back of a car moving east at 95 mph.

5.	If the velocity of a train doubles, the frequency shift _____.

a) halves
b) doubles
c) cannot be determined since direction is not known

6.	If the velocity of a train doubles, the positive frequency shift _____.

a) halves
b) doubles
c) cannot be determined since direction is not known

7.	Which represents a greater Doppler shift, +2 kHz or –3 kHz?

a) +2 kHz
b) –3 kHz
c) Cannot be determined

8.	If the transmit frequency is 4 MHz and the detected signal is 3.998 MHz which of the following statements is NOT true?

a) The object could be moving toward the observer.
b) The shift is 2 kHz.
c) The shift is –2 kHz.

2. Relationships in the Doppler Equation

2.1 Velocity (v) and Wavelength (λ)

From the experiments we have conducted, we have learned that the Doppler effect is principally caused by a change in wavelength caused by motion relative to an observer. As the relative motion increases, the Doppler effect also increases. This proportional relationship makes sense since a higher velocity implies a greater distance traveled. Since the effect is caused by the relative distance change as a percentage of the wavelength, anything which results in a greater relative distance will result in a greater percentage change.

To illustrate this point, imagine that the wavelength is 10 meters. Now consider what happens if a train moves two meters instead of one meter during the period. One meter is 10% of the wavelength whereas two meters is 20% of the wavelength. Clearly, the greater distance results in a greater change. Since the distance traveled is related to the velocity, we again arrive at the relationship discovered earlier that the Doppler shift is proportional to the velocity, or: $f_{Dop} \propto v$.

2.2 Wavelength (λ) and the Transmit Frequency (Operating Frequency f_0)

The wavelength equation dictates that there is an inverse relationship between the wavelength and the operating frequency:

$$\lambda = \frac{c}{f}.$$

Since the Doppler effect is affected by the wavelength, and since the wavelength is affected by the operating frequency, we know (by the transitive property) that the Doppler effect must be affected by the operating frequency. Now all we need to do is to determine the mathematical relationship between the Doppler shift and the operating frequency.

Consider what happens to the wavelength if the operating frequency increases. Since there is an inverse relationship, as the operating frequency increases, the wavelength decreases. Now recall that the Doppler effect is caused by the percent relative change in the wavelength caused by the train's motion. Therefore, as the wavelength decreases, the Doppler effect increases. As we did in Section 2.1, we will use a numerical example to make this point clear (See *Figure 4*).

For a given operating frequency, imagine that the wavelength is 10 meters. Now further imagine that the train moves one meter during a period of time, equivalent to 10% of the wavelength. Now presume that the operating frequency is doubled. Since there is an inverse proportionality between the operating frequency and the wavelength, if the operating frequency doubles, the wavelength is reduced by a factor of 2.

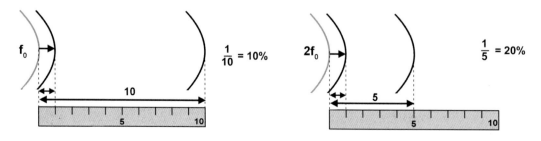

Fig. 4   **Effect of Frequency on the Doppler Effect**

Therefore, at the higher operating frequency the wavelength is reduced from 10 meters to 5 meters. The train's velocity is independent of the frequency of its whistle, therefore the train still moves 1 meter during the same period of time. One meter relative to a 5 meters wavelength now represents 20%, or a doubling in the Doppler effect relative to the lower operating frequency. Therefore, as the operating frequency increases, the Doppler shift increases. Mathematically, this is written as:

$$f_{\text{Dop}} \propto f_0$$

2.3 Wavelength (λ) and the Propagation Velocity (c)

The wavelength equation also dictates that there is a direct relationship between the wavelength and the propagation velocity:

$$\lambda = \frac{c}{f}.$$

Again since the Doppler effect is affected by the wavelength, and since the wavelength is affected by the propagation velocity, we know (by the transitive property) that the Doppler effect must be affected by the propagation velocity. Now we need to determine the mathematical relationship between the Doppler shift and the propagation velocity.

Consider what happens to the wavelength if the propagation velocity increases. Since there is a direct relationship, as the propagation velocity increases, the wavelength increases. Now recall that the Doppler effect is caused by the percent relative change in the wavelength caused by the train's motion. Therefore, as the wavelength increases, the Doppler effect decreases. As we just did with illustrating the effect of the operating frequency, we will use a numerical example to make this point clear.

For a given propagation velocity, imagine that the wavelength is 5 meters. Now further imagine that the train moves 1 meter during a period of time, equivalent to 20% of the wavelength. Now presume that the propagation velocity is doubled. Since there is a direct proportionality between the propagation velocity and the wavelength, if the propagation velocity doubles, the wavelength is doubled.

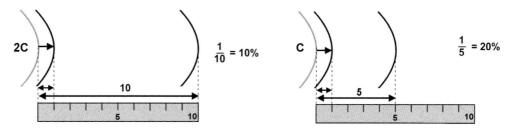

Fig. 5   **Effect of Propagation Velocity on the Doppler Effect**

Therefore, at the higher propagation velocity, the wavelength is increased from 5 meters to 10 meters. The train's velocity is independent of the propagation velocity of the whistle, therefore the train still moves 1 meter during the same period of time. One meter relative to a 10 meters wavelength now represents only 10%, or half of the Doppler effect that occurred with a lower propagation velocity.

Therefore, as the propagation velocity increases, the Doppler shift decreases. Mathematically, this is written as:

$$f_{\text{Dop}} \propto \frac{1}{c}$$

2.4 Roundtrip Effect

In each of our thought experiments so far, the Doppler effect was measured by the observer. However, in ultrasound, the measurement is not made by the observer but rather by measuring the reflected frequency back to the transducer. In other words, there is a roundtrip effect that must be considered. In essence, as the wave travels to the moving structure, there is an associated shift. The structure then acts as the source of the reflected wave. Recall that movement by the source or by the observer both cause a frequency shift. Therefore, since the structure is moving as it reflects the wave back to the transducer, there is a doubling effect. As a result, we should expect to see a factor of two in the mathematical expression which determines the Doppler shift (the Doppler equation).

3. A Simplified Doppler Equation

3.1 Equation with No Angle Effects

As we saw in the various scenarios, the Doppler shift can be positive or negative depending on the direction of motion relative to the observer. In the examples we have analyzed, the relative motion was either directly toward or directly away from an observer. For now, we will deal only with this simplified case. In Level 2 we will add the next level of complexity which expresses mathematically what happens when the motion is neither directly towards nor directly away from the source (transducer for ultrasound).

Cognizant of this simplification, if we combine all of the relations we have just discussed into one equation, we arrive at a simplified form of the Doppler equation:

$$f_{Dop} = \frac{2 f_0 v}{c}$$

where:

f_{Dop} = Doppler shifted frequency

f_0 = transmit frequency

v = velocity of target through medium

c = speed of interrogating beam through medium (c = 1540 m/sec for sound in tissue)

Notice that the absolute equation expresses all of the following relationships.

$$f_{Dop} \propto v$$

$$f_{Dop} \propto f_0$$

$$f_{Dop} \propto \frac{1}{c}$$

Notice that the factor of 2 which accounts for the round trip effect is not demonstrated in the relationships. Recall from Chapter 1 that relationships exist between variables. The number 2 is a constant, and hence, cannot change in response to changes with other variables.

3.2 Simplified Numeric Form

In many textbooks you may see a further simplified form in which an assumption is made for the propagation velocity, and the assumed value plugged into the equation. Assuming a propagation velocity of 1540 m/sec, the equation can be rewritten as:

$$f_{Dop} = \frac{2f_0\ v}{c} = \frac{2f_0\ v}{1540\ \frac{m}{sec}} = \frac{f_0\ v}{770\ \frac{m}{sec}}.$$

Note: I am not a big proponent of learning the Doppler equation in this simplified numeric form, since it usually leads to pure memorization instead of intuitive understanding of the equation and its application. I believe that seeing the variable for propagation velocity in the equation is a reminder that the Doppler effect is wavelength related and that the wavelength is determined by both the operating frequency and the propagation velocity. This form is included here so that no confusion develops should you see the equation written in this form in any other literature. You should realize that this equation still presumes that the direction of motion is either directly toward or directly away relative to the observer, and therefore does not take into account angle effects.

3.3 Examples of Doppler Relations Applied

◊　　*Example 1:*

For a given interrogating frequency, if the velocity triples, what happens to the Doppler shift frequency?

Answer:

Since the Doppler shift is proportional to the velocity ($f_{Dop} \propto v$) a tripling of the velocity implies a tripling of the Doppler shift.

◊　　*Example 2:*

For a specific target velocity, if the transmit frequency is decreased by a factor of 1.63, what happens to the Doppler shift frequency?

Answer:

Since the Doppler shift is proportional to the operating (transmit) frequency ($f_{Dop} \propto f_0$) a decrease in the operating frequency by a factor of 1.63 implies a decrease in the Doppler shift by a factor of 1.63.

◊　　*Example 3:*

Assuming no other changes, if the propagation velocity increased by a factor of 1.1, what happens to the Doppler shift frequency?

Answer:

Since the Doppler shift is inversely proportional to the propagation velocity ($f_{Dop} \propto \frac{1}{c}$), an increase in the propagation velocity by a factor of 1.1 implies a decrease in the Doppler shift by a factor of 1.1.

◊ **Example 4:**   If the transmit frequency is changed from 2 MHz to 10 MHz, what happens to the Doppler shift frequency?

Answer: Since the Doppler shift is proportional to the operating (transmit) frequency ($f_{Dop} \propto f_0$) an increase in the operating frequency by a factor of 5 implies an increase in the Doppler shift by a factor of 5.

◊ **Example 5:**   Using 2 MHz, the measured Doppler shift was -3 kHz. If the transmit frequency is changed from 2 MHz to 4 MHz, what will the Doppler shift frequency be?

Answer: Since the Doppler shift is proportional to the operating (transmit) frequency ($f_{Dop} \propto f_0$), an increase in the operating frequency by a factor of 2 implies an increase in the Doppler shift by a factor of 2. Since the original Doppler shift frequency was -3 kHz, the new Doppler shift frequency is -6 kHz.

In the case of diagnostic ultrasound, the target is usually red blood cells and the observer is the transducer. However, any motion which occurs, such as wall motion, respiration, transducer movement, etc., will cause a frequency shift.

4. Solving the Doppler Equation for Velocity

The simplified Doppler equation is expressed in terms of the Doppler shift frequency. Since in general, the Doppler shift is the measured parameter, what we would like to calculate is the velocity. To express the equation in terms of velocity, all that is needed is to manipulate the equation. As you learned in Chapter 1, the rules for equation manipulation are simple, whatever you do to one side of the equation must be done to the other side. So by using the property of reciprocals we can manipulate the equation as follows:

$$f_{Dop} = \frac{2f_0 \; v}{c}$$

$$f_{Dop} \times \frac{c}{2f_0} = \frac{2f_0 \; v}{c} \times \frac{c}{2f_0}$$

$$v = \frac{c \times f_{Dop}}{2f_0}.$$

Remember, this equation is simplified and does not contain angle correction.

5. Conceptual Questions   Answers: Pg. 959-960

1.   The _____ _____ is a shift in frequency caused by relative motion between the observer and target.

2.   A positive shift is caused by motion _____ the observer.

3.   A _____ shift is caused by motion away from the observer.

4.   A Doppler shift will _____ if both the target and observer are moving away from each other faster.

5.   A Doppler shift will _____ if both the target and observer are moving towards each other faster.

6.   In comparison to a target and an observer moving in opposite directions, a Doppler shift will _____ if both the target and observer are moving in the same direction.

7.   The _____ the target moves, the higher the Doppler shift.

8.   The Doppler shift frequency is _____ to the target velocity.

9.   The Doppler shift frequency is _____ to the operating frequency.

10.   The Doppler shift frequency is _____ _____ to the propagation velocity.

6. Completing the Doppler Equation

6.1 Removing the "Directly Toward or Directly Away" Assumption

When we derived the Doppler equation, we took note that the Doppler shift would change depending on where the observer was located relative to the moving train. We then made the assumption that the motion was always either directly toward or directly away, so as to simplify the Doppler equation. Real world conditions pretty much guarantee that the flow direction we measure in the body is rarely directly towards or directly away from the transducer. The probability of flow directly toward or away is more probable in cardiac imaging and much less probable in vascular studies. Even in the cardiac world, there is a plethora of times where the "direct" assumption will not hold. Therefore, we will now remove this assumption and develop the mathematical correction for angle in Doppler.

6.2 Relative Motion and Angle

Interestingly, in our first thought experiments, observer A and observer B saw inverse frequency shifts. Observer A experienced a negative shift and observer B experienced a positive shift. In the figure below, we will use a -1 to represent a negative shift and a +1 to represent a positive shift.

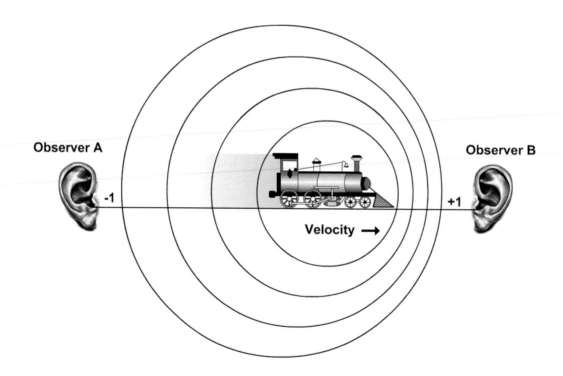

Fig. 6   **Positive and Negative Frequency Shifts**

Because the train is coming directly toward observer B, we will call the angle between the motion of the train and the observer B 0 degrees. In contrast, the train is moving directly away from observer A. We will therefore call the angle between the train's direction of motion and observer A 180 degrees. Imagine now if we were to add a third observer, C, as indicated in *Figure 7*. Observer C is located at 90 degrees relative to the train's direction of motion. At the very instant when the train first starts blowing the whistle, the train is neither going toward (decreasing the distance to) observer C nor going away from (increasing the distance to) observer C. Since there is no motion toward or away relative to observer C, observer C experiences no change in the frequency.

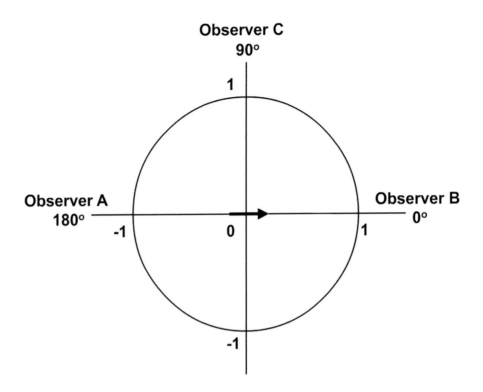

Fig. 7 **Doppler Angle Dependence**

You have already studied a mathematical function in Chapter 1 which expresses this very relationship between angle and perceived effect. This mathematical function is called the cosine of the angle. Not surprisingly, since the Doppler effect is a based on motion relative to an observer, the angle between the observer and the motion affects the Doppler effect. In Level 1, we started with the assumption that the motion was either directly towards or directly away. We can now add the cosine term to the Doppler equation yielding:

$$f_{Dop} = \frac{2 f_0 v}{c} cos(\theta).$$

where:

f_{Dop}	=	Doppler shifted frequency
f_0	=	transmit frequency
v	=	velocity of target through medium
c	=	speed of interrogating beam through medium (c = 1540 m/sec for sound in tissue)
$cos(\theta)$	=	mathematical correction for angle effect
θ	=	insonification angle (or angle to flow)

Note: Understanding this equation is the foundation for understanding all Doppler techniques. There is a wealth of information within the mathematical relationships expressed within this equation.

7. Doppler Shifts from Red Blood Cells

7.1 The Rayleigh Scattering/Frequency Paradox

In Chapter 3 we discussed types of reflection, referring to specular, scattering, and Rayleigh scattering. The criterion for when Rayleigh scattering occurs is when the diameter of the reflector is small relative to the wavelength of the interrogating wave. For red blood cells (RBCs), the typical diameter is approximately 7 μm, and the thickness about 2 μm, whereas the typical wavelength for diagnostic ultrasound ranges from 154 μm (at 10 MHz) to 770 μm (at 2 MHz). With respect to these numbers, we can be quite certain that red blood cells meet the requirement for Rayleigh scattering. Since Rayleigh scattering is such a weak reflective mode, extra caution must be taken in choosing the appropriate operating frequency for performing Doppler studies.

In Chapter 3 we also introduced a paradox. Since the amount of scattering increases with increasing frequency (as the frequency increases, the wavelength decreases making the structures appear larger relatively), it would be presumed that a higher frequency would produce stronger Doppler signals. In fact, Rayleigh scattering is related very non-linearly to the frequency. The amount of scattering is related to the frequency to the fourth power. This relationship implies that changing from a 3 MHz to a 6 MHz operating frequency should increase the amplitude of the Doppler signal by a factor of 16 (the factor of 2 increase in frequency raised to the fourth power). However, the reality is that higher frequencies for most imaging situations produce weaker Doppler signals. Therein lies the paradox.

The problem is that increasing the frequency increases reflectivity, but also results in significantly increased attenuation. Therefore, these two effects work inversely, and the increased attenuation with higher frequency very quickly dominates the increase in reflectivity.

7.2 The Optimal Frequency for Doppler

The following graph demonstrates the "optimal" Doppler frequency versus Doppler depth in cm. Since very few systems allow for Doppler below a frequency of 1.8 MHZ, you will notice that past the depth of 5 cm, the optimal frequency is artificially fixed at 1.8 MHz.

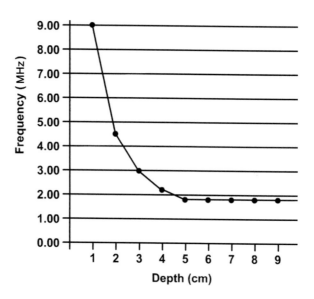

Fig. 8   **Optimal Doppler Frequency versus Depth of Doppler**

Pegasus Lectures, Inc.

Shallower than 1 cm, the optimal Doppler frequency is 9 MHz; from 1 cm to 2 cm, the optimal Doppler frequency drops below 5 MHz. By 5 cm, the optimal frequency is actually at the limit of how low most ultrasound systems produce transducers for Doppler. Therefore, excluding very superficial imaging, the lowest Doppler frequency possible should be used to optimize sensitivity.

Note: To create this graph, certain assumptions about attenuation and blood reflectivity had to be made. Although there are no assumptions that will be absolutely true for all patients and situations, absolute predictive value is not the purpose or requirement of this graph (Figure 8). Instead, this graph is intended to serve only as a guideline for appropriate frequency selection and a warning that errors can occur when the frequency used for Doppler is even slightly higher than optimal.

7.3 Red Blood Cell Aggregation and Reflectivity

Most theoretical work which has analyzed the reflective behavior of ultrasound from blood comes to the conclusion that in reality it is not the individual RBC that acts as the source of the reflection but rather the interference that results from the point source scattering from the inhomogeneities in the RBC concentration. The reflected spherical waves from an individual RBC are small enough so as to be undetectable with ultrasound; however, the constructive interference of spherical waves from multiple blood cells increases the signal strength. Also, changes in blood cell concentration give rise to larger reflections than could be attributed to a collection of individual RBCs. This is presumed to be the reason why the blood signal in the presence of turbulence tends to increase in amplitude relative to the same "hematocrit" blood in a laminar state. In general, there is a weak correlation between the number of red blood cell scatterers and the reflected energy. With aggregation, as occurs in low volume states, the reflectivity increases. This fact is also in support of the theory that changes in cell concentration are responsible for the reflectivity of blood.

7.4 Rouleau and Spontaneous Contrast

In low shear flow states, red blood cells tend to aggregate, creating what is referred to as rouleau flow. A rouleau refers to a small row or coil of coins, or anything which forms a similar coiled shape. With respect to blood, the erythrocytes (red blood cells) actually change their shape and form an adhesion to other erythrocytes. The chain of connected red blood cells resembles a coil and hence the name rouleau. Since a rouleau becomes larger with respect to the wavelength, the reflectivity tends to increase. In some imaging situations, rouleau formation can lead to the visualization of blood within a 2-D image. This appearance is often described as "smoke" or "spontaneous contrast". The conditions under which spontaneous contrast becomes more likely are related to volumetric flow, hematocrit, shear, and the interrogating frequency. The presence of "spontaneous contrast" can therefore be indicative of a greater likelihood of a hemodynamic problem such as increased risk for embolism or thrombus, or can be perfectly normal. With the increased use of higher frequency imaging through harmonics (discussed in Chapter 10), "spontaneous contrast" has become much more commonplace. Still, it is useful to recognize that there are times when the presence of "smoke" is a warning that increased risk exists.

The following image of *Figure 9* demonstrates normal rouleau formation in venous flow in the common femoral vein. Harmonic imaging was used, increasing the visibility of the blood pool in this image.

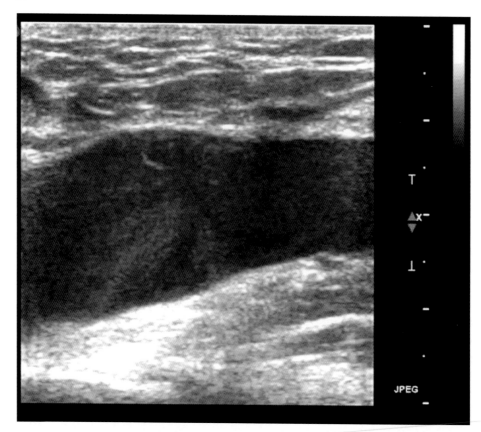

Fig. 9 **Rouleau Resulting in Spontaneous Contrast (visualization of blood) in the Common Femoral Vein**

 **View Animation and Image Library CD**

8. Identifying the Doppler Angle (Insonification or Insonation Angle)

8.1 Standardized Angle Determination

The Doppler angle is defined as the angle that is formed between the observer's line of sight and the direction of the target object. In terms of ultrasound, this angle is often referred to as the insonification angle or the angle of insonation, measured between the beam steering direction and the direction of the flow. The ability to correctly identify the insonification angle is critical for many reasons including:

1. The ability to determine flow direction.
2. The ability to assess Doppler measurement accuracy.
3. The ability to minimize Doppler error sources.
4. The ability to assess likelihood of artifact related issues such as spectral broadening.

8.2 Examples of Insonification Angles

The following series of diagrams indicate how the Doppler angle is determined.

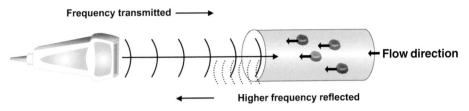

Fig. 10   **Doppler Insonification Angle = 0⁰**

Figure 10 illustrates measuring the angle between the beam direction and the flow direction. Since there is no angular displacement between the two directions, the angle is specified as 0°, or directly towards the transducer.

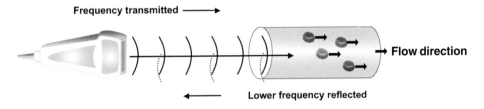

Fig. 11   **Doppler Insonification Angle = 180⁰**

Figure 11 represents the exact opposite of *Figure 10*, since the blood flow is directly away from the transducer beam, or 180°.

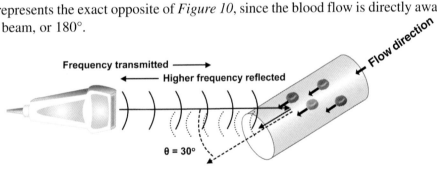

Fig. 12   **Doppler Insonification Angle = 30⁰**

In *Figure 12* the angle is measured between the flow direction (where the flow is going to - indicated by the arrowhead) and the beam direction. Since the angle is less than 90 degrees, and since the cosine of an angle less than 90 degrees is positive, this represents a positive frequency shift. However, you will note that the flow is not directly toward the transducer, hence, the shift detected will be less than 100%. Recalling that the cosine of 30° is 0.86, we know that only 86% of the true shift is detected.

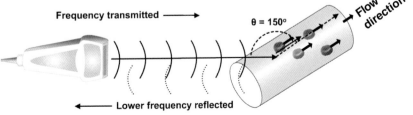

Fig. 13   **Doppler Insonification Angle = 150⁰**

In *Figure 13* the angle is measured between the flow direction (where the flow is going to, indicated by the arrowhead) and the beam direction. You need to pay particular attention to the difference between this case and the previous case represented by *Figure 12*. Although the angle formed between the vessel and the ultrasound beam is the same, the angle to flow is not the same. Since the flow is now in the opposite direction in the vessel, the angle to flow must be different. By drawing the angle between the head of the flow (the flow arrowhead) and the beam direction, it is clear that this angle is now greater than 90 degrees. Since the cosine of an angle greater than 90 degrees is negative, this represents a negative frequency shift. However, you will note that the flow is not directly away from the transducer, hence, the shift detected will be less than 100%. Recalling that the cosine of 150° is 0.86, we know that only 86% of the true shift is detected. Therefore, the same shift is detected as when the angle was 30 degrees, except now the shift is negative instead of positive.

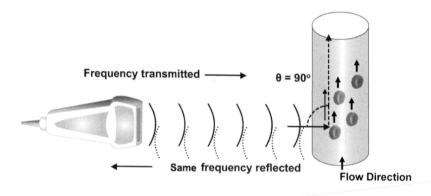

Fig. 14 **Doppler Insonification Angle = 90⁰**

In *Figure 14* the angle to flow is 90 degrees. With a 90 degree insonification angle, there is no motion towards or away from the transducer and hence, no Doppler effect. The cosine of 90 degrees is 0 and the Doppler equation predicts the absence of a shift at 90 degrees. In other words, if the insonification angle equals 90°, or is close to 90°, then there is no Doppler information:

$$\cos\left(90°\right) = 0 \Rightarrow f_{\text{Dop}} = \frac{2f_0\text{v}}{\text{c}}\left(0\right) = 0.$$

(So even though the target is moving, you have not detected this movement!!)

Note: The ability to determine the angle to flow is relatively straightforward given that you are taught the standardized definition of the insonification angle. The ability to determine flow direction, measurement accuracy, minimize error sources, and assess artifact related issues is also relatively straightforward given that you have reviewed basic trigonometry. In lieu of this understanding, you will be relegated to "techniques" which only give the right answer some of the time in some very specific cases.

8.2.1 Reviewing the Cosine

Because of the cosine dependence of the Doppler effect, it is important that you review the behavior of the cosine. Specifically, you should make certain that you can calculate the cosine of the basic angles (0°, 30°, 45°, 60°, 90°, 120°, 135°, 150°, 180°, 270°, and 360°). Additionally, you should know for what range of angles the cosine is positive and for what range of angles the cosine is negative. Later in this chapter, we will analyze the slope of the cosine function as a means of assessing error and measurement accuracy. If you are not comfortable with determining the cosine of various angles, it is highly recommended that you review Chapter 1. (Isn't it great how your earlier work is now paying dividends?)

View Animation and Image Library CD

9. Exercises   Answers: Pg. 960-961

What is the Doppler shifted frequency in soft tissue if the transmit frequency is 1 MHz, the angle is 0°, and the blood velocity is 1.54 m/sec?

$$f_{Dop} = \frac{2f_0 v}{c} \cos(\theta)$$

$$= \frac{2 \bullet \left(1 \bullet 10^6 \text{ Hz}\right)\left(1.54 \dfrac{m}{sec}\right)}{1540 \dfrac{m}{sec}} \cos(\theta)$$

where $\cos\left(0^0\right) = 1$

$$f_{Dop} = \frac{2 \bullet \left(1 \bullet 10^6 \text{ Hz}\right)\left(1.54 \dfrac{m}{sec}\right)}{1540 \dfrac{m}{sec}} \bullet (1)$$

$$f_{Dop} = 2 \bullet 10^3 \text{ Hz} = 2 \text{ kHz} \quad \text{or} \quad 2,000 \text{ Hz}$$

Use the above information to solve the following four problems.

1. What would the Doppler shifted frequency be if 2 MHz ultrasound was used instead of 1 MHz? (assume soft tissue, angle = 0°, blood velocity = 1.54 m/sec)

2. What would the Doppler shifted frequency be if the angle was 60°, instead of 0°? (assume soft tissue, 1 MHz transmit, blood velocity = 1.54 m/sec)

3. What would the Doppler shifted frequency be if the blood velocity was 3.08 m/sec instead of 1.54 m/sec? (assume soft tissue, 1 MHz transmit, angle = 0° .)

4. What would be the velocity of the blood, if the frequency shift were 6 kHz? (assume soft tissue, 1 MHz transmit, angle = 0°)

10. Spectral Doppler System Operation

10.1 The Value of a Block Diagram

Just as we reviewed a high-level system block diagram as the foundation for discussing system operation for 2-D imaging, we will use a high-level block diagram of how Doppler functions. At the highest level, the block diagram for a pedof (pencil, blind, Doppler only transducer) is very similar to the block diagram for performing Doppler with a phased array transducer. (With the exception of the beamforming functions for phased arrays, the core functions are the same.) Therefore, instead of going through the process twice, we will use the same diagram for both Doppler systems.

The value of the block diagram will not derive from your ability or inability to design a Doppler circuit, or even memorize the diagram and draw it yourself. Rather, the value derives from the block diagram serving as means of integrating all of the various aspects and controls related to spectral Doppler. As you review each Doppler function and process, you should relate the function to its location in the block diagram, and then ultimately to the controls that exist on your ultrasound system.

10.2 Why You Need to Also Know About Analog Waveform and Unidirectional Doppler

The block diagram described here is for a high end, bi-directional, spectral Doppler. There are lower complexity approaches which provide waveforms and use less precise techniques such as zero crossing detector schemes. These simpler devices are now becoming less common, and are now frequently only found as dedicated, stand-alone Doppler devices. As a result, we will concentrate much more heavily on what you will use most of the time in the clinical world. However, for two reasons we will point out how a simpler device operates:

1. There is a chance you might use an analog waveform Doppler and you should be aware of the limitations.
2. You may be still expected to know about unidirectional Doppler, analog waveform Doppler, and zero-crossing detection techniques on credentialing exams.

11.3 Amplification: (Amplifier)

When the reflected echoes are received, the amplitude of all of the echoes is very low, therefore amplification is necessary. The amplification in the receiver is not under user control. Typically 40 dB to 60 dB of gain is applied before any other processing occurs. For phased systems, the beamformer has the extra task of steering and focusing the returning echoes by applying the appropriate phase delays to the signals from each transducer element and then summing the channels together.

11.4 Doppler Shift Detection: (Mixers)

The returning signal is a combination of back scattered data from tissue and frequency shifted data from the moving targets. The signals reflected from stationary structures are still at the same frequency as the transmit frequency. Therefore, the combination of signals returning can be notationally written as:

$$\underbrace{f_0\,(\text{MHz})}_{\text{Stationary Structures}} \quad \pm \quad \underbrace{\sum f_{\text{Dop}}\,(\text{kHz})}_{\text{Moving Structures}}.$$

Since Doppler is interested in determining the velocity of the moving structures, the reflected signals from the stationary structures are subtracted from the combined signal, leaving just the shifted frequencies from the moving structures:

$$\underbrace{\pm \;\sum f_{\text{Dop}}\,(\text{kHz})}_{\text{Moving Structures}}.$$

This process is called demodulation or signal detection. From the old radio days, this process is also called "heterodyning" or "mixing to baseband."

The mixing to baseband is performed using two channels in what is called quadrature detection. A quadrant of a circle is 90°. Quadrature detection signifies that the information is detected at two different phases, 90° apart. This separation is created by multiplying the received Doppler signal by the sine and cosine. (As we learned in Chapter 1, the sine and the cosine have a phase separation of 90 degrees.) Later in the Doppler processing, the channels are rotated another 90 degrees resulting in a phase separation of 180°. Since 180° represents exact opposite directions, forward flow is now distinguished from reverse flow. Therefore, the reason for quadrature detection is to separate the signal into its forward and reverse components so that flow directionality is known.

Early Doppler systems did not perform the quadrature detection and as a result yielded uni-directional Doppler. In these systems, both flow towards and away from the transducer would be represented above the baseline, as demonstrated in *Figure 17*. Fortunately, the days of non-directional (uni-directional) Doppler have been extinct for many years. *Figure 18* demonstrates a bi-directional Doppler waveform of a femoral artery. This waveform was generated by a zero-crossing detection Doppler circuit. For a pure frequency, the frequency can be detected by counting the number of times the signal crosses through the baseline (zero). With many simultaneous frequencies (as commonly occurs when measuring blood flow), a zero-crossing yields a value loosely related to a mean velocity (root mean squared velocity). For comparison, *Figure 19* demonstrates a typical spectral Doppler waveform for a femoral artery.

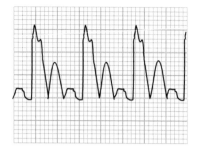 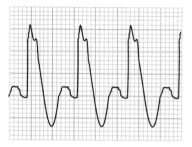 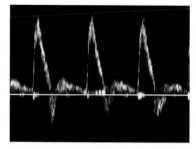

Fig. 17 **Uni-directional Doppler Waveform** *Fig. 18* **Bi-directional Doppler Waveform** *Fig. 19* **Spectral Doppler**

11.5 Wall Filtering

11.5.1 Dynamic Range of Doppler

In Chapter 6, we discussed how the large dynamic range of the signals presented such an enormous problem. In that section, we learned that the dynamic range of the signal typically spanned more than 80 dB. In comparison, the situation is much worse for Doppler. Depending on the imaging situation, the dynamic range may be as great as 140 dB in PW Doppler and 160 dB in CW Doppler. As way of review, we will convert 160 dB into the equivalent signal ratio.

$$20\times\log\left(\frac{A_{biggest}}{A_{smallest}}\right)=160 \text{ dB}$$

Dividing both sides by 20 yields:

$$\log\left(\frac{A_{biggest}}{A_{smallest}}\right)=8$$

(The base is 10 - recall if not expressly written, we assume a base of 10)

$$\log_{10}\left(\frac{A_{biggest}}{A_{smallest}}\right)=8$$

Solving the logarithm yields:

$$\left(\frac{A_{biggest}}{A_{smallest}}\right)=\frac{10^8}{1}=100,000,000:1$$

This calculation shows that the largest signals returning in CW Doppler can be one hundred million times larger than the smallest signals. This is problematic for two reasons. First, recall that human visible dynamic range is less than 36 dB (fewer than 64 shades of gray), so there is an enormous dynamic range issue. Second, the signals from blood are the ones that we care most about and, unfortunately, these signals are most likely at the very bottom of the dynamic range. If we do not eliminate the enormous signals, there will be no way of detecting the tiny signals associated with the Rayleigh scattering of the blood. Before we discuss a solution, we need to first understand the source of the problem.

11.5.2 Clutter Signals

Recall that any relative movement between target and transducer will create a Doppler shift. In addition to blood flow - wall motion, valve motion, respiration induced movement, transducer movement, etc., will create Doppler shifts. These Doppler shifts are usually much bigger in amplitude than the amplitude of the associated blood signals because of the specular nature of these reflectors. These high amplitude signals from relatively stationary, strongly reflecting structures are generally referred to as "clutter" signals.

Note: You need to make certain you pay attention to the difference between amplitude and frequency. In Chapter 2 we made of point of making this distinction by stating that "amplitude and frequency are disjoint." The amplitude corresponds to the signal strength. The frequency shift corresponds to the velocity of the blood and all of the related parameters through the Doppler equation.

11.5.3 Graphic Depiction of Dynamic Range Issues

Figure 20 illustrates the dynamic range issues associated with processing Doppler data.

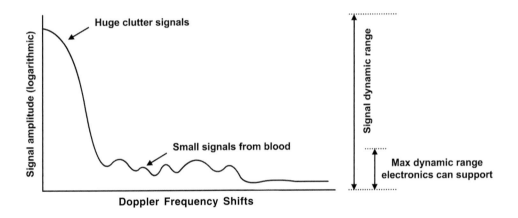

Fig. 20   **Doppler Dynamic Range and Clutter**

Notice how the (clutter) signals at the lower Doppler frequency shifts are extremely high amplitude, and much larger in amplitude than the signals from the blood flow. Also note that the overall signal dynamic range (the ratio of the biggest signal to the smallest signal) is much larger than the dynamic range of the electronics. If we were to consider the dynamic range of the human eye, that range would be even smaller than the supportable dynamic range of the electronics. Since the dynamic range of the Doppler signal is much larger than the dynamic range supported by the electronics and much larger than the dynamic range visible to the human eye, something must be done with the large clutter signals.

11.5.4 Wall Filter Theory

Luckily, the reflectors that cause these enormous clutter signals usually move slowly relative to most blood flow. From the Doppler equation, we know that low velocities result in low frequency shifts. Therefore, if we discriminate signals based on their frequency shifts, we have the potential to filter out the clutter signals. The technique for filtering out these clutter signals is called wall filtering. Wall filters allow the user to attenuate the lower frequency shift (velocity) signals which are usually the highest amplitude signals. By reducing or eliminating the high amplitude signals, the signal dynamic range is reduced.

11.5.5 Graphic Depiction of Wall Filters

Wall filters are high pass filters. As the name suggests, high pass filters allow the high frequency signals to pass through while rejecting the lower frequency signals. A high pass filter is designed to have a specific cutoff frequency. The cutoff frequency is the breakpoint frequency above which the signal frequencies are passed, and below which the signal frequencies are attenuated.

Figure 21 depicts the relation of the wall filter to the signal data.

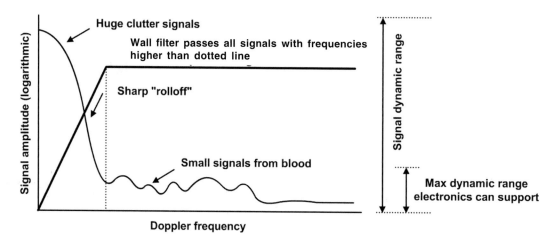

Fig. 21　**Applying a Wall Filter**

Notice that the bold line represents the function of the wall filter. The dotted line indicates the frequency below which signals are attenuated and above which signals are passed. The frequency at which the attenuation begins is commonly referred to as the "corner" frequency or "cutoff" frequency of the wall filter. Signals with frequency shifts above this corner are multiplied by 1, or passed through unchanged (hence the name "high pass" filter). Frequencies below the corner frequency are multiplied by a number less than 1. As displayed graphically, the lower the frequency, the lower the multiplier applied. Note that the filter drawn in this diagram has a very sharp "roll-off," implying that frequencies just below the corner are attenuated a fair amount. If the roll-off were more gradual (slower slope), then more of the signals with frequencies below the corner would still pass through the filter, albeit with a lower amplitude (weaker signal displayed).

View Animation and Image Library CD

11.5.6 Effects of Wall Filters

Once the wall filter has been applied, if the wall filter corner frequency is set appropriately, then the signal dynamic range should be significantly reduced. The following diagram depicts the reduced signal dynamic range after the wall filters are employed.

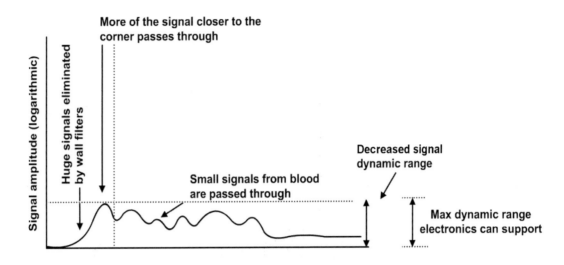

Fig. 22   **Reduced Dynamic Range After Wall Filters**

Note: The dynamic range is greatly reduced by attenuating the large clutter signals at the lower frequency shifts. Also note that the wall filter is not a pure reject filter, and therefore still allows larger signals closer to the corner frequency to still pass through, although with a much lower amplitude. The result is a much smaller dynamic range which now can be more easily processed by the system and visualized by the human eye.

11.5.7 Wall Filter Appearance on Doppler Spectrum

In spectral Doppler, the wall filters are visualized as a black band around the baseline of the spectrum. This black band represents the low frequency signals that were attenuated and mapped to very low amplitudes.

The black band above and below the baseline represents the signals attenuated by the wall filters.

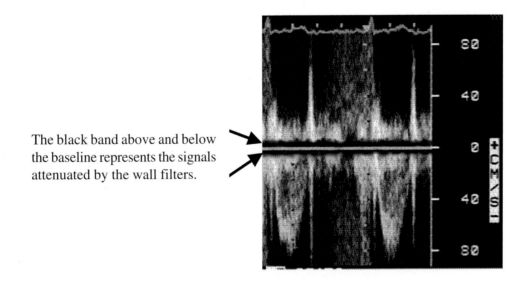

Fig. 23   **Spectral Appearance of the Wall Filter**

As the corner frequency of the wall filters is increased, this black band becomes broader. The wall filters also affect the Doppler audio signal. As the wall filters are increased, less of the base frequencies are audible, allowing only the higher frequency signals to be heard.

11.5.8 Appropriate Wall Filter Settings for Various Clinical Applications

Different applications require different wall filter settings. For example, venous Doppler detection generally requires the ability to detect lower frequency shifts than arterial Doppler studies. As a result, the wall filters must be set to a lower cutoff frequency for venous Doppler studies, or the desired venous signals may actually be eliminated by the wall filter.

Typical ranges for wall filters are from about 10 Hz to as high as 1600 Hz. Venous Doppler is usually performed with wall filters of 50 Hz or less. Arterial studies are usually performed at 50 Hz to 100 Hz. Adult echo typically uses a range of 200 Hz to 600 Hz, while pediatric echo typically uses a range of 600 Hz to 800 Hz.

11.5.9 Effect of Operating Frequency on Wall Filter Settings

An important point is that the operating frequency affects what wall filter settings should be used. From the Doppler equation, we know that the Doppler shift is proportional to the operating frequency. For the same velocity, using a higher operating frequency results in a higher frequency shift. Assume a wall is moving at a velocity such that it produces a Doppler shift of 40 Hz when using a 2 MHz transducer. Also assume that the wall filters are set at 50 Hz, so that these "clutter" signals are eliminated. Now imagine that the transducer frequency is changed to 4 MHz. The exact same wall velocity will now create a Doppler shift at 80 Hz and the 50 Hz wall filter will pass the clutter through. This fact is the principal reason why pediatric Doppler generally uses higher cutoff wall filters than adult Doppler.

11.5.10 Saturation of Wall Filters

Note that if the wall filters are set too low, saturation of the electronics will occur. When the electronics saturate, there is a very distinct bright symmetric band about the baseline, usually from top to bottom of the spectrum (see *Figure 24* below). Additionally, the audio will have a characteristic loud thump or banging sound. Saturation occurs when the signals become larger than the voltage rails of the electronics. In essence, the electronics can only handle a certain voltage dynamic range. If the signals become larger than the maximum of this range, then the circuit saturates and the electronics ring. During this ringing phase, the Doppler circuit is not really working. The result is that the desired Doppler spectrum is obscured by the "clutter" signal.

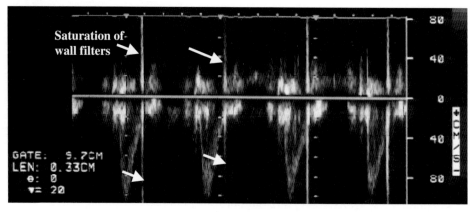

Fig. 24   **Wall Filter Saturation**

11.6 Variable Gain (Gain)

Recall that some amplification was applied in the receiver. However, since in the system design the receiver is before the wall filters, it could not amplify the signal as much as is necessary or the large clutter signals would have saturated the circuit. Once the large clutter signals have been removed by the wall filters, more amplification can be applied. Since the echoes from the blood are so small, the signal must be significantly amplified to be in an appropriate range for viewing. For conventional Doppler processing techniques, this amplification is referred to as the "Doppler gain" and is controlled by the user.

As with all "gain" related controls on the system, the Doppler gain is logarithmic. By this point, you have hopefully become accustomed to the idea that since the attenuation is non-linear, the amplification controls are most usable if designed to also perform non-linearly.

Figure 25 demonstrates the need for amplification of the Doppler signal after wall filtering.

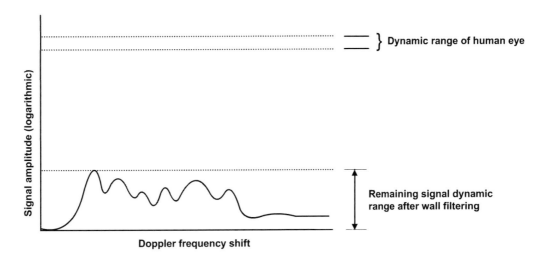

Fig. 25   **Reduced Dynamic Range After Wall Filters**

Note that there are really two existing issues that must be overcome. First, even the highest amplitude signal is less than the visual threshold as indicated by the dynamic range of the human eye, *Figure 25*. This fact is precisely why user controlled amplification is applied at this point in the processing chain. Second, even though we have reduced the dynamic range by wall filtering, the dynamic range of the signal is still significantly greater than the dynamic range of the eye. Not unlike 2-D, this dynamic range issue will force the need for compression.

11.7 Audio (speakers)

The signals are "cleaned up" to drive the speakers. Since the frequency shifts of diagnostic ultrasound are generally within the audio range (± 10 kHz), you can "detect" the different blood velocities as different frequencies with your ears. If the detection is performed in quadrature, as discussed earlier) forward flow is presented in one speaker channel and reverse flow is presented in the other channel. As a result, stereo separation is useful to help distinguish signal phasicity.

Note: Learning to interpret Doppler audio is critical. There is a wealth of information in the audio signal. In general, I recommend that anyone teaching Doppler should first focus only on Doppler audio without a spectral display. Begin with normal studies until the student can identify the characteristics of the normal blood flow for each study type. Next, progress to audio only from abnormal studies. Once students have mastered the audio, then allow them to correlate what they see spectrally with what they hear audibly. The next step is to allow the students to see the 2-D or B-mode image in addition to the spectrum and the audio. The last step is to allow the students to see color Doppler in conjunction with the image and the spectrum.

11.8 Analog to Digital Conversion (A/D)

In addition to hearing, there is a definite desire to see and quantify the Doppler spectrum. The human ear is capable of hearing multiple frequencies simultaneously, and detecting the presence of various frequency ranges. If this were not the case, it is not likely that many of us would ever listen to music. Recall that the output of the mixing process was an entire spectrum of frequency shifts associated with the flow situation. In order to display all the different velocities (the spectrum) so that the signal characteristics can be interpreted visually, more work must be done to the signal for spectral Doppler than for audio Doppler.

In order to perform an FFT (Section 11.9), post processing (Section 11.10), and store the spectrum into digital memory for comparison and measurement, the analog Doppler signal must be sampled or converted from an analog signal to a digital signal. We have discussed the process of A/D conversion multiple times so that there is no need to repeat the discussion here. The only other note is that digital Doppler systems perform the function of A/D conversion much earlier in the processing chain than at this step. Analog Doppler systems perform the conversion right after the wall filtering and amplification, whereas digital systems can convert just before or just after the mixing process. Luckily, you should never be asked this information unless you plan to design a Doppler circuit.

11.9 Fast Fourier Transform (FFT)

The Fast Fourier Transform is a mathematical technique for separating a spectrum into its individual frequency components. The following figure illustrates graphically the role of FFT processing.

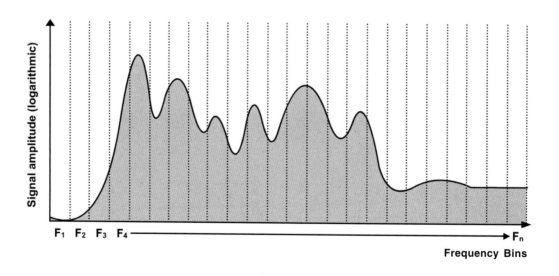

Fig. 26 **FFT Processing**

Notice that the full range of frequency shifts is divided into individual frequency bins. Each bin corresponds to a narrow range of frequency shifts, which by the Doppler equation, can be converted into a calculated velocity. Clearly the lowest frequency bin corresponds to virtually zero velocity The last bin, F_n, corresponds to the Nyquist limited maximum Doppler frequency detectable. (This will be coming up in Section 13.6, so no need to panic). In addition to dividing the summation of frequencies into individual frequency bins, the FFT also determines how much energy, if any, is in each frequency bin. The energy in the bin is weakly related to the number of red blood cells traveling at that particular velocity. If a bin has no signal, then no blood cells were detected with that particular frequency shift. If a bin has a large signal, then it is presumed that there were many blood cells which caused the associated frequency shift.

Notice in the graphical representation of the FFT process in *Figure 26* that the first two bins (F_1 and F_2) have no signal. This absence of signal is the result of the wall filtering applied. If the wall filter were increased, more of the lowest bins would have no signal, or virtually no signal.

11.10 Post-processing (Compression and Reject or Grayscale)

As was demonstrated in *Figure 25*, (Section 11.6), the Doppler signals still span a greater dynamic range than the visible dynamic range, even after wall filtering. Just as was needed for 2-D images, compression is employed to further reduce the dynamic range. The compression maps for Doppler are non-linear. Care must be taken to make certain that weak signals are not compressed out just as can occur with 2-D images. Since the compression maps occur after the Doppler data has been stored, compression is a post processing technique. In other words, the compression of the Doppler spectral data can be changed on frozen data as well as in real time.

Names for spectral Doppler compression are very similar to the names used for compression mapping for B-mode, including compression, grayscale, dynamic range, video compression, and post processing curves. Some systems also have a function called reject which sets the threshold, below which signals are mapped to black. For systems with both controls, compression and reject together determine the mapping of signal amplitudes to brightness on the screen.

11.11 Display

The Doppler display actually demonstrates three quantities on a two-dimensional display. Obviously the frequency (or equivalent velocity through the Doppler equation) is displayed on the vertical axis. Time is swept across the horizontal axis. Most systems allow the user to change the time base of the sweep, also referred to as the sweep speed. Higher sweep speeds result in less time displayed on the horizontal axis such that only two cardiac cycles might appear whereas in a lower sweep speed four or five cardiac cycles might be visualized. The third axis is "imaginary" and represents the amplitude. Amplitude display is achieved by the variations in brightness levels.

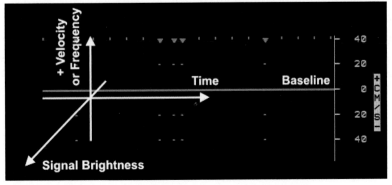

Fig. 27   **The Display Axes of Spectral Doppler**

12. Frequency vs. Amplitude

Earlier in this chapter we reiterated the fact that amplitude and frequency are disjoint (or independent). In other words, knowing the frequency tells you nothing about the amplitude and vice versa. This concept is very important for Doppler. The frequency shift in Doppler is dictated by all the terms in the Doppler equation [f_o, v, c, cos(θ)]. The amplitude of the signal is determined by the scattering properties of the blood. In other words, the wavelength relative to the size of the RBCs, the number of RBCs, discontinuities in concentration of the blood cells, as well as the attenuation properties of the tissue through which the ultrasound beam travels all contribute to the strength of the signal. The velocity of the blood determines the frequency shift, NOT the amplitude or strength of the signal. The following four Doppler spectrals demonstrate the disjoint nature of frequency and amplitude.

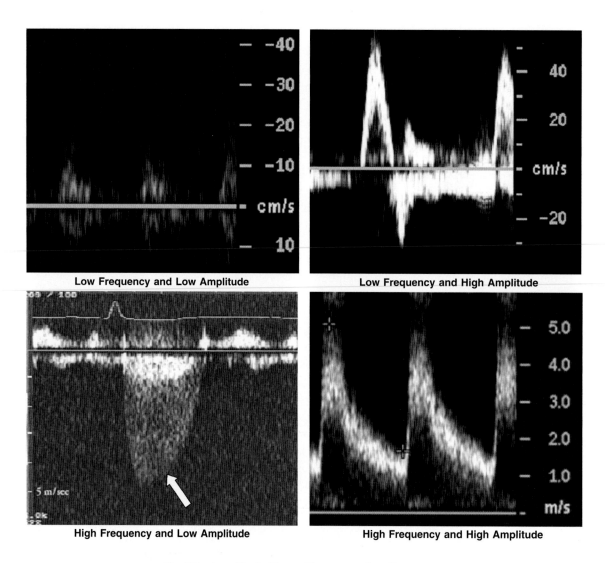

Fig. 28   **Amplitude Versus Frequency in a Spectrum**

13. PW vs. CW Comparison

13.1 Trade-offs

Ultrasound, like life, is all about trade-offs. The winner is the person who trades off what they don't need for what they do need. The loser is someone who doesn't understand that there is a trade-off, or worse yet, gives up something needed for something not needed. PW and CW Doppler both exist as ultrasound modalities since each has a primary benefit and a primary drawback.

13.2 Timing and Basics of CW Doppler

Continuous wave Doppler is performed by one crystal or group of elements continuously transmitting while a second crystal or group of elements continuously receives the echoes. Since the transmit is continuous, there are echoes being generated from all depths simultaneously. Hence the receiver continuously receives echoes from all locations at once.

13.3 Timing and Basics of PW Doppler

In contrast to CW Doppler, PW Doppler is performed by transmitting a pulse on either a single crystal or a group of crystals followed by a "dead time" or "dead period." During this dead period, the system is not transmitting, nor receiving. The dead period is really the roundtrip propagation time required for the pulse to arrive at and reflect back from the depth of interest as specified by the Doppler gate location placed by the user. Recall that 1 cm imaging depth requires 13 μsec travel time, so the dead time until listening can begin is simply the gate depth in centimeters multiplied by 13 μsec. When the "dead time" has transpired, the crystal or group of elements are allowed to receive the echoes. The transition from using a crystal or an element as a transmitter to receiver is achieved through the use of a T/R switch. (You can probably guess what T and R stand for.) The switch changes the connection of the element from the transmit circuit to the receive circuit. During the "dead time" the T/R switch is open and the echoes are not registered. Therefore, echoes from depths shallower than the gate are not received.

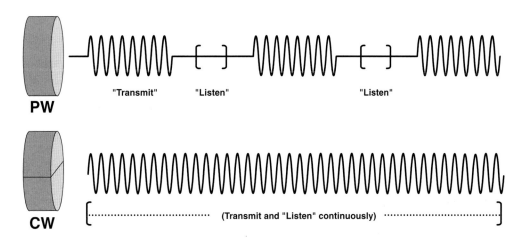

Fig. 29 **PW and CW Comparison**

13.4 Range Specificity: Advantage PW

The fundamental advantage of PW over CW is good range specificity. In fact, the motivation for creating the more complex approach of PW was the inability of CW to offer any range resolution.

There are two fundamental misconceptions that we must address concerning CW versus PW and range specificity.

1. *When using CW Doppler, there is no means by which to create range specificity.*
    Other modalities can be used in conjunction with CW to effectively create range specificity. Although there is no range specificity in CW as a modality by itself, the use of other modalities in conjunction with CW effectively yields range specificity. For example, if you are "Dopplering" flow through a stenotic valve or stenosed vessel, and the image and/or color Doppler shows that there is only one narrowed region in the area of the CW Doppler beam, then the peak velocity obtained can pretty safely be attributed to that specific region in the image.

2. *PW Doppler has no range ambiguity.*
    PW offers good range specificity, not perfect range specificity. If you notice, the fundamental advantage of PW relative to CW was written as "good" range specificity, not perfect range specificity. Contrary to popular misconception in the field, PW Doppler always suffers from potential range ambiguity. In fact, every Doppler modality based on pulsed wave operation suffers from range ambiguity including 2-D imaging, color Doppler, M-mode, and PW spectral Doppler. This range ambiguity is responsible for artifacts which are rarely identified. The range ambiguity is so predictable that an entire new Doppler modality called HPRF Doppler was created which exploited the range ambiguity effect. Range ambiguity and HPRF Doppler will be discussed thoroughly in Section 18.

13.5 Aliasing: Advantage CW

The fundamental advantage of CW relative to PW is no aliasing. In Chapter 1, we discussed aliasing as the phenomenon that occurs when a signal is sampled below the Nyquist criterion. For CW, since the receiver is always "listening" the sampling rate is essentially infinite. For PW Doppler, "listening" occurs only (periodically) when the receivers are turned on. In the PW figure below, we see that the time between "listens" is the same as the time between "transmits." We have already learned in Chapter 4 that the time between the repeat of a transmit pulse is called the pulse repetition period (PRP). Therefore, the time between "listens" is also referred to as the PRP. Expressed as a frequency, the reciprocal of the time between "listens" is referred to as the pulse repetition frequency.

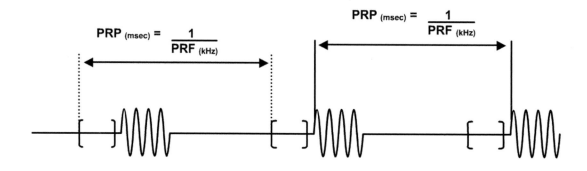

Fig. 30   **The Listening Rate in PW is the PRF**

13.6 The Maximum Detectable Frequency Shift (PW)

For consistency with the language used to describe the Nyquist criterion, we will refer to the time of "listening" as "sampling." Therefore, the frequency at which sampling occurs in PW Doppler is the PRF. We know that by the Nyquist Criterion, the maximum detectable frequency is half of the sample rate.

Therefore, for PW Doppler, the Nyquist limit is the PRF divided by 2. Since the frequencies we are sampling are the Doppler shift frequencies, we can write the relationship between the maximum detectable frequency shift and the existence of aliasing simply as:

$$f_{Dop}(\text{maximum}) = \frac{PRF}{2}.$$

From this equation it is evident that higher frequency shifts are more likely to cause aliasing. Fortunately, we have already learned the Doppler equation which dictates what causes higher Doppler frequency shifts. According to the Doppler equation, higher velocity flow, higher operating frequencies, lower propagation velocities, and insonification angles closer to 0 degrees or 180 degrees all result in higher Doppler frequency shifts. From this equation, it is also evident that lower PRFs are more likely to cause aliasing. We learned in Chapter 4 that the PRP, and hence the PRF, are determined by the depth. (The propagation speed theoretically also affects the PRF, but from a practical standpoint, since the system always assumes 1540 m/sec, the propagation velocity is no longer treated as a variable but instead as a constant.) A deeper imaging depth requires a longer line time, resulting in a longer PRP and a lower PRF. As a result, we can now compile a table which expresses when aliasing is most likely to occur.

13.7 Parameters Affecting Aliasing in PW Doppler

Related Parameter	Parameter Affecting Aliasing
Doppler Shift	Higher velocity of blood
	Insonification angle closer to $0°$ or $180°$
	Higher transmit frequency
PRF	Deeper gate depth

Table 1: **Increased Likelihood of Aliasing for PW Doppler**

Note: Although this table was included for completeness, it is hoped that you will analyze the Doppler equation and the physical situations which control the PRF to arrive at the same conclusions on your own.

13.8 Appearance of Aliasing in a Doppler Spectrum

The following Doppler spectrum in *Figure 31* demonstrates aliasing. When true aliasing occurs, it is not possible to increase the Doppler scales any more so as to unwrap the true peak velocity. Aliasing appears in the spectrum as a "wrapping" of the signal from either the top of the spectrum to the bottom of the spectrum or vice versa. Flow toward the transducer (presuming spectral invert is not on) will extend to the top of the spectrum and then continue at the bottom of the spectrum.

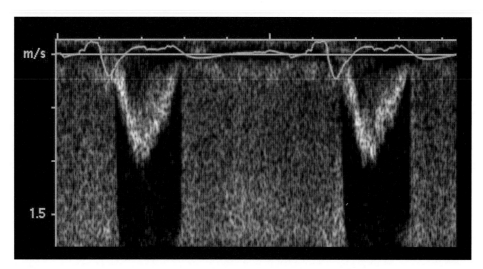

Fig. 31 **Doppler Aliasing**

The following Doppler spectrum in *Figure 32* is often referred to as aliasing, but is really just a "display alias." A display alias implies that the signal is wrapped in the spectrum but can actually be "unwrapped" by increasing the scales or shifting the Doppler baseline.

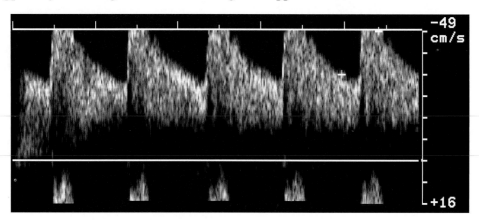

Fig. 32 **Doppler "Display" Alias**

13.9 Practical Limit in CW Doppler and Aliasing

In reality, there is a practical limit imposed on the sampling rate of CW Doppler, but by design, this limit is so high that it rarely becomes a limiting factor clinically. Since the listen is continuous in CW Doppler, the receiving of the CW signal does not limit the ability to detect Doppler shift frequencies as with PW Doppler. Recall that in the processing of Doppler, the signal is converted from analog format to digital format. The A/D converter samples the analog signal at the frequency determined by the sampling clock. If the sample rate of the A/D converter is 50 kHz, then the maximum detectable frequency shift would be half of that or 25 kHz. Since it is possible in some extreme cases to achieve Doppler shifts as high as 50 kHz, the 50 kHz converter would cause aliasing in CW. In order to avoid cause aliasing for a 50 kHz Doppler shift, the converter would have to convert at a rate of at least 100 kHz. In earlier days, there were very few technologies capable of producing higher conversion rate A/D converters. As a result, the cost of the high speed converters was prohibitive. However, following Moore's law describing technology advancement, converters with conversion rates much higher than 100 kHz now cost essentially pennies. Therefore, the A/D converter rate is pushed up high enough so as to never be a practical concern in CW Doppler anymore.

13.10 Changing the Scale in PW Doppler

As a review of the concept of reciprocals, the reciprocal of a maximum is a minimum. The maximum PRF is the reciprocal of the minimum PRP. The minimum PRP is determined by the gate depth. In other words, since we can't make sound travel any faster into the body than 1540 m/sec, the time we must wait for the reflection to return to the transducer is purely a function of the depth. If the gate is set deep, then the echo will arrive much later than if the gate is set shallow. Unfortunately, as a sonographer, you do not have the power to make all blood flow occur at shallow depths. As a result, long PRPs are possible and probable, implying low PRFs. The low PRFs lead to greater likelihood of aliasing in PW Doppler. Specifically if the PRF is not at least twice the Doppler frequency shift, aliasing occurs.

Let us consider the converse case. What if the maximum PRF is much higher than twice the Doppler frequency shift detected? The following spectrum of *Figure 33* demonstrates this situation.

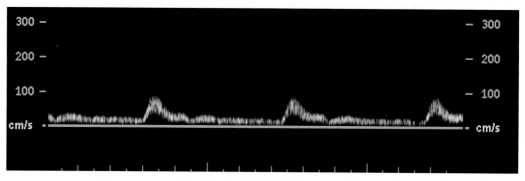

Fig. 33   **Doppler Scales Too High**

The ability to accurately measure the velocity of this spectrum is clearly compromised by the scale being too high. If the Doppler scale (PRF) is lowered, the spectrum will appear as a greater percentage, and hence more appropriately scaled. *Figure 34* demonstrates the same signal with the Doppler scale lowered.

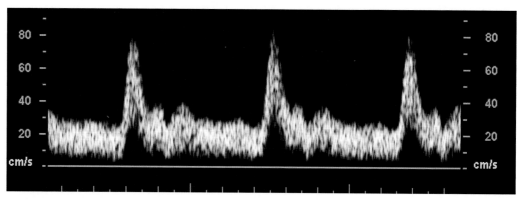

Fig. 34   **Appropriate Doppler Scale**

View Animation and Image Library CD

To demonstrate what physically happens when the scales are changed, we will return to our pulse wave picture. Let's imagine that the depth is set so that the maximum PRF is 8 kHz as shown below.

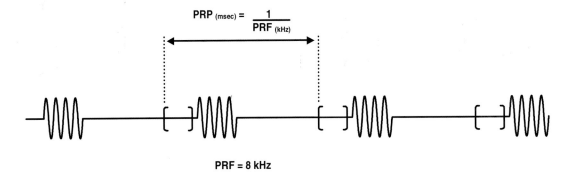

$$\text{PRP}_{\text{(msec)}} = \frac{1}{\text{PRF}_{\text{(kHz)}}}$$

PRF = 8 kHz

Fig. 35 **Minimum PRP (no dead time)**

Now imagine that the user wants to decrease the Doppler scale so as to make the spectrum a more appropriate percentage of the scale as just shown with the two spectrums of *Figures 33* and *34*. A lower PRF is achieved by increasing the gate depth. However, the gate depth, although under user control, must be placed wherever the flow to be measured exists. Therefore, we need a way to increase the PRP without changing the gate location. The following figure, *Figure 36*, demonstrates how this can be achieved.

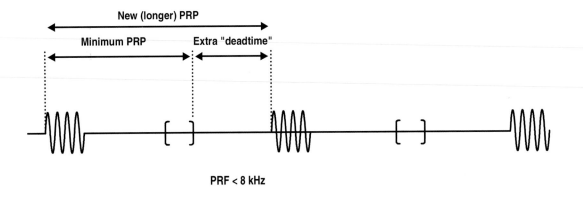

New (longer) PRP

Minimum PRP   **Extra "deadtime"**

PRF < 8 kHz

Fig. 36 **Increasing the PRP (adding "dead time")**

Notice that additional "dead time" has been added after the Doppler gate, but that the time between the transmit and the Doppler gate remains unchanged. This means that the Doppler gate is still listening to signals from the same depth as in the previous example. However, since the time between transmits has now increased (similarly the time between listens has increased), the PRF is now lower. If the PRF is lower, the maximum detectable frequency shift is now lower which means that the Doppler signal now occupies a larger percentage of the displayed spectral frequency range. If the Doppler scales are lowered repeatedly, more dead time is added repeatedly until the desired PRF is reached.

When the Doppler scales are increased, the exact opposite process occurs. Each time the scale is increased, some of the extra dead time between the Doppler gate and the next transmit pulse is removed. Eventually, all of the dead time is removed and the maximum scale (for that particular depth) is reached. If aliasing is still occurring, there are only a few choices:

1.   Use a lower frequency transducer.
2.   Find a view that results in a shallower gate depth to interrogate the same flow.
3.   Use CW Doppler.
4.   Use HPRF Doppler (described later in this chapter).

14. The Maximum Detectable Velocity

In Section 13.6 we developed the equation which specifies the maximum detectable frequency shift as dictated by the Nyquist criterion. Although Doppler displays can display either the Doppler frequency shift or the velocity on the vertical axis (and some systems allow for both simultaneously), velocity has pretty much become the norm. We would therefore like to be able to convert the maximum detectable frequency shift into an expression for the maximum detectable velocity.

We will start with the Doppler equation. We will presume that no variables are changing so that we can write that the maximum Doppler shift detectable is directly related to the maximum velocity detectable, or:

$$f_{\text{Dop}}(\text{maximum}) = \frac{2 f_0 \text{v}(\text{maximum})}{\text{c}} \cos(\theta)$$

Solving for v (maximum detectable) by manipulation yields:

$$\frac{\text{c} \times f_{\text{Dop}}(\text{maximum})}{2 f_0 \cos(\theta)} = \text{v}(\text{maximum})$$

Since we have another expression for the maximum detectable Doppler shift frequency according to Nyquist,

$$\left(f_{\text{Dop}}(\text{maximum}) = \frac{\text{PRF}}{2} \right), \text{ we can substitute as follows:}$$

$$\frac{\text{c} \times PRF}{4 \times f_0 \cos(\theta)} = \text{v}(\text{maximum})$$

We now have an expression which relates the maximum detectable velocity to the system parameters that are known when scanning. Specifically, we know the relationship between the maximum detectable velocity and the transmit frequency and the PRF. Not surprisingly, this equation shows that as the PRF increases, the maximum detectable velocity increases. Also evident is the fact that as the operating frequency increases the maximum detectable velocity decreases. This inability to detect higher velocities with higher frequency transducers is yet another reason why Doppler should be performed with lower transmit frequencies.

Note: Lowering the transmit frequency decreases the likelihood of aliasing.

The following table demonstrates the maximum detectable velocities for imaging depths from 10 cm to 20 cm, using varying transmit frequencies. Shading has been used to break the velocity ranges into bands of 10 cm/sec.

Depth (cm)	PRP (msec)	PRF/2 (kHz)	fo = 2.0 MHz	fo = 2.5 MHz	fo = 3.0 MHz	fo = 3.5 MHz	fo = 4.0 MHz	fo = 5.0 MHz
10	154.87	3.2	124.3	99.4	82.9	71.0	62.1	49.7
11	167.86	3.0	114.7	91.7	76.5	65.5	57.3	45.9
12	180.84	2.8	106.4	85.2	71.0	60.8	53.2	42.6
13	193.83	2.6	99.3	79.5	66.2	56.8	49.7	39.7
14	206.82	2.4	93.1	74.5	62.1	53.2	46.5	37.2
15	219.81	2.3	87.6	70.1	58.4	50.0	43.8	35.0
16	232.79	2.1	82.7	66.2	55.1	47.3	41.3	33.1
17	245.78	2.0	78.3	62.7	52.2	44.8	39.2	31.3
18	258.77	1.9	74.4	59.5	49.6	42.5	37.2	29.8
19	271.75	1.8	70.8	56.7	47.2	40.5	35.4	28.3
20	284.74	1.8	67.6	54.1	45.1	38.6	33.8	27.0

Table 2: **Max Detectable Velocity (± cm/s) for Given Transmit Frequency (f_0)**

Note: The observant reader will have noticed that the PRP listed is greater than the imaging depth multiplied by 13μsec per cm. A certain amount of overhead is necessary for setting up each transmitted line. This "overhead" time has been included so as to yield more accurate line time estimates.

15. The Presence of a Spectral Window

Notice in the PW spectrum of *Figure 37* that there is a spectral window (the open area between the spectrum and the baseline). The sample volume is 0.05 cm. In this case, the sample volume is small relative to the diameter of the vessel and is placed in the center of the vessel. Since most of the blood traveling through the sample volume is traveling at the same velocity, there is relatively little spread around the mean velocity. The presence of a spectral window indicates the presence of laminar flow. However, the absence of a spectral window may or may not indicate turbulence. (See Chapter 12 on hemodynamics.) Caution must be taken not to over interpret this criterion in the absence of a spectral window.

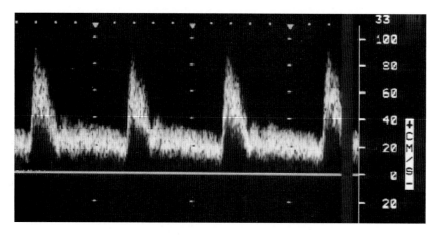

Fig. 37 **PW Doppler Spectral Window**

Pegasus Lectures, Inc.

For example, the spectrum in *Figure 38* is taken from the exact same vessel using the same size sample volume, located closer to the vessel wall in the elevation direction. In this case, the sample volume incorporated lower velocity flow close to the vessel wall. Note how the spectrum is filled in at lower velocities (closer to the baseline) from the slower blood velocities registered along the vessel walls. It is important to realize that increasing the sample volume size will also fill in the spectral window. If the sample volume were made large enough to interrogate the entire vessel, the peak velocity would remain as in the previous spectrum. A spectrum with little or no spectral window similar to this spectrum would be created using CW Doppler, which is effectively an infinitely large PW sample volume.

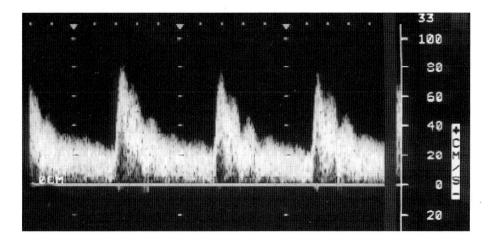

Fig. 38   **PW Doppler (decreasing spectral window)**

16. PW Versus CW Comparison

PW	CW
Good range resolution *(Not perfect: see range ambiguity)*	No range specificity *(Unless derived from other modalities)*
Aliasing: limited maximum detectable velocity *(Nyquist limited)*	Virtually unlimited maximum detectable velocity *(High A/D converter rate is limit)*
Deeper maximum focus *(Can use full-aperture since transmit and receive are separated in time)*	Shallower maximum focus *(Can only use half aperture since transmit and receive are concurrent)*
Possible to visualize spectral window for laminar flow *(For small sample volumes in the center of large healthy vessels, with appropriate gain and insonification angle, spectral window exists)*	Rarely visualize spectral window *(Low and high velocities are received simultaneously so filling to baseline is normal)*
Greater potential sensitivity *(Can use full aperture for transmit, receive, and are not as restricted by thermal issues)*	Potentially less sensitive *(Usually less sensitive than PW, but depends on gate size, alignment to flow, thermal limits, depth of focus, etc.)*
Less restricted by thermal bioeffect risks *(Lower I_{SPTA})*	More restricted by thermal bioeffect risks *(Higher I_{SPTA} implies potentially lower sensitivity)*

Table 3: **PW Versus CW Comparison**

17. PW Range Ambiguity

17.1 Dispelling the Myth

PW Doppler is often said to have perfect range resolution. This statement implies that the Doppler signal from a PW Doppler can only emanate from the desired Doppler gate depth. This statement is not true. In reality, standard PW Doppler always receives signals from depths which correspond to multiples of the pulse repetition period (PRP). This artifact has been well understood in radar for many years and is called range ambiguity.

17.2 The Mechanism that Causes Range Ambiguity

We will use *Figure 39* to illustrate the cause of this artifact. Assume that the first transmit pulse occurs at time T_0. From time T_0 to time T_1, the sound has traveled from the transducer to the desired gate depth. From time T_1 to time T_2, the transmit pulse continues to travel within the medium to the 1st ambiguous gate depth. Simultaneously the echo from the desired gate depth returns to the transducer. At time T_2, since the echo from the first transmit is received, a second transmit pulse is fired. From time T_2 to time T_3, the pulse from the second transmit pulse has reached the desired gate depth. Simultaneously, the echo of the first transmit pulse has traveled from the 1st ambiguous gate location and arrived at the Doppler gate location. The 1st ambiguous gate echo from the first transmit is added to the echo from the desired Doppler gate of the second transmit. From time T_3 to time T_4, this combined echo returns to the transducer. At time T_4, the echo is received and the third transmit occurs. The process continues such that every subsequent echo is really a sum of echoes from multiples of the roundtrip distance that the sound travels in the time between transmits, or the pulse repetition period, (PRP). Hence PW Doppler is actually always receiving echoes from multiple gates at the same time.

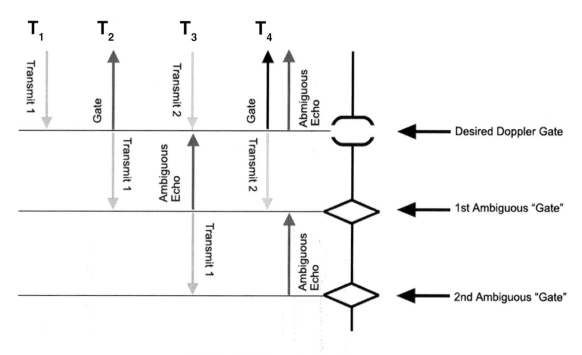

Fig. 39   **PW Range Ambiguity**

View Animation and Image Library CD

17.3 Important Questions about Range Ambiguity and Mitigating Factors

Given that this artifact always exists in PW Doppler, there are two very important questions to answer: "How often does this artifact occur and go unrecognized?" and "How can you tell when this artifact is affecting the Doppler spectrum?"

This artifact affects the Doppler spectrum somewhat frequently and is almost always unrecognized. There are, however, mitigating factors which reduce the occurrence or severity of the range ambiguity artifact in PW Doppler, such as:

1. There may be no blood flow at the ambiguous gate locations.
2. The signals from the ambiguous gates are generally weaker than from the desired Doppler gate.
3. There is more attenuation from deeper depths.
4. Electronic (phased) transducers focus the beam at the Doppler gate, making the beam more diffuse (less intense) at the ambiguous gate locations. (This is not true for fixed focus transducers which generally experience range ambiguity worse than phased arrays.)

17.4 Risk Factors
The greatest risk of range ambiguity occurring exists when the Doppler gate is shallow. When the Doppler gate is shallow, the ambiguous gate locations are still relatively shallow. The resulting echoes from these ambiguous locations may or may not be strong enough to affect the Doppler spectrum. The probability is increased when mechanical transducers are used. Since mechanical transducers have a fixed focus, usually set as deep as possible, the beam cannot intentionally be made more diffuse at the ambiguous gate location. As a result, attenuation due to beam divergence cannot be utilized to help discriminate signals from the desired gate location and the ambiguous gate location.

17.5 Determining if Range Ambiguity is Present
The easiest way to ascertain whether or not range ambiguity is present is to change the PRF (Doppler scales). Changing the Doppler scales should only scale the Doppler spectrum and not change the basic characteristic of the spectrum. Changing the PRF changes the PRP and hence, the location of the ambiguous gate. If changing the scale results in a change in the characteristic shape of the spectrum, range ambiguity is present.

18. HPRF Doppler

18.1 Using the Trade-offs
As we have just learned, PW generally has good range resolution but is prone to aliasing. CW has virtually no range resolution but virtually unlimited maximum detectable velocities. High pulse repetition frequency Doppler (HPRF) is a compromise of these two modes. HPRF Doppler intentionally utilizes the artifact of range ambiguity to increase the maximum detectable velocity without aliasing, at the expense of some range resolution.

18.2 Using Range Ambiguity to Create HPRF Doppler
In PW, the minimum PRP (maximum PRF), is determined by the Doppler gate depth. A deeper gate results in a longer travel time and hence, a lower maximum PRF. The first schema depicted in *Figure 40* shows standard PW Doppler with a relatively deep Doppler gate depth such that the PRF is relatively low. Note that the beam is focused at the Doppler gate depth. The second schema depicts standard PW Doppler with a shallower gate depth. Note that the ambiguous gate happens to align with the desired gate depth of the first schema. Since the gate depth is shallower, the PRF is higher than the first schema. Note that the beam focus is again set at the Doppler gate depth. The third schema demonstrates how high pulse repetition frequency (HPRF) Doppler functions. HPRF uses the timing of the shallower gate depth with the focusing of the deeper depth to achieve higher PRF's with improved sensitivity at the desired depth.

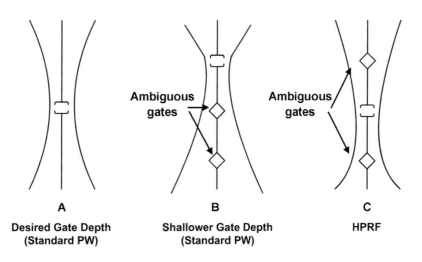

A

Desired Gate Depth
(Standard PW)

Ambiguous
gates

B

Shallower Gate Depth
(Standard PW)

Ambiguous
gates

C

HPRF

Fig. 40   **Range Ambiguity Exploited to Create HPRF Doppler**

Note that the diamonds on the HPRF Doppler steer line demonstrate the locations of the ambiguous gates.

The value of HPRF Doppler is the ability to achieve higher PRFs at deeper gate depths. The trade-off is that HPRF allows for some range ambiguity shallower than the Doppler gate to achieve the higher PRFs. Therefore, HPRF Doppler has range ambiguity both above and below the desired gate location. Standard PW also has range ambiguity, but the ambiguous gates are only at locations deeper than the desired gate depth. In HPRF, these "ambiguous" gate locations are usually indicated by diamonds on the steer line. If these diamonds do not overlay any regions of flow, then no extraneous flow is being registered and there is no source for problems or confusion. If these diamonds overlay a region of low velocity flow, then there is also not likely a significant issue since there must be high velocity in the actual Doppler gate or HPRF would not be activated in the first place. The only real issue occurs when the diamond overlays a region where there is also very high velocities. By changing the scales, the location of the ambiguous gates (represented by the diamonds) can be moved in the hopes of registering only the high velocity flow from the desired gate location. On most systems, the activation of HPRF is automatic when the user increases the Doppler scales past the depth-restricted limit. When HPRF is activated, all systems notify the user with the display of the diamonds and many systems usually add the title HPRF above the spectrum.

19. Doppler Insonification Angle and Error Sources

19.1 Cardiac and Alignment with Flow
Since the Doppler effect is angle dependent, modern systems allow for angle correction of Doppler measurements. In cardiac, the insonification angle is presumed to be 0 degrees or 180 degrees such that 100% of the Doppler shift is detected, and no correction is needed. For vascular Doppler, the angle can vary considerably, and angle correction is commonly employed.

In cardiac imaging, because of the number of different imaging windows (apical, parasternal, sub-costal, and the suprasternal notch) as well as the ability to move to different intercostal spaces, the ability to achieve insonification angles close to either 0 degrees or 180 degrees generally holds true. When the angle deviates from these ideal angles, the angular error is generally small enough relative to other error sources in ultrasound so as to be ignored. However, there are times when the angle to flow deviates more than normal where the velocities recorded will have enough error so as to be significant. To fully understand the relationship between the angle and the velocity measurement accuracy, we will need to review the cosine function.

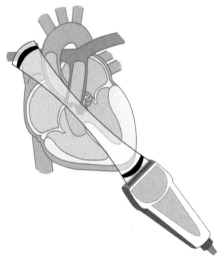

Fig. 41   **CW Doppler Beam Alignment with Ascending Aorta (180°)**

19.2 Vascular Doppler and the Need to Angle Correct

Before reviewing the cosine, we should also discuss the prevalence of angle errors in vascular Doppler. Unlike cardiac, vascular Doppler applications frequently are restricted to views where the vessel is parallel to the skin surface. The result is a less than optimum angle formed between the beam and the flow. In fact, quite frequently, without steering or transducer angulation, the insonification angle is the worst possible, 90 degrees. Through steering and angulation, angles of 60 degrees or less are generally achievable. Since the cosine of 60 degrees is only 0.5, clearly, angle correction is going to be a critical component of an accurate assessment.

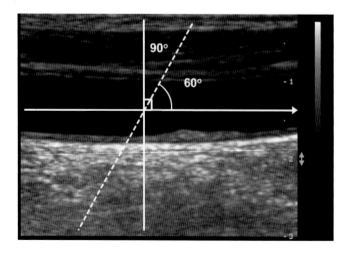

Fig. 42   **With No Steering, Doppler Angle to Flow is Commonly Close to 90⁰**

19.3 Review of the Cosine

In Chapter 1 we discussed the details of the cosine of a varying angle. The following is a plot of the cosine of the angle (y-axis) versus varying angles (x-axis).

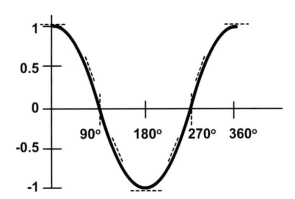

Fig. 43   **The Slope of the Cosine Function and Error**

From the shape of the cosine curve, the non-linear aspect of the cosine is most likely evident. Notice that the rate of change of the cosine is very slow at angles close to zero degrees. The rate of change is determined by the slope and is indicated by the dotted tangential lines on the graph. In other words, for small deviations in angles around zero degrees, the associated measurement error is relatively small. Notice that as the angle becomes larger, the rate of change increases (slope steepens). The rate of change reaches a maximum at 90 degrees, where the cosine itself reaches zero. The registered Doppler shift will be zero at an angle of 90 degrees or close to 90 degrees because of the rejection caused by the wall filters. At this point, the error in the measurement is infinite. As the angle progresses from 90 degrees towards 180 degrees, the rate of change decreases. At 180 degrees, the slope flattens out, and the error associated with angular error is as small as it was at 0 degrees.

19.4 Peak Velocity and Pressure Gradient

The peak velocity measurement is usually made so that a pressure gradient can be calculated (discussed in Chapters 12 and 13). The pressure gradient is calculated from the modified Bernoulli' equation, by squaring the peak velocity. Any error in the peak velocity thereby is squared, making the error in the pressure gradient explode rapidly with increasing velocity error. Since the angular error associated with the cosine is non-linear, and the pressure gradient relationship is non-linear, it is imperative that you understand how significant "small angular errors" can become.

19.5 Angle Correction Error (5 Degree Table)

Table 4 demonstrates the velocity error and the pressure error associated with only a 5 degree error in angle correction, relative to various insonification angles from 0 degrees to 80 degrees. The first column represents the assumed insonification angle. The second column represents the cosine if the actual angle is 5 degrees larger than the presumed angle represented in Column 1. Similarly, the third column represents the cosine if the actual angle is 5 degrees less than the presumed angle of Column 1. Column 4 represents the associated percentage overestimation in velocity. Column 5 represents the associated percentage underestimation in velocity. Column 6 represents the associated percentage overestimation error in the calculated pressure, and the last column represents the associated percentage underestimation in the calculated pressure.

Angle	Cosine		% Velocity		% Pressure	
Degrees	> Angle (5°)	< Angle (5°)	Overestimation	Underestimation	Overestimation	Underestimation
0	0.99619	0.99619	0.38%	0.38%	0.77%	0.77%
10	0.96593	0.99619	1.95%	-1.14%	3.95%	-2.27%
20	0.90631	0.96593	3.68%	-2.72%	7.50%	-5.36%
30	0.81915	0.90631	5.72%	-4.44%	11.77%	-8.69%
40	0.70711	0.81915	8.34%	-6.48%	17.36%	-12.55%
50	0.57358	0.70711	12.07%	-9.10%	25.59%	-17.36%
60	0.42262	0.57358	18.31%	-12.83%	39.97%	-24.01%
70	0.25882	0.42262	32.15%	-19.07%	74.63%	-34.51%
80	0.08716	0.25882	99.24%	-32.91%	296.96%	-54.99%

Table 4: **Angle Correction Error (5 degree error)**

This table represents the errors of only a 5 degree angular error. You should note that even if you were always capable of specifying the insonification angle within 5 degrees in the lateral plane, (which is not probable), you still have not accounted for the angular error in the elevation plane. As you can see from the table, as the insonification angle gets larger, the error grows extremely rapidly. In fact, at larger angles, there are other error sources which have not been accounted for such as spectral broadening. The take home lesson is that extreme care must be made when assessing Doppler angles. Effort should be made to completely interrogate the vessel to make certain of the appropriate alignment in the elevation direction. Additionally, it should be clear how even well performed studies can have significant error sources which must be accounted for when interpreting.

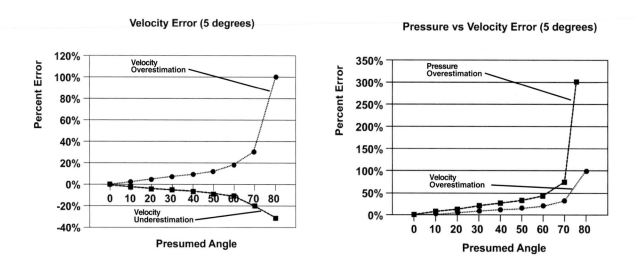

Fig. 44 **Velocity Over and Underestimation**   *Fig. 45* **Pressure Versus Velocity Overestimation**

In Level 3, another table is included which demonstrates the effects of a 10 degree error in angle.

20. Color Flow

The Blessing and the Curse
The addition of color imaging to ultrasound has been both a blessing and a curse. On the one hand, color is an invaluable tool that generally makes detecting disease simpler and faster. Unlike spectral Doppler (a non-scanned modality), color offers a wonderful survey tool to quickly assess a large region of the patient. These are the blessings, now for the curse. Color does not give full spectral information. Color Doppler yields only an estimate of the mean velocity. There are many hemodynamic situations where the mean will appear normal whereas the spectral Doppler will indicate the presence of disease. The temptation to over interpret color information is great. Color is certainly a powerful, useful, and even indispensable tool, but rarely should color Doppler be used as the sole means of assessing severity of disease, if ever. As long as this fact is always part of the equation, the curse goes away and color becomes what it should be, a powerful tool that corroborates the findings of all other modalities being utilized.

21. Color Doppler Versus Spectral Doppler

Differences in Gating Techniques for Doppler Modalities
Color Doppler uses the Doppler effect and then correlates the frequency shifts recorded to estimate the mean flow velocity and variance. In juxtaposition to spectral Doppler, color Doppler has a distinct advantage of providing flow information over a large spatial area; whereas spectral Doppler provides information along a specific line or within a specified gate range. Color is able to provide this spatial information because of two distinct differences with respect to how spectral Doppler is performed. First, color Doppler is a scanned modality, whereas spectral Doppler is a non-scanned modality. The scanning in color Doppler produces the lateral dimension not present in spectral Doppler. Second, after producing the transmit pulse, color Doppler listens with a series of "range gates" which span the entire time until the next transmit pulse is produced. In this way, color receives pixel-by-pixel information to determine the spatial data for the depth direction. *Figure 46* demonstrates the difference between pulsed wave Doppler, CW Doppler, HPRF Doppler, and color Doppler.

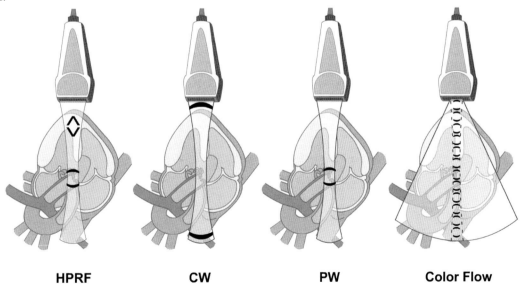

HPRF   **CW**   **PW**   **Color Flow**

Fig. 46   **Comparison of "Receive Gates" for HPRF, CW, PW, and Color Flow Doppler**

Although color provides information over spatial dimensions, color does not provide peak velocities, velocity gradients, or spectral broadening characteristics. Note that no FFT is performed on color Doppler. In spectral Doppler, an FFT is performed so that spectral analysis and quantification can be performed. In color Doppler, no FFT is performed since there are not enough data samples per individual location (color is a scanned modality) and furthermore there would be no way of displaying the results. In spectral Doppler, the physical display axes are frequency and time. For color Doppler, the two physical display axes are the spatial coordinates of depth and width. For spectral Doppler, the imaginary third axis is amplitude; for color it is a mean velocity estimator.

22. Overview of How Color Doppler is Performed

22.1 Similarities of Color to Spectral Doppler and 2-D Imaging

In terms of how data is processed in ultrasound, the processing for color Doppler is perhaps the least understood by ultrasound practitioners. This lack of understanding most likely stems from the fact that color Doppler behaves in some aspects like spectral Doppler, in some aspects like 2-D, and in other aspects like neither. Color Doppler creates an image by repeatedly scanning a single line in the same direction to create what is called a color packet (or color ensemble) and then scans the packets across the body to produce a frame. So in some sense, color data is produced like spectral Doppler data in that a single line is transmitted repeatedly in the same direction (non-scanned). In another sense, color data is produced like a 2-D image since packets of acoustic lines are scanned across the body. Furthermore, color Doppler relies on Doppler frequency shifts like spectral Doppler but also relies on spatial information to produce an image, like 2-D. Unlike spectral Doppler, color Doppler produces an estimate of the mean velocity, not a full distribution of signals. Unlike 2-D imaging, the signal intensity is not interpretable from the brightness of a pixel on the color image.

22.2 Creating the Color Scan

As already mentioned, color Doppler is produced by transmitting a single line in a specific direction and then repeating that single line a number of times (usually between 4 and 12) creating what is called a packet. The Doppler information is obtained by a series of range gates within each acoustic line of the packet. A correlation is then performed using each of the lines within the packet to yield an estimated mean velocity at each range gate along the line (where each successive range gate in time corresponds to deeper depths). The direction of the line is then changed and a new packet is then transmitted in the new direction. The same correlation process is repeated, and a new transmit direction chosen until eventually information is acquired from the scan region in the area of interest.

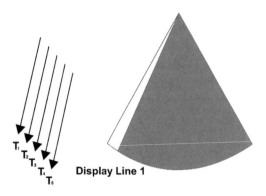

Display Line 1

Fig. 47 **Illustration of a Color Packet of 5 Acoustic Lines to Produce One Color Display Line**

View Animation and Image Library CD

22.3 Temporal Resolution and Color

In Chapter 4 we learned how to calculate the acoustic frame rate. At that time, we made reference to the fact that color Doppler has the worst temporal resolution of all the ultrasound modalities. From the description of how a scan is created, the reason should now be clear. Since every color line displayed on the screen represents an entire packet of acoustic lines, creating an entire color scan requires many more acoustic lines than creating an entire conventional 2-D scan. As a result, a higher frame time results in a lower frame rate (frequency). A lower frame rate implies a greater likelihood of not capturing a short duration event. For this reason, color Doppler is not well suited for determining timing parameters or timing accuracy.

22.4 Color Display and Velocity Interpretation

The processing of color data is really a series of steps. Once a packet has been transmitted and a correlation performed, the data is filtered and colors assigned on a pixel-by-pixel basis based on a color scale or color bar. The color bar is really a "key" which relates mean frequency shifts detected with a color. When a certain color is displayed on the screen, the user can then look at the color scale to determine approximately what mean frequency shift corresponds with that color. As we have already shown through the Doppler equation, the frequency shift can be translated into a velocity measurement. However, interpreting velocity from color Doppler can be somewhat misleading since the frequency shift detected is greatly affected by the angle formed between the ultrasound beam and the flow direction (the insonification angle). As a result, if the angle is close to 0 degrees or 180 degrees, then the velocity displayed potentially can be relatively close to the true mean velocity. However, as the angle varies and becomes closer to 90 degrees or 270 degrees, then the velocity displayed may only be weakly related to the true mean velocity.

22.4.1 Toward and Away

Since it is desirable to know direction as well as velocity, the color bar has a plus and minus direction. The plus direction implies that the flow is toward the transducer, or equivalently that the insonification angle is less than 90 degrees. The negative direction implies that there will be a negative frequency shift and that the insonification angle is greater than 90 degrees. If no plus and minus are indicated on the scale, and there is no text such as "color invert" then the plus is assumed to be on top and the minus assumed to be on the bottom. In the center of the color bar is a black band which represents the baseline and the color wall filters. If no frequency shift is detected or a low frequency is detected but filtered out, there is an absence of color in the image.

22.4.2 How the System Applies a Color Map

The way in which the color map is applied by the system is to look pixel-by-pixel across the scanned color region. Each pixel is assessed for whether or not there is a signal above a color noise threshold, and if so, what is the associated frequency shift. If the signal is too weak (below the color noise threshold) no color will be assigned to that pixel. In other words, even if there is motion, if the signal is too weak, then the pixel will present as black, which may then be misinterpreted as the absence of flow. If the signal is stronger than the threshold, the frequency shift and direction is compared against the maximum frequency shift of the color scale (the Nyquist limit) and a color assigned. In essence, the display of color images goes through a digital "go, no go" process. Once a signal is determined to be above the threshold, a higher signal causes no change in how that particular pixel is displayed.

Since color is performed over a region, the spatial distribution of the signal is often interpreted to give an estimate of many flow parameters. Color flow is widely valued because it is relatively quick and simple to appreciate global hemodynamic conditions.

23. Time Correlated Color

Besides the Doppler based approach to color just described, there is another approach called "time correlated" color. Time correlated color effectively uses the distance equation and correlates the most commonly occurring time shifts to determine blood velocity. This technique provides a modal velocity (the most commonly occurring velocity) and like color Doppler, cannot supply peak velocity quantification, flow gradients, or spectral broadening characteristics.

Mean velocities (from color Doppler) and modal velocities (from time correlated color) generally cannot be compared with peak velocities. Both the mean and modal velocities can change with the presence of turbulence or even as the result of using different range gate sizes. In addition, using different receive gain, wall filtering, and pre and post processing settings can significantly alter these measurements.

24. Color Gain

Like the receiver gain for 2-D imaging, the color gain amplifies the signal after it has been received back from the patient. Also like 2-D, increasing the color gain can affect the "apparent signal-to-noise" but not the true signal-to-noise ratio since both the signal and the noise are amplified together.

Color Doppler gain behaves differently than 2-D imaging and spectral Doppler gain. With 2-D imaging or spectral Doppler, increasing or decreasing the gain increases or decreases the display intensity of the signal on the screen. For color Doppler, increasing the color gain may have no visible effect on the signal over a certain range of the gain knob for certain signals. On the other hand, increasing the gain may have a profound effect on the amount of color displayed. This behavior is very different than 2-D or spectral Doppler where an increase in gain results in an increase in display intensity no matter what the imaging situation. For color, a pixel is either colorized to represent a specific flow velocity or is not based on a threshold. Every pixel that represents a specific velocity will have the same intensity, regardless of the signal strength. Thus, if the color signal at a certain location is higher than the noise threshold, the pixel is colorized. If the signal is lower than that same threshold, then the pixel is not colorized. Therefore, if there is very poor signal-to-noise, there may be no apparent effect on the color image over a wide range of gain increase. Similarly, very strong signals may show no change in appearance over a wide gain range. Ultimately, if the color is overgained, the color noise floor will become visible as color speckle within the image.

24.1 Setting the Appropriate Color Gain
The correct way to set the color gain is to increase the gain until noise speckle just becomes apparent and then decrease the color gain until the color speckle disappears. The noise will appear as random speckles of color distributed throughout the entire color region. The idea behind this technique is to optimize the ability to display weak signals, while not displaying artifacts associated with overgaining. When overgaining occurs, the color signals tend to bleed into neighboring regions, making the color region appear larger than reality. The following panel of images demonstrates the presence of moderate noise speckle, excessive noise speckle, and then appropriate color gain so that noise speckle is absent.

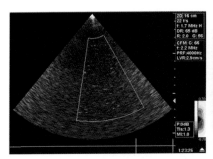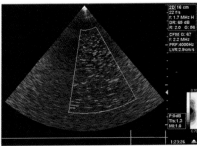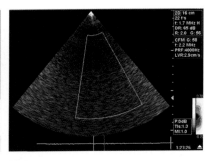

Fig. 48   **The Color Noise Floor (Color Speckle)**

View Animation and Image Library CD

25. Interpreting the Color Bar Relative to Spectral Doppler

Recall that directionality is known from the Doppler equation by determining if the Doppler shift is positive or negative relative to the operating frequency. Flow towards the transducer creates a positive frequency shift, while flow away from the transducer creates a negative frequency shift. In spectral Doppler, the direction is indicated by whether the flow is presented above or below the baseline, unless spectral invert is activated, which results in flow towards the transducer displayed below the baseline and flow away from the transducer displayed above the baseline. For color Doppler, directionality is indicated by the colors on the color bar. Using the figure below, you should note the similarities between the color bar and the display parameters of the Doppler spectrum.

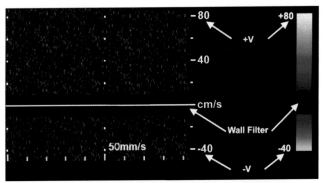

Fig. 49   **Color Bar Relation to Spectral Display**

26. Color Invert and Aliasing

Just as with spectral Doppler, attention must be paid to whether or not the spectral or color invert is on, so as to appropriately determine flow direction. For the color bar in *Figure 49*, since color invert is not on, flow towards the transducer is represented by the color above the baseline (red in this case). In spectral Doppler, higher velocity flows are represented higher above the baseline. Similarly, as the velocity increases, the color transitions up the color bar (from shades of red to shades of yellow for this color bar). If the velocity, or, equivalently, frequency shift, goes beyond the maximum detectable velocity or frequency shift, aliasing occurs. With spectral Doppler, when aliasing occurs, the spectrum wraps over the top and returns from the bottom. Similarly, with color Doppler, the color representation wraps from the color at the top of the color bar to the color which appears at the bottom of the color bar (yellow to light blue). Obviously, the reverse occurs if the flow aliasing occurs in the opposite direction.

27. Color Wall Filters

27.1 Wall Filter and Color Scale Integrated

In spectral Doppler, separate controls are given for both the wall filters and the PRF (Doppler scales). The user is therefore allowed to change either of these parameters independent of the other. In color Doppler, most systems build the function of wall filtering into the PRF knob. In other words, by changing the color PRF (Nyquist limit), the wall filter is also (usually unwittingly) changed. As a result, increasing the color scale increases the corner frequency of the color wall filter. Similarly, decreasing the Nyquist limit on the color bar (PRF) decreases the corner frequency of the color wall filter.

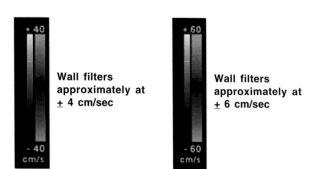

Wall filters approximately at ± 4 cm/sec

Wall filters approximately at ± 6 cm/sec

Note: When trying to detect low velocity flows with color, you must make certain to lower the color scale. If you do not lower the color scales, the integrated wall filters will be too high, and will eliminate the very signals you are trying to detect.

Fig. 50   **Wall Filters as a Percentage of Color Scales**

27.2 The Absence of Color

As already mentioned, for color Doppler, the wall filters are represented as the black band in the center (around the baseline) of the color bar. This black band represents that either the flow was not detected (velocity or frequency shift of 0), or that the detected velocity (or frequency shift) was low enough such that they were eliminated by the wall filters. Therefore, a black area on a color image could be the result of no flow, an angle at or close to 90°, or low frequency shifts rejected by the wall filters. Additionally, a black region could represent an area where the signal was too weak to be detected by the color Doppler circuitry or too weak to overcome the noise threshold (poor signal-to-noise). It is critical to understand that a black region within a region where there is blood does not necessarily represent blood that is static. *Figure 51* demonstrates how changing the scales (which affect the wall filters) can dramatically affect visualization of flow. In *Figure 51*, the flow is in the portal vein.

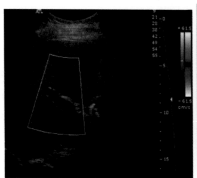 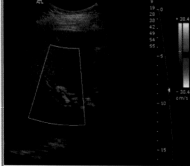 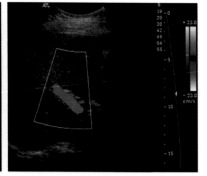

High scales (61.5 cm/sec)
High wall filter

Intermediate scales (38 cm/sec)
Intermediate wall filter

Low scales (23 cm/sec)
Low wall filter

Fig. 51   **Color Wall Filter Effects**

27.3 Interpreting the Color Bar Relative to Nyquist and the Wall Filters

The following color bar illustrates how a typical color bar is interpreted relative to the Nyquist limit (PRF) and the color wall filter. Notice that the black band in the center is approximately 10% of the Nyquist limit.

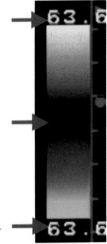

This value represents that the highest mean velocity detectable is 63.6 cm/sec toward the transducer. Flow toward the transducer with a mean velocity of 63.6 cm/sec would be displayed as yellow according to this color scale.

The black band vaguely expresses the fact that signals with detected velocities in this range are not likely to be visualized (colorized as black). However, weak signals at higher velocities also may not be visualized because the color wall filters do not have a sharp corner frequency like spectral wall filters (as discussed in the upcoming paragraphs and graphs.)

This value represents that the highest mean velocity detectable is 63.6 cm/sec away from the transducer. Flow "away" with a mean velocity of 63.6 cm/sec would be displayed as aqua, according to this color scale.

Fig. 52 **Interpreting the Color Bar**

Some systems allow the user to adjust the wall filter percentage. In other words, the user can determine at what percentage of the PRF the wall filter corner frequency is set. For example, imagine that filter setting 1 represents 10% and filter setting 2 represents 20%. If the PRF is set to $\pm$ 100 cm/sec, the first wall filter setting would put the wall filter corner at 10 cm/sec, whereas the second wall filter setting would set the wall filter at 20 cm/sec. If the PRF were changed to 150 cm/sec, the filter 1 setting would set the wall filters at 15 cm/sec, and the filter 2 setting would result in the wall filters being set at 30 cm/sec.

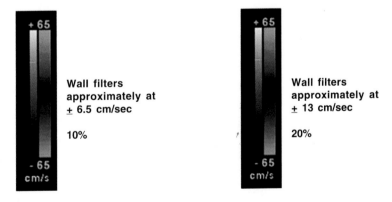

Fig. 53 **Variable Percentage of Nyquist Wall Filter Control**

View Animation and Image Library CD

28. Determining Flow Direction in Color Doppler

28.1 Why Colors Change Even When Velocity Doesn't

Figure 54 nicely demonstrates how flow in a straight vessel, with no flow disturbance can be displayed with colors at either end of the color bar just by variations in the angle between the observer line and the flow direction (the insonification angle). Because a sector transducer steers the beam at different angles to create an image, the steering direction is different across the entire image. As a result, the angle to flow changes across a straight vessel.

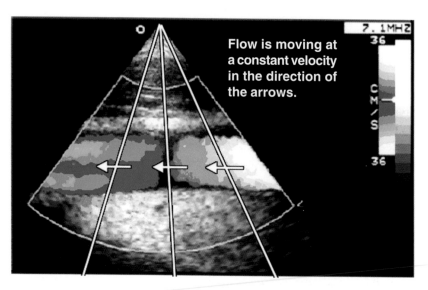

Fig. 54 **Insonification Angle and Displayed Color**

 **View Animation and Image Library CD**

Notice how in the center of the vessel, there is a black band, or color dropout. This color dropout exists not because there is an absence of flow, but because the insonification angle is close to 90 degrees and because the wall filters are eliminating low frequency shifts at that particular location in the image. On the far extreme right of the vessel notice that the velocity displayed looks higher (lighter hues) than the velocity closer to the center (darker red). Similarly, notice how the flow just to the left of the centerline of the image looks as if it is traveling more slowly (darker blue hues) than the flow farther to the left side of the image (lighter blue hues). This perception of changes in velocity is purely the result of the angular effects, and not because there is an actual change in velocity within the vessel.

Note: This type of image is frequently included on the credentialing boards. Besides asking about the color dropout related to insonification angle, the direction of flow is commonly asked. In the upcoming sections, we will learn how to correctly interpret flow direction, regardless of image shape, steering versus non-steering, aliasing, and even tortuosity.

28.2 Defining the Insonification Angle

In Section 8.2 of Level 1, we specified that the Doppler insonification angle is always measured between the head of the flow (where the flow is going to) and the steered beam direction. Since color is a Doppler technique dependent on the same equation as spectral Doppler, the angle to flow in color is measured the same way as in spectral Doppler. Any approach to determine color Doppler direction which does not start out with recognizing the true insonification angle is a "trick" which will lead to mistakes, not just on exams but also in the clinical world. The insonification angle must be properly identified since the angle is precisely what determines how color is presented on the system. Unlike "trick" techniques sometimes used (which only work for non-aliased flow in a non-tortuous vessel using a sector transducer), this technique will work for non-steered linear images, steered linear images, curved-linear images, sectors, and even in the presence of tortuosity.

28.3 Cosine Revisited

Once the angle is correctly identified, determining the directionality is a relatively straightforward task. When the angle to flow is less than 90 degrees, the flow direction is considered toward the transducer. Since the cosine of an angle less than 90 degrees is positive, the flow will be presented in whatever color is associated with the plus on the color bar. (If no plus sign exists, the color on top is assumed to be positive.) When the insonification angle is greater than 90 degrees, the cosine is negative and hence the color of the flow will match the colors associated with the negative sign on the color bar.

Figure 55 demonstrates the use of color invert, imaging the same flow during the same phase of the cardiac cycle.

Note: Be careful not to presume that red always means towards the transducer and that blue always indicates away from the transducer. There are an infinite number of color maps possible, and the mere application of color invert can reverse what you have come to expect.

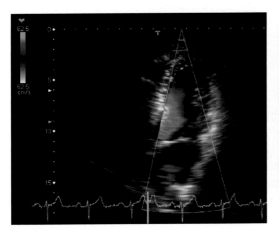 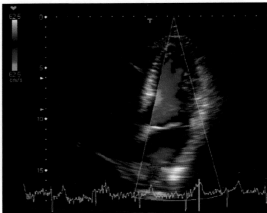

Fig. 55   **Color Invert**

View Animation and Image Library CD

28.4 Step-by-Step Approach
1. Determine the Steering Direction Throughout the Image

The critical first step to determining flow direction is identifying the steer directions throughout the image. Changing the steer direction alters the insonification angle and hence, can easily result in flow perceived as "towards" becoming flow perceived as "away." This need to be able to determine steer direction in an image was one of the motivating factors for learning how different transducers function. From an image, the color steer angle can be determined by looking at the direction of the color wedge or sector. The steer angle can also often be determined by looking for color dropout where the insonification angle equals 90°.

The following images demonstrate how the steering direction is indicated for various image formats. Note that in each image, three or four locations were arbitrarily chosen to assess the steering directions.

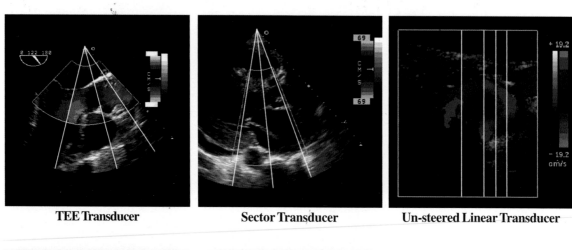

| TEE Transducer | Sector Transducer | Un-steered Linear Transducer |

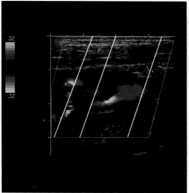
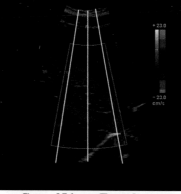

Beam Directions for each Format
A. Sector phased arrays produce beams that fan out from the top of the image to the bottom.
B. Linear arrays always produce an image with parallel beams (both steered and un-steered color boxes).
C. Curved-linear arrays always produce beams that are perpendicular to the very top and very bottom of the image.

Steered Linear Transducer   Curved Linear Transducer

Fig. 56 **Determining the Steering Direction**

2. Draw Directionless Flow Lines

In Step 1 we specified the steering direction. Since the angle to flow is formed between the steering direction and the flow direction, we now need to indicate the direction of flow. We will perform this step in two stages by first drawing in directionless flow lines and then assessing actual flow direction.

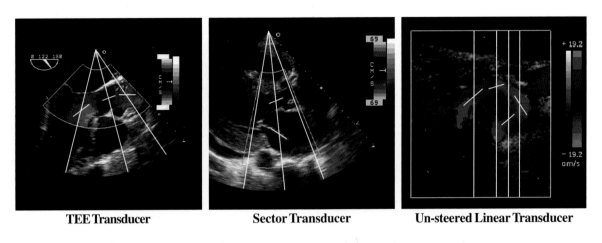

TEE Transducer Sector Transducer Un-steered Linear Transducer

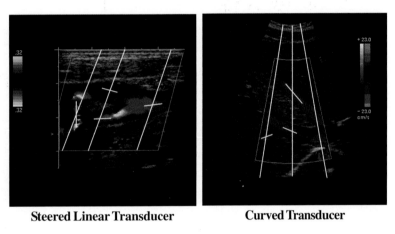

Steered Linear Transducer Curved Transducer

Fig. 57 **Directionless Flow Lines**

3. Read the Color Bar

The color bar is the "legend" or "key" which dictates the presentation color for positive and negative shifts. First check to make sure that color invert is not activated. If color invert is activated, then you must find the color which is associated with the positive sign. If color invert is not on, then the color on the top of the bar represents flow "toward" the transducer, or an angle that is less than 90 degrees. You must also now assess the "negative" direction color from the color bar.

4. Assign Directions (arrowheads)

Within the image, find the regions that are presented in the "positive" colors. Excluding aliasing (discussed in a moment), the angle that is formed between the steer line and the flow indicator must be less than 90 degrees. Therefore, you can now add the arrowhead on the side of the flow indicator that results in an angle less than 90 degrees. Similarly, find the negative colors in the image. Again excluding aliasing, you should now be able to add a directional arrow to the flow indicator, since these angles should be greater than 90 degrees.

Remember - the insonification angle at a point in an image is always measured between the arrow head back toward the line of sight (steering line) from the transducer.

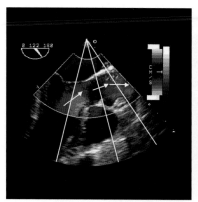

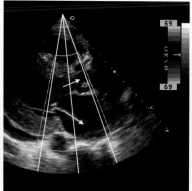
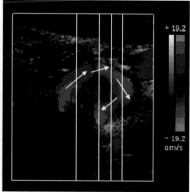

TEE Transducer   **Sector Transducer**   **Un-steered Linear Transducer**

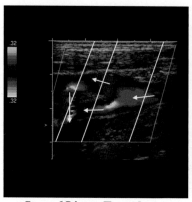

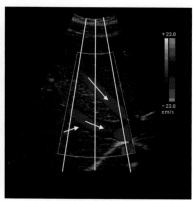

Steered Linear Transducer   **Curved Transducer**

Fig. 58   **Assign Flow Directions**

View Animation and Image Library CD

5. Recognizing Aliasing and Applying Common Sense

Within the steered linear image of *Figure 58*, you will notice that the flow indicator farthest to the left is actually an angle much greater than 90 degrees. From the color scale, this region of flow should be presented as red. However, the flow is blue and the flow direction indicated is correct. The reason is simple, there is aliasing occurring. The reason for this aliasing is twofold: first the flow has gone around a corner which requires acceleration, and second and more importantly, the angle to flow has become almost 180 degrees. Recall that the greatest Doppler shifts are recorded at 0 degrees and 180 degrees. A higher Doppler shift implies a greater likelihood of aliasing. The other insonification angles specified are very close to 90 degrees where very little shift is recorded. Therefore, it should make sense that aliasing would occur in this one location.

You must always consider the reasons why higher Doppler shifts can be detected in assessing the likelihood of aliasing as well as the color scale setting. Low color scales are much more likely to result in aliasing than high scale settings. In addition to angular effects, geometric flow conditions such as a narrowing, a corner, and being closer to the center-stream all result in higher velocities which should result in higher frequency shifts.

Consider the following example:

To avoid being tricked by aliasing, always start by assessing flow direction in regions where the lowest Doppler shifts would be detected such as near vessel walls, away from narrowings in the flow path, and where the Doppler angles are worst (away from 0 and 180 degrees).

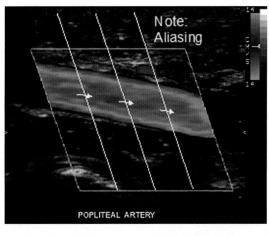

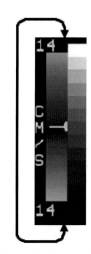

Fig. 59 **Centerstream Aliased Color Flow**   *Fig. 60* **Aliasing in Color**

Without paying attention to aliasing, the flow direction in this image would be misinterpreted. The angle formed between the steering direction and the flow is greater than 90 degrees, which according to the scale should be red. However, notice how low the color scales are set. Additionally, look at the color close to the vessel walls. The dark red near the vessel wall is consisten with flow in the direction of the arrows drawn in the image.

With increasing distance from the vessel walls, notice that the color hue lightens, representing higher velocities as indicated by the color scale, and is still consistent with the flow direction indicated. Only in the more central regions of the vessel where the higher velocity flow occurs does the color seem "inconsistent" with the drawn color direction. In fact, at the very center of the vessel where the highest velocities occur, even darker hues of blue are reached, which is a clear indication that the color has wrapped back around the color bar, hence, aliasing.

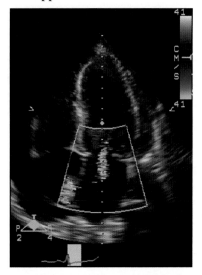

Fig. 61 **Aliased Mitral Regurgitation**

View Animation and Image Library CD

29. Color Persistence

29.1 The Purpose and Effects of Color Persistence

In Chapter 6 we discussed "averaging techniques" with the goal of improved signal-to-noise benefits. The goal of color persistence, like the goal of 2-D persistence, is to "average" frames over time so as to improve the signal-to-noise ratio. Improving the signal-to-noise ratio is especially desirable when there is poor sensitivity resulting in weak signals. Recall that in Chapter 6, we learned that persistence was usually not a pure averaging but rather followed a recipe of adding together some of the existing frame data with smaller percentages of the data from previous frames. Since the noise from frame to frame is random (incoherent), averaging (coherent) signals over time reduces the effects of the noise and increases the signal strength.

29.2 Persistence and Temporal Distortion

Of course, the trade-off with all averaging techniques is a reduction in temporal resolution. With persistence, this trade-off is often misconstrued. This confusion stems from the fact that persistence has the exact opposite effect on signals that are present in many frames than signals that are present in only one or two frames. Signals that are present in only one or two frames generally disappear with high persistence. Conversely, signals that are present in many frames can be persisted into other frames. The reason for this difference is clear. If a signal is present in many frames and absent in only one, averaging all of the frames together will add the event into the one frame in which it was not contained. In reverse, an event which occurs in only a single frame, averaging with the data in the other frames, makes the signals weaker or even disappear. As a result, by using higher persistence there is the potential to miss events which occur over a short duration, and also possibly introduce a temporal discordance, or time delay, between the actual occurrence of the event and the display of that event. For short duration events, such as non-holosystolic regurgitant jets, using too much persistence can mask the appearance of the jet, especially when the color frame rate is low. Conversely, long duration events, such as relatively continuous, uniform diastolic flow, are generally persisted into frames in which the flow doesn't actually exist. This potential for temporal distortion is another reason why timing and time duration estimates are better assessed by spectral Doppler than by color Doppler.

 **View Animation and Image Library CD**

29.3 Important Points about Persistence

- There are many different recipes which can be used for persistence. Most use a time weighting function, giving more "weight" to the last frame obtained and successively less weight to each earlier frame.
- Higher color persistence is generally used when the color signal is weak and some color (speckle) noise is present.
- Higher color persistence can distort the temporal aspects of the visualized flow.
- Very short duration signals that exist for only one color frame may potentially be "persisted" out.
- Longer duration signals that persist for multiple frames may potentially be "persisted" into future frames.

30. Color Priority

30.1 How Color Priority Works

Color priority is a threshold technique set by the user. When an individual pixel has both a grayscale (tissue) signal and a color signal, the color priority determines if the color is displayed or the grayscale is displayed. The threshold equates to the tissue amplitude above which grayscale is presented and below which color is presented. In other words, for a particular pixel, if both a grayscale (tissue) signal and a color signal exist, the pixel will be displayed as grayscale if the tissue signal amplitude is above the threshold. Increasing the color priority is equivalent to increasing the threshold. Therefore, a higher threshold implies that the tissue signal amplitude must be higher for the grayscale value to take precedence over the color value. At pixel locations where only color or only tissue signals exist, color priority has no effect.

30.2 Important Points about Color Priority:

- Axial resolution of color is generally not as good as that of 2-D so it is common for there to be a color "tail". Color priority helps reduce related tissue/color overlap.
- A higher color priority implies a higher tissue amplitude threshold.
- Color priority will not "create" a signal where no Doppler shift was recorded; color priority just votes between competing signals at the same location.
- High 2-D gain can cause dropout based on color priority setting.
- Color noise from overgaining can be reduced by color priority but this is not a good idea.

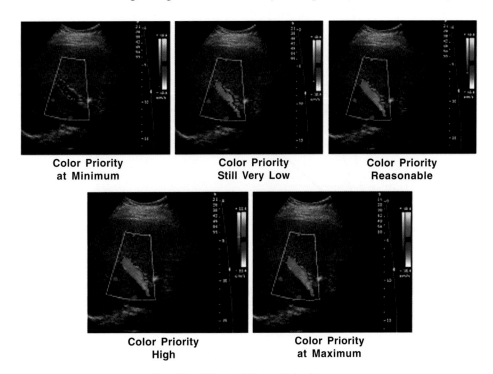

Color Priority at Minimum   Color Priority Still Very Low   Color Priority Reasonable

Color Priority High   Color Priority at Maximum

Fig. 62   **Effect of Color Priority**

From these images you should notice that a very high color priority only slightly "overfilled the vessel relative to the "reasonable" setting. In contrast, using too low color priority caused significant underfilling. As the signal-to-noise decreases, you should make certain to increase the color priority appropriately, or color filling will be difficult to achieve. This fact should make sense if you consider the weak reflective mechanism responsible for color Doppler signals.

31. Understanding the Behavior of Color Wall Filters

31.1 Digital Filtering

Predicting the behavior of the wall filters in color Doppler is much more difficult than predicting the behavior of the wall filters for spectral Doppler. Although the concept of the wall filters is the same, the electronic implementation is very different. In contrast to spectral Doppler, color Doppler wall filters are almost always designed as pure digital filters. Usually these filters take on the form of an infinite impulse response filter (IIR). Since the number of samples used in the filter must be small (usually around eight, corresponding to the color packet size), the filters have a very gradual roll-off. As a result, to achieve enough attenuation of the large clutter signals at the lower frequencies, the wall filters must be designed to begin attenuating at much higher frequencies than the wall filters for spectral Doppler. The significance of this fact is that the color wall filters, although designed to perform a similar function to the wall filters of spectral Doppler, behave extremely differently. Whereas, a spectral Doppler wall filter has a sharp corner frequency at a relatively low frequency with very steep attenuation (roll-off), a color wall has a much higher "corner" frequency and tends to gradually roll-off. This difference is graphically depicted in the *Figure 63*.

31.2 Comparing Spectral Doppler Wall Filters with the Color Wall Filter

The following graph depicts the differences between a bank of selectable spectral Doppler wall filters and the color Doppler wall filter which results for a specific PRF. For spectral Doppler, the wall filters can be set independent of the PRF, whereas for color Doppler, the wall filters are automatically adjusted by changing the PRF.

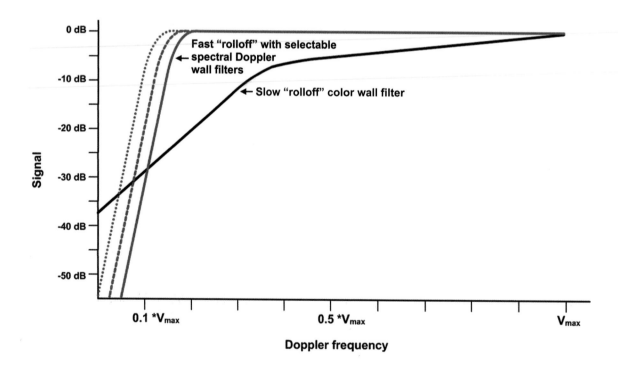

Fig. 63   **Spectral Doppler vs. Color Doppler Wall Filter**

The wall filters for spectral Doppler attenuate at a much faster rate ("roll-off") than the wall filter for color Doppler. The wall filter for color begins attenuating at a much higher frequency than the spectral Doppler wall filters. This higher "corner" frequency is an attempt for the color wall filter to compensate for the much slower roll-off. Since the attenuation rate is so much slower with the color wall filters, the corner frequency must be set higher to try to achieve adequate attenuation of the large clutter signals at the lower frequency shift ranges. As a result, for color Doppler, signals at lower percentages of V_{max} may or not be displayed depending on their signal strength. This point will be illustrated in a later graph (*Figures 66* and *67*).

31.3 Color Wall Filters and Nyquist

The following graph depicts the behavior of the color wall filters for two different Nyquist settings. The blue curve and blue labels on the x-axis represent the wall filters for a Nyquist limit half of that for the red curve and red labels on the x-axis.

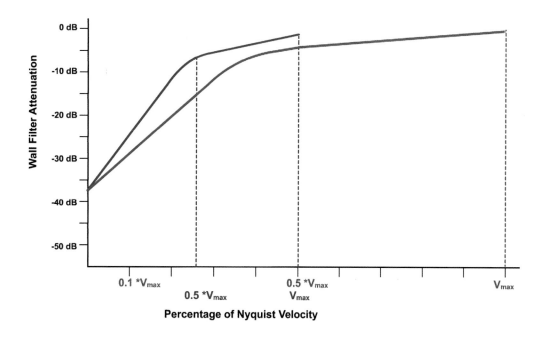

Fig. 64   Color Doppler Wall Filters for Two Different Nyquist Settings

As the maximum detectable velocity is reduced (by reducing the PRF), the effective corner frequency of the wall filter is also reduced. A signal with a frequency shift at the second tick mark on the x-axis is attenuated very differently by the red curve (lower wall filter setting) than the blue curve (higher wall filter setting).

31.4 Effect of Signal Strength on Color Wall Filtering

It already has been shown how the wall filter affects the signal for spectral Doppler. For spectral Doppler, the wall filters are very discriminating, attenuating very rapidly below the corner frequency and passing, virtually unchanged, signals above the corner frequency. In comparison, the wall filters for color Doppler are much less discriminating. The following graph, *Figure 65,* depicts the effect that the same wall filter has on two signals of different amplitudes (signal strength). Note that in both cases (the stronger signal indicated in red and the weaker signal indicated in blue), the flow conditions are identical, implying that the results ideally would be the same.

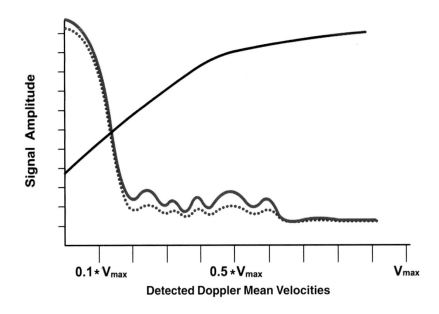

Fig. 65   **Effect of Wall Filters on Strong and Weak Signals**

Again, the red solid-line signal represents a stronger signal than the blue dotted-line signal, but for the identical flow situation. A weaker signal could result from having to travel a greater distance (larger patient), using a higher frequency transducer, a less efficient transducer, or by using a lower transmit power.

Figure 66 depicts the same two signals after attenuation by the wall filter and some applied amplification. Using the given color bar, the resulting flows are then depicted in *Figure 67*. Since these two signals are from identical hemodynamic situations, the resulting color image, ideally, would be the same.

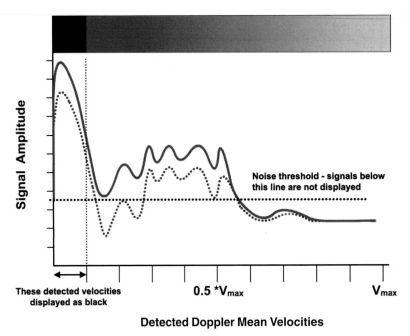

Fig. 66   **Effect of Wall Filters on Strong and Weak Signals**

From this graph it is clear that the lower velocity flow of the blue dotted-line signal (just beyond the black band of the color bar) was attenuated so that the resulting signal was too weak to be displayed (below the visible threshold). In comparison, the same range of frequencies for the red solid-line signal is still above the visible threshold, and hence, is displayed.

Imagine that the signal in question represents a flow with a velocity gradient from the center of the flow to the outside edge, as commonly occurs. In this case we will depict this flow as a regurgitant jet, but any flow situation can be utilized. Since the lower velocities will be found at the outer bounds of the regurgitant jet, the result of wall filtering a weaker signal will be a smaller perceived jet area. This decrease in area is shown pictorially in the figure below:

**Larger area detected
from stronger signal**
(red signal of *Figure 66*)

**Smaller area detected
from weaker signal**
(blue signal of *Figure 66*)

Fig. 67 **Perceived Jet Size and Signal Strength**

If we take this effect to its logical conclusion, it is clear that poor signal-to-noise can play a major role in affecting perceived color. As the signal-to-noise ratio decreases, the detected region of color decreases non-linearly. If the signal strength becomes weak enough, a color jet can be significantly underestimated or even not detected. The following figure demonstrates how signal-to-noise can affect perceived jet size.

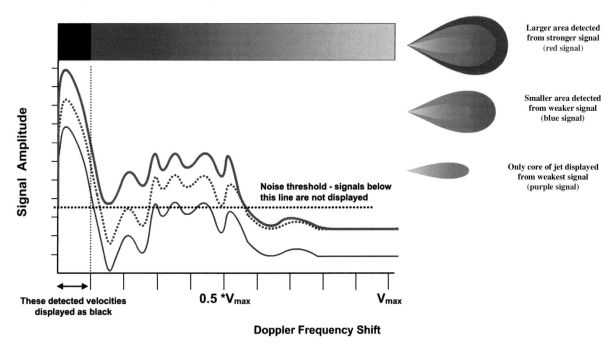

Fig. 68 **Effect of Signal Strength on Color Jet Size**

As a result, we can see that there is a complex interaction between Nyquist, the color wall filter settings, the signal-to-noise and perception of color. The size of a color jet can vary considerably with any changes in an entire host of parameters. If the wall filters are set very low, then low velocity entrained flow will inflate the perceived jet size. If the sensitivity is too low, then the perceived jet size will be smaller than "reality." The thresholding behavior of color Doppler does not serve well as a low variance, high repeatability measurement technique. Therefore, extreme caution must be taken when color measurements are made for a "numerical" assessment of severity.

31.5 Angle Correction Error (10 degree error)

Angle	Cosine		% Velocity		% Pressure	
Degrees	> Angle (10°)	< Angle (10°)	Overestimation	Underestimation	Overestimation	Underestimation
0	0.98481	0.98481	1.54%	1.54%	3.11%	3.11%
10	0.93969	1.00000	4.80%	-1.52%	9.83%	-3.02%
20	0.86603	0.98481	8.51%	-4.58%	17.74%	-8.95%
30	0.76604	0.93969	13.05%	-7.84%	27.81%	-15.06%
40	0.64279	0.86603	19.18%	-11.54%	42.03%	-21.76%
50	0.50000	0.76604	28.56%	-16.09%	65.27%	-29.59%
60	0.34202	0.64279	46.19%	-22.21%	113.72%	-39.49%
70	0.17365	0.50000	96.96%	-31.60%	287.94%	-53.21%
80	0.00000	0.34202	infinite	-49.23%	infinite	-74.22%

Table 5: **Angle Correction Error (10 degree error)**

This table is analogous to the table of Section 19.5, except the error is now 10 degrees from the presumed angle. A 10 degree angular error is certainly possible and even quite probable.

View Animation and Image Library CD

Pegasus Lectures, Inc.

Level 3

32. Conceptual Questions   Answers: Pg. 961-962

1. The _____ term in the Doppler equation corrects for the decrease in detected shift due to insonification angle.

2. A _____ filter is used to decrease the signal dynamic range by attenuating (lessening) high amplitude, low frequency signals.

3. A wall filter is a _____ pass filter, allowing higher frequency signals to pass and eliminating lower frequency signals.

4. A _____ _____ _____ is used to separate the spectrum of signals into its individual frequency components.

5. A typical Doppler frequency shift is within the range of plus or minus _____, but can be much higher.

6. Since the typical Doppler frequency shift is approximately plus or minus 10 kHz, the Doppler shift is within the _____ range.

7. The amplitude of a Doppler signal is displayed by the _____ of the spectrum.

8. The horizontal axis of a Doppler display corresponds to _____.

9. Range resolution is an advantage of _____ Doppler.

10. Aliasing is a disadvantage of _____ Doppler.

11. Aliasing occurs when the _____ limit is violated.

12. The _____ _____ requires a sampling twice as fast as the highest frequency.

13. _____ Doppler provides flow information over two dimensions.

14. Color Doppler uses a _____ technique to estimate the mean velocity of blood flow.

15. To determine a peak _____ spectral Doppler must be used.

16. If a color scale goes from blue below the baseline to red above the baseline, non-aliased flow towards the transducer will be encoded as _____.

17. If a color scale goes from blue below the baseline to red above the baseline, non-aliased flow away from the transducer will be encoded as _____.

18. The use of persistence with color flow will lower _____ resolution.

- The Doppler effect is caused by motion relative to an observer. Movement by either a target, the observer, or both can cause the effect.

- The Doppler effect is an apparent change in frequency caused by a change in wavelength as a result of relative motion between the target and the observer.

- The Doppler shifted frequency is the difference between the transmitted frequency and the returned frequency.

- The Doppler shift depends on the relative velocity. The faster the movement between structure and observer, the greater the shift: $\left(f_{Dop} \propto v \right)$.

- Since the Doppler effect is caused by a change in wavelength, any wave parameter which affects the wavelength also affects the Doppler shift.

- The wavelength is inversely related to transmit frequency. As the frequency increases, the wavelength decreases, making the object's distance traveled a greater percentage of the wavelength. The Doppler shift is proportional to the operating (transmit) frequency: $\left(f_{Dop} \propto f_o \right)$.

- The wavelength is proportional to the wave propagation velocity. As the propagation velocity increases, the wavelength increases, making the object's distance traveled a lesser percentage of the wavelength. So the Doppler shift is inversely proportional to the propagation velocity: $\left(f_{Dop} \propto \dfrac{1}{c} \right)$.

- Since the Doppler effect is due to motion relative to the observer, the direction relative to the observer (angle between observer and motion) affects the Doppler shift. The angle is referred to as the insonification angle. The Doppler shift is proportional to the cosine of the Doppler angle: $\left(f_{Dop} \propto \cos(\theta) \right)$.

- The Doppler equation is:

$$f_{Dop} = \frac{2 f_o v \, \cos(\theta)}{c}$$

- The Doppler angle is assumed to be 0 degrees or 180 degrees (parallel to flow) in cardiac scanning. The sonographer's role is to get as close to parallel to flow as possible.

- In general, Doppler modalities other than cardiac scanning should strive for a Doppler angle of 45° - 60° when possible.

- In vascular studies, the user indicates the Doppler angle by placement of the flow indicator. Proper alignment to flow is critical since error with Doppler angle is non-linear and can become very significant.

- The advantage of CW (relative to PW) is the ability to detect flow of virtually any velocity without aliasing.

- The primary advantage of PW (relative to CW) is good range specificity.

- Aliasing occurs in any pulsed mode when the Nyquist criterion is violated.

- For PW Doppler, aliasing occurs when the Doppler frequency shift is more than half of the PRF.

$$f_{Dop}(max) = \frac{PRF}{2}$$

- Although PW has good range specificity, it is not perfect. All PW modalities (including PW Doppler, color Doppler, B-mode imaging, and M-mode) suffer from range ambiguity.

- Range ambiguity results in echoes from deeper in the patient from the previous transmit line to add to the echoes from shallower depths from the current transmit line.

- Range ambiguity effects are most apparent when the imaging depth is set shallow.

- Aliasing is more likely to occur with:
    - Deep Doppler gate depths
    - Higher transmit frequencies
    - High velocity flow
    - Angles to flow closer to 0 or 180 degrees

- Wall filters are high pass filters which reduce the signal dynamic range by eliminating low frequency signals which are generally produced by slowly moving and stationary specular reflectors ("clutter" signals).

- If the wall filter is set too low, circuit saturation occurs.

- If the wall filters are set too high when measuring low velocity flow, the actual low velocity flow may not be detected.

- A single color Doppler display line is produced by transmitting multiple lines (a "packet" or "ensemble") in the same direction and then correlating the data within the packet.

- To produce a color scan, the process is repeated by transmitting packets at varying angles or locations across the scan region.

- Since color is produced using packets of lines, the frame times are very high resulting in low frame rates.

- Low frame rates result in poor temporal resolution.

- Larger packet sizes produce smoother color with less noise, but further degrades temporal resolution.

- Color yields an estimate of the mean velocity, not the distribution of velocities as does spectral Doppler.

- Determining flow direction is a process involving assessing the angle formed between the steered direction and the "head" of the flow (the direction to where the flow is going).

- If the angle is less than 90 degrees, the flow direction is encoded with the color on the color bar that corresponds with positive frequency shifts (excluding aliasing).

- If the angle is greater than 90 degrees, the flow direction is encoded with the color on the color bar that corresponds with negative frequency shifts (excluding aliasing).

- Aliasing must always be considered. Factors to consider are:
    - Higher velocity flows are more likely with certain hemodynamic situations: (i.e., a vessel narrowing, bending, kinking, high pressure, and small flow cross-sectional arrow areas, etc.)
    - The frequency of the transducer (higher operating frequencies alias earlier than lower operating frequencies).
    - The angle to flow (angles closer to 0 or 180 yields higher frequency shifts and therefore are more likely to alias).
    - The color scale setting (aliasing is more likely to occur with lower color scales).

- Color wall filters are often misunderstood. The wall filters are set as a percentage of the color scales (Nyquist setting). Increasing the color scales increases the color wall filters.

- To detect low velocity flow in color, the color scales must be set low or the wall filters will eliminate the low velocity signals.

- Color priority is a user controlled thresholding technique.

- Setting a higher color priority specifies that when a pixel has conflicting data (both a color signal and a 2D signal), if the 2D signal is below the threshold value, then color is displayed instead of the tissue signal. If the 2D signal is above the threshold value then the color is not displayed.

- Color persistence is a user controlled, time based averaging technique.

- Persistence reduces random noise through averaging.

- Persistence potentially can eliminate short duration events and potentially increase duration of long duration events.

Note: See Appendix N: Physical Units and Appendix O: Equations for additional review.

CHAPTER 8

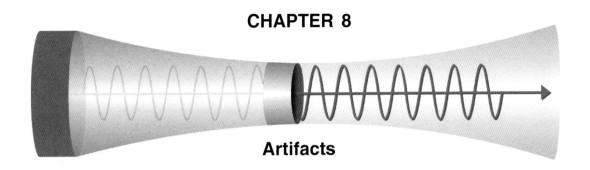

Artifacts

Introduction

The term artifact has many different meanings even within the "narrow" field of ultrasound. The word artifact refers to something made through skill by man, hardly the definition we would use in ultrasound. In its simplest form, an artifact is any representation in the image or on a spectrum which is not indicative of "truth". To quote Shakespeare and Socrates in a mixed metaphor of sorts, "therein lies the rub for what is truth but a shadow on the cave wall." In other words, "truth" and artifact are often extremely difficult to discern, and sometimes present only a shadow by which to determine "reality". In essence, determining what is "real" is often more nebulous than we would like to admit.

One thing is for sure, not all artifacts are bad. Paradoxically, some artifacts can be very useful as an indication of a very specific mechanism in the body. For example, the bright white "spike" which occurs on the Doppler spectrum often referred to as a "valve click" is in reality an artifact caused by circuit saturation. Yet, it is a useful artifact when controlled since it helps to quickly identify timing in the cardiac cycle. Artifacts such as shadowing and enhancement can be very useful since understanding the mechanisms which cause the artifact leads to information about the associated tissues and structures. For example, shadowing may indicate the presence of a calcification and enhancement may indicate the presence of a fluid. Of course there are other artifacts which are absolutely not useful such as susceptibility artifacts which result from receiving radio frequency signals from outside sources. These signals from sources such as radio signals, television signals, pulse oximeters, Bovie electrosurgical units, etc. are not related to what is physically occurring in the body and therefore are not at all useful as artifacts.

Throughout the entire book we have been discussing artifacts within the context of each chapter topic. For example, we have already discussed the concept of speed error when discussing the assumed propagation velocity in Chapter 2, specular reflection as a main source of imaging artifacts and refraction related artifacts when discussing attenuation in Chapter 3, range ambiguity when discussing timing issues in pulsed wave operation in Chapter 4, grating lobes when discussing transducer design in Chapter 5, contrast issues and detail resolution in Chapter 6, and aliasing when discussing Doppler in Chapter 7. In fact, many more artifacts were discussed, but we would virtually have to list every topic covered in the book to be complete. Great effort has been expended to make sure that the physics of the mechanisms which cause artifacts has been thoroughly taught in the previous chapters so that this chapter on artifacts can simply serve as a compilation of artifacts, rather than trying to teach all of the underlying physics in one chapter. In other words, this chapter presumes that the previous seven chapters have been read. Because understanding artifacts requires some clinical background, the entire chapter is Level 2. In an effort to make the integration of artifacts easier, we will group artifacts either by common mechanisms (source of the artifact) or by common appearance attribute (location, intensity, etc.). The result of this classification scheme is that the same artifact may be listed in more than one category. Additionally, there are many more artifact images included in the Animation and Image Library CD, intended to make identification of artifacts both more comfortable and systematic.

1. Categorizing Artifacts

1.1 Image Detail Resolution Related

We have already discussed artifacts associated with ultrasound beam characteristics generated by transducer and system designs. These artifacts are often, but not always, the limiting factor in detail resolution.

Detail resolution artifacts for 2-D and color Doppler are associated mainly with:

- Limited axial resolution
- Limited lateral resolution
- Limited elevation ("slice thickness") resolution

1.2 Locational Artifacts

Locational artifacts result in structures appearing either displaced in the image from the true location, or the presence of a structure or signal which does not even exist in the patient. Most of the locational artifacts can also affect detail resolution. The locational artifacts that generally affect detail resolution are indicated by an asterisk (*) in the list below.

- Refraction
- Reverberation
- Comet tail
- Ring down
- Multipath
- Grating lobes *
- Side lobes *
- Speed error
- Range ambiguity
- Mirror images

1.3 Attenuation Artifacts

Attenuation artifacts may result in a change in intensity of the signal, and potentially the location of a signal. As a result, you will notice that some of the artifacts listed in this section are also included in the locational artifact list.

- Acoustic shadowing
- Enhancement
- Reverberation
- Comet tail
- Ring down
- Refraction
- Speckle

1.4 Doppler Artifacts

Almost all spectral Doppler artifacts affect the spectrum such that error is introduced into the velocity measurement. Some artifacts tend to cause overestimation while others tend to cause an underestimation. For color Doppler, almost all artifacts result in the presence of a color signal where no signal should exist, or the absence of a color signal where color should exist.

- Aliasing (spectral and color)
- Range ambiguity (spectral and color)
- Spectral mirroring
- Spectral spread (broadening)
- Blossoming (spectral and color)
- Wall filter saturation (spectral and color)

2. Detail Resolution

2.1 Lateral and Axial Resolution

The following test phantom image *Figure 1* demonstrates limited axial and lateral resolution.

- The "V" shaped group of pins near label 1 is used for testing axial resolution. Notice how the two pins indicated by the arrow tip have converged into nearly one object in the image.
- The pin group identified by the white arrow labeled number 2 is used to demonstrate lateral resolution. In this pin group there are actually six pins spaced laterally at varying intervals. On the right side of the arrow, it is possible to distinguish each pin distinctly. To the left of the arrow tip, the limited lateral resolution causes the pins to appear as one "blurred" object.
- The pin indicated by the white arrow labeled number 3 has the same physical dimension as the entire row of pins linearly located directly above. Notice that the pin dimension is "smeared" laterally so as to appear approximately five times wider than the second and third pin down from the top. The reason for this lateral distortion is twofold. First, as the depth increases, the beamwidth is increasing, decreasing lateral resolution. Also, for a curved linear transducer, since the beams angle away from the transducer face, the beam density in the near field is higher than the beam density in the far field. Therefore, the received beam must be drawn wider in the far field. In Chapter 6, this point was discussed relative to the non-linear transformation needed by the scan converter for non-rectangular image shapes.

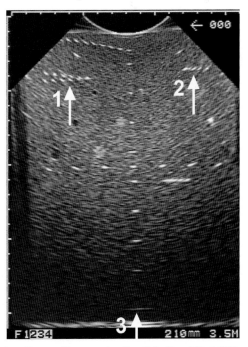

Fig. 1   **Phantom Image Demonstrating Limits of Detail Resolution**

2.2 Elevation Resolution

A 2-D image does not have a means of indicating the slice thickness of an image. The following image in *Figure 2* demonstrates how the elevation resolution (discussed in Chapter 5) can impact an image, and potentially lead to an incorrect conclusion.

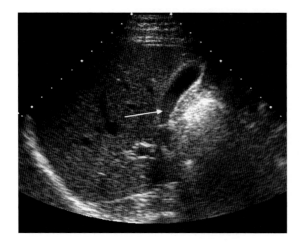

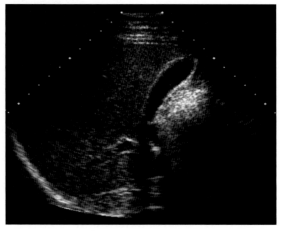

Fig. 2   **"Noise" in the Gallbladder from "Slice Thickness"**

Fig. 3   **Elimination of "Noise" Related to Slice Thickness**

The image of *Figure 2* demonstrates lower level signals within the gallbladder that are the result of the beam elevation thickness. The image in *Figure 3* is from the same patient using harmonic imaging. The use of harmonics makes the beamwidth narrower both laterally and elevationally. Because of the improved elevation resolution, the low-level echoes of *Figure 2* are no longer present in the gallbladder in *Figure 3*.

3. "Locational" Artifacts

3.1 Refraction

As discussed in Chapter 3, refraction can result in a lateral displacement of an object. The line drawing of *Figure 4* represents the basic refractive mechanism that results in lateral displacement. Notice that the beam is directed away from the correct path (refracted). The redirected beam insonifies a structure ("strong reflector real") and the echo is refracted back to the transducer. Since the system always assumes echoes are received from the straight ahead direction (indicated by the dotted line) the structure is artificially drawn in the image, laterally displaced. In other words, the structure is artifactually drawn along the presumed straight ahead dotted path even though the real structure causing the reflection is from the bent path indicated by the solid line.

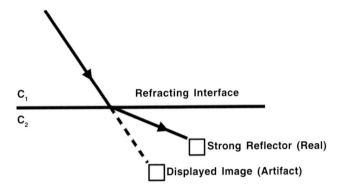

Fig. 4   **Lateral Displacement Caused by Refraction**

Recall that the amount of refraction can be determined by employing Snell's law. As the incident angle increases (the further from perpendicular), the amount of refraction increases (given that there is a change in propagation velocity across an interface between two media).

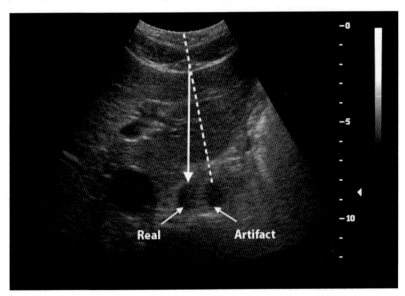

Fig. 5   **Refraction Artifact Creating a "Second" Abdominal Aorta**

In *Figure 5* there is an artifactual, laterally displaced second abdominal aorta. The mechanism which produces this artifact is refraction from the rectus sheath. At approximately 2 cm, there is a bright curved "line" which represents the liver capsule. Since the beam is perpendicular to this interface, there is no associated refraction. However, just above the liver capsule are the rectus sheath and the rectus muscles. As indicated by the dotted line, when transmitting in the direction of the artifactual aorta, the beam is refracted and insonifies the true aorta. On the return path, the beam is refracted back toward the transducer. The system always assumes that the signals arrive from the steered direction. Therefore, a second (artifactual) aorta is drawn laterally displaced from the true abdominal aorta. The refraction indicated in this figure would also occur for color Doppler and spectral Doppler. Therefore, this artifact will not be "identified" by turning on color Doppler or by performing spectral Doppler in the artifactual abdominal aorta. The color Doppler and the spectral Doppler will both produce artifactual signals from the region where the 2-D artifactual aorta is drawn. The image of *Figure 6* demonstrates how the artifactual abdominal aorta has color filling similar to the color filling of the actual abdominal aorta. This image is also included on the Animation and Image Library CD to allow for appreciation of color.

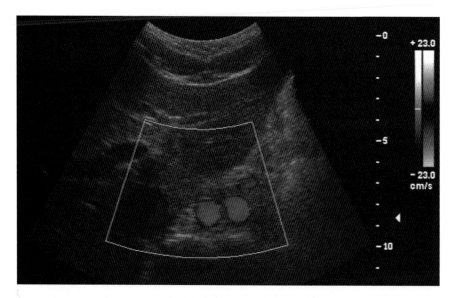

Fig. 6 **Refraction Artifact in Color Doppler Creating a "Second" Abdominal Aorta**

 **View Animation and Image Library CD**

3.2 Reverberation

As the name suggests, reverberation is an artifact caused by sound bouncing between multiple structures. Reverberation can occur between any two, or more, strong specular reflectors. In general, reverberation artifacts occur more commonly from relatively superficial reflectors since the reverberation paths for deep structures result in greater attenuation. The mechanisms of reverberation and how the artifact presents can be very complex. Unfortunately, many texts give such an oversimplified and rudimentary treatment of reverberation that the artifact is often misunderstood and misinterpreted. You must realize that when reverberation occurs, all "tissues" between the reverberating structures can be replicated, not just the specular reverberating structures. This fact implies that it is possible for reverberated tissue signals to be superimposed over a blood pool, giving the impression of a thrombus which does not truly exist.

3.2.1 A Simple Case: Between a Specular Reflector and the Transducer Face

In Chapter 3 we learned that sound reflects based on the acoustic impedance mismatch and the geometric aspect of the reflecting surface relative to the wavelength. As the sound returns to the transducer, some of that sound gets reflected back into the body since there is a large acoustic impedance mismatch between the transducer and the body. This reflected sound acts as a second "undesired" transmit. Again, some of the sound reflects back towards the transducer, of which some is received and some is reflected. In general, this "second" reflection does not cause too much degradation to the image since the second reflections are generally relatively weak. However, when there is a strong specular reflector in the relative near field, the "second" signal can be quite strong and result in a second appearance of the reflecting structure. This second appearance is called reverberation artifact since the sound is "reverberated" between two structures. Depending on signal strength, this process can occur multiple times. In this simple case, the result is the appearance of the strongly reflecting structure multiple times at constant depth increments with diminishing intensity.

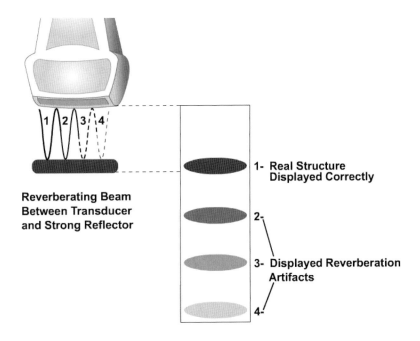

Reverberating Beam
Between Transducer
and Strong Reflector

1- Real Structure
Displayed Correctly

2-

3- Displayed Reverberation
Artifacts

4-

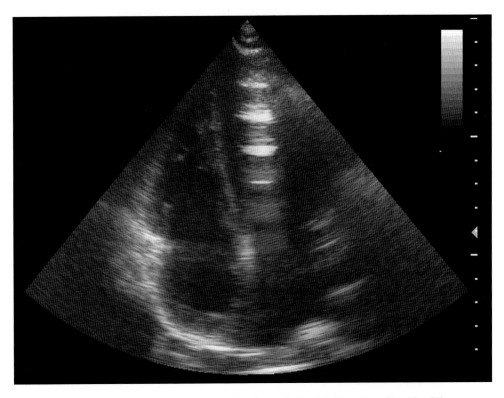

Fig. 7   **Reverberation Artifact in an Apical 4-Chamber Cardiac View**

View Animation and Image Library CD

3.2.2 A More Complex Case: Between Multiple Specular Reflectors

Reverberation can become significantly more complex when the reverberation occurs between multiple strong specular reflectors within the body. The mechanism for the artifact is the same as explained previously, except now the reverberation artifacts are not necessarily equidistantly spaced. Additionally, when there is reverberation between specular reflectors within the body, there is often also reverberation between these same structures and the transducer face. The result can be a very confusing compounding of image and artifacts. The image below of the subclavian artery demonstrates reverberation caused from both the surface of the transducer and between multiple reflectors within the body.

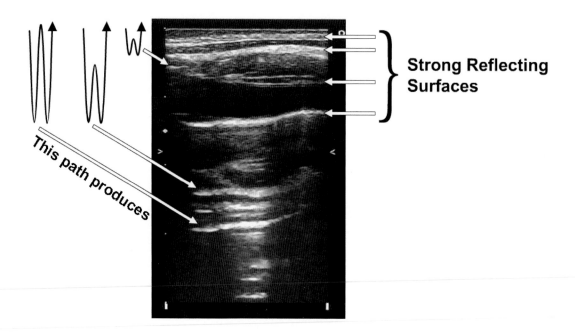

Fig. 8 **Subclavian Artery with Multiple Reverberation Paths**

3.2.3 A Very Complex Case: "Ghosting" or "Mirrored" Arteries

As already mentioned, reverberation artifacts can become complex and can occur much more frequently than most people recognize. Another way in which reverberation can manifest is when there is a scattering from another structure which then reverberates between two strong specular reflectors. This situation occurs frequently with signals from blood, causing the signals to then reverberate between the vessel's walls.

The color image in *Figure 9* demonstrates what many texts call mirror artifact due to the almost perfect "mirror" of the subclavian artery about the pleura. In reality this artifact is caused by reverberation. True mirror artifact occurs with a strong specular reflector acting as a mirror and an object which also yields a relatively specular reflection. The reflection from blood cells is Rayleigh scattering and will not create the multiple reflections necessary to create the mirror artifact. The reverberation path which creates the spurious subclavian artery is demonstrated in the image. In essence, the reverberation is between the anterior wall and the pleura, as shown by the extended path length (the solid path line). Note that the color in the actual artery appears at the correct location as indicated by the normal reflection path (the dashed line).

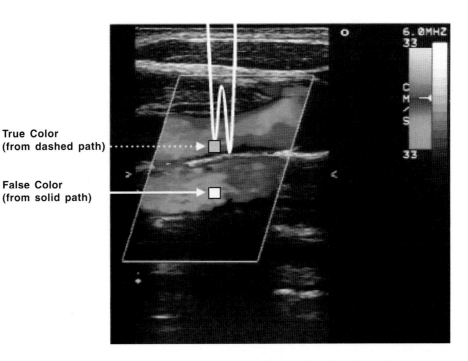

True Color
(from dashed path)

False Color
(from solid path)

Fig. 9 **Subclavian Artery with False Color from Reverberation**

So how do you answer questions on mirror versus reverberation artifact? It is unfortunate that most textbooks refer to the dual artery in this example as a "mirror artifact," since in reality it is caused by reverberation. Whenever you see a "false image" relatively symmetric about a strong specular reflector, the artifact will most likely be deemed as mirror artifact on an exam. Also recall that most texts assume that reverberation artifacts are uniformly spaced, multiple reflections only.

View Animation and Image Library CD

3.2.4 Be Vigilant Not to Confuse a Reverberation Artifact with a Thrombus
You should always be vigilant for reverberation related artifacts. The simple cases of reverberation present as exact replications of the reverberating structure at equidistant depths of the true depth. As shown, reverberation can have very complex paths creating spurious images at many different depths, and sometimes causing an area of haze which could be misinterpreted as thrombus. The best way not to miss this artifact is to always watch for imaging situations in which there are strong specular reflectors in the relative near field. Recall that specular reflection is highly angularly dependent. Changing the imaging or steering angle will often change the reflection path and hence, change the image. It is your job to prove what is real and what is artifact.

The images of *Figure 10* and *Figure 11* show examples in which reverberation can easily be confused with thrombus.

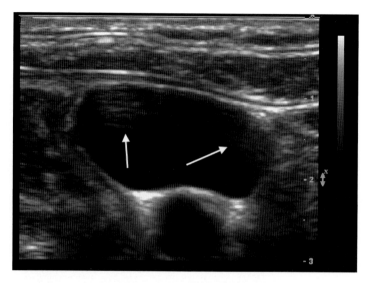

Fig. 10 **Reverberation Artifact in the Jugular Vein Appearing Like Thrombus**

 **View Animation and Image Library CD**

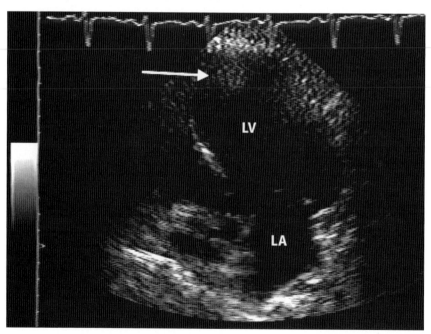

Fig. 11 **Apparent Pedunculated Mass Caused by Reverberation Artifact**

In the apical view, reverberations in the apex of the ventricle often appear as a mass or thrombus (as indicated by the white arrow in *Figure 11*). Correct identification as artifact or actual thrombus can be difficult, since the artifact can move with ventricular contraction just as an actual thrombus would. In this case, color flow imaging was instrumental in correct identification of the artifact.

3.2.5 Ring Down and Comet Tail (Specific Forms of Reverberation)

When sound reverberates within an air sac, the boundaries of the air sac are redrawn repeatedly creating a bright "tail-like" image below the air sac. This artifact has been given the name of ring down. *Figure 12* is a transverse image of a patient with a biliary stent causing pneumobilia (air in the biliary system). The bright white echoes (indicated by the white arrows) represent the strong reflection from the large acoustic impedance mismatch with the air. Below the bright reflectors are white "flashlights" caused by the sound reverberating within the air bubbles.

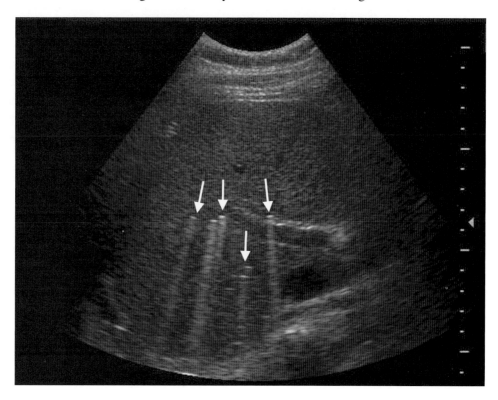

Fig. 12   **Ringdown Artifact Caused by Air in the Biliary System**

A similar phenomenon called comet tail occurs when the sound reverberates within a calcific structure or a metallic structure such as a surgical clip, catheter, or needle tip. In these cases, there is usually a striated tail of bright reflection below the structure, representing the front and back impedance mismatch of the structure. Sometimes these striations are even more obvious than in *Figure 13*. In this case, the metal discs of the St. Jude valve are causing reverberation which is seen well below the extent of the disc. You should also notice the dark regions on either side which are caused by acoustic shadowing from the valve struts.

View Animation and Image Library CD

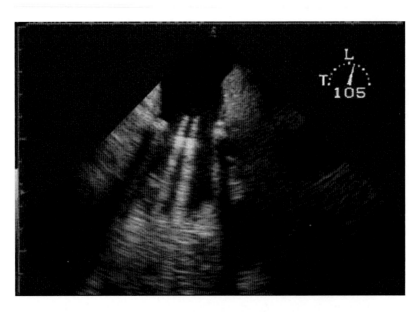

Fig. 13   **Comet Tail Artifact - Reverberation**
(disks are in open position)

 **View Animation and Image Library CD**

3.3 Multi-Path Artifact

Multi-path artifact incorrectly displays the depth of a structure. This artifact is generally the result of insonification of a specular reflector at an oblique angle (not perpendicular). Since specular reflection is very directional and the reflection angle equals the incident angle, the reflection is not directed toward the transducer.

If the reflection encounters another strong reflector off-axis (which redirects the beam toward the transducer), the path lengthens and therefore, acoustic transit (travel) time is longer than expected, and the structure is represented too deep.

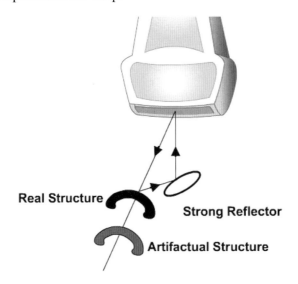

Fig. 14   **Multi-path Artifact Resulting in Artificially Deeper Appearance of a Structure**

3.4 Side Lobe (Single Element) and Grating Lobe (Arrays) Artifacts

Actual beam patterns are extremely complex (especially in the Fresnel zone). The beam profiles drawn to teach about beams and resolution in ultrasound are highly simplified. One known complexity to the beam shape is the existence of lower pressure or weaker beams pointing off-axis. These weaker beam artifacts are called side lobes for single element transducers and grating lobes for multi-element transducers.

These grating lobe beams exist, in part, because of partial constructive interference. Ideally, we would be able to create beams that added completely constructively in the desired direction, and completely destructively in all other directions. In reality, the waves created from each of the elements are never completely out-of-phase off-axis of the main beam. The result is that energy propagates in undesired directions, returning echoes from undesired locations. Generally the energy in these lobes is much less than the main beam and therefore goes unnoticed. However, if these lobes encounter a strong specular reflector, the reflected energy will be added to the reflected energy of the main beam either creating a spurious structure or "clouding" over the image. When a spurious structure is created, it appears laterally displaced from the real structure in the image. Caution must be taken since this artifact is sometimes misinterpreted as a thrombus or mass.

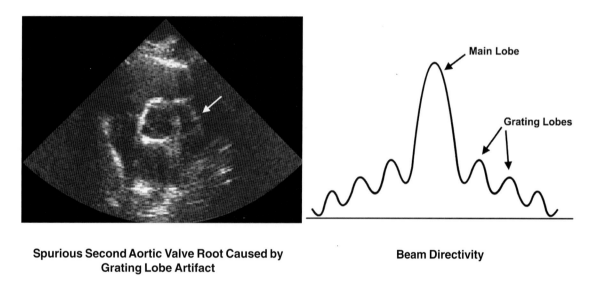

Spurious Second Aortic Valve Root Caused by Grating Lobe Artifact

Beam Directivity

Fig. 15 **Grating Lobe Artifact**

Note: The other principal mechanism that results in an artifactual lateral translation of a structure is refraction. Depending on the refractive path length, refraction usually causes the spurious structure to be slightly deeper, as well as lateral, to the true structure. From this still image alone, it is not possible to determine if the artifact in the above figure is caused by grating lobes or by refraction from the rib. However, analyzing the appearance and disappearance with angle in real time demonstrates this artifact to be a grating lobe artifact.

3.5 Speed Error Artifact

In diagnostic ultrasound, a propagation velocity of 1540 m/sec is assumed. By the distance equation, an ultrasound system calculates the depth based on this assumed propagation velocity and the time from the transmit until receiving the echo. If the propagation velocity is different at anytime within the path, the system will display structures at an incorrect depth.

Speed Assumed By System = 1540 m/s

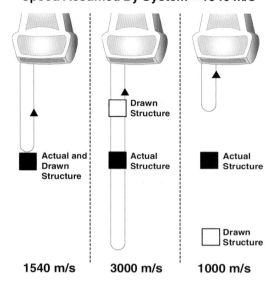

1540 m/s   3000 m/s   1000 m/s

Fig. 16 **Speed Error Artifact**

If the propagation speed is higher than 1540 m/sec, the echoes will return sooner, and the structures will be drawn artificially shallow. Conversely, if the propagation speed is slower than 1540 m/sec, echoes will arrive later in time and hence, be displayed deeper than reality.

You should expect speed error anytime the sound propagates through a medium that has a significantly different propagation velocity than the presumed 1540 m/sec of soft tissue. Besides the obvious candidates of air and bone, just about everything man-made which is put into the body should be suspected (the silastic rubber of a ball and cage valve, metal discs, wires, clips, etc.).

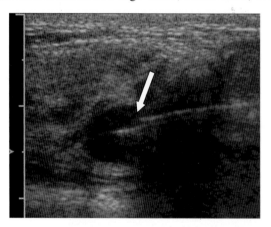

Fig. 17 **Speed Error Associated with a Needle**

In the image of *Figure 17*, the needle appears as if broken as a result of speed error. Since the propagation velocity is faster in the tissue than in the fluid of the cyst, the echo from the needle returning through the cyst takes more time than the echo returning from the needle through the tissue. As a result, the tip of the needle is displayed deeper in the image, given the appearance of a bend or break at the point of entry into the cyst. This artifact is sometimes referred to as a "bayonet sign" and is useful in that it confirms that the needle is within the cyst/mass. If the propagation velocity of a mass is close to the propagation velocity of the surrounding tissue, the bayonet sign may not be evident.

3.6 Range Ambiguity Artifact

Range ambiguity usually occurs only for very shallow depth settings. (The exact same artifact occurs in PW Doppler and was described in detail in Chapter 7.) A pulse will travel in a medium until all the energy is scattered or absorbed. At shallow depth settings, the acoustic transit time for a line is very short, which means transmit pulses can be fired rapidly. If an echo from a previous pulse (prior acoustic line) arrives after the transmit of a new pulse (a new acoustic line), the system cannot discriminate between the echo of the prior transmit pulse and the echo from the new pulse. The result is that echoes from two locations are superimposed. This artifact often results in a grayish haze and/or scintillations in the relative near field of an image, sometimes referred to as "herbies", (commonly seen in the apical views of the left ventricle).

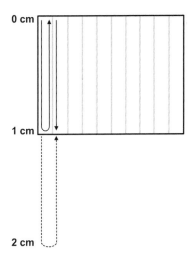

Fig. 18   **Range Ambiguity Diagram**

3.7 Mirror Artifact

The mechanism for a mirrored image is an oblique incidence to a specular reflector. The specular reflection directs the reflected beam toward a structure. The reflection from the structure is then reflected by the specular reflector back to the transducer. The result is a spurious structure "mirrored" through the specular reflector. The diaphragm is a good example of a structure which often acts as an acoustic mirror.

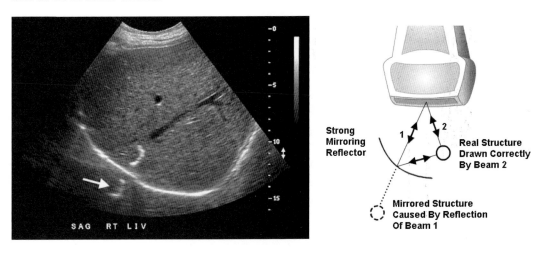

Fig. 19   **Mirror of Calcification in Liver from the Diaphragm**

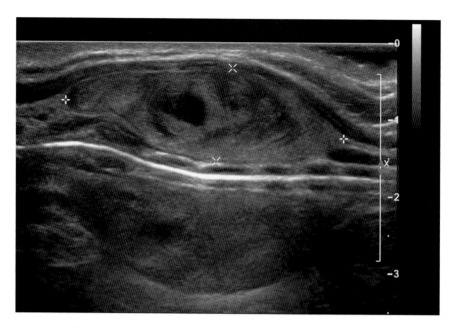

Fig. 20   **Large Mirror Artifact Reflected Across the Trachea**

The image of *Figure 20* is a large heterogenous thyroid isthmus between calipers compatible with a multi-nodular goiter. The bright white specular reflection running horizontally through the image is the trachea. Below the strong reflection of the trachea you will note a remarkable mirror image of the multi-nodular goiter.

4. Attenuation Artifacts

4.1 Shadowing

As the name suggests, a "shadow" is a darker than normal appearance. Shadowing is caused by any form of attenuation stronger than the attenuation of the surrounding area. A shadow can be cast on the image below by a strong reflector or absorber. Both strong reflection and absorption decrease the beam intensity thereby attenuating the echoes from deeper structures more than usual. Additionally, a shadow can be cast by beam refraction.

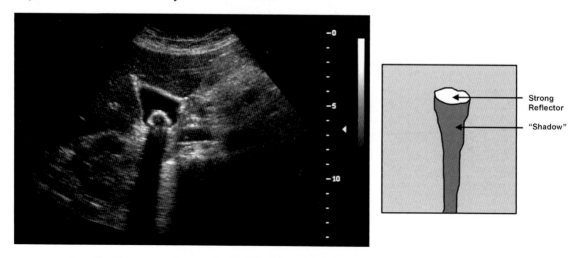

Fig. 21   **Transverse Image of a Gallbladder with Acoustic Shadowing from a Gallstone**

In the following fetal cranial image, the shadowing is caused by refraction.

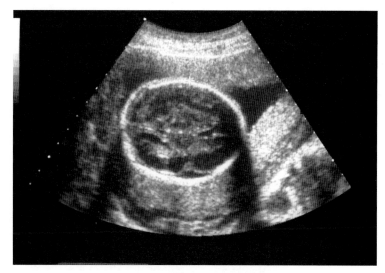

Fig. 22 **Shadowing Artifact**

Applying Snell's law, the critical angle is determined as approximately 25°.
The shadowing which occurs is the result of total internal reflection.

c_i = 1540 m/sec
c_t = 4080 m/sec
θ_t = 90° (for total internal reflection)

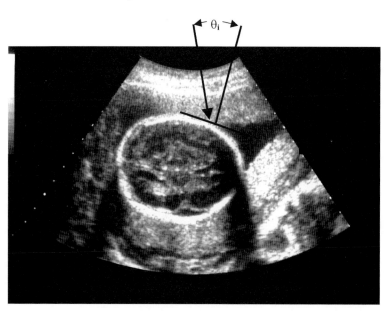

Fig. 23 **Measuring, the Critical Angle**

View Animation and Image Library CD

4.2 Enhancement Artifact

Enhancement is the "reciprocal" of shadowing. If a structure is a weaker reflector than normal or less absorbing than normal, the beam is attenuated less than normal "enhancing" the amplitude of echoes below the weak reflector or poor absorber. The term "increased through transmission" is also sometimes used to refer to the same effect as enhancement.

Typically fluids are relatively homogenous and less absorbing than tissues. As a result, enhancement often occurs when sound propagates through a fluid-filled region. The most common examples are cystic structures, the bladder, and frequently, a blood pool.

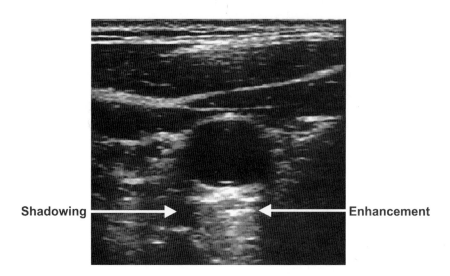

Fig. 24 **Shadowing and Enhancement from the Femoral Artery**

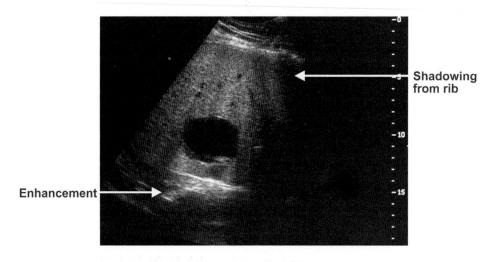

Fig. 25 **Enhancement From an Anechoic Cyst in the Liver**

 **View Animation and Image Library CD**

4.3 Speckle

Speckle appears as pseudo tissue texture. The scattering from multiple structures occurs simultaneously, and adds either constructively or destructively (as explained by wave addition in Section 22 of Chapter 1) creating bright and dark spots. Since higher frequencies have shorter wavelengths, higher frequency waves go in and out of phase in a shorter distance than do lower frequency waves. The result is that higher frequencies produce finer speckle patterns making tissue appear to be finer in texture.

5. Doppler Artifacts

5.1 Aliasing

Aliasing is the result of violating the Nyquist criterion (which states that to detect a given frequency, you must sample at greater than twice that frequency). For PW Doppler the sample rate is equivalent to the PRF, so the maximum detectable frequency shift is determined by one half the PRF.

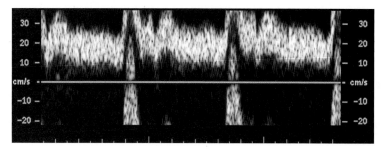

Fig. 26 **Aliased Doppler Spectrum**

Note: Although the signal in the above spectrum is "aliased," shifting the baseline down will almost "unwrap" the signal. When the aliasing gets worse, the signal wraps so far around that it is not possible to infer the true peak velocity. This of course presumes that the Doppler scales have already been increased to the maximum possible.

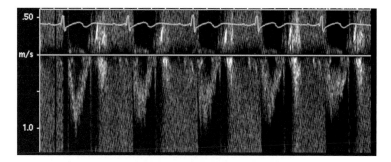

Fig. 27 **Aliased Doppler Spectrum**

In the spectrum of *Figure 27*, you will note that the peak velocity of the regurgitant jet wraps completely around and cannot be determined by a baseline shift.

View Animation and Image Library CD

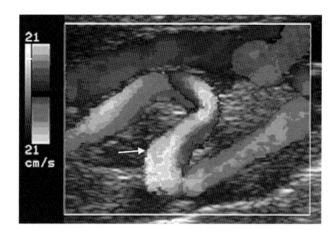

Fig. 28   **Color Aliasing**

Notice that in the tortuous internal carotid artery (the lower vessel), the color changes with flow direction. In the middle region in which the flow is almost directly toward the transducer, the recorded Doppler shifts increase leading to color aliasing. Notice that the two specific regions where the aliasing occurs are near bends in the vessel where acceleration occurs, increasing the Doppler shift. *Figure 28* is included on the Animation and Image Library CD to allow for appreciation of color.

 View Animation and Image Library CD

5.2 Range Ambiguity

As discussed in the last section, if a second transmit pulse is transmitted before all of the echoes from the first are received, the system might actually detect flow from deeper vessels as if at the shallower depth. This is particularly disturbing to sonographers when the sample volume is placed in tissue and blood flow is detected. Fortunately, this rarely happens due to attenuation and the unlikelihood of flow at the ambiguous depth. Range ambiguity is more likely to occur with shallow gate depths and also with a fixed focus transducer.

5.3 Mirroring (Spectral)

Bidirectional Doppler uses quadrature detection to determine flow toward and away from the transducer. If the signal amplitude is greater than the separation between the two channels of forward and reverse flow, a mirrored spectrum (which is weaker in amplitude) will appear in the opposite direction of the real flow.

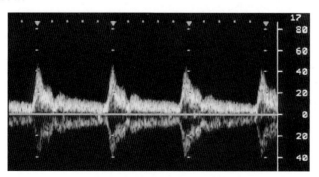

Fig. 29   **Spectral Mirroring**

View Animation and Image Library CD

The primary cause for spectral mirroring is poor electronic design with inadequate "separation" between the forward and reverse channels (I and Q). Additionally, the angle of insonation can increase the likelihood of spectral mirroring as demonstrated in *Figure 30*. Recall that the beam has physical width. When the beam is close to perpendicular to flow (90° insonification angle), part of the beam may be at an angle less than 90°, resulting in forward flow, and part of the beam may be at an angle greater than 90°, resulting in reverse flow. Spectral mirroring can be exacerbated by very strong signals as the result of very superficial Doppler with high frequency transducers, high transmit power, and too high receive gain.

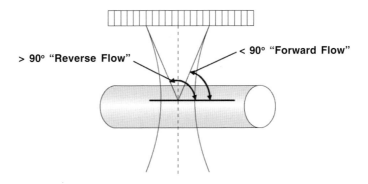

> 90° "Reverse Flow"   < 90° "Forward Flow"

Fig. 30   **Spectral Mirroring Caused By Angle**

5.4 Spectral Spread (Broadening) Artifact

In addition to normal spectral broadening, which results from differing blood velocities within a sample volume, an artificial spectral broadening exists. Artificial spectral broadening (spectral spread) artificially smears out the spectrum, increasing the peak velocity. The principal cause for this artifact is that the angle to flow from each element of an array is slightly different. For small insonification angles, small transducer apertures, and deeper gate depths this effect is negligible. For large linear arrays with insonification angles of 70° or greater, and more superficial gate depths this effect becomes very substantial. The result can be inaccurate measurements, leading to peak velocity overestimation and pressure gradient overestimation.

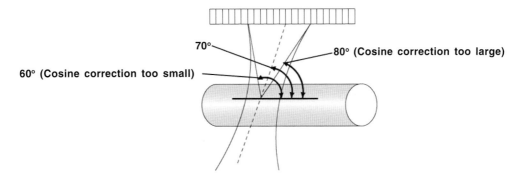

70°   80° (Cosine correction too large)

60° (Cosine correction too small)

Fig. 31   **Spread of Angles when Insonifying at 70⁰**

Notice from *Figure 31* that the angle to flow from some elements is greater than the central angle of 70^0 and that the angle to flow to other elements is less than the central angle of 70^0. However, the system assumes a 70^0 angle such that some signals are overcompensated and other signals are under-compensated. This over and under-compensation leads to a spreading of the Doppler spectrum as depicted in *Figure 32*.

Correction by Cosine (80°)
Causes higher peak velocity

Correction by Cosine (60°)
Causes window filling

True Spectrum   **Spread Spectrum**

Fig. 32   **Spectral Broadening**

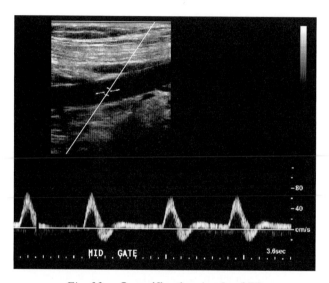

Fig. 33a   **Insonification Angle of 55°**

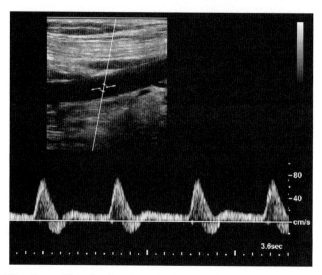

Fig. 33b   **Insonification Angle of 70° Producing Spectral Broadening**

The spectrum in *Figure 33a* is the result of using a 55 degree insonification angle whereas the spectrum in *Figure 33b* is the result of approximately a 70 degree insonification angle. Notice how the peak is slightly overestimated, and that the spectral window is diminished.

5.5 Blossoming

The term blossoming is used to refer to a signal that is essentially overgained such that the signal "bleeds" into neighboring regions of the spectrum. Overgaining can be the result of too high a transmit power for very superficial flow, or too much receiver gain for superficial flow. In the presence of blossoming artifact, the peak velocity is usually artificially high. Also, in PW Doppler blossoming can cause the loss of a spectral window when a window should be present.

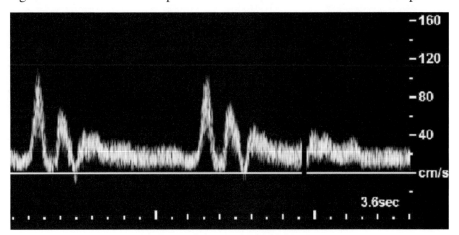

Fig. 34 **Appropriate Doppler Gain**

The Doppler gain in *Figure 34* is appropriate. Notice that the peak velocity is slightly over 100 cm/sec in *Figure 34*.

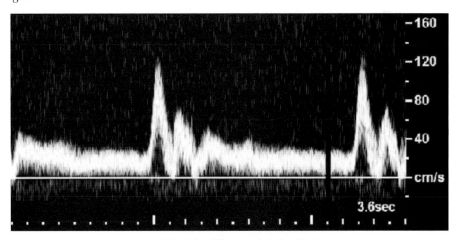

Fig. 35 **Blossoming Artifact**

The Doppler gain in *Figure 35* is excessive, causing blossoming artifact. Notice that the peak velocity is over 120 cm/sec, a 20% increase from *Figure 34*.

View Animation and Image Library CD

5.6 Wall Filter Saturation

In Chapter 7, we reviewed the function of wall filters. We also discussed the fact that when the "clutter" signals are not adequately attenuated, the signal dynamic range becomes too large causing circuit saturation. The following example demonstrates saturation of the wall filters when using CW Doppler.

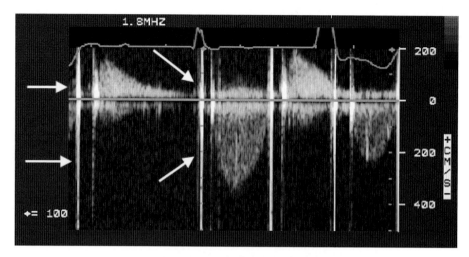

Fig. 36 **Saturation of Doppler Wall Filters**

In this case, the saturation occurs from the strong specular reflection from a mechanical valve. Notice that as the valve opens and closes, the Doppler insonification angle changes. When the incident angle is close to 0 degrees, (the beam is close to perpendicular to the valve leaflets), the specular reflection returns to the transducer and drives the Doppler circuit to saturation. During this period of time, the electronics are ringing between the voltage supply rails.

5.7 Refraction

Refraction artifact can significantly weaken Doppler signals, and in extreme cases, make the signal completely disappear. Recall from Chapter 3 that when the incident angle reaches the critical angle, the beam is totally internally reflected, and no energy actually transmits across the interface between two structures. Using the figure below, it should be clear that, with diving vessels, there is frequently the possibility of reaching the critical angle. Approaching the critical angle, the Doppler signal will weaken. Once the critical angle is reached, the Doppler signal will completely disappear.

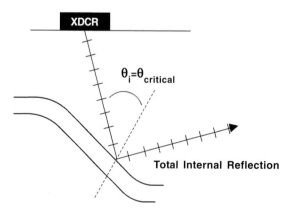

Fig. 37 **Critical Angle and Spectral Dropout**

6. Conceptual Questions   Answers: Pg. 963-964

1. Refraction, which is governed by _____ law, results in objects appearing _____ displaced from their true position.

2. _____ results in the appearance of strongly reflecting structures multiple times at constant depth increments.

3. Two specular reflectors are located in the same vicinity. If the first reflector is insonified at an oblique angle and the second reflector is off-axis, a _____ -path artifact will most likely result.

4. The multi-_____ artifact causes a strongly reflecting structure to appear too deep.

5. Off-axis beams which result from single element transducers are called _____ _____.

6. Off-axis beams created by multi-element transducers are called _____ _____.

7. The general effect of _____ _____ and _____ lobes is a creation of a spurious lateral structure or a clouding or haze over the image.

8. _____ error results in a misregistration of a structure because the actual propagation velocity is not the assumed propagation velocity of 1540 m/s.

9. If the propagation velocity is _____ than 1540 m/sec, an ultrasound system will represent a structure shallower than reality.

10. If the propagation velocity is _____ than 1540 m/sec, an ultrasound system will represent a structure deeper than reality.

11. _____ _____ occurs in shallow depth settings in PW Doppler. The result is an echo from a deeper depth registering as if from the shallower depth setting.

12. The PW Doppler gate placed in myocardium and mitral flow is registered from a depth that is approximately twice the Doppler gate depth. The most likely explanation is _____ _____.

13. High PRF Doppler utilizes _____ ambiguity to achieve a higher Nyquist _____.

14. _____ image is an artifact similar to multi-path, however, as the name suggests, with _____ image, one structure is spuriously displayed twice, once at its current position and once at its mirrored position.

15. _____ is the reduction or absence of echo below a highly _____ structure.

16. _____ is the opposite of shadowing.

17. _____ is a brighter than normal echo below a structure which is less _____ than normal.

18. _____ results when the Nyquist criterion is violated.

19. The Nyquist limit dictates that to detect a frequency of "f" you must sample at a frequency of at least _____.

20. Spectral mirroring is evident as a mirrored spectrum in the _____ direction of strong flow.

21. _____ _____ is an artifactual smearing of the Doppler spectrum resulting in peak velocity overestimation or and possibly the diminishing of the spectral window.

22. Spectral broadening generally becomes a significant concern when using large _____ arrays and insonification angles of _____ or greater.

KEY CONCEPTS
Artifacts

- Artifacts can result from interactions within the body, processing within the equipment, incorrect imaging technique, or from external sources such as radio signals.

- Understanding artifacts originates with an understanding of all of the principles taught throughout the earlier chapters. Without the fundamentals, it is very difficult to recognize or identify artifacts.

- The presence of artifacts in an image is not always bad. For artifacts that result from interactions within the body, quite frequently the artifact reveals information about the tissue or imaging situation.

- Lateral displacement generally occurs as the result of either grating lobe artifact or refraction artifact.

- Incorrect location in depth can result from speed error artifact, multi-path artifact, reverberation artifact, range ambiguity artifact, and mirroring artifact.

- Most imaging artifacts result from sound's interaction with specular reflectors.

- Since most (but not all) imaging artifacts are caused by specular reflections, you should always assess the presence of specular reflectors as well as the angle of insonation of the reflectors so as to identify artifacts or the likelihood of artifacts.

- Since specular reflection is highly angle dependent, changing the angle (steering, rocking the transducer, using a different imaging plane, etc.) is one of the most effective techniques to identify artifact from reality.

- Reverberation artifact is often broken into many sub-categories such as ring down, comet tail, and mirroring.

- Attenuation based artifacts include shadowing and enhancement.

- Doppler artifacts include:
  - Aliasing
  - Range ambiguity
  - Spectral broadening
  - Spectral mirroring
  - Blossoming
  - Wall filter saturation
  - Signal dropout from refraction

Note: See Appendix N: Physical Units and Appendix O: Equations for additional review.

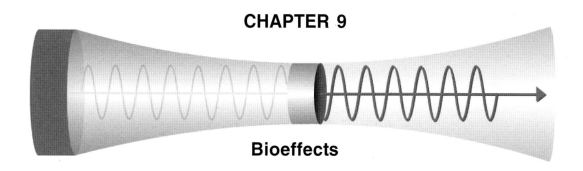

CHAPTER 9

Bioeffects

Overview

The foundation for discussing bioeffects has been discussed virtually throughout the entire book. In Chapter 2, Waves, we learned that sound is a mechanical wave and that all waves are a cyclical transference of energy. We also learned that as the wave propagates, the wave physically interacts with the medium causing changes within the medium. These changes are measurable in four different quantities called the acoustic variables. Recall that the changes are related to pressure, temperature, particle displacement, and density. Chapter 2 also introduced the general concept of acoustic power and intensity.

In Chapter 3, Attenuation, we learned that the principal form of attenuation for soft tissue is absorption. Recall that absorption is the conversion of some of the mechanical wave energy into heat within the body. As we will learn, absorption rates are one of the key indicators of the risk of inducing a thermal bioeffect. Additionally, the concept of non-linear frequency dependent absorption was introduced.

In Chapter 4, Pulsed Wave Operation, we learned different ways of timing the transmitted pulse so as to achieve some longitudinal resolution. Within Chapter 4, the foundation was laid for discussing temporal issues as relates to bioeffects. Specifically, the concepts of the duty factor, frame rates, and scanned versus non-scanned modalities, were introduced and explained.

In Chapter 5, Transducers, we learned about transducers and beam shapes. We learned that the beam is narrowest at the focus and hence, will always have a higher intensity at the focus or shallower than the focus. Great effort was taken to consider how the intensity of the beam changes with convergence and divergence.

In Chapter 6, System Operation, we learned about signal-to-noise ratio and how the output power increases the beam intensity, thereby increasing the signal-to-noise ratio. We also learned about receiver gain, and improving "apparent" signal-to-noise.

In Chapter 7, Doppler, we learned about the non-scanned modalities of spectral Doppler as well as the differences between PW and CW Doppler. In Chapter 7, the intricacies of how color is produced as a scan of non-scanned packets was also explained.

As should be evident from summarizing most of the previous chapters, the content we have learned to this point is almost all related to the risks and mechanisms of bioeffects. When all of these facts are considered together there is a very solid foundation for discussing bioeffects.

1. Mechanisms of Bioeffects

The term "bioeffect" refers to an undesired biological change to tissues as a result of interaction with the insonating beam. The fact that the potential for bioeffects exists should have been evident with the very description of sound as a transport of energy. Since energy can perform work, the possibility that the work performed leads to adverse biological situations is well within the realm of reasonable speculation. Since there are myriad interactions, and myriad uses of ultrasound, we also expect that there is more than one mechanism by which damage could potentially result. Fortunately, the list of potential effects can be categorized according to the mechanisms which create the effects. There are two principal mechanisms for creating bioeffects: thermal and mechanical.

1.1 Thermal Bioeffects

Although extremely complex in terms of identifying, measuring, and accurately predicting thermal bioeffects, understanding the basic mechanism of thermal bioeffects is relatively simple. Recall that absorption is a conversion of the sound energy into heat. If the temperature in a region rises too high metabolic breakdown occurs, and cellular damage can occur.

The following quoted passage is copied with permission from Bioeffects & Safety of Diagnostic Ultrasound (AIUM) Page 20:

> *Temporal Effects*
> *Healthy cellular activity depends on chemical reactions occurring in the proper location at the proper rate. The rates of chemical reactions and thus of enzymatic activity, are temperature dependent. The overall effect of temperature on enzymatic activity is described approximately by the relationship known as the Q_{10} Rule. This rule states that for each 10ºC increase in temperature, there is a corresponding doubling in enzymatic activity. Thus, an immediate consequence of a temperature increase is an increase in biochemical reaction rates. However, when the temperature becomes sufficiently high (i. e., approximately [3] 45ºC), enzymes become denatured. Subsequently, enzymatic activity decreases and ultimately ceases, which can have a significant impact on cell structure and function.*

1.2 Mechanical Bioeffects

In addition to thermal bioeffects, there is a risk of mechanical damage from interaction between the wave and the tissues in the body. This fact should not be surprising since sound is a mechanical wave. Although there is more than one type of "mechanical" mechanism, the principal mechanical mechanism of bioeffects is called cavitation. The word cavitation has as its root the word cavity or "cavus" which means a hollow space. In the presence of surrounding fluids, a bubble represents a "cavity." Therefore, when a bubble is created within a structure, there is a production of a cavity and hence the term cavitation. In the simplest definition, cavitation is essentially when bubbles are produced, vibrate or oscillate, and in extreme cases burst or implode. There are two types of cavitation described, one type is referred to as stable and the other type is referred to as inertial (sometimes referred to as transient).

1.2.1 Stable Cavitation

Stable cavitation occurs when the oscillation of the microbubbles does not lead to collapse. In general, when bubbles undergo stable cavitation, the bubbles oscillate with the varying acoustic pressure field in a "stable" manner. In the presence of stable cavitation, fluids surrounding the bubbles may begin to flow or stream. This flow is the result of eddy currents which develop as energy is imparted to the fluid through the oscillating bubbles. This effect of fluid streaming as a result of bubble oscillation is referred to as "micro-streaming." The momentum of the flow is potentially capable of inducing cellular wall stresses that can cause cellular harm.

View Animation and Image Library CD

1.2.2 Inertial Transient Cavitation

Unlike stable cavitation, inertial cavitation results in implosion of the microbubbles. The microbubbles may completely fragment or the "destruction" may lead to a collection of smaller microbubbles. The likelihood of implosion is related to the peak rarefactional pressure. During the rarefactional phase, the pressure within the bubble relative to the lower decreasing pressure external to the bubble causes the bubble to expand. Clearly, during compression, the increasing external pressure causes the bubble to contract. With increasing "negative" pressure of rarefaction, the bubble expands more and more.

Eventually, the bubble expands so much that when the compression begins, there is so much inertia from the surrounding fluid, that the bubble collapses inwardly (implodes). This collapse can be extremely violent generating high amplitude shock waves and producing extremely high temperatures (as high as 10,000 degrees Kelvin). These shock waves and localized high-temperature increases can cause damage to surrounding regions. In the case of metals such as propellers, turbine blades, regulator valves, and pressurized hydraulic pipes this violent collapse results in pitting and eventually structural damage. In the case of surrounding tissue, this cavitation can cause localized cellular death. Fortunately, the affected region is very small, potentially damaging only a few cells. The term "transient" is also used synonymously with the term inertial cavitation. The term transient is indicative of the fact that there is a change in "state" of the bubble. The word inertial is indicative of the fact that the dramatic change in state is the result of inertia.

View Animation and Image Library CD

1.3 The Concept of a Threshold Effect

In order to relate the principal bioeffect mechanisms to parameters of ultrasound, a fundamental understanding of the concept of a threshold effect is extremely helpful. A threshold is a limit or boundary. A threshold effect implies that there is a limit or boundary above which a specific outcome is achieved, and below which a different outcome occurs. As an example, a threshold effect could be that if you score above a certain number on a test you graduate and if you score below that threshold, you don't. With respect to bioeffects, threshold bioeffects will force different scanning behavior and protocols than non-threshold effects.

To date, the best science indicates that inertial cavitation is a threshold effect. Cavitation is stable up to a certain threshold, above which inertial cavitation occurs. In other words, long periods of time at lower rarefactional pressures will not produce inertial cavitation. On the other hand, even a very brief exposure at a pressure level exceeding the threshold rarefactional pressure will result in bubble collapse.

With respect to cellular damage, whether or not thermal bioeffects exhibit a threshold behavior depends on the reference point. On the one hand, there is no specific point at which a slight increase in power or scan duration will cause a dramatic increase in tissue temperature. Instead, the temperature change tends to be gradual over periods of time. This behavior is in stark contrast to the threshold behavior of cavitation, where stable cavitation will occur right up to a threshold and only a slight increase above this intensity will cause an abrupt change in bubble response. On the other hand, relative to a threshold temperature, temperatures below 40 degrees Celsius seemingly produce no irreversible bioeffects. From this perspective, thermal bioeffects exhibit a threshold behavior. Regardless of "threshold" perspective, the most important aspect of this discussion is the fact that temperature related bioeffects have a time-dependence and that cellular damage increases with increased exposure time and with increased intensities above 40 degrees Celsius. In contrast, mechanical effects of cavitation are related to the short-term event during the transmit burst and are not related to longer time periods.

2. The Desire to Safeguard the Patient

The ultimate goal of studying ultrasound related bioeffects is to assure that no harm is induced. Since the potential exists, studies must be performed to understand the mechanisms, identify the parameters of each mechanism which correlate best with bioeffects, create restriction guidelines, and create usage models so as to safeguard from inducing damage. In this endeavor, countless hours of research and work has been devoted.

2.1 Confirming Safe Levels

Confirming the existence of potential bioeffects is not the challenge that exists. If the acoustic power is set at levels beyond what is currently used in diagnostic ultrasound, the existence of bioeffects is easily confirmed. The true challenge is to determine guidelines and ultrasound use models that ensure patient safety.

The task of determining a verifiable standard which guarantees that ultrasound is always safe while preserving efficacy is daunting at best and intractable (unsolvable) at worst. The complexity of the interactions between the waves and tissue types, the various ways in which ultrasound is used, the wave parameters which are routinely varied, differences in patient body habitus, and physiology all enter into the equation. The following is a very partial list of issues that relays some of the impediments to conclusive findings regarding bioeffects and definitive thresholds.

1. In vitro testing cannot adequately address the complexity of live mammalian tissues or the interactions that result. This is not to say that in vitro testing has no value, but that extrapolating the results as they apply to clinical situations is tenuous.
2. Differences in tissue composition, tissue thicknesses, fluid content, and regional blood volume all can have significant impact on bioeffect mechanisms.
3. There is an inability to test in a graduated manner on live human tissues until levels are reached at which bioeffects are observed.
4. Adverse effects of ultrasound may become evident only after a latency period.
5. Adverse effects can potentially be attributed to many interdependent parameters; isolation to just the use of ultrasound is very challenging.
6. Epidemiologic studies have a potential built-in bias since many of the patients being tested are already infirmed.
7. In vivo studies may not be predictive of effects for all patients.

And the list could go on indefinitely. The point of displaying this list is not to state that there is no good information on which to base safety standards. On the contrary, there is a wealth of information that has been gathered over many years through much diligence and effort. The point is to stress that:

1. Definitive results relating to bioeffects and safety limits do not exist and are not likely to ever exist.
2. Results of new tests should be constantly assessed and assimilated into the body of knowledge.
3. Changes in use models of diagnostic ultrasound (new modalities and techniques) may lead to situations which have not thoroughly been tested.

Taken together, these points should lead to an understanding of a need for a cautious but balanced approach to the use of ultrasound. As an analogy, consider how different your driving behavior would be given the following two scenarios. First imagine that every time you drive your car at exactly 43 miles per hour or faster, the wheels start to shake, you lose control, and you crash the car. In comparison, imagine if the potential for the tires to start shaking increases with increasing speed, but there are many other parameters that can affect this less than desired outcome such as the changing conditions of the road, the temperature of the air, and the atmospheric pressure. In the first case, there is a known threshold beyond which you will never drive your car, insuring safety. In the second scenario, you will need to exercise more caution in certain situations, and weigh the risk of greater likelihood of crashing the car with the benefit of getting to your work on time.

3. Research and Standards

Owing to the wide acceptance of ultrasound, there are many groups which have published guidelines, standards, or research regarding bioeffects. A few of the most notable are:

1. American Institute of Ultrasound in Medicine (AIUM)
2. National Council on Radiation Protection and Measurements (NCRP)
3. World Federation of Ultrasound in Medicine and Biology (WFUMB)
4. National Institutes of Health (NIH)
5. Food and Drug Administration (FDA)

A Congressional amendment was passed in 1976 requiring the FDA to regulate all medical devices including diagnostic ultrasound. The resulting restriction on power limits by the FDA was based on performance and power predating their regulatory period. In essence, the regulatory standard became the existing "performance" levels including maximum power levels prior to 1976. In the parlance of FDA approval for new designs and devices, comparisons are made with a "predicate" device. If data is in evidence supporting that a "new" system behaves similarly to an existing device, then FDA approval is granted through a process called a 510K submission. If a predicate device cannot be shown, a much more elaborate FDA approval process is required with full clinical trial testing for safety and efficacy. Interestingly, equipment power levels predating the FDA regulation charter were not necessarily determined strictly by rigorous science, but rather on historical experience and empirical results which indicated no serious existing bioeffects. Since no bioeffects had been confirmed at the existing power levels, it was believed that there was a margin of safety built into these power limits.

Since 1976, all of the organizations listed above have produced official statements regarding bioeffects and safety. Additionally, the FDA has allowed ultrasound equipment manufacturers the ability to increase transmit power levels beyond the pre-existing 1976 limits by presenting an output standard as a guideline for the user to interpret and weigh benefits versus increased risk. We will concentrate primarily on the conclusions of the AIUM. Specifically, the AIUM formed a bioeffects committee with the express purpose of monitoring and evaluating research reports related to biological effects. In 1987 and again in 1992, the committee held an AIUM sponsored conference. The meeting in 1992 reexamined the publication which resulted from the 1987 meeting. The amended guidelines were published in 1993 and form the foundation of much of the accepted body of information regarding ultrasound bioeffects and ultrasound safety. The official statements published in this 1993 document will be reviewed once we have developed a basis to understand the intensity and mechanical indices referenced within the guidelines.

4. Power Measurements as a Basis for Gauging the Risk of Bioeffects

In Chapter 2, we discussed the concept of relating a transmit voltage to the power in an acoustic pressure field. Since power is a measure of the ability to perform work, power seems like a reasonable parameter by which to restrict ultrasound to limit the risk of bioeffects. However, as we also discovered in Chapter 2, the power of the beam can be distributed in many different ways. If the same power is distributed over a narrow region, there certainly will be a different risk of harm than if the power is distributed over a large spatial area. This fact led us to the concept of intensity. The general form of intensity is simply the power in the beam divided by the beam area, or:

$$\text{Intensity} = \frac{\text{power}}{\text{beam area}}$$

Although the general intensity is intuitively a better indicator of risk, there are many different ways of assessing the intensity. For example, over spatial distribution, the beam intensity can be measured at the one point at which the highest acoustic intensity occurs, or the average intensity over the region of the beam. Additionally, for pulsed operation, the intensity can be measured over the very short duration of the peak pressure in the pulse, or over the short duration of the transmit pulse (PD), or even over the longer duration between repeating the transmit pulse (PRP). In other words, there are many different means of assessing the intensity. Unfortunately, there is no one intensity measurement that relates to all different mechanisms for bioeffects. Instead, some intensity measurements are more indicative of thermal bioeffects, and others are better suited for indicating mechanical risks. Later in this chapter we will learn the AIUM's statement regarding the safety of ultrasound and "prudent use." In order to comply with the AIUM's statement about the safety of ultrasound and prudent use, we must therefore develop an understanding of the various intensity measurements (referred to as the common intensities) and indices used to assess and minimize bioeffect risks.

5. Common Intensities

5.1 Pulsed Wave Timing Revisited
Before we begin reviewing the common intensities, we will find it helpful to briefly review the foundational PW timing drawing from Chapter 4. You will notice that we have replaced the uniform multi-cycle pulse (more commonly used in PW Doppler and color Doppler) with a short duration transmit pulse more commonly used for 2-D imaging.

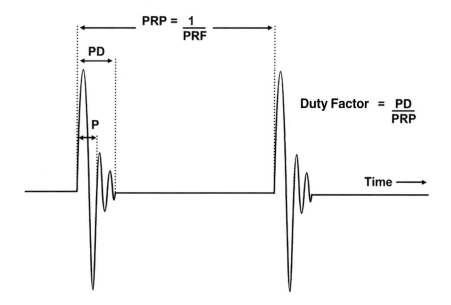

Fig. 1 **Pulsed Wave Timing Diagram**

5.2 The Common Intensities

The format for specifying a common intensity is the capital letter "I", followed by 2 clusters of 2 letters each, generally subscripted. The following list indicates the interpretation for each of these abbreviated terms:

I_{SPTP}	·	Spatial Peak, Temporal Peak
I_{SPPA}	·	Spatial Peak, Pulse Average
I_{SPTA}	·	Spatial Peak, Temporal Average
I_{SATP}	·	Spatial Average, Temporal Peak
I_{SAPA}	·	Spatial Average, Pulse Average
I_{SATA}	·	Spatial Average, Temporal Average
I_{m}	·	Maximum Intensity

5.3 Deciphering the Common Intensities by Concepts

To help decipher this seemingly complex list, we will subdivide the topic into four relatively simple concepts.

1st Concept: A peak is always greater than or equal to the average.

◊   ***Example:*** *Given the numbers 3, 5, & 7, which is the peak? What is the average?*

$$Peak = 7$$

$$Average = \frac{3+5+7}{3} = 5$$

◊ **_Example:_**   Given the numbers 12, 12, & 12, which is the peak? What is the average?

$$\text{Peak} = 12$$

$$\text{Average} = \frac{12+12+12}{3} = 12$$

As a result, we expect peak values to be at least equal to and usually greater than the average values.

2nd Concept: The first letter (S) represents the word "spatial" and refers to how the beam is distributed over space: I_{SP**} or I_{SA**}.

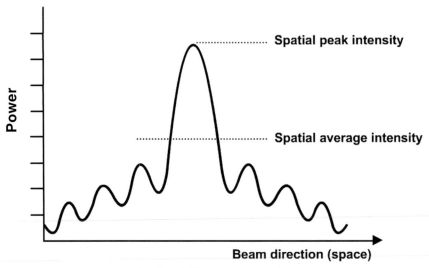

Fig. 2   **Spatial Beam Distribution**

3rd Concept: The first letter of the second letter "cluster" refers to an intensity measurement over time. If this letter is "P" the intensity measurement is taken during the Pulse Duration: I_{**PP} or I_{**PA}.

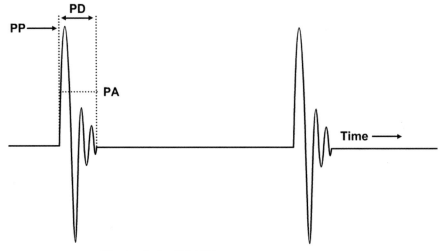

Fig. 3   **Pulse (PD) Measurements**

Clearly the pulse peak is where the pulse reaches its highest amplitude. The pulse average is a measure of the power in the pulse divided by the pulse duration time.

4th Concept: If the first letter of the second letter cluster is "T" the intensity measurement is taken during the Pulse Repetition Period (PRP): I_{**TP} or I_{**TA}.

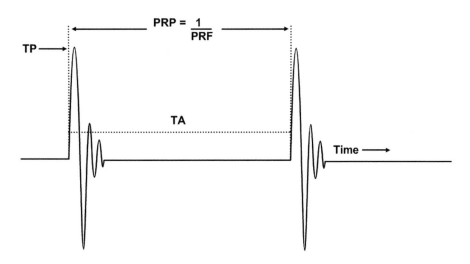

Fig. 4 **Temporal (PRP) Measurements**

As depicted in the figure above, the temporal average (TA) is almost always smaller than the pulse average (PA). This should make sense as the TA is all of the energy in the pulse divided by the pulse repetition period whereas the PA is the same energy divided by the pulse duration. Since the PRP is a bigger number than the PD, the TA is smaller than the PA. There is only one exception to this rule: CW Doppler. In CW, since the pulse is continuously "on," the pulse duration is effectively the same as the pulse repetition period.

5.4 Putting the Concepts Together
From comparing the two figures above, it is obvious that both the temporal peak (TP) and the pulse peak (PP) refer to the exact same parameter of the wave. Therefore, there is no need to use both terms. The abbreviation TP is used and the abbreviation PP is dropped.

In Chapter 4, we also learned that the ratio of the PD to the PRP was called the duty factor. Do you see how the PA (pulse average) and the TA (temporal average) are related?

Since the PA is the energy of the pulse divided by the PD, and the TA is the energy in the pulse divided by the PRP, the ratio of the TA and the PA is also the duty factor.

$$\frac{(TA)}{(PA)} = \frac{\left(\dfrac{Energy}{PRP}\right)}{\left(\dfrac{Energy}{PD}\right)} = \left(\frac{Energy}{PRP}\right) \bullet \left(\frac{PD}{Energy}\right) = \left(\frac{PD}{PRP}\right) = Duty\ Factor$$

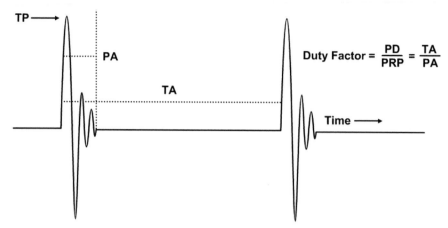

Fig. 5 **All Temporal Intensity Measurements**

As measured, the greatest intensity is where the intensity is maximum both spatially and temporally, or:

$$I_{SPTP} \text{ (}\underline{S}\text{patial } \underline{P}\text{eak, } \underline{T}\text{emporal } \underline{P}\text{eak).}$$

Since a pulse average is less than a temporal peak, the measured spatial peak, pulse average must be less than the spatial peak, temporal peak, or:

$$I_{SPTP} \text{ (}\underline{S}\text{patial } \underline{P}\text{eak, } \underline{T}\text{emporal } \underline{P}\text{eak)} > I_{SPPA} \text{ (}\underline{S}\text{patial } \underline{P}\text{eak, } \underline{P}\text{ulse } \underline{A}\text{verage).}$$

The smallest measured intensity is where the intensity is minimum, both spatially and temporally, or:

$$I_{SATA} \text{ (}\underline{S}\text{patial } \underline{A}\text{verage, } \underline{T}\text{emporal } \underline{A}\text{verage).}$$

6. The Significance of the Common Intensities

6.1 Common Intensity Analogy
Knowing that there are multiple ways in which to measure an intensity, and knowing that there are multiple mechanisms for bioeffects is not the same as intuitively understanding the differences between the common intensities, why each exists, and which bioeffect mechanism is associated with which intensity. The following analogy should help develop some insight.

Imagine that you have a bathtub that you would like to fill. However, whatever you do, you must make certain not to overfill the tub, allowing the water to spill over and ruin the bathroom floor. In this analogy, the tub is the equivalent to the patient, the water is equivalent to the energy in the transmitted waveforms, and an overflow is the equivalent to bioeffects.

There are two extreme cases that can cause the tub to overflow. One extreme is to turn the faucet on full so that in a short time there is an overflow. The other extreme is to allow the faucet to trickle flow into the tub, but allow the trickle to continue for a long period of time. Either case results in an overflow and a bioeffect. Of course, there is an inverse relationship between the flow rate and time. As the flow increases, the time until overflow decreases.

6.2 Mechanical Bioeffects and the I$_{SPPA}$

This first extreme overflow scenario is analogous to the mechanical bioeffect of cavitation. If there is enough energy in the short duration pulse, cavitation occurs. Therefore to predict cavitation, the intensity measurement is made over the short duration of the transmit pulse, referred to as the pulse average. Since the common intensities measure intensity with respect to space and time, we must also consider the spatial component more likely to predict cavitation. Clearly, where the beam reaches the highest intensity in physical space would have a greater likelihood of cavitation than where the beam is at average intensity. Therefore, in terms of common intensities, the best indicator for cavitation is the spatial peak, pulse average, or the I$_{SPPA}$. Common I$_{SPPA}$ values are below 190 W/cm^2.

Note: Frequently confusion arises from the fact that the relationship with cavitation is with the pulse average and not the temporal peak. In terms of the analogy, the overflow of the bathtub is associated with too much volume over a short time, not the instantaneous peak volume. In terms of the cavitation of bubbles, because of inertia, it takes time to mechanically oscillate the bubble. Therefore, it is the average energy of the pulse that is the "better" indicator of cavitation, not the instantaneous peak.

6.3 Thermal Bioeffects and the I$_{SPTA}$

The second overflow scenario is analogous to the risk of thermal bioeffects. Heating occurs over time. The intensity parameter that would best relate to a thermal bioeffect should measure the intensity with respect to longer time intervals. Therefore, the temporal average is the best indicator to predict thermal conditions and hence thermal related bioeffects. Since the common intensities reference the beam intensity both over space and distance, we must consider the spatial distribution and the likelihood of increased heating. Again, we would expect that where the beam reaches the highest intensity in physical space would have a greater likelihood of generating heat than where the beam is at average intensity. Therefore, in terms of common intensities, the best indicator for thermal bioeffects is the spatial peak, temporal average, or the I$_{SPTA}$. Common I$_{SPTA}$ values are below 720 mW/cm^2.

6.4 Conversion Between a PA and a TA intensity: (Duty Factor)

In Section 5.4, we learned that the ratio of a temporal average intensity to a pulse average intensity is the same as the ratio of the PD to the PRP, referred to as the duty factor. Therefore, the duty factor can be thought of as the constant of conversion between a temporal average and a pulse average.

$$Duty\ Factor = \frac{PD}{PRP} = \frac{TA}{PA}$$

To convert from a pulse average to a temporal average (PA $\Rightarrow$ TA), you multiply the pulse average by the duty factor, or:

PA • DF = TA.

And similarly, to convert the (TA $\Rightarrow$ PA), you divide the TA by the duty factor as follows:

PA=TA/DF.

Note: Recall that the duty factor represents the percentage of time the transducer is producing energy that will interact with the patient. The highest possible duty factor is 1, or 100%, which occurs in continuous wave. All pulse wave modalities must have a duty factor less than 1. A higher duty factor implies a greater potential for heat to build up within the patient, increasing the likelihood of thermal bioeffects.

6.5 Conversion Between SP and SA Intensity: (BUF)

6.5.1 The Beam Uniformity Factor (BUF)

The beam uniformity factor or coefficient is defined as the spatial peak divided by the spatial average. The BUF is a measure of how uniform a beam is distributed spatially.

$$BUF = \frac{SP}{SA}$$

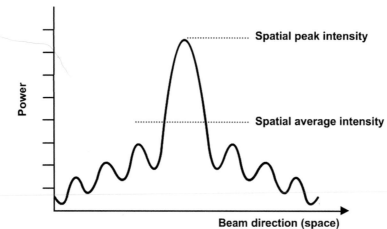

Fig. 6 **Beam Uniformity**

◊ ***Example:***   What is the BUF if the spatial peak intensity is 700 mW/cm² and the spatial average intensity is 400 mW/cm²?

$$\text{Beam Uniformity Coefficient} = \frac{700}{400} = \frac{7}{4} = 1.75$$

As noted above, the beam uniformity factor is defined as the spatial peak divided by the spatial average. Since a peak is always greater than or equal to an average, the BUF is always greater than or equal to one, and in reality always greater than 1. A perfectly uniform beam would have a BUF equal to 1.

6.5.2 Converting between the SA and the SP

To convert a spatial average to spatial peak, you multiply the spatial average by the BUF as follows:

$$SA \bullet BUF = SA \bullet \frac{SP}{SA} = SP$$

Pegasus Lectures, Inc.

7. Exercises   Answers: Pg. 965

1. Define (from memory) each of the following:

   a) I_{SPTP}
   b) I_{SPTA}
   c) I_{SATP}
   d) I_{SPPA}
   e) I_{SAPA}
   f) I_{SATA}
   g) I_m

2. Of the above intensities which must always be the greatest? The smallest?

3. "Pulse" refers to the energy only during the "pulse on" time or pulse duration (PD). Temporal refers to the energy distribution over the entire _____ .

4. The "BUF" beam uniformity coefficient is defined as:

   $$BUF=?$$

5. To convert an SP value to an SA value you need to know the _____ .

6. The peak is always _____ than or equal to the average.

7. A spatial peak is always _____ than or equal to a spatial average.

8. A temporal peak is always greater than or equal to a _____ _____.

9. Spatial refers to the energy distribution over physical space whereas _____ refers to a beam's energy distribution over time.

10. The pulse average must be _____ than the pulse peak.

11. The _____ _____ factor equals the spatial peak divided by the spatial average, and is a measure of how uniform a beam is spatially.

8. Relating Risks of Bioeffects to Ultrasound Modes

8.1 Scanned Versus Non-scanned Modalities

In Chapter 4, we began the discussion about scanned versus non-scanned modalities. Recall that non-scanned modalities such as PW Doppler, CW Doppler, A-mode, and M-mode, repeatedly transmit in the same direction whereas scanned modalities (such as 2-D and color Doppler) transmit in differing directions over time. With respect to thermal bioeffects, the risk is higher for non-scanned modalities. For a scanned modality the energy is distributed line-by-line over a wide area, allowing time for heat generated through absorption to dissipate. In comparison, a non-scanned modality repeatedly transmits energy in the same direction leaving little time between transmit pulses for heat to dissipate. Therefore, the propensity for localized heating is greater in modes like CW Doppler and PW Doppler than in modes like color Doppler and 2-D imaging. How much heating occurs depends on the beam intensity (power and spatial distribution), the pulse duration and pulse repetition period (the duty cycle), the absorption rate of the tissues, and the ability of that region of the body to duct away heat.

8.2 Ultrasound Modalities in Order of Thermal Risks

If we consider the effect of duty cycle in conjunction with non-scanned modalities, it becomes clear that the ultrasound mode with the greatest potential risk of thermal bioeffects is CW Doppler. As a non-scanned modality with a duty factor of 1, CW is the mode which usually generates the highest I_{SPTA} values. The next modality on the thermal list is PW Doppler. PW Doppler is also a non-scanned modality but generally has a considerably lower duty factor than 1. The modality with the lowest risk of thermal bioeffects is generally 2-D imaging. The reason is not only because 2-D is a purely scanned modality, but also because the transmit pulses are designed to be as short as possible for optimal axial resolution, producing a very low duty factor.

Of the conventional modes still in use, we have not yet specified the ranking of thermal rank for color Doppler and M-mode. For many reasons there is no easy means by which to determine which of these two modalities will have potentially worse thermal effects. Although M-mode is a non-scanned modality, M-mode usually has a very low duty factor like 2-D imaging, so as to achieve high axial resolution. Color is a partially scanned, partially non-scanned modality and generally has a higher duty factor than M-mode. The imaging situations which make color more likely to produce higher temporal average intensities are when there are narrower color sectors, shallower imaging depths, larger color packet sizes, and of course, higher transmit power. The most that can be said about the relative heating from M-mode and color Doppler is that these two modalities are generally not the most likely to be restricted by thermal issues, and they are also not the least likely to be restricted by thermal issues.

8.3 Transmit Voltages for Various Modalities

As a result of the thermal restriction imposed by the high I_{SPTA} values for CW Doppler, the maximum allowed transmit voltage is relatively low. Typical peak transmit voltages for CW Doppler are on the order of 8 Volts (peak-to-peak). For the same transmit voltage, PW has a lower I_{SPTA} value. As a result, the maximum transmit voltage is higher for PW Doppler than CW Doppler. How high the transmit voltage can go depends on the Doppler gate depth, Doppler gate size, and the PRF, but in general, the maximum voltage is approximately 30 Volts (peak-to-peak). For 2-D imaging, a transmit voltage of 35 Volts would produce a very low I_{SPTA} value. As a result, the maximum allowed transmit voltage is as high as 150 or even 200 Volts peak. This relationship is analogous to the bathtub analogy. When the faucet is left running for a long duration, the flow is only allowed to trickle (CW transmit voltage). As the duration is shorter, the flow is allowed to increase. In the extreme, if you want to fill a bathtub in one short burst of water, the flow is allowed to be extremely high during that short duration (2-D imaging). *Figure 7* demonstrates the relative relations of the transmit voltage between CW Doppler, PW Doppler, and 2-D imaging. Note that these voltages cannot be drawn to scale because of the significant differences in amplitude.

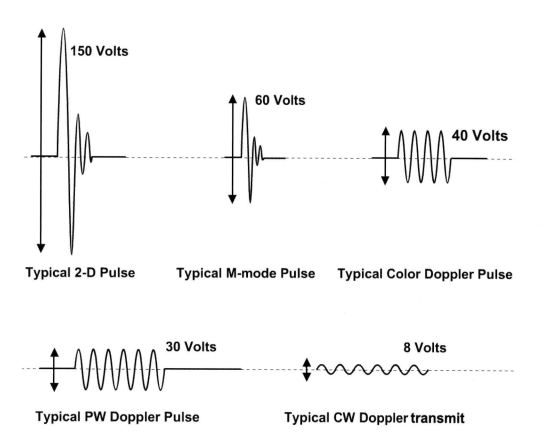

Fig. 7   **Relative Transmit Voltages**

8.4 Ultrasound Modalities in Terms of Cavitation

As already discussed, the likelihood of inertial cavitation is a threshold effect which does not, for the most part, depend on the duration of the imaging. As a result, first order determination of which modalities have the greatest risk of cavitation is a simple process of looking at the "maximum allowed" transmit voltages in *Figure 7*. Clearly, 2-D imaging presents the greatest "potential" risk whereas CW offers relatively little, if any, risk of cavitation. In essence there is an inverse relationship between the modalities with the highest risk of thermal damage and the corresponding risk of mechanical damage.

8.5 Theory of FDA Limits

In theory, if all testing and predictive models are correct, no modality would have any real risk of producing bioeffects. By measuring the various beam intensities and guaranteeing the system never goes above threshold limits, bioeffects should not exist. Therefore, in a perfect world, even though CW Doppler runs closer to the I_{SPTA} limit than 2-D, no real thermal risk should exist. This is precisely the reason why CW transmit voltages are so low in comparison to 2-D transmit voltages. Similarly, in a perfect world, the risk of bioeffects with 2-D imaging would also be zero for allowed imaging situations. The difficulty, as discussed in Section 2.1, is that no mathematical models are perfect and not all imaging situations can be anticipated and factored in a priori. As a result, relatively conservative intensity limits have been set to try to safeguard the patient. As you will see from the AIUM statements regarding the safety of ultrasound, this approach has been relatively successful. On the other hand, you must appreciate that there are still potential risks, and that these risks must be minimized while simultaneously producing the best diagnostic quality data possible. This "trade-off" will be covered by the AIUM's ALARA principle regarding prudent use of ultrasound.

9. Acoustic Power Measurements

9.1 Overview of Acoustic Power Measurements

Equipment manufacturers use power models and acoustic power testing to determine an acceptable range for the acoustic intensity parameters. The models are used to help limit the tests required by predicting the worst-case scenarios. Specifically, the computer models predict the "worst case" by analyzing each of the imaging modalities at various power levels, focal configurations, depth settings, and PRF's. The "worst case" modes are the imaging situations which are predicted to generate the highest temporal and pulse average intensities.

From this data, a system is tested by attaching a transducer and placing the face of the transducer in a water tank. The system is configured so as to be in one of the expected "worst-case" modes. A special ultrasound sensitive transducer in the water tank is then used to measure the acoustic pressure and calculate the various intensity measurements. The system configuration is then changed to another "worst case" predicted mode, and the measurement process repeated. Multiple transducers are put through the same testing procedure and the resulting power data is analyzed. If the computer modeling was correct, then all of the transducers tested, for all of the various system configurations will have intensities which fall within the accepted power limits. If any specific system configurations, or any transducers result in measurements above the power limits, the maximum allowed power is "dialed back" in the system software and the tests repeated. For new products, the data collected is then submitted to the FDA for verification of meeting predicated device standards. In this way, a system is tested to "assure" safe power levels.

Pegasus Lectures, Inc.

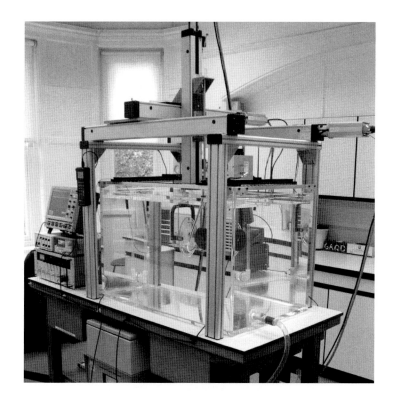

Fig. 8   **Acoustic Power Measurement Test Tank**

9.2 The Hydrophone

A hydrophone is a specialized ultrasound transducer, designed to measure acoustic pressure fields. Since hydrophones are used in water baths, the sensitivity requirements are not nearly as rigorous as for imaging transducers. On the other hand, to be useful, a hydrophone must be very stable over time, with a near flat response (or correctable response) over a wide frequency range. If the hydrophone sensitivity were to vary significantly, the acoustic power testing data would be completely unreliable. As a result, hydrophones used for acoustic power measurement testing are routinely tested and calibrated. This calibration must also take into account the temperature of the water.

There are a few different types of hydrophones which can be used for acoustic power testing. The two most commonly used hydrophones for diagnostic ultrasound transducer testing are the needle hydrophone and the membrane hydrophone. Parameters of importance are bandwidth, sensitivity, directivity, and flatness of response. A comparison table with descriptions for one manufacturer is included in Level 3, Section 16.

Fig. 9a **Membrane Hydrophone**

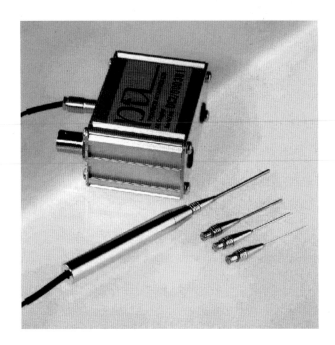

Fig. 9b **Needle Hydrophone**

9.3 Six Degrees of Freedom

As simple as the principle of acoustic testing sounds, reality is in sharp juxtaposition. For accurate power measurements there are actually six different degrees of freedom. The hydrophone must be aligned to the beam laterally, elevationally, and axially. In addition to the normal scan plane dimensions, since the surface of the hydrophone represents a specular reflector, the hydrophone must be aligned in the three angles referred to as pitch, yaw, and roll. As a result, the process of testing a transducer and the associated power field is time consuming. Very large, semi-automated tanks have been designed to help reduce the complexity, but the fact still remains that power testing using a hydrophone in an acoustic tank is still time consuming.

9.4 Beamplots

While scanning the acoustic field over the imaging scan planes (power testing), the measurement system actually digitizes and stores the power registered by the hydrophone. This data can then be plotted and analyzed. Analysis can include maximum sensitivity, bandwidth, sensitivity over bandwidth, lateral beam dimensions, elevation beam dimensions, beam shape over depth, changes with changes to the focus, and grating lobes to name a few. In addition to testing for safety (relative to the guidelines and power restriction to minimize risk of bioeffects), and for quality assurance (to ensure adequate performance), these results are used in the design process. For engineers, these output results of the acoustic testing frequently become what drives iterations of design and system implementation. Computer models are the beginning, but given the complexities of ultrasound beams, ultimately, the models do not always accurately predict what happens in real life.

Recently a new approach to testing has been developed called a pulse Schlieren system. A Schlieren system uses an intense focused light source to illuminate a transparent medium. The light source is strobed in time, very accurately synchronized with the transmit pulse driving the transducer. Since the sound wave interacts with the medium as it propagates, the medium is "perturbed" from its normal state. The perturbations in the medium cause phase disturbances in the reflected light. Optics are used to create an image from the very weak phase perturbed scattered light. The phase disturbances are on the order of a few wavelengths of the light. These phase disturbances are converted into an intensity and displayed. This new approach holds the promise of significantly faster beam assessment and power measurements.

The following images (courtesy of Onda Corporation) are of a beam pattern produced using Schlieren imaging.

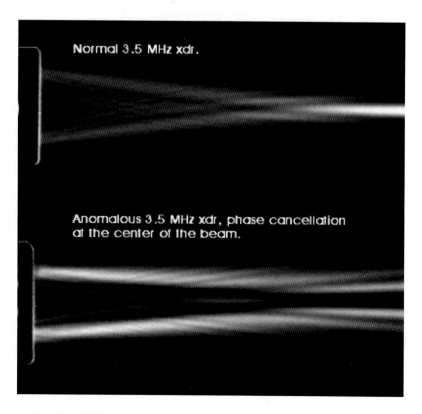

Fig. 10 **Schlieren Image of a Normal and Abnormal 3.5 MHz Beam**

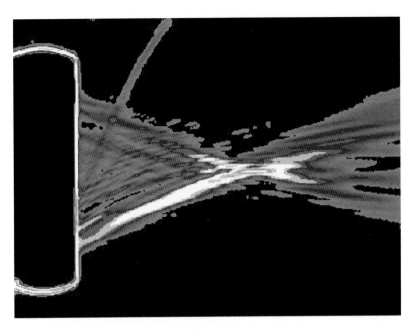

Fig. 11   **Schlieren Image of a Focused Beam from a Transducer with a Bad Element**

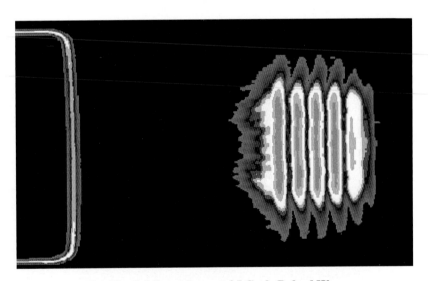

Fig. 12   **Schlieren Image of 5 Cycle Pulsed Wave**

View Animation and Image Library CD

10. Output Display Standards

In 1985, a joint committee formed by the AIUM, the FDA, and NEMA (National Electrical Manufacturers Association) developed an alternative to the existing paradigm for FDA approval of ultrasound devices. The previous standard was based on the I_{SPTA} maximums as follows:

Trans-ophthalmic	17 mW/cm²
Fetal imaging	94 mW/cm²
Small parts	94 mW/cm²
Pediatric echo	94 mW/cm²
Adult echo	430 mW/cm²
Vascular	720 mW/cm²

Table 1: I_{SPTA} **Limits Prior to 1985**

The new output standard removed the individual limits, opting for one overriding limit that the maximum I_{SPTA} allowed never exceed 720 mW/cm². As part of the new paradigm, ultrasound equipment was required to post one of two mechanical indices, the mechanical index (MI) or the thermal index (TI). The user is then expected to make a decision based on the posted mechanical index as to whether presumed increased risk was outweighed by the expected improvement in diagnostic quality. Equipment manufacturers were now given an option of following the old track for FDA approval or the new track. Almost all systems today follow the new paradigm, and have done so for at least the last 5 years.

11. Mechanical Index (MI)

Before the mechanical index, the restriction on acoustic output power levels most closely associated with the risk of cavitation was the spatial peak pulse average. The pulse average intensity measurement refers only to the distribution of the power temporally and spatially, but does not take into account the fact that the risk of cavitation also has a frequency relationship. The MI is now considered the index which best correlates with the likelihood of cavitation. A higher MI implies a greater likelihood of cavitation, but does not actually specify when cavitation occurs.

The mechanical index is defined as the peak rarefactional pressure divided by the square root of the operating frequency, or:

$$MI = \frac{\text{peak rarefactional pressure}}{\sqrt{\text{operating frequency}}}.$$

The mechanical index mathematically expresses the fact that the risk of inertial cavitation has been found to increase proportionally with increasing rarefactional pressure and decrease by a square root relationship with increasing frequency.

As a result of the new standard, most ultrasound systems now present mechanical indices instead of following the old acoustic output standards. The standard only specifies that one index be displayed per application. The MI is always present when performing 2-D imaging, since 2-D is the modality which presents the greatest potential for mechanical bioeffects. Since thermal effects are highly improbable, there is very little need to post a thermal index as well. As we will see, Doppler modes are likely to present a thermal index, but not an MI.

12. Thermal Indices

12.1 Absorption Rates of Various Mediums

Absorption in the body tends to increase with an increase in collagen content. Therefore, the highest rate of absorption is expected in tissue types such as bone, cartilage, tendons, scar tissue, and fascia. At the opposite end of the absorption spectrum are fluids. The absorption rate in water is 0.0022 dB per cm at 1 MHz of operation. In comparison, the absorption rate in bone varies from around 14 dB per cm to 25 dB per cm at 1 MHz. This is a ratio of approximately 10,000 to 1. Since absorption rates differ so dramatically, clearly the risk of thermal bioeffects will vary significantly with the tissue types within the ultrasound path. A table including absorption rates for some biological tissues is given in Level 3 of Chapter 3.

12.2 Thermal Indices Defined

The thermal index actually represents the collective title for three different indices:
- Thermal Index in Soft Tissue (TIS)
- Thermal Index in Bone (TIB)
- Thermal Index in Cranial Bone (TIC)

The thermal index is a predictive value which estimates the "maximum" temperature rise expected for the current imaging situation. Therefore, a TI of 1 indicates that the maximum temperature rise expected over time would be 1 degree Celsius. A TI of 1 does not imply a temperature increase of 1 degree, but rather what the model predicts as the "worst-case." How accurately the worst-case model predicts the actual temperature rise depends on many parameters including:
- How and where the beam is focused
- What tissues and absorption rates occur in the path
- Blood flow and fluids in the region which can dissipate heat
- How well the assumed attenuation rates match the values assumed in the model

12.3 The Three Thermal Indices

The reason that three different thermal indices exists is the fact that absorption rates vary significantly depending on the medium. The TIS predicts the temperature rise presuming the predominant presence of relatively homogenous soft tissue. The TIC indicates the likely worst-case temperature rise for a bone at the surface such as cranial bone when performing transcranial imaging. The TIB is the predictive value for bone presuming that the surface of the bone is near the focus of the beam, as occurs commonly with fetal imaging.

12.4 Underestimation of Worst Case

In general, it is presumed that a thermal index gives the maximum possible temperature rise, but this is not always the case. As with all algorithmic based models, the conclusions are only accurate when the situation modeled is covered by parameters within the model. In other words, clinical situations can occur which could potentially produce higher temperature increases than predicted by the models. One such example would be the TIS in the presence of a large cystic structure. Since absorption within fluids is very low, less attenuation occurs in the beam path than expected. As a result, there is an "enhancement" effect where more power reaches greater depths. As a result, a higher than predicted temperature rise might occur deeper than the cystic structure. There are other possible parameters which potentially could affect the accuracy such as dehydration and severe fever. Although these possibilities exist, for the most part, the TI is a pretty fair estimate of the worst-case temperature rise.

Pegasus Lectures, Inc.

13. AIUM Statements Regarding Ultrasound and Bioeffects

13.1 Acknowledging the AIUM

Special thanks to the American Institute of Ultrasound in Medicine (AIUM) for granting permission to copy the following pages. The report is entitled <u>Bioeffects & Safety of Diagnostic Ultrasound</u> and can be purchased at $17.00 for members and $34.00 for nonmembers. Given the importance of understanding the potential risks of ultrasound, it is suggested that every lab possess a copy of this document, and all practitioners of ultrasound should read the full document. To that end, information is included at the end of this chapter to facilitate purchase.

In addition, the AIUM has produced two subsequent documents to further promulgate the dissemination of information pertaining to bioeffects. These two documents are referenced at the end of the chapter as well.

13.2 How Best to Use the Following Pages

Although all of the information in the following pages is relevant, the most critical information has been set in bold type. I debated heavily whether to include just the "conclusive" statements, or the conclusive statements with the surrounding text to give greater context. I decided to include the context as well in the hope that greater insight might result from contextual reading. To facilitate recognition of direct quoting, all excerpts from the AIUM guide is written in italics, with page references following the excerpt.

It is strongly suggested that when you read these statements, you relate the information to the fundamental concepts discussed about the mechanisms for bioeffects. It should make sense that some of the statements will be related to the risk of mechanical damage, some statements will be related to the risk of thermal bioeffects, some statements related to how to minimize the risks, and some statements to describe how this information was developed and tested. If you attempt to categorize each statement and distill the information to its core purpose for being included, learning and comprehending this complex but important topic should become a little easier.

13.3 Conclusions Regarding the Safety of Ultrasound

Although we have focused on the risk associated with bioeffects, it must be stressed that conservative use has proven ultrasound to be a very safe modality. To date there have been no confirmed bioeffects with diagnostic ultrasound. However, you must realize that the statement "no confirmed bioeffects" does not necessarily mean that there have been no bioeffects. The potential for bioeffects exists, and the possibility that some bioeffects have occurred and do still occur is very real. This possibility of bioeffects mandates that caution be exercised so as to minimize risk while maximizing clinical utility (prudent use).

The AIUM Statement on Clinical Safety (ARM, 1988) provides general guidance on the use and safety of diagnostic ultrasound. This statement is based on a review of what is known regarding ultrasonically induced experimental biological effects, epidemiological studies, and understanding of the differences between experimental conditions and clinical practice:

American Institute of Ultrasound in Medicine Official Statement on Clinical Safety. Approved October 1982; Revised and approved March 1988; Reaffirmed March 1993.

Diagnostic ultrasound has been in use since the late 1950s. Given its known benefits and recognized efficacy for medical diagnosis, including use during human pregnancy, the

American Institute of Ultrasound in Medicine herein addresses the clinical safety of such use: No confirmed biological effects on patients or instrument operators caused by exposure at intensities typical of present diagnostic ultrasound instruments have ever been reported. Although the possibility exists that such biological effects may be identified in the future, current data indicate that the benefits to patients of the prudent use of diagnostic ultrasound outweigh the risks, if any, that may be present.

(Page 86)

13.4 ALARA Principle

The ALARA Principle is a simple acronym which stands for "as low as reasonably achievable." In essence, the ALARA principle is a guideline to define "prudent" use. The word "low" refers to exposure. As we have learned there are a two principal components to exposure: the intensity (related to the output power) and the scan time duration. ALARA mandates that the lowest possible power be used as well as minimizing the scan time. The term "achievable" is a balancing word which expresses the recognition of a potential trade-off between quality of a scan and exposure parameters. In other words, using higher transmit powers and increasing scanning time may be perfectly appropriate when the trade-off is improved diagnostic information. The goal of diagnostic testing is to "achieve" accurate clinical results. Therefore, the lowest exposure that yields good clinical results is the appropriate condition. In a paraphrased form of the safety statement, remember that although the possibility of biological effects exists, the benefits to the patient of diagnostic ultrasound, to date, have outweighed those risks.

The ramifications of the ALARA principle to you the sonographer include:
- understanding the mechanisms which cause bioeffects,
- understanding the parameters which increase the risk of bioeffects,
- learning the system controls and functions that directly control these parameters,
- understanding the control of post processing controls that can secondarily affect where the power related controls are set,
- understanding the differences in modalities (applications), and
- performing clinical studies only when there are potential benefits which outweigh the risks.

13.5 Prudent Use

The use of ultrasound for non-medical purposes is discouraged. Remember that although ultrasound has proven to be a safe modality there is still a potential risk. The AIUM statement regarding prudent use defines responsible use for fetal imaging by specifying that non-medical scans including obtaining images of a fetus to determine fetal gender without a specific medical need is inappropriate.

Prudent Use Approved May 2, 1999

The AIUM advocates the responsible use of diagnostic ultrasound. The AIUM strongly discourages the non-medical use of ultrasound for psychosocial or entertainment purposes. The use of either two-dimensional (2D) or three-dimensional (3D) ultrasound to only view the fetus, obtain a picture of the fetus or determine the fetal gender without a medical indication is inappropriate and contrary to responsible medical practice. Although there are no confirmed biological effects on patients caused by exposures from present diagnostic ultrasound instruments, the possibility exists that such biological effects may be identified in the future. Thus ultrasound should be used in a prudent manner to provide medical benefit to the patient.

13.6 Safety Concerns Regarding the Use of Ultrasound in Training and Research

The question always arises as to what constitutes prudent use when using ultrasound in educational and research settings. In these cases, the person being scanned may not present with a medical need for imaging. However, in these cases when the intended purpose may result in an indirect instead of a direct medical benefit, the AIUM has made a specific recommendation as included in the Safety in Training and Research statement included below.

Safety in Training and Research Approved March 26, 1997

Diagnostic ultrasound has been in use since the late 1950s. There are no confirmed adverse biological effects on patients resulting from this usage. Although no hazard has been identified that would preclude the prudent and conservative use of diagnostic ultrasound in education and research, experience from normal diagnostic practice may or may not be relevant to extended exposure times and altered exposure conditions. It is therefore considered appropriate to make the following recommendation.

In those special situations in which examinations are to be carried out for purposes other than direct medical benefit to the individual being examined, the subject should be informed of the anticipated exposure conditions, and of how these compare with conditions for normal diagnostic practice.

13.7 Statement Regarding Non-Human Mammalian In Vivo Biological Effects

The term "in vivo" literally means "in the living." As mentioned, direct testing to threshold levels on living human patients is ethically not an option. This presents difficulty with acquiring data which relates directly to the application of ultrasound in common practice. The use of non-human "in vivo" testing is a means by which to provide recommendations for appropriate use models of ultrasound. Of course, results from "in vivo" tests on non-human subjects must be kept in perspective, and may not accurately predict the presence of threshold levels of bioeffects in humans.

American Institute of Ultrasound in Medicine Statement on Non-Human Mammalian In Vivo Biological Effects. Approved October 1992.

Information from experiments utilizing laboratory mammals has contributed significantly to our understanding of ultrasonically induced biological effects and the mechanisms that are most likely responsible. The following statement summarizes observations relative to specific ultrasound parameters and indices. The history and rationale for this statement are provided in (reference).

In the low megahertz frequency range there have been no independently confirmed adverse biological effects in non-human mammalian tissues exposed in vivo under experimental ultrasound conditions, as follows.

a)   *When a thermal mechanism is involved, these conditions are unfocused-beam intensities* below 100 mW/cm², focused^-beam intensities below 1 W/cm², or thermal index values less than 2. Furthermore, such effects have not been reported for higher values of thermal index when it is less than*

$$6 - \frac{\log_{10} t}{0.6}$$

where t is the exposure duration ranging from 1 to 250 minutes, including off-time for pulsed exposure.

b)   *When a nonthermal mechanism is involved, # in tissues that contain well-defined gas bodies, these conditions are* **in situ** *peak rarefactional pressures below approximately 0.3 MPa or mechanical index values less than approximately 0.3. Furthermore, for other tissues no such effects have been reported.*

*Free-field spatial peak, temporal average (SPTA) for continuous wave and pulsed exposures.
^A Quarter-power (-6 dB) beam width smaller than four wavelengths or 4 mm, whichever is less at the exposure frequency.
#For diagnostically relevant ultrasound exposures.

COMMENTARY

Observations of biological effects from ultrasound experiments do not necessarily imply hazard to patients receiving diagnostic ultrasound examinations. Dimensions of tissues and organs in laboratory animals often have different relationships to beam width, tissue paths, and energy dissipation than in patients. Laboratory conditions are frequently selected to maximize the likelihood of producing, and detecting, effects in order to establish cause/effect relationships, and to provide details of the physical interactions of ultrasound and the biological specimen but not for direct use in the clinical setting.

The **in vivo** *statement can assist the clinical user in putting experimental data in perspective, but it should not be misconstrued to represent safety limits for exposure during diagnostic exams. It is helpful in arriving at recommendations for wise use of ultrasound in medicine. However, the statement does not, in itself, imply specific advice on "safe levels" which might be universally valid. Determination of recommended maximum levels will require consideration of such difficult topics as: adequacy of present knowledge of bioeffects, expected reliability of equipment specifications, assessment of patient benefits, and others. Current diagnostic equipment may exceed the conditions described in the statement. In such situations, the user should be aware of alternative equipment settings and conditions which might be employed to decrease acoustic exposure.*

(Pages 84 and 85)

13.8 The Mechanical Index and Conclusions Regarding Gas Bodies

The adoption of the MI as an acceptable standard for users to base risk benefit determination is based on the many advantages of the MI relative to the shortcomings of the I_{SPPA}. The following excerpt from the AIUM defines both the MI term, its relationship to cavitation, and the shortcomings that are eliminated based on its adoption. It is important to note, that the adoption of the MI has been beneficial to the use of contrast agents as a means of standardizing performance across manufacturers platforms as well as allowing for more predictable and controllable use.

Mechanical Index

After a theoretical investigation of cavitation, Apfel and Holland (1991) developed a simple relationship between acoustic pressure and the onset of inertial cavitation under the assumption that the optimum bubble size is present. The theory assumed isothermal growth, adiabatic collapse, an incompressible host fluid and neglected gas diffusion into the bubble. Short pulse durations, e.g., single cycles, were used in the calculations. The criterion for an inertial event was the generation of a collapse temperature of 5,000° K. As shown in Figure 3.2, the threshold pressure vs. initial bubble radius curve for a given carrier frequency has a minimum at a particular radius, termed the "optimum radius" by the authors. Furthermore, that minimum threshold acoustic pressure level increases approximately in proportion to the square root of the carrier frequency.

These analyses have been the basis for the adoption by a consensus group from the American Institute of Ultrasound in Medicine and other professional organizations of **a Mechanical Index (MI), which is defined as the derated peak rarefactional pressure (in MPa) at the location of the maximum pulse intensity integral divided by the square root of the center frequency (in MHz) (AIUM/NEMA, 1992). The position of the maximum pulse intensity integral in the sound field is just a specific definition for the focal point. The MI avoids the averaging problem inherent in the definition of the pulse average intensity; it avoids reliance upon the compressional pressure spike that dominates the maximum intensity; and, it incorporates a reasonable frequency dependence in the definition itself so that, in principle, it provides a single number that should be related to the occurrence of cavitation in the worst case** *(i.e., the optimum bubble size is assumed to be present). Although the special environment of tissues is not considered in the formulation of* MI, *it has the potential to be a useful predictor of bubble-related effects in tissues as long as it is "calibrated" against specific experimental observations* in vivo. *Such a "calibration" might take into account the pulse length dependence of the effects.*

(Page 15)

CONCLUSIONS REGARDING GAS BODIES
Approved March 18, 1993

1. The temporal peak outputs of some currently available diagnostic ultrasound devices can exceed the threshold for cavitation in vitro and can generate levels that produce extravasation of blood cells in the lungs of laboratory animals.

2. A Mechanical Index (MI)* has been formulated to assist users in evaluating the likelihood of cavitation-related adverse biological effects for diagnostically relevant exposures. The MI is a better indicator than derated spatial peak, pulse average intensity ($I_{SPPA.3}$) or derated peak rarefactional pressure ($p_{r.3}$) for known adverse nonthermal biological effects of ultrasound.

*The MI is equal to the derated peak rarefactional pressure (in MPa) at the point of the maximum pulse intensity integral divided by the square root of the ultrasonic center frequency (in MHz) *(see* Standard for Real-Time Display of Thermal and Mechanical Acoustic Output Indices on Diagnostic Ultrasound Equipment, *AIUM/NEMA, 1992).*

3. Thresholds for adverse nonthermal effects depend upon tissue characteristics and ultrasound parameters such as pressure amplitude, pulse duration and frequency. Thus far, biologically significant, adverse, nonthermal effects have only been identified with certainty for diagnostically relevant exposures in tissues that have well-defined populations of stabilized gas bodies. For extravasation of blood cells in postnatal mouse lung, the threshold values of **MI** *increase with decreasing pulse duration in the 1-100 μs range, increase with decreasing exposure time and are weakly dependent upon pulse repetition frequency. The threshold value of* MI *for extravasation of blood cells in mouse lung is approximately 0.3. The implications of these observations for human exposure are yet to be determined.*

4. No extravasation of blood cells was found in mouse kidneys exposed to peak pressures in situ corresponding to an **MI** *of 4. Furthermore, for diagnostically relevant exposures, no independently confirmed, biologically significant adverse nonthermal effects have been reported in mammalian tissues that do not contain well-defined gas bodies.*

(Page 3)

13.9 Conclusion Regarding Heat and the Thermal Indices (TIS, TIB, TIC)

The absorption rates for tissue types found in the body can vary significantly. As presented earlier in this chapter, tendons and bones absorb acoustic energy at a much greater rate than tissue, which absorbs at a much greater rate than fluids. A spatial average intensity is a measure of how acoustic energy is distributed over time. The problem with the spatial average metric is that it does not reflect the fact that heat generation is a function not only of the beam distribution, but also of the absorption coefficient. The thermal indices, although not perfect, reflect the impact of both of these parameters. To make an informed decision so as to perform prudent ultrasound, the thermal indices must be heeded.

CONCLUSIONS REGARDING HEAT
Approved March 26, 1997

1. Excessive temperature increase can result in toxic effects in mammalian systems. The biological effects observed depend on many factors, such as the exposure duration, the type of tissue exposed, its cellular proliferation rate, and its potential for regeneration. Age and stage of development are important factors when considering fetal and neonatal safety. Temperature increases of several degrees Celsius above the normal core range can occur naturally; there have been no significant biological effects observed resulting from such temperature increases except when they were sustained for extended time periods.

   a. **For exposure durations up to 50 hours, there have been no significant, adverse biological effects observed due to temperature increases less than or equal to 2° C above normal.**

   b. **For temperature increases greater than 2° C above normal, there have been no significant, adverse biological effects observed due to temperature increases less than or equal to 6 - (log10t/0.6) where t is the exposure duration ranging from 1 to 250 minutes. For example, for temperature increases of 4° C and 6° C, the corresponding limits for the exposure duration t are 16 min and 1 min, respectively.**

   c. **In general, adult tissues are more tolerant of temperature increases than fetal and neonatal tissues. Therefore, higher temperatures and/or longer exposure durations would be required for thermal damage.**

2. *The temperature increase during exposure of tissues to diagnostic ultrasound fields is dependent upon (a) output characteristics of the acoustic source such as frequency, source dimensions, scan rate, power, pulse repetition frequency, pulse duration, transducer self heating, exposure time and wave shape and (b) tissue properties such as attenuation, absorption, speed of sound, acoustic impedance, perfusion, thermal conductivity, thermal diffusivity, anatomical structure and nonlinearity parameter.*

3. For similar exposure conditions, the expected temperature increase in bone is significantly greater than in soft tissues. For this reason, conditions where an acoustic beam impinges on ossifying fetal bone deserve special attention due to its close proximity to other developing tissues.

4. *Calculations of the maximum temperature increase resulting from ultrasound exposure in vivo should not be assumed to be exact because of the uncertainties and approximations associated with the thermal, acoustic and structural characteristics of the tissues involved. However, experimental evidence shows that calculations are capable of predicting measured values within a factor of two. Thus, it appears reasonable to use calculations to obtain safety guidelines for clinical exposures where temperature measurements are not feasible. To provide a display of real-time estimates of tissue temperature increases as part of a diagnostic system, simplifying approximations are used to yield values called Thermal Indices.* **Under most clinically relevant conditions, the soft-tissue thermal index, TIS, and the bone thermal index, TIB, either over estimate or closely approximate the best available estimate of the maximum temperature increase ($\ddot{A} T_{max}$). For example, if TIS = 2, then $\ddot{A} T_{max} = 2°$ C.***

*The Thermal Indices are the non-dimensional ratios of the estimated temperature increases to $1°$ C for specific tissue models (see the Standard for Real-Time Display of Thermal and Mechanical Acoustic Output Indices on Diagnostic Ultrasound Equipment, AIUM/NEMA, 1992).

5. *The current FDA regulatory limit for $I_{SPTA.3}$ is 720 mW/cm². For this, and lesser intensities, the best available estimate of the maximum temperature increase in the conceptus can exceed $2°$ C.*

6. The soft-tissue thermal index, TIS, and the bone thermal index, TIB, are useful for estimating the temperature increase in vivo. For this purpose, these thermal indices are superior to any single ultrasonic field quantity such as the derated spatial-peak, temporal-average intensity, $I_{SPTA.3}$. That is, TIS and TIB track changes in the maximum temperature increases, ÄTmax, thus allowing for implementation of the ALARA principle, whereas $I_{SPTA.3}$ does not. For example,

    a. *At a constant value of $I_{SPTA.3}$ TIS increases with increasing frequency and with increasing source diameter.*

    b. *At a constant value of $I_{SPTA.3}$ TIB increases with increasing focal beam diameter.*

(Pages 3 and 4)

13.10 Thermal Effects on the Fetus

For numerous reasons, many of the greatest concerns with respect to thermal bioeffects is the use of ultrasound for fetal scanning. Part of the reason for concern is just the sheer number of studies performed. It is now estimated that well more than 3 million fetal studies are performed a year in the US alone. By itself, sheer volume does not constitute reason for concern. What does constitute reasons for concern is that fetal scans generally involve scanning through bones which have much higher absorption rates than other tissue types. This issue is exacerbated by the fact that the fluid surrounding the fetus is primarily water and hence, not very absorptive. As a result, the potential for significant temperature rise exists. Furthermore, there is certainly reason to be concerned with cellular damage in the presence of rapid fetal growth and specialization. For adults, the damage to a "few cells" seemingly is less problematic than damage to a similar number of cells for a fetus.

*The fetal temperatures requisite for damage appear to be several degrees above the normal, and involve exposure durations that decrease with increasing temperatures. In other words, the higher the temperature, the shorter the exposure time to achieve a deleterious effect. Second, it is not unusual for temperatures of pregnant women to have brief excursions into the "fever range." However, there is no clear relationship between these temperatures and any resulting fetal abnormalities in humans (Warkany, 1986). **Third, the relationship between elevated fetal temperatures and fetal abnormalities is strongest for animal studies. Fetal temperatures of 41° C for extended periods of time appear to be "threshold" for induction of fetal anomalies.** Adverse effects following hyperthermia are most likely if exposure occurs during organogenesis (Edwards, 1986). Fourth, it is clear that local temperatures in the body can vary widely without apparent adverse effect, e.g., as when drinking hot beverages.*

(Page 23)

13.11. The AIUM Statement Regarding "In Vitro" Biological Effects

The term "in vitro" literally means "in glass" and refers to testing that is performed or modeled outside of living tissues. Included in this classification of tests is algorithm based computer modeling. These models may use parameters derived from in vivo testing as part of the algorithmic basis. With respect to studying, identifying, and classifying bioeffects, much testing is performed in vitro. The value of in vitro testing is not that the results necessarily predict bioeffects with great specificity or accuracy, but rather that the results serve as a means by which to limit testing on live tissue (in vivo studies) as well as to serve as a guideline to design more specific testing.

Approved March 26, 1997, November 16, 2003

It is often difficult to evaluate reports of ultrasonically induced in vitro biological effects with respect to their clinical significance. The predominant physical and biological interactions and mechanisms involved in an in vitro effect may not pertain to the in vivo situation. Nevertheless, an in vitro effect must be regarded as a real biological effect.

***Results from in vitro experiments suggest new endpoints and serve as a basis for design of in** vivo experiments. In vitro studies provide the capability to control experimental variables and thus offer a means to explore and evaluate specific mechanisms. Although they may have limited applicability to in vivo biological effects, such studies can disclose fundamental intercellular or intracellular interactions.*

While it is valid for authors to place their results in context and to suggest further relevant investigations, reports which do more than that should be viewed with caution.

13.12 AIUM Conclusions Regarding Epidemiology for Obstetric Ultrasound

Epidemiologic studies in ultrasound involve analyzing populations of which some individuals have been exposed to ultrasound and of which some have not been exposed so as to determine if there is a statistical prevalence of an adverse outcome. Epidemiologic studies can be extremely useful, but can also be quite inaccurate. For example, if 10 of 100 patients who come into a hospital have the flu, the assumption that 10% of the population at large has the flu may be completely erroneous. Quite simply, people experiencing severe flu symptoms are more likely to go to a hospital than people who are not sick with the flu. The value of an epidemiologic study with respect to ultrasound is that a very large number of patients is included so that regional biases become statistically smaller or insignificant. The problem with an epidemiologic study is the only "adverse" outcomes recognized are those that are presumed as possible outcomes by the test. In other words, if ultrasound makes hair turn prematurely gray, but the study uses as metrics fetal weight, height, and hearing loss, the "adverse effect" or premature hair loss will not be identified.

Approved March 29, 1995; Revised June 22, 2005

*Based on the epidemiologic data available and on current knowledge of interactive mechanisms, there is insufficient justification to warrant conclusion of a causal relationship between diagnostic **ultrasound and recognized adverse effects in humans. Some studies have reported effects of exposure to diagnostic ultrasound during pregnancy, such as low birth weight, delayed speech, dyslexia and non-right-handedness. Other studies have not demonstrated such effects. The epidemiologic evidence is based on exposure conditions prior to 1992, the year in which acoustic limits of ultrasound machines were substantially increased for fetal/obstetric applications.***

14. Conceptual Questions   Answers: Pg. 965-966

1. There have been no recorded biological effects observed due to temperatures less than or equal to _____ above normal for exposure duration up to 50 hours.

2. The _____ _____ assists the user in evaluating the likelihood of cavitation-related adverse biological effects.

3. _____ _____ is the violent collapse of cells caused by the energy of the wave.

4. Transient cavitation is known to occur at pressures exceeding _____ .

5. _____ _____ occurs at energy levels lower than transient cavitation and is basically when bubbles begin to expand and oscillate.

6. The threshold for fetal anomalies over extended periods of time is _____ .

7. No significant biological effects in mammalian tissues exposed in vivo have been confirmed for unfocused ultrasound with intensities below 100 mW/cm^2, or for focused ultrasound with intensities below _____ .

8.   The _____ official statement on clinical _____ basically states no confirmed bio-
        logical effects have ever been reported on patients or instrument operators caused by exposure at
        intensities typical of present diagnostic ultrasound instruments. In addition, although future risks may
        be found, prudent use of diagnostic ultrasound outweighs the risks, if any, that may be present.

9.   Tissue heating is caused by absorption. The most important common intensity which predicts thermal
        effects is the _____ .

10.   _____ studies are studies done in a "test tube."

11.   _____ studies are studies done within living tissue.

12.   The AIUM's position on _____ studies is that it is difficult to make conclusions about
        _____ effects; however, in vitro studies are valuable for designing appropriate in
        _____ studies.

13.   The AIUM's position on diagnostic ultrasound safety, training and research is

        a) don't perform _____ without reason,
        b) don't prolong studies without _____, and
        c) use the minimum output _____ and maximum receiver gain to optimize
            image quality.

14.   The AIUM's position in the electrical and mechanical hazards of ultrasound are as follows:

        a) Use proper _____ to avoid electrical shock.
        b) Routinely _____ equipment for proper condition.
        c) Ultrasound presents no special electrical _____.
        d) Since the _____ comes in direct contact with the patient, the transducer is most
            likely to pose a threat, albeit small, to a patient's safety.

15.   The _____ _____ (MI) is a better indicator of cavitation-related adverse biological
        effects than the derated spatial peak, pulse average intensity *(I_{SPPA}).

15. Review Sheet For Converting Intensities

15.1 Conversion Between Spatial Peak and Spatial Average
Recall that:

$$\frac{SP}{SA} = BUF \;\; (\geq 1)$$

To convert between a Spatial Peak (SP) and a Spatial Average (SA), you must use the BUF.

(Think about the fact that the SP should be greater than the SA and the BUF ≥ 1.)

So:
The SP divided by the BUF yields the SA.
The SA multiplied by the BUF yields the SP.

15.2 Converting Between the Pulse Average and the Temporal Average
Recall that:

$$\frac{PD}{PRP} = Duty\ Factor \;\; (\leq 1)$$

(Think about the fact that the PRP should be greater than the PD and the DF ≤ 1.)

So:
The PD divided by the duty factor yields the PRP.
The PRP multiplied by the duty factor yields the PD.

15.3 Steps for Converting Between Intensities
Following is a step by step recipe for converting between one intensity measurement and another intensity measurement.

    Step 1: Break the four letter cluster into two letter clusters (SP, SA, TP, PA, TA).
    Step 2: Analyze which letter cluster or clusters is changed.
    Step 3: Determine what factor(s) are needed to perform conversion.
    Step 4: Determine if the value should become larger or smaller.*
    Step 5: Multiply or divide accordingly by conversion factor(s).
    Step 6: Sanity check (make sure that the answer makes sense).

*Note:
a) Multiplying a number by a number greater than one makes the number bigger.
b) Multiplying a number by a number less than one makes the number smaller.

Since division is the inverse operation of multiplication:
c) Dividing a number by a number greater than 1 makes the number smaller.
d) Dividing a number by a number less than 1 makes the number larger.

Chapter 9

◊ *Example:* Convert the I_{SPPA} into an I_{SAPA}, given that the $I_{SPPA} = 200$ mW/cm² and the BUF = 2.

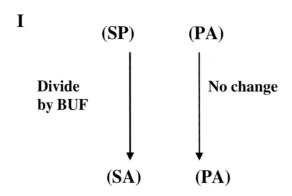

So the $I_{SAPA} = \dfrac{I_{SPPA}}{BUF} = \dfrac{\left(200\,\dfrac{mW}{cm^2}\right)}{2} = 100\,\dfrac{mW}{cm^2}$.

◊ *Example:* Convert the I_{SPPA} into an I_{SPTA}, given the $I_{SPPA} = 700$ mW/cm² and the DF = 10%.

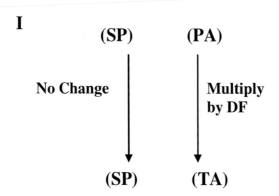

So the $I_{SPTA} = I_{SPPA} \bullet DF = \left(700\,\dfrac{mW}{cm^2}\right) \bullet 0.10 = 70\,\dfrac{mW}{cm^2}$.

◊ **Example:** Convert the I_{SATA} into an I_{SPPA}, given the $I_{SATA} = 100$ mW/cm², the DF = 10%, and the BUF = 3.

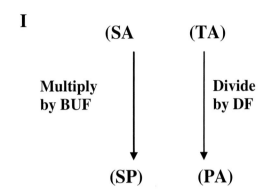

So the $I_{SPPA} = \dfrac{I_{SATA} \bullet BUF}{DF} = \dfrac{\left(100\,\dfrac{mW}{cm^2}\right) \bullet 3}{0.1} = 3{,}000\,\dfrac{mW}{cm^2} = 3\,\dfrac{W}{cm^2}$.

16. Hydrophones

The following data regarding types of hydrophones and performance characteristics was provided by the ONDA Corporation. The purpose for inclusion is to demonstrate some of the parameters that matter relative to accurate acoustic testing.

16.1 Comparison Table

	HM Series (Membrane)	HGL Series (Capsule)	HNV Series (Needle)	HNZ Series (Needle)	HNR Series (Needle)
Aperture Size (μm)	200/500	85 – 1000	200 - 1500	200 - 1500	500/1000
Frequency Response (useable range) (MHz)	0.2 – 20 ($\pm$3dB)	0.2 – 40 ($\pm$3dB)	1 – 20 ($\pm$6dB)	1 – 10 ($\pm$6dB)	0.2 – 20 ($\pm$6dB)
Normal Sensitivity	Medium +	Medium	Medium	High	Medium
Ruggedness	Low	Medium	Low	Low	High
Field Disturbance	High	Low	Low	Low	Medium
Typical Application	Standard regulatory test (pulse), reference hydrophone	General regulatory test (CW + pulse), working hydrophone	General purpose medium intensity, confined space	General purpose low intensity, confined space	Industrial rugged duty applications, ultrasonic cleaning tanks, lithotripters

Chapter 9

16.2 Membrane Hydrophones (HMA and HMB)*

For most pulsed wave applications that require a flat response over a broad bandwidth, membrane hydrophones are the type of choice. With their uniform sensitivity these devices provide accurate reproduction of a pulse including harmonic distortion up to 45 MHz. The single membrane HMA model has a traditional laminar construction that does not significantly affect the wave as it interacts with the device. The backed membrane HMB model has additional ruggedness because of its lossy backing. and because the backing is carefully designed to match the properties of water, it also does not affect the acoustic wave — as long as it does not contain large amounts of energy. If exposed to a high intensity field such as from a lithotriptor, the energy absorbed in the backing is likely to generate blisters and destroy the device.

16.3 Capsule "Golden Lipstick" Hydrophones (HGL)*

This unique design, created by Alan Selfridge, bridges the gap between membrane and needle hydrophones. It has an extremely flat sensitivity similar to membrane devices, yet it does not have a frame that affects the acoustic field and is very convenient for moving around a tank. Onda's AH amplifiers mate directly to these hydrophones, allowing for a water-tight, optimal configuration for measuring acoustic fields with minimal disturbance.

16.4 Needle Hydrophones (HNZ and HNV)*

The ceramic-based HNZ models have the most sensitivity for their size, but their frequency response is less flat. The polymer-based HNV models' needles have a smoother frequency response, with about 10 dB less sensitivity for a given size. With all hydrophones, frequency response varies somewhat among individual production units, and is quite difficult to control. Throughout the industry there are no standards on the range of variability that can be found among devices.

Note that because of their needle shape, you can poke them into objects like foams or soft materials, which makes them very convenient for many experiments. However, it is also very easy to scratch the device and remove isolation around the edges. The active element has very little separation between its two electrodes, so even a slight tap against a solid object can completely destroy the hydrophone. Any fixture that requires inserting the hydrophone through a hole is NOT recommended. Instead, the recommendation is to use "V" groove holders with clamping bars, into which the hydrophone can be laid without threatening the fragile tip.

16.5 Needle Reflecting Hydrophones (HNR)*

In general shape these hydrophones are still needle-like, however they have flat tips, about 2.4 mm in diameter. The active element diameter is still much smaller (see data sheet). The angular responses are about what we expect for the specified aperture, and the sensitivity tends to roll off above 10 MHz. The main advantage these devices have is that they are TOUGH, and able to withstand pressures and cavitation that would ruin a needle type device. A typical use might be to measure fields in ultrasonic cleaners ("Megasonic") and other high intensity fields. The frequency response usually has a 2 to 3dB sharp resonance near 2 MHz, probably a radial resonance.

* Information provided by Onda Corporation

Bioeffects

- There are two principal mechanisms of bioeffects: mechanical and thermal.

- Mechanical bioeffects are primarily related to cavitation.

- Cavitation is the production, oscillation, or destruction of bubbles.

- Cavitation is believed to be a threshold mechanism: below certain power levels cavitation tends to be stable, above certain power levels cavitation tends to be transient (inertial).

- Stable cavitation occurs when the oscillations does not lead to bubble collapse.

- Inertial (transient) cavitation results in bubble destruction (implosion).

- Although the potential for bioeffects exist, ultrasound is considered a very safe modality.

- Thermal bioeffects are related to the beam intensity, the duration of the scan, the absorption rate of the medium, the ability to duct away heat from the region being scanned, and whether the technique being performed is a scanned or non-scanned modality.

- According to the AIUM, no confirmed bioeffects have occurred using accepted power levels.

- You should know the ALARA (as low as reasonably achievable) principle and its meaning. In essence, the lowest power necessary to achieve good clinical results should be used, constituting prudent use of ultrasound.

- Furthermore, you should be aware that scan times should not be extended needlessly, nor should needless scans be performed.

- The common intensities are a way of assessing the potential risk of bioeffects.

- Spatial measurements refer to the power distribution over physical dimensions.

- Temporal and pulse measurements refer to the distribution of power over time.

- The largest intensity measurement is the spatial peak, temporal peak. The smallest is the spatial average, temporal average.

- CW Doppler has the highest potential risk of thermal bioeffects since the duty factor is 1 (always transmitting) and CW is a "non-scanned" modality.

- In terms of the common intensities, the best indicator for the risk of thermal bioeffects is the spatial peak temporal average (intensity over the long period of time).

- The mechanical index (MI) has become the standard for indication of risk of bioeffects.

- The MI is the indicator for the risk of mechanical damage.

- There are three thermal indices to indicate the potential risk of thermal related bioeffects:
    - TIS: thermal index in soft tissue
    - TIC: thermal index in cranial bone
    - TIB: thermal index in bone

- The thermal index indicates the model based prediction of the highest expected temperature rise for the current imaging situation. A thermal index of 1 implies the maximum temperature rise expected is 1 degree Celsius.

- It is possible that the models underestimate the worst-case situations, and that the temperature could rise above the value predicted.

- The maximum temperature rise allowed in fetal imaging is 2 degrees Celsius.

- The maximum beam intensity allowed is 100 mW/cm^2 for an unfocused beam and 1 W/cm^2 for a focused beam.

- Acoustic power measurements are made to assure transducer performance both in terms of adequate sensitivity as well as safety.

- Hydrophones are routinely used to make power measurements in a water bath.

- Power measurements are difficult to make and very time consuming.

- There are hopes of newer technologies to make power measurements simpler, faster, and better.

Note: See Appendix N: Physical Units and Appendix O: Equations for additional review.

Contact Information:

AIUM
14750 Sweitzer Lane
Suite 100
Laurel, MD 20707-5906
1-301-498-4100

References:

* <u>Bioeffects & Safety of Diagnostic Ultrasound</u>. American Institute of Ultrasound in Medicine, 1993.

* <u>Medical Ultrasound Safety: Part One: Bioeffects and BioPhysics, Part Two: Prudent Use, Part Three: Implementing ALARA</u>. American Institute of Ultrasound in Medicine, 1994.

* <u>Medical Bioeffects From Diagnostic Ultrasound: AIUM Consensus Statements</u>. Journal of Ultrasound in Medicine, Volume 19, Number 2, February 2000.

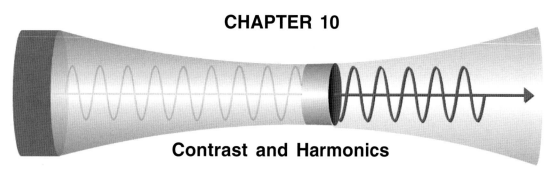

CHAPTER 10

Contrast and Harmonics

Co-authored by Patrick Rafter, MS

1. Motivation for Contrast Imaging

1.1 Overcoming Too Much Attenuation

One of the motivating factors for creating contrast imaging is how incredibly low-level the signals are when imaging red blood cells. As we have already discussed, reflections from blood can be very weak due to the nature of the Rayleigh scattering and the minimal acoustic impedance mismatch within the blood itself. The weak reflection often causes very poor signal-to-noise, sometimes poor enough so that the signal is either non-diagnostic or even not detected.

Recall the equation which relates the operating frequency, the propagation speed, and the wavelength: $\lambda = \dfrac{c}{f}$. Substituting 1540 m/sec for c and using the range of 2 MHz to 10 MHz as the normal range for diagnostic ultrasound, the typical range for the wavelength is calculated as 770 μm to 154 μm. The typical red blood cell has a diameter of approximately 6 - 7 μm. Clearly, red blood cells look small in comparison to the wavelength, and therefore yield weak Rayleigh scattering.

1.2 Conventional Approaches

The approaches usually taken to overcome poor signal-to-noise are to use a lower frequency transducer, use a different imaging approach, use a higher transmit power, or even to use a more invasive approach such as transesophageal (TEE). All of these approaches rely on trying to create a better interrogating signal. The question is, "Is there anything which can be done to enhance the strength or mechanism of reflection?"

1.3 Increasing the Acoustic Impedance Mismatch

There are clearly two ways in which to increase the amount of backscatter: increase the surface of the reflector, or increase the acoustic impedance mismatch. Consider if an agent was added to the blood to enhance the signal. It is obviously a very poor idea to try to add an agent with a large backscattering surface, since the diameter of the agent must be able to pass through the capillaries without causing obstruction. Therefore, the idea of contrast imaging is not to increase the backscattering surface, but rather to use a contrast agent which increases the acoustic impedance mismatch within the blood.

Given that the contrast agent will reside in the blood pool, the agent needs to have an acoustic impedance which varies significantly relative to the plasma and red blood cells. The most obvious choice is to use a gas.

Recall that the acoustic impedance is given by the equation: $Z = \rho * c$. Since gases tend to have relatively low densities and high compressibility, it is expected that gases will also have a low propagation velocity. Therefore, since the density and propagation speed in a gas are low, the acoustic impedance of a gas is extremely low. In comparison, the density and propagation speed of the blood are both significantly higher, resulting in a significantly higher acoustic impedance. Also recall that the amount of reflection is dependent on the acoustic impedance mismatch, given by the equation:

$$Reflection\% = \left[\frac{Z_2 - Z_1}{Z_2 + Z_1} \right]^2$$

1.4 Increase in Signal Amplitude with Contrast

Since with a contrast agent there is a significant mismatch within the blood, there will be significantly more backscattered energy, and hence significantly better signal-to-noise. In fact, the increase in signal strength using a contrast agent, in comparison to the signal strength of normal blood, is typically on the order of 30 dB, as shown in *Figure 1*.

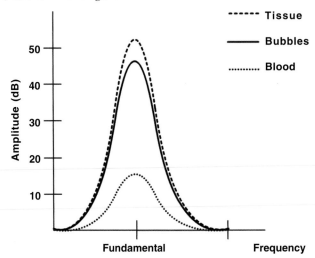

Fig. 1   **Relative Signal Amplitudes**

The specifics of contrast imaging are further discussed in Level 3 of this chapter.

2. Fundamentals of Harmonics

2.1. Motivation for Harmonic Imaging

The clear advantage of using a higher transmit frequency for imaging is better detail resolution (resolution is discussed in Chapters 4, 5, 6 and 8). One of the clear disadvantages of using a higher transmit frequency is significantly greater attenuation (recall that the amount of absorption increases exponentially with increasing frequency). The question is, "Is there a way to get better resolution while still preserving the ability to visualize deeper structures without having to use more invasive techniques?"

Figure 2a depicts how using a high frequency is inappropriate when penetration is necessary. *Figure 2b* shows how using a lower frequency provides the penetration required, but does not yield optimal resolution.

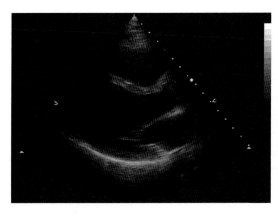
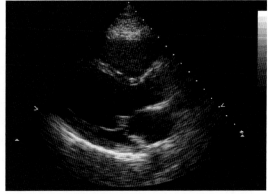

Fig. 2a   **High Frequency with Inadequate Penetration**

Fig. 2b   **Low Frequency with Poor Resolution**

The concept of harmonic imaging is to transmit at a lower frequency and receive at a higher frequency. Specifically, the word harmonics refers to a multiple of the operating frequency. For example, the first harmonic refers to the fundamental frequency or operating frequency, the second harmonic refers to the frequency that is twice the fundamental frequency, while the third harmonic refers to the frequency that is three times the fundamental frequency. There is sometimes confusion between the naming convention of overtones and harmonics. The first overtone is the same as the second harmonic, whereas the second overtone is the same as the third harmonic.

Transmitting at the lower frequency (the fundamental frequency) allows for better penetration, while receiving at the higher frequency (the harmonic frequency), generally yields better resolution. Compare the image of *Figure 3* with *Figure 2a* and *Figure 2b*. Notice the significant improvement in resolution and reduction in reverberation. The question is, "How does this work?"

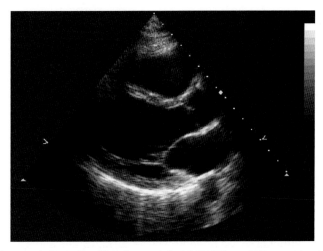

Fig. 3   **Harmonic Imaging (Fundamental at 1.8 MHz and Harmonic at 3.6 MHz)**

2.2 Mechanisms that Produce Harmonic Signals
There are two different mechanisms for producing harmonic signals used in diagnostic ultrasound:

- Non-linear propagation through tissue producing "native" or "tissue harmonic imaging"
- Resonance of contrast agents producing "contrast harmonic imaging"

Chapter 10

3. Technology Advances

The first attempt to develop techniques specifically to image ultrasound contrast agents led to the development of harmonic imaging. Initial uses of contrast agents were somewhat limited by some of the same general types of problems which plague conventional imaging, and a few new problems. Specifically, reflection from near field specular structures still generated many imaging artifacts. New problems arose such as shadowing from the increased reflectivity due to the large acoustic impedance mismatch of the bubbles, and the too rapid destruction of the contrast agent. As a result, a new approach was desired. It was well known that bubbles could reach resonant frequencies where non-linear excitation would produce harmonic energy. The "new approach," called harmonic contrast imaging, was to change the system operation so as to enhance the non-linear resonance effects and then process the resulting harmonic signals.

While improving the system operation for contrast harmonic imaging, a few technological advancements in the mid 1990's made harmonic imaging a possibility. Specifically, the combination of broadband transducers capable of transmitting at one frequency and receiving at twice that frequency (as depicted in *Figure 4* and discussed in Chapter 4) and broadband digital beamformers (discussed in Chapter 6) with programmable digital filtering, made harmonic imaging feasible. At the time, to improve harmonic contrast imaging, it was hoped, and even expected, that the harmonic signal would be purely generated by the contrast agents. Therefore, by processing only the frequency range of signals in the harmonic band, the source of many imaging artifacts would be completely eliminated.

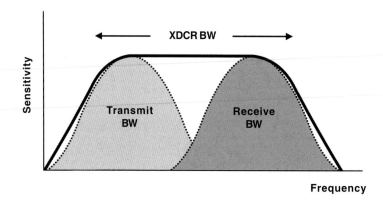

Fig. 4   **Broadband Transducer Capable of Harmonic Imaging**

Somewhat surprisingly, the reflected signal was not purely comprised of harmonic energy from the contrast agent. Instead, the reflected signal also was comprised of harmonic content generated by the tissue as well as the contrast agent. Although the harmonic contrast signal was of higher amplitude than the signal from the surrounding blood, the harmonic tissue signals were quite strong and often masked the desired contrast signal. Therefore, even without the use of contrast agents, harmonic energy is generated by the propagation of sound waves through the body as depicted in *Figure 5*.

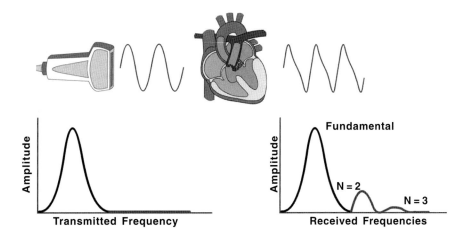

Fig. 5   **Generation of Harmonic Energy from Propagation Through Tissue**

4. Relative Amplitudes

Figure 6 demonstrates the relative amplitudes of tissue, blood, contrast bubbles, and tissue harmonic signals.

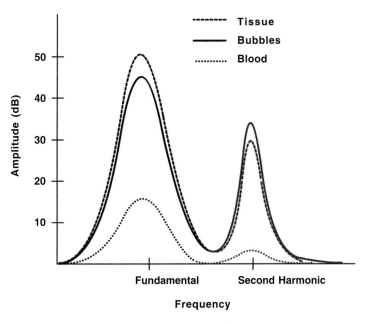

Fig. 6   **Relative Amplitudes**

Notice that at the harmonic frequency, the amplitude of the contrast signal has enhanced the harmonic blood signal by approximately 30 dB to 40 dB. Also notice that in general, the contrast signal has a higher amplitude than the harmonic tissue signal and that the difference in amplitude is not that large.

5. Generation of Harmonics

5.1 Non-linear Wave Propagation

To understand how tissue harmonic energy is generated, you must reconsider the mechanism by which a mechanical wave propagates. Recall that a mechanical wave propagates through a series of compressions and rarefactions. Also recall that the propagation speed changes with the density and stiffness of the medium. During the compression phase of the wave the material becomes denser. As a result, the propagation speed increases slightly. During the rarefactional phase, the medium becomes a little less stiff and is a little more elastic. As a result, the propagation speed decreases slightly. These changes in propagation speeds are noted in *Figure 7*.

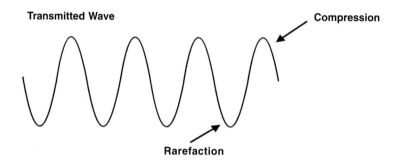

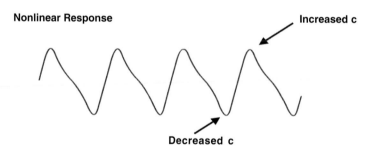

Fig. 7 **Generation of Harmonics from Non-linear Wave Propagation Through Body**

Notice that the wave propagating through the body has a characteristically different shape than the the transmitted wave. Notice how there are sharp edges to the wave propagating through the body due to the changes from lower to higher and higher to lower propagation speeds. These "quick" changes represent higher frequency energy. In reality, there is energy at many different harmonics of the fundamental frequency. If the signal is decomposed into individual frequency bands (much like the FFT process described in Chapter 7 on Doppler processing), energy will exist not just at the second harmonic, but also at the third harmonic, fourth harmonic, etc. The amplitude of each successive higher harmonic reduces non-linearly, so that the third harmonic is much weaker than the second, and the fourth harmonic much weaker than the third. The following diagram, *Figure 8*, demonstrates the relative amplitudes of the various harmonics generated by non-linear propagation.

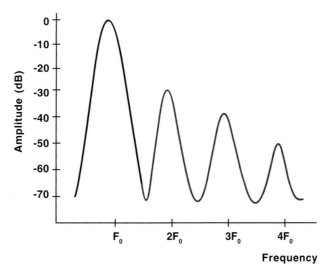

Fig. 8   **Relative Amplitudes of Harmonic Series**

5.2 Harmonics and Depth Dependence

As illustrated in *Figure 7*, as the sound wave propagates through the body, the characteristic shape of the wave changes. In general, this "distortion" of the transmitted signal accumulates as the waveform propagates through tissue, leading to an increasing level of second harmonic signal with depth. Where the wave starts out at the face of the transducer there are no harmonic components. As the wave propagates into the body, distortion resulting in harmonic energy begins to occur. The rate at which harmonic energy builds up is dependent on multiple factors such as the acoustic transmit pressure, the transmit frequency, and the attenuation rate. As the beam converges towards the focus, the acoustic pressure increases (higher beam intensities) leading to a higher level of distortion. The increase in harmonic energy with higher intensities is the result of greater variation in propagation velocity resulting from higher amplitude compressions and rarefactions.

With increasing depth, there is increased beam attenuation, decreasing the pressure intensity. As we learned in Chapter 5, past the focus, the beam diverges rapidly reducing the acoustic pressure field. As a result of the increased attenuation, eventually, the rate of increase in harmonic energy will decrease, and the harmonic generation rate will drop well below the rate of attenuation at the fundamental frequency. In other words, the rate of decreasing harmonic energy will be faster than the already high rate of attenuation at the fundamental frequency. Recall that the harmonic signal is weaker than the fundamental signal. Furthermore, since the harmonic signal is at a higher frequency, the attenuation rate on return to the transducer is higher than the attenuation rate of the fundamental signal. The combined effect (weaker harmonics, higher attenuation rates, and decreased harmonic production because of decreasing beam intensity) leads to significantly lower levels of harmonic signal in the far field. Therefore, in the very near field and in the far field, there are times when fundamental imaging will outperform harmonic imaging in terms of signal-to-noise ratio. The loss of harmonic signal in the far field is most noticeable at higher transmit frequencies (e.g., > 2.5 MHz) due to the greater rate of absorption at these frequencies. The following diagram, *Figure 9*, illustrates the gradual "build up" and decrease of harmonic energy as a function of depth.

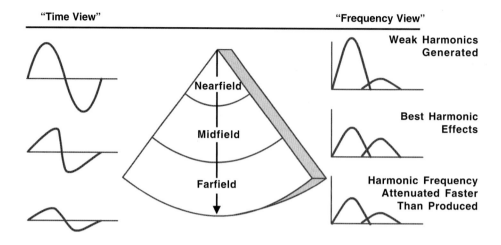

Fig. 9 **Harmonic Generation versus Depth**

5.3 Effective Harmonic Beam Shape

As a result of the increasing harmonic generation with depth, the effective harmonic beam shape differs greatly from the transmitted fundamental beam shape. *Figure 10* demonstrates these differences.

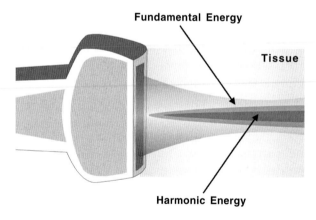

Fig. 10 **Comparison of Harmonic Beamwidth and Fundamental Beamwidth**

6. Advantages and Disadvantages of Conventional Harmonics

6.1 Improved Lateral Resolution

When there is adequate signal-to-noise, there are many possible improvements in image quality from tissue harmonic imaging (THI) such as improved lateral resolution relative to fundamental imaging. This improvement leads to the question: "To improve lateral resolution, why not just use a higher transmit frequency?" The answer is, there are other benefits to tissue harmonic imaging such as improved penetration relative to fundamental imaging at higher frequencies and more importantly, dramatic reduction in imaging artifacts.

6.2 Reduction in Grating Lobes

One source of noise and artifact in an ultrasound image is from off-axis objects mapping energy into the main beam (grating lobe artifact as discussed in Chapter 8). Since grating lobes result in lateral translation of signal in an image, real anatomical structures may be obscured, or artificial structures "manufactured." The use of harmonics significantly reduces the deleterious effects of grating lobes. As already discussed, higher harmonic energy generation is very dependent on incident pressure. Higher pressure fields result in much greater harmonic energy. Recall that the energy in the grating lobe is significantly less than the energy in the main lobe (usually 30 dB to 60 dB less). As a result, the harmonic energy produced by the undesired grating lobe of the beam is much lower in amplitude than the harmonic energy produced by the main lobe of the beam. Therefore, there is significantly less noise and artifact associated with the grating lobes. The following illustration in *Figure 11* depicts the decrease in grating lobes with harmonic production.

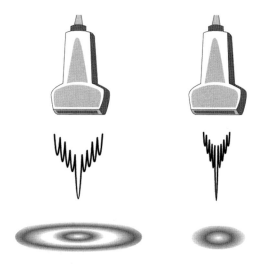

Fig. 11   **Decreased Grating Lobes with Harmonic Imaging**

6.3 Reduction in Reverberation and Clutter Artifacts

Another important source of artifact and noise is multi-path reverberations. As discussed in many chapters including Chapter 8, reverberation is caused by large acoustic impedance mismatches, usually from specular reflectors, which result in the sound beam being redirected back and forth between structures or between structures and the transducer face. For example, in cardiac imaging sound will reverberate between the skin, the chest wall, the ribs, and the transducer. Since multiple reflections have occurred, the actual path the ultrasound wave has traveled when reflected back to the transducer is longer than the distance from the transducer to the original structures that redirected the energy. To the ultrasound scanner, this energy appears to come from deeper in the body, often appearing as a haze in the image that obscures structures, or worse, appears as an artifactual thrombus. There are two effects that work in tandem to reduce reverberation with harmonic imaging. First, the intensity of each reverberation is lower than the intensity of the actual reflection. Lower intensity waves produce less distortion and hence less harmonic energy. Second, most imaging artifacts are caused by specular reflectors in the relative near field where the beam is still converging and hence producing relatively weak harmonic energy.

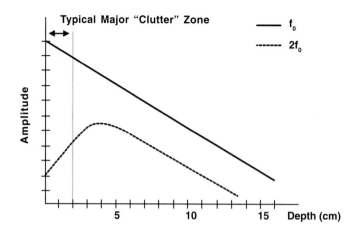

Fig. 12 **Reduction in "Clutter" from Harmonics**

Referring to *Figure 12*, notice that in the near field, the source of most imaging artifacts, the harmonic signal is significantly weaker than the fundamental signal. The result is that the strong "clutter" signals responsible for the majority of artifacts are reduced, and artifacts are either diminished or eliminated entirely. This is perhaps one of the biggest benefits of harmonic imaging.

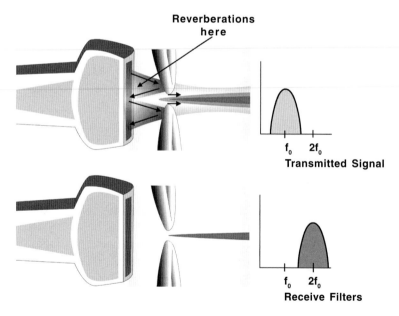

Fig. 13 **Reduction in Reverberation Artifact**

Figure 13 demonstrates how reverberation from ribs in a cardiac setting is significantly reduced by harmonic imaging. Note that there is very little attenuation of the fundamental frequency in the near field such that the system is very sensitive to these reverberating signals when using conventional imaging (at the fundamental). In contrast, since the harmonic effect increases as the beam intensifies while converging, the harmonic system is less sensitive to these reverberating signals.

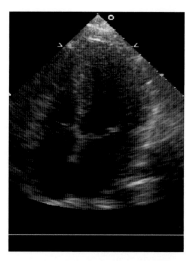

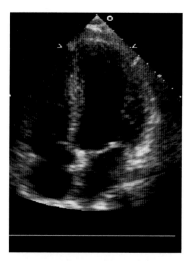

Fig. 14a **Conventional Imaging**   *Fig. 14b* **Harmonic Imaging (Apical 4-Chamber)**

View Animation and Image Library CD

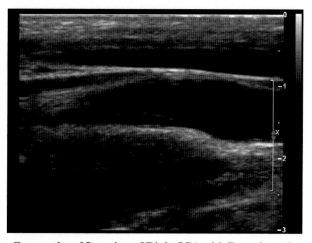

Fig. 15a **Conventional Imaging of Right ICA with Reverberation Artifact**

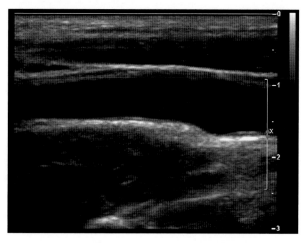

Fig. 15b **Harmonic Imaging of Right ICA**

Chapter 10

6.4 Reduction in Phase Aberration

Another benefit of harmonic imaging relative to transmitting at a higher frequency is the reduction in effects from phase aberration. Phase aberration is a distortion of the ultrasound beam caused by differences in the speed of sound due to inhomogeniety in tissue. For example, fat has a lower speed of sound (1440 m/sec) than muscle (1560 m/sec). As the spherical waves from each of the transducer elements propagates through different distances of tissues with varying propagation speeds they arrive at a point along the beam at different times. In other words, the differences in the acoustic path of each spherical wave have caused a phase delay. In essence, this phase delay counteracts the phase delays produced by the system to steer and focus the beam. The result is a less directed and less focused beam, referred to as "aberration." The result of this aberration is a decrease in the "main lobe" energy and an increase in the grating lobe energy. This effect is reduced by harmonic imaging since the focusing of lower frequencies is less affected by changes in the speed of sound than higher frequencies. Recall that higher frequencies produce shorter wavelengths. For shorter wavelengths, less of a time delay results in more destructive interference. Therefore transmitting at a lower frequency, as done with harmonic imaging, reduces phase aberration effects.

6.5 Degradation in Axial Resolution

A drawback of harmonic imaging relative to higher frequency conventional imaging is a degradation of axial resolution. In order to gain the full benefit of THI, separation of the fundamental and harmonic bandwidths is required. Any overlap of the fundamental and receive bandwidth can cause noise and haze in the image. The overlap of the bandwidths can be reduced by transmitting a narrower bandwidth of frequencies. As we learned in Chapter 4, the bandwidth is inversely related to the pulse duration. Therefore, to create a narrower bandwidth, the transducer is allowed to ring for more cycles. This relationship is depicted in *Figure 16*. Since the number of cycles also affects the spatial pulse length, an increase in the number of cycles increases the spatial pulse length, decreasing axial resolution. In the cardiac world, this decrease in axial resolution often results in an apparent "thickening" of the valve leaflets. Therefore when axial resolution is critical, conventional harmonics should be turned off.

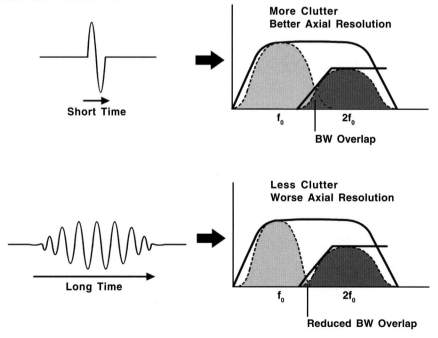

Fig. 16 **Narrow Banding Reduces Clutter but also Decreases Axial Resolution**

7. Pulse or Phase Inversion

Pulse inversion has proven very beneficial in reversing the degradation in axial resolution that occurs with conventional harmonic imaging. To understand how pulse inversion works, we will first need to demonstrate a very interesting phenomenon. A fundamental pulse 180 degrees out of phase with another fundamental pulse, will generate the same phase harmonic signal. In the following figure (*Figure 17*) notice that the fundamental frequency at both 0 degrees and at 180 degrees corresponds to the same phase for the harmonic signal. This result is fortuitous, since it becomes the basis for how pulse inversion works.

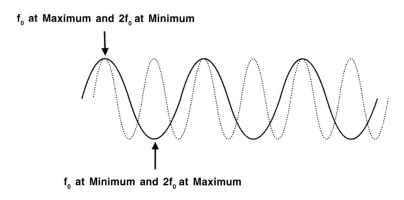

f_0 at Maximum and $2f_0$ at Minimum

f_0 at Minimum and $2f_0$ at Maximum

Fig. 17 **Phase of 2ⁿᵈ Harmonic is the Same for the Maxima and Minima of the Fundamental Frequency**

Unlike conventional harmonics, pulse inversion harmonics requires multiple acoustic lines to produce a single display line. A transmit pulse is generated creating the first acoustic line. A second transmit pulse is then transmitted in the same scan direction, but this time with the phase inverted (180 degrees out of phase). The received response from the first pulse is then summed with the response from the second pulse. Any energy that reflects linearly (at the fundamental frequency) will be 180 degrees out of phase between the first and second transmit pulses. When added together destructive interference occurs (as discussed in Chapter 1), and the fundamental energy is cancelled out. In comparison, any energy that reflects non-linearly (harmonics) will be in phase (0 degrees out of phase) between the first and second pulses. When added together, two signals in phase add constructively, producing a larger signal. There are therefore two major advantages to pulse inversion: since the fundamental energy is cancelled out, no narrowbanding is needed to preserve axial resolution, and the averaging effect improves the signal-to-noise ratio by a factor of 1.4 (the square root of 2). *Figure 18* demonstrates the basic principle of pulse inversion harmonics. The one disadvantage is that since two acoustic lines are transmitted per display line, the frame rate, and hence the temporal resolution, is degraded by a factor of 2.

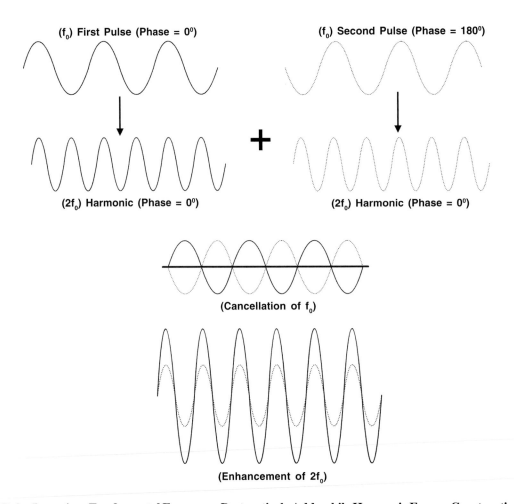

Fig. 18 **Pulse Inversion: Fundamental Frequency Destructively Adds while Harmonic Energy Constructively Adds**

Figure 19b shows how dramatic the improvement from pulse inversion harmonics can be relative to fundamental imaging. In this case a large thrombus becomes evident using pulse inversion harmonics which is not visualized with conventional imaging.

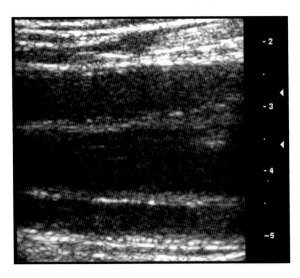

Fig. 19a **Fundamental Imaging**

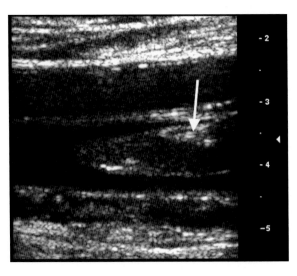

Fig. 19a **Pulse Inversion Harmonics**

8. Current Uses of Contrast Imaging

Ultrasound contrast agents have been commercially available in the U.S. since 1994. However, the only currently approved indication by the FDA is for left ventricular opacification (LVO) to aid in the delineation of endocardial borders. In the coming years a myocardial perfusion indication is hoped for as well as indications for other organs. Currently in Europe and Asia, use of contrast for detection and characterization of focal liver lesions is on the rise. Today's ultrasound contrast agents consist of microbubbles that act as intravascular tracers – moving at the same velocities as red blood cells and going everywhere red blood cells go. A typical contrast agent is less than 6 microns diameter and is designed with the goal of passing through the pulmonary microcirculation when administered with an intravenous injection. After reaching the arterial side of the heart, they are pumped everywhere red blood cells go and are therefore ideal for imaging and studying the microcirculation.

9. Properties of Contrast

9.1 Composition of Bubbles

Today's contrast agents consist of bubbles encapsulated by a stabilizing shell. In order to be effective, it is necessary for the contrast agent to last several minutes in the blood stream to allow for ample imaging time. Since the bubbles are micron sized, a shell is necessary to keep them from dissolving quickly in the blood stream. Typical shells consist of sonicated albumin, phospholipids or more recently, synthetic polymers. Since the shell used in a particular agent can cause it to be either stiff or pliable, the shell plays an extremely important role in determining acoustic properties. The gas plays an important part as well – especially in determining the longevity of the contrast effect. Early contrast agents were air-based but due to the high diffusibility of air, they would dissolve rather rapidly in the bloodstream. More recently higher density gases such as sulfur hexafluoride and perfluorocarbons have been introduced which allow for greater longevity. However, pharmaceutical companies have also shown that with the right shell composition it is possible to construct a stable air filled microbubble.

9.2 Microbubble Interaction with Ultrasound and Resonance

Microbubbles, around the size of contrast agent bubbles, generally have a strong acoustic response when excited by waveforms with frequencies in the low MHz range, corresponding nicely with the typical range of diagnostic ultrasound frequencies (typically > 1 MHz and < 10 MHz). This natural response frequency is referred to as a "resonance". *Figure 20* demonstrates the increase in signal amplitude which results from insonating a bubble at its resonant frequency.

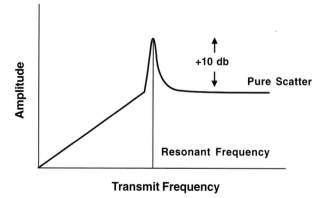

Fig. 20   **Microbubble Resonance**

To understand resonance, we will need to consider the bubble response to the mechanical wave.

During the compressional phase of the mechanical wave, there is increased pressure on the microbubble and the microbubble gets smaller or contracts. During the rarefaction phase of the ultrasound wave, the pressure surrounding the microbubble decreases and the microbubble becomes larger or expands. As the microbubble oscillates in the varying acoustic field, it reradiates an ultrasound wave back towards the transducer. The amplitude, frequency, and duration of the driving pulse all play very important roles in determining the acoustic response from microbubbles. However, the actual dynamics of the microbubble oscillation is altered by the microbubble's "desire" to resonate at its natural frequency.

This resonance effect is very similar to a string of a guitar. The length of the string and its tension help define the tone or frequency that results when the string is plucked. In a similar manner, a microbubble's natural resonance frequency is strongly influenced by its radius as well as its shell properties. For an unencapsulated "free" air bubble the resonance is given by:

$$Frequency(MHz) = \frac{330}{Resting\ Radius(\mu m)} .$$

For example, a 2 micron bubble will resonate at 1.65 MHz. A typical contrast agent is comprised of a wide range of bubble sizes with varying shell thickness and therefore has a corresponding wide range of responses. The combination of these factors has made it extremely challenging to mathematically predict microbubble behavior under various ultrasound conditions. To date, most of the understanding of interaction of ultrasound with microbubbles has come from observed acoustic behavior when imaging microbubbles in vitro and in vivo. Recently, a great deal of understanding has come from high-speed cameras capable of taking pictures of single microbubbles under ultrasound excitation at very fast frame rates.

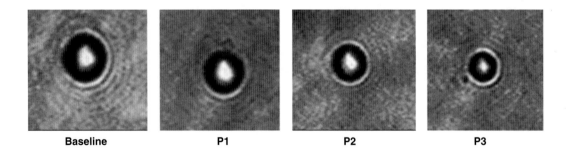

Baseline   **P1**   **P2**   **P3**

Fig. 21   **Stable Oscillation of a Lipid Bubble**

Referring to *Figure 21*, the first frame labeled "baseline" is a light microscopy image of a lipid bubble prior to excitation. The frame labeled "P1" is the bubble after one pulse with an MI of 0.4. Note that the bubble has been compressed. The frames labeled "P2" and "P3" are the bubble after the second and third pulse.

10. The Mechanical Index (MI)

10.1 Understanding the MI

One of the keys to optimizing ultrasound images with contrast agents is to understand more about the interaction between output power and the contrast effect. Not only does output power have a dramatic influence on contrast enhancement level, it has also been observed in vivo that diagnostic levels of ultrasound output power can cause microbubble disruption. The (MI) was introduced several years ago as an indicator of the likelihood of cavitation in tissue. (The MI is discussed in Chapter 9: Bioeffects.) The MI is currently displayed on all newer ultrasound systems since its adoption as a standard. The MI is the primary indicator of output power on ultrasound equipment and is the most critical parameter in determining microbubble response. For a given transmit frequency, the MI is directly related to the peak rarefactional, or negative, pressure. The equation is:

$$MI = \frac{Peak\ Negative\ Pressure\ (MPa)}{\sqrt{frequency\ (MHz)}}$$

Since the actual acoustic pressure that tissue is exposed to can vary a great deal depending on the patient and the acoustic window, the displayed MI is only an estimate. A constant level of attenuation (0.3 dB/MHz/cm) is assumed when equipment manufacturers determine the MI. Due to the complexities of making these measurements, there are also slight variations between manufacturers. Therefore, machines reporting the same MI may in fact be somewhat different in terms of their actual output.

10.2 Non-uniformity of the MI

It is important to understand that the reported MI is for only one location throughout the entire image. Often, the point of peak MI is much closer to the face of the transducer than the actual placement of the transmit focus. Due to directivity of the elements of transducers, the scan lines at angles will also tend to have lower MIs than the centerline — the one fired "straight ahead" or perpendicular to the transducer face (as indicated in *Figure 22*). This variation in signal strength with angular direction is very similar to the effect of sound being louder when you are standing right in front of a speaker rather than off to the side. Also, it is important to realize that the movement of the transmit focus will alter the distribution of power in the image, even if the reported MI remains the same. For example, when the focus is in the far field the transmit beam will tend to be more uniform and less variable with depth.

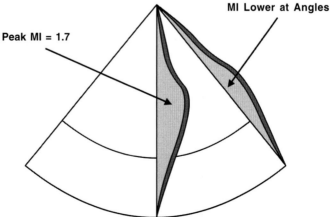

Fig. 22 **Dependence of MI on Steer Angle**

10.3 Effect of MI on Microbubbles

10.3.1 Linear Response for Low MIs

The mechanism for microbubble destruction is highly dependent on the MI as well as the properties of the contrast agent. For simplification purposes, it is possible to break up the realm of responses into different ranges of MIs. At very low MIs (typically < 0.1) there is essentially a "linear" response from the microbubbles. This means that during a transmit pulse the signal reflected from the microbubble looks similar to the excitation pulse. With low MIs, the variations in radius of a microbubble are very small and the bubble grows the same amount as it shrinks, or the bubble undergoes symmetric oscillation. Since the reradiated returning signal looks very much like the transmitted signal, the frequency response will be composed of primarily the fundamental frequencies. The linear response of contrast bubbles at low MIs is demonstrated in *Figure 23*.

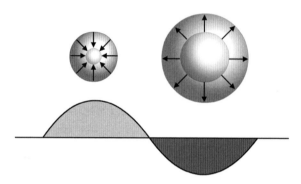

Fig. 23   **Linear Response to Compression and Rarefaction of Wave: Symmetric Oscillation**

10.3.2 Non-linear Response for Higher MIs

For slightly higher MIs (typically > 0.1) there are certain microbubbles within the population of a contrast agent that begin to respond in a "non-linear" fashion. If the transmit frequency is close to the resonant frequency of a particular size bubble, the bubble will undergo larger excursions. Because there are high internal pressures as the microbubble contracts, it is easier for the bubble to expand than it is for the bubble to contract. As a result, the bubble radius increases more during the rarefactional phase of the wave than it contracts during the compressional phase of the wave. This non-symmetric oscillation implies that the reradiated response from these resonating bubbles is no longer symmetric and the reflected wave is distorted. The frequency content of the acoustic response is now comprised of higher order harmonics as well as the fundamental frequency. The strongest harmonic signal is usually located at twice the transmit frequency, referred to as the "second harmonic." It is this second harmonic signal that plays a very important part in helping to discriminate contrast signal from tissue signal at these low MIs.

The distorted waveform from non-linear resonance is illustrated in *Figure 24*.

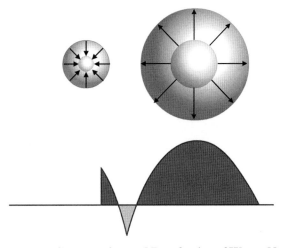

Fig. 24 **Non-linear Response to Compression and Rarefaction of Wave: Non-symmetric Oscillation**

The result of the non-linear resonance of the bubbles to insonification is a harmonic reflected wave as illustrated in *Figure 25* below. In this example, a 2 MHz fundamental frequency results not only in a reflected signal at 2 MHz (linear response) but also a reflected signal at 4 MHz (the harmonic or non-linear response).

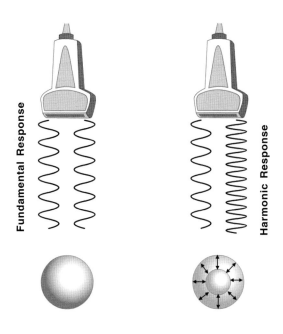

Fig. 25

The following frames of *Figure 26* were captured from stable non-linear oscillations of a lipid microbubble using as high speed camera. A video is included on the Animation and Image Library CD so that time variance can be appreciated.

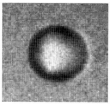

Fig. 26 **Non-linear Bubble Oscillation**

 **View Animation and Image Library CD**

10.4 Bubble Disruption

Even at these low MIs, where bubbles can exhibit stable non-linear behavior, some microbubbles begin to be disrupted or "destroyed." Since a given contrast agent is comprised of a wide range of microbubbles with varying sizes and shell thickness, the disruption occurs over a continuum of MIs rather than at a certain threshold. A typical range where this may occur would be between an MI of 0.1 and 0.4. However, if the MI is kept below 0.2, most contrast agents will "survive" and continue to work effectively.

The composition of the shell of a particular contrast agent can lead to differences in the mechanism for disruption. Lipid encapsulated microbubbles tend to be more pliable than albumin shelled microbubbles and thus tend to be more acoustically responsive at lower MIs. At these low MIs microbubble disruption can be caused by the forced outward diffusion of gas, often referred to as acoustically driven diffusion. The oscillation of the microbubble will cause some gas to be "squeezed" out with each transmit pulse. This effect has been seen more in lipid-encapsulated microbubbles than in albumin-shelled microbubbles. It has been proposed that this is due to the increased flexibility of the lipid shell coupled with the high concentration gradient of the gas. Larger excursions about the resting radius cause a larger pressure gradient to be created during maximal compression which leads to an increase in outward diffusion. At low MIs even small changes in resting microbubble size can have a significant effect in terms of the acoustic response. For bubbles close to resonance size, there will be a significant decrease in response before the microbubble has completely dissolved.

With stiffer shelled microbubbles, such as those that are albumin based, there is often the creation of a shell defect caused by the ultrasound pulse. This is followed by subsequent diffusion through the "crack" and dissolution of the free gas into the surrounding blood. This dissolution can occur quickly if the gas is nitrogen based (e.g., 10 ms) or much slower if it contains a higher density, less diffusible gas such as a perfluorocarbon. The signal from a free perfluorocarbon bubble can last for hundreds of milliseconds before it dissolves. As in the forced-diffusion case, there will be significant decrease in received signal intensity even before the microbubble is completely dissolved.

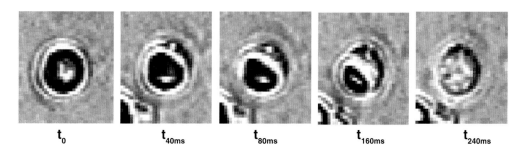

t_0 t_{40ms} t_{80ms} t_{160ms} t_{240ms}

Fig. 27 **Shell Defect Produced by Ultrasound Pulse**

Figure 27 demonstrates diffusion of gas from the microbubble followed by dissolution. The first frame labeled "t_o" represents the bubble prior to excitation. The subsequent frames indicate the time transpired from excitation and make apparent the diffusion of gas from a shell defect produced by the ultrasound pulse.

View Animation and Image Library CD

As the MI continues to increase, single pulse destruction can occur. Under the appropriate conditions, large excursions in microbubble radius can lead to fragmentation or can break up a single microbubble into multiple microbubbles. In this case, one ultrasound pulse can cause a microbubble to be "pinched" off or to be split into multiple smaller microbubbles that then dissolve very quickly. The decrease in intensity from the microbubble will happen almost instantaneously, over microseconds. This effect can happen to either nitrogen based bubbles or perfluorocarbon based bubbles. High-speed cameras confirm that the conditions under which fragmentation will occur are when the maximum-to-minimum variation of microbubble radius during excitation from the ultrasound pulse approaches a factor of 10. Transmit waveform properties such as frequency and duration as well as microbubble properties such as size and shell thickness lead to a continuum of MIs over which fragmentation will occur.

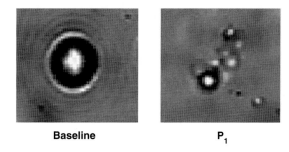

Baseline **P$_1$**

Fig. 28 **Rapid Destruction of a Lipid Bubble from a Pulse with a High MI of 1.6.**

Chapter 10

As illustrated in *Figure 29*, during fragmentation, strong, transient broadband signals are radiated from the microbubble with significant energy not only at the harmonics but also *between* the harmonics. This specific signature can be used to distinguish microbubbles from tissue. Compared to tissue signal that only appears at harmonics, microbubble destruction leads to broadband response. Improvement in contrast-to-tissue ratio can be obtained when filters are applied that remove the tissue harmonic signals. The lines in the figure demonstrate the frequency band at which RF filters could be applied to remove tissue signal.

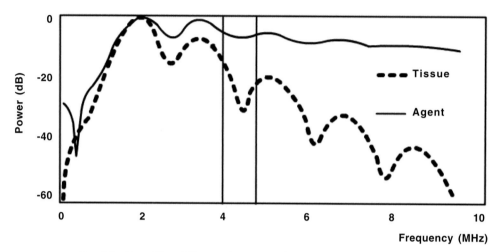

Fig. 29   **Broadband Signals from Bubble Defragmentation and RF Filtering**

11. Transmit Focus

Besides the MI, there are other imaging parameters under control of the user that play an important role in the interaction of ultrasound and contrast. As mentioned earlier, moving the transmit focus changes the distribution of MI in the image. This is not only important along the direction of the transmit pulse (i.e., in the axial direction), but also in areas where the transmit beams overlap (laterally) enough to cause some microbubble disruption. For sector images, this area of transmit beam overlap often occurs very close to the face of the transducer. As an example, consider how the transmit beam changes when the focal depth is increased. To create a deeper focus, a wider beam is produced in the near field. Since a sector image "fans out" the result of laterally wider beams is greater beam overlap in the near field. This increase in overlap can cause an artifact in some patients such as decreased concentration of contrast agent resulting in a decreased acoustic response in the near field. Moving the focus closer to the transducer will cause a tightening of the beam and will generally reduce the overlap. This shallower focus will often entirely eliminate this artifact, of course at the expense of signal-to-noise in the far field. While equipment manufacturers strive to find a solution to this trade-off, it is important to be aware of the effect of transmit focus on contrast detection.

11.1 Bubble Concentration and Signal Amplitude
When the first commercial agents, Albunex and Levovist, became approved in various countries, it was hoped that the signal enhancement in standard fundamental imaging would allow visualization of microbubbles in the myocardium. Since higher concentrations of contrast leads to an increase in scattering and therefore increased received signal intensity, it seems plausible that adding more agent would allow visualization of microbubbles in the myocardium. However, there is in fact a limit to how much contrast can be successfully administered. Within a certain range of microbubble concentrations, scattered intensity is directly related to the local concentration of microbubbles. Above this linear

range, interference from scattering from multiple microbubbles leads to a loss of linearity with contrast dose. This means a higher concentration will no longer give a proportional enhancement. At even higher dosages, bubble concentration is so high that an "acoustic shield" is created actually decreasing the signal dramatically, particularly when "looking" through large pools of blood such as the left ventricular cavity (as illustrated in *Figure 30*). Essentially, so much ultrasound energy is scattered back that very little is available at deeper depths (shadowing artifact). Therefore, there is a need for contrast specific imaging modalities to enhance bubble detection.

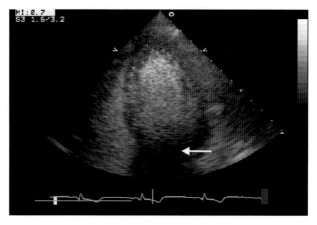

Fig. 30 **Attenuation from Excessive Contrast in LV**

 **View Animation and Image Library CD**

12. Contrast Specific Detection Techniques

Over the last several years there has been an increase in the understanding of the interaction between ultrasound and ultrasound contrast agents. This knowledge has fueled equipment manufacturers' progress and has resulted in the invention and introduction of new contrast specific detection techniques and image acquisition methods and tools. The goal of these new modalities has been to improve the visualization of ultrasound contrast agents within tissue.

12.1 Contrast Harmonic Imaging
Figure 31 illustrates typical relative amplitudes of tissue versus contrast at a mid level MI (around a value of 0.5). The graph compares the received frequency components from tissue to the signal from a typical contrast agent in a large blood pool such as the left ventricular (LV) cavity. At the fundamental, or transmitted frequency, the tissue signal is greater than the signal from the contrast agent. Therefore, if the ultrasound system filters are set up to remove the harmonic signal and process the fundamental frequency, the tissue signal will be brighter than the contrast signal in the LV cavity. This was the result that motivated harmonic imaging techniques. By removing the fundamental frequencies and processing the harmonic frequencies, the contrast-to-tissue ratio is dramatically improved. However, in many cases this increase in contrast-to-tissue ratio is not enough

to image microbubbles inside the tissue which is necessary to obtain information regarding tissue perfusion. The blood volume in tissue is often < 5% and therefore the concentration of microbubbles inside the tissue is a small fraction of that inside a large vessel or large cavity which is 100% blood. Due to the low concentration of microbubbles in the tissue, the signals from the tissue will often dominate the contrast signals, leading to difficulty in bubble detection and discrimination.

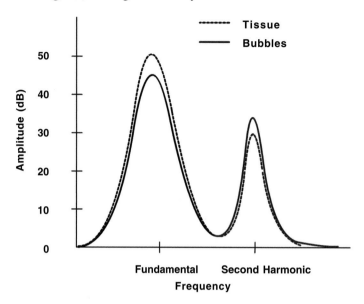

Fig. 31   **Relative Amplitudes of Tissue and Bubbles**

As we have already discussed, higher MIs produce much larger tissue harmonic signals. Therefore, when using higher MIs with contrast agents, the increased tissue harmonics will further dominate the harmonics produced by the contrast agent in the tissue. Therefore there will be a reduction in contrast-to-tissue ratio at the high MIs. However, the signal returning from the microbubbles is still very large and well above the noise floor of the system. Therefore, high MI imaging, although destructive in nature, offers the possibility for extremely sensitive contrast detection given a method or technique for suppressing the tissue harmonic signals. On the other hand, lowering the MI will have the benefit of preserving microbubbles and will also reduce the tissue harmonic signal resulting in better contrast-to-tissue ratios. However, lowering the MI will also result in lowering the amplitudes of the returning signals. Since the goal of any contrast specific imaging technique is to reduce the tissue signal while maximizing the signal from the contrast agent, it is important that the techniques maintain an excellent "contrast-to-tissue" ratio *and* "contrast-to-noise floor" ratio. In other words, not only does the technique need to do a great job of suppressing tissue but it also has to have excellent signal-to-noise, such that the contrast signal is well above the noise floor of the system. Effective techniques have been developed to improve contrast to tissue ratio at high MIs. Also, extremely sensitive techniques have been developed to improve signal to noise at low MIs.

12.2 High MI Techniques

12.2.1 Triggered Imaging
Imaging contrast agents with MIs that are high enough to cause disruption of the majority of microbubbles require much slower frame rates to be effective than with nondestructive MIs. The velocity in a typical capillary is on the order of 1 mm/s and each scan plane of ultrasound will destroy a slice of microbubbles of several millimeters in width. With standard frame rates, bubbles are subjected to continuous exposure and thus don't have the opportunity to flow back

into the scan plane in time for the next image acquisition. It is therefore necessary to pause scanning and to wait several seconds for contrast to replenish the capillary bed after destruction. For cardiac imaging this can correspond to five or more cardiac cycles between images. For imaging skeletomuscular muscle, this may be 20 seconds or more. To deal with this issue, equipment manufacturers have developed triggered or intermittent imaging techniques. With triggered imaging geared towards imaging myocardial perfusion, the transmission of ultrasound frames is synchronized to the ECG such that the frames will always be acquired during the same phase of the cardiac cycle. The displayed image is no longer updated at a frame rate of 30 frames per second but instead potentially only one frame acquired every five cardiac cycles. Precisely because of the lack of a real-time display, it is crucial to maintain the same transducer position, making it possible to see the refilling of microbubbles into the exact same scan plane in which they were disrupted. If the acquisition were not synchronized to the cardiac cycle, cardiac rotation and translation would cause different scan planes to be visualized yielding inaccurate contrast replenishment information.

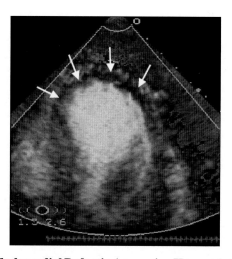

Fig. 32 **Endocardial Defect in Apex using Harmonic Power Doppler**

12.2.2 Harmonic Power Doppler

Contrast harmonic power Doppler using high MIs results in a contrast-to-tissue ratio improvement over standard, high MI, B-mode harmonic imaging. In order to understand the source of this improvement, it is important to first review how power Doppler works.

Power Doppler has been available for many years in vascular and abdominal imaging, where it is used primarily to look at slow flow in smaller vessels. Power Doppler is similar to color Doppler since both are "multi-pulse" correlation techniques. Like color Doppler, power Doppler is created by transmitting a packet of acoustic lines (usually between 4 and 12) to form a single display line. The returning echoes from each acoustic line are "compared" or correlated to the echoes of the previous acoustic line: the 2nd pulse is compared to the 1st; the 3rd is compared to the 2nd and so on. Power Doppler is also similar to B-mode in that intensity is displayed rather than velocity. In short, power Doppler displays the intensity of particles that are moving or changing, whereas color Doppler displays the velocity of particles moving.

When imaging contrast agents there are potential sources of "change" other than movement. The pulse of the first acoustic line fragments some of the microbubbles, breaking them into several smaller bubbles. This change in bubble structure is detected as a change by power Doppler. Other mechanisms of destruction can occur as well such as the shell can become damaged allowing the gas inside to "leak out." These free bubbles then dissolve over time, at a rate that depends on the density of the gas and its diffusivity in blood. Furthermore, it is also possible that the pulse doesn't destroy a particular microbubble but instead alters its size or shape—such as in the case of acoustically forced diffusion. Within a population of microbubbles, it is likely that more than one of these change mechanisms occurs. Throughout the length of the packet, each successive acoustic line detects changes from the previous acoustic line while simultaneously acting as the source of change in the microbubbles for the subsequent acoustic line. Free bubbles have vastly different resonance and backscatter characteristics than encapsulated microbubbles. The system detects these bubbles due to differences in backscattered intensity as well as changes in frequency or phase shifts between pulses. These changes produce a power Doppler signal. The greater the change observed between pulses, the larger the Power Doppler signal.

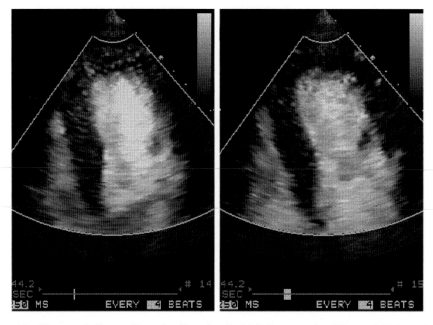

Fig. 33 **Harmonic Power Doppler Showing Bubble Destruction Through Triggering**

12.2.3 Benefits of Lower than Conventional Fundamental Frequencies

There are many more benefits of using transmit frequencies lower than conventionally used for diagnostic B-mode imaging (less than 2 MHz). Since many of the contrast detection techniques use receive frequencies that are much higher than the transmit frequency, such as with harmonic modes, even though very low transmit frequencies are used, resolution can still be maintained.

One such benefit to using lower transmit frequencies for harmonic contrast is the reduction in the undesirable tissue harmonic signal. The amount of harmonic distortion that builds up in a propagating wave depends on the distance traveled in wavelengths of the transmit frequency. Lower frequencies have longer wavelengths, and therefore for the same distance traveled in the patient, there will be less harmonic generation than for a higher frequency. In other words,

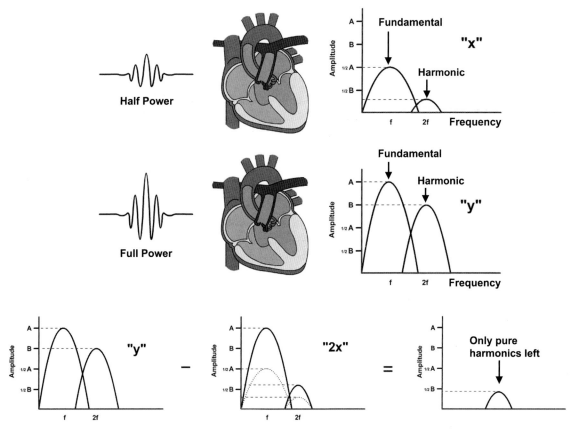

Fig. 34 **Power Modulation for Harmonics**

View Animation and Image Library CD

14.4 Importance of Low Frequencies

Just as with high MI techniques, the use of low frequencies plays an important role in low MI techniques. As mentioned previously, low frequencies provide lower levels of tissue distortion and a more homogeneous MI throughout the scan plane. These advantages apply to low MI techniques as well.

At high MIs, lower frequencies destroy (and therefore detect) a larger portion of the contrast agent population. Although greater "destruction" with lower transmit frequencies does not necessarily occur with nondestructive low MI techniques, there is still a benefit to using lower than conventional frequencies with low MIs. Larger bubbles have lower resonant frequencies. Therefore, lower frequencies will resonate larger microbubbles, producing higher amplitude signals. Also, at low MIs, there is a significant response from bubbles whose resonance frequency is at integer multiples of the transmit frequency. For example, a 1 MHz transmit will get a strong non-linear response from microbubbles that resonate close to 1 MHz, 2 MHz, 3 MHz, etc. Therefore when imaging non-destructively, low frequencies will potentially induce a greater acoustic response from a larger portion of the contrast agent population than will higher frequencies. The combination of these factors as well as a reduction in attenuation, leads to enhanced nondestructive detection at low transmit frequencies.

15. Challenges at Low MIs: Signal-to-Noise

As mentioned above, the major drawback for low MI imaging modalities is the reduction in signal-to-noise relative to high MI approaches. For low MI techniques, the amplitude of the transmitted signals are up to 20 dB (10 times) smaller than those for high MI techniques. Additionally, the amount of energy scattered from a free or destroyed microbubble is much higher than that of an encapsulated microbubble undergoing stable resonance. Therefore, as discussed throughout, increasing the MI improves microbubble response but increases tissue non-linearity faster. Also, as was discussed earlier, an increase in MI increases microbubble destruction and may actually *decrease* contrast signal due to the lower contrast bubble concentration. The range over which contrast-to-tissue ratio and signal-to-noise ratio are optimized is both patient and contrast agent dependent. To optimize real-time low MI techniques, it is usually necessary to maintain MIs in the 0.1-0.2 range. In order to increase signal-to-noise of low MI techniques, the best method is to increase the dosage or infusion rate of the contrast agent. Therefore, low MI techniques may use considerably more contrast agent to get sufficient signal-to-noise. The extra contrast used is usually offset by the increase in speed of the acquisition that low MI real-time offers. Although optimizing the contrast concentration is crucial with all techniques, it can be more challenging with low MI techniques.

16. The Future

16.1 Coded Pulses
There are a myriad of possible techniques that are being looked at to improve contrast imaging. The use of coded pulses is one of these techniques. Coded pulses involve transmitting very long pulses encoded in a certain manner and then decoding the received echoes. One example of the type of possible coding that could be used is frequency coding, where the frequency changes during the transmit pulse (CHIRP frequencies). The hope with such a technique is that long pulses could be used at low MIs and that the signal-to-noise could be improved from the increase in energy in the transmit pulse. The resolution will not be degraded much since the decoding process will create a high-resolution received pulse. This is done by trying to "look" for, or match, the original transmitted signal with the returning signal.

16.2 Direction
Excellent contrast agents are FDA approved for LVO and are available in the United States. Equipment manufacturers provide excellent contrast detection techniques with high sensitivity and contrast-to-tissue ratio. Techniques operating at low MIs offer real-time acquisition capabilities and lead to faster examinations while high MI techniques offer the highest sensitivity. All techniques remain viable alternatives for imaging contrast agents. The contrast field remains fast moving and new contrast-specific detection techniques and improvements are likely to continue.

16.3 Molecular Imaging Field
Ultrasound contrast agents are also playing a key role in the developing molecular imaging field. Research is ongoing to detect disease states earlier by identifying and targeting molecular signatures that occur in the early stages of disease. Contrast agents can then be modified by the addition of ligands to bind to or target those molecular signatures and imaging techniques such as those described previously and can be used to image these disease states. The hope is that early identification of disease as well as the optimization of treatment strategies will lead to improvement in patient outcome. Angiogenesis (the growth of new blood vessels), and inflammation both play an important role in many disease states such as vulnerable plaques and cancer, and are therefore the focus of much of this work.

16.4 Therapeutic Applications

The next step beyond diagnostics is the use of ultrasound and contrast for therapeutic applications. One area that has had some initial promising results is in lyses of blood clots. The combination of ultrasound and contrast has been shown to improve the efficacy of thrombolytics in animal studies. Also, once a contrast agent is targeted to a disease state it is then possible to optimize drug delivery or to research gene delivery. Higher effective dosages of a drug may be possible while minimizing systemic side effects by targeting the actual delivery sites and delivering the drug through ultrasound activated microbubble destruction. Delivery of genes is also an area of ongoing research including the promotion of angiogenesis by delivery of genetic growth factors.

Contrast and Harmonics

- Harmonic imaging currently implies that the received frequency is at the second harmonic frequency (twice the fundamental, or transmit, frequency).

- Harmonic imaging currently processes harmonic energy produced through two different mechanisms: contrast agents and non-linear tissue propagation.

- The premise for using tissue produced harmonic imaging is basically a tradeoff between conventional imaging at the fundamental frequency and conventional imaging at the harmonic frequency. With harmonic imaging, the fundamental frequency produces good penetration and the harmonic response generates relatively good resolution.

- One of the greatest benefits of harmonic imaging is the reduction of "clutter" related artifacts in the nearfield.

- The harmonic energy is weaker than the energy at the fundamental frequency, so the use of harmonics is not always optimal when significant penetration is required.

- The strongest harmonic response is generated in the midfield.

- The harmonic response is non-linear with the intensity of sound (MI). Higher MIs produce much more harmonic energy than lower MIs.

- In order to perform harmonic imaging, transducers must have enough bandwidth to support transmitting at the lower frequency and receiving at the higher frequency.

- In order to reduce the overlap between the transmit and receive bandwidth, conventional harmonic imaging usually narrowbands the transmit pulse by increasing the pulse duration (recall that bandwidth and pulse duration are inversely related). Increasing the pulse duration also results in an increase in the spatial pulse length, reducing axial resolution.

- New approaches to relieve the need to narrowband the transmit have resulted in powerful techniques such as power modulated harmonic imaging and pulse inversion harmonic imaging.

- Contrast imaging can be performed at the fundamental frequency (conventional contrast imaging) or at the harmonic frequency (harmonic contrast imaging).

- The harmonic response from a microbubble is the result of non-linear expansion and contraction of a bubble.

- In the presence of high intensity fields (high MIs) the bubble can expand much more than it can contract.

- The contrast agent is designed to significantly increase the reflectivity of the blood by a dramatic increase in the acoustic impedance mismatch (highly compressible and low density gas in contrast to much higher density and much less compressible red blood cells and plasma).

- High MI techniques can result in a rapid destruction of bubbles as well as difficulty distinguishing bubble harmonic response from tissue harmonic response.

- As a result of the tradeoffs with high MI techniques, many low MI techniques have been created such as pulse inversion and power modulation (the same fundamental approaches as used for harmonic imaging to improve signal-to-noise).

- The future of contrast and harmonics is very promising, including more therapeutic and treatment related ultrasound.

Note: See Appendix N: Physical Units and Appendix O: Equations for additional review.

CHAPTER 11

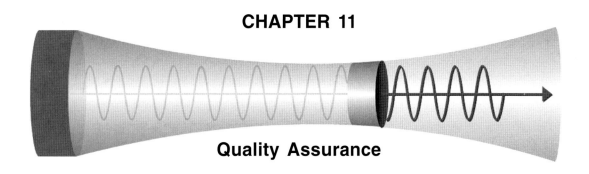

Quality Assurance

Introduction

There are many facets of quality assurance. Quality assurance can include everything from routine maintenance of the ultrasound and laboratory equipment through record keeping, patient tracking, and making certain that the correct exams are performed on the correct patient. Quality assurance can also include statistical processing to compare a testing procedure against a "gold standard" testing procedure, peer review, QA meetings, and how to ascertain the overall accuracy of the laboratory studies. Intricately tied to quality assurance is the process of lab accreditation and individual certification.

In this book we will not go into extensive detail regarding patient tracking and appropriate clinical testing. However we will briefly discuss the role and importance of lab accreditation and a good quality assurance program. In general, good practice is dictated by lab protocols. Your lab should develop consistent, methodical protocols to minimize the number and severity of oversights and errors. In general, the more rigorous the process and the process controls prescribed by the protocol, the less likely there will be major errors within your lab.

The two aspects of quality control we will discuss in greater detail are related to statistical indices and equipment performance testing. As you will see both of these topics present challenges to providing quality in day-to-day ultrasound.

1. The Laboratory Accreditation

1.1 Accreditation Providers
The laboratory accreditation process is designed to recognize laboratories that provide quality services. An accredited laboratory requires that their interpreting physicians and practicing sonographers be adequately trained and experienced to perform and/or interpret sonography. Currently, there are several organizations that provide ultrasound lab accreditation including the American College of Radiology (ACR), the American Institute of Ultrasound in Medicine (AIUM), the Intersocietal Commission for the Accreditation of Vascular Laboratories (ICAVL) and the Intersocietal Commission for the Accreditation for Echocardiography Laboratories (ICAEL). (Contact information for these organizations can be found in Appendix G.)

1.2 Commitment to Quality
Most states require accreditation for full Medicare reimbursement. Beyond the financial reasons, lab accreditation demonstrates a full commitment to quality patient care and self-assessment. The accreditation process requires the lab to assess every aspect of daily operation and its impact on the quality of health care provided to patients. While validating their quality assurance programs for the

accreditation process, labs often identify and correct potential problems before they occur, thereby saving time and money and reducing stress. Once a lab has gained accreditation, they must continue their commitment to quality and self-assessment by renewing their accreditation every few years.

The natural tendency of anyone with too many demands on their time is to claim that there is inadequate time to develop and review a quality program. "Brown et. al, Recent data collected by ICAVL accredited vascular laboratories has shown that repeat carotid duplex examination of patients referred for surgical evaluation for carotid endarterectomy have documented clinically significant differences in as high as 61% of the reexamined patients. It was found that the common thread amongst these outside (unaccredited) laboratories was the lack of a quality assurance program which would have identified the reason for these errors and provided the laboratories with the data necessary to adjust their criteria, or refine technical errors that may have contributed to the erroneous results." *Brown OW, Bendick PJ, Bove PG, Long GW, Cornealius P, Zelenock GB. Shanley CJ " Reliability of Extracranial Carotid Artery Duplex Ultrasound Scanning: Value of Laboratory Accreditation." Journal of Vascular Surgery 2004; 39: 366-371.* As mentioned earlier, taking the time required to create a quality program ultimately saves time and reduces the number of errors.

As a note, it is always good to put information into perspective. Imagine if you were the patient, what would you prefer?

1.3 The Individual Credential

Individual credentialing goes hand-in-hand with laboratory accreditation. Since lab accreditation requires one or more of the lab employees to be registered, there is clear job security in becoming Registry certified. Several organizations provide credentialing in ultrasound including The American Registry for Diagnostic Medical Sonography (ARDMS,) Cardiovascular Credentialing International (CCI), and the American Registry of Radiologic Technologists (ARRT). (Contact information for these organizations can be found in Appendix G.)

The field of sonography is ever changing with an increasingly rapid pace of advancement in technology and applications. As a result, it is extremely important that ultrasound professionals keep up-to-date with the latest innovations, new procedures and the "best practices" in patient care. The rules for being "certifiable" are fluid and vary according to the requirements of each credentialing organization. However, most credentials require proof of completing an ultrasound education program and clinical instruction in sonography and/or other allied health education. Furthermore, requirements for sitting for the credentialing exam often include documentation of adequate experience in clinical settings. Obviously, a passing score on the certifying exam is also required. Once "registered," individuals are required to complete continuing medical education credit hours (CMEs) every few years. The rules regarding the number of CMEs to maintain credentials varies with the credentialing organization. For sonography based credentials, the requirement is typically 30 CME hours per triennium. This requirement again represents a commitment to lifelong learning and quality patient care.

1.4 Personnel Qualifications

Accreditation specifies roles that must be fulfilled in each laboratory to meet quality standards. Specifics on all of the various roles may vary between accrediting body, and not all specific roles are addressed in this text. For details on the specific roles of the physician directors, interpreting physician, nursing, clerical, and administrative support, documentation is easily found on the websites from any of the accrediting organizations included in Appendix G. The following information describes, in general terms, the role of the clinical staff related to the accreditation process.

Medical Director

The medical director must be a legally licensed medical practitioner with a thorough understanding of indications for ultrasound examinations as well as familiarity with the basic physical principles and limitations of the technologies that are performed in the laboratory. Additional criteria may include completion of a formal six to twelve month training program, demonstration of interpretation of ultrasound examinations (may vary from 75 – 1800 cases depending on ultrasound specialty) and/or successful completion of board certification examinations. Requirements will vary depending on the accreditation body and the area of specialty.

The Medical Director is responsible for the entire operation of the laboratory, clinical services provided, quality and appropriateness of services offered as well as adherence of the clinical staff to accreditation standards. Specific operations may be delegated to the Technical Director and/or associated directors.

Technical Director

Ideally, the technical director should hold appropriate credentialing in all areas of accreditation application. Each of the accrediting bodies specifies certification, training and experience qualifications in their standards. Responsibilities of the Technical Director may include general supervision of the technical and ancillary staff, daily technical operation of the laboratory, technical training, operation and maintenance of laboratory equipment, compliance of the technical and ancillary staff to the accreditation standards, and coordination with the Medical Staff to ensure quality patient care.

Medical Staff

All medical staff must be legally qualified physicians and demonstrate competency in interpretation of ultrasound. Requirements generally include demonstration of a formal or informal training program with further documentation of experience interpreting under the supervision of physicians who have already met the standards of accreditation.

Technical Staff

Again, ideally all technical staff should strive to be credentialed in all areas they are performing examinations. All technical staff should demonstrate an appropriate level of training, technical certification or documented experience. With respect to certification, during the initial accreditation application phase most accrediting bodies offer a "grace" period for technical staff who are eligible for certification by the American Registry of Diagnostic Medical Sonographers (ARDMS), Cardiovascular Credentialing International (CCI), or American Registry of Radiologic Technologists (ARRT). Most accrediting bodies require proper technical certification upon reapplication.

Continuing Education Requirements

All medical and technical staff must meet the specific continuing medical education requirements of the accreditation standards. Continuing education should be relevant to the areas of accreditation.

Examination Protocols and Documentation of Examinations

One of the principal areas of the accreditation application process is the evaluation of exam protocols and documentation of examinations. Laboratory protocols are carefully evaluated to ensure that comprehensive examinations are performed with sufficient documentation for interpretation. Representative clinical images, films or audio/video recordings including spectral Doppler and/or color Doppler are submitted for review. Diagnostic criteria is evaluated for appropriateness and consistency throughout all the technical and medical staff. Interpretive reports should be standardized with uniform diagnostic criteria and report format. Reports should include clinical indications, description of examinations performed and a complete description of pertinent positive and negative findings. Final reports should be signed by the interpreting physician and available in a timely fashion to the referring physician.

1.5 Document Storage and Record Keeping

Accreditation standards generally have specific requirements regarding record keeping and storage of documentation. The specific requirements may vary between credentialing organizations, but usually require specifications for access and retrieval, the type of media on which studies are saved, and shelf life of the storage medium used.

1.6 Instrumentation and Quality Assurance

System testing for performance and degradation is naturally part of every quality assurance program. Again, there is no national "standard" policy that must be adopted. Instead many organizations have created guidelines, recommendations, and standards that are adopted by various accrediting organizations. Almost all quality testing programs include the basic categories of having up-to-date equipment, making sure the system and transducers are in proper operating condition and regularly serviced, and that no degradation in performance has occurred. In Section 2, we will devote considerable effort to discussing the concept of testing for performance and degradation in performance, the mechanisms for testing, and the related issues. Some recommendations go further in stressing which test should be performed daily, which monthly, and which semi-annually or annually.

Laboratories must demonstrate a written policy regarding quality assurance for all procedures performed in the laboratory. Documentation should include a description of the goals of the quality assurance program and the responsibilities involved. In addition to instrument maintenance, annual volume statistics should be recorded for laboratory procedures and for individuals. Records should include information on examination indications, tests performed, and test findings, as well as correlation and confirmation of results. Intermittent peer review of the performance and interpretation of studies is invaluable to determine the quality, accuracy and appropriateness of examinations. Physicians and sonographers alike should be involved in the process.

2. Equipment Testing

2.1 The Need for Tight Testing Controls

Testing and maintenance of ultrasound equipment is an interesting, complex topic. On the one hand, there is a desire for equipment testing to make certain that the system performance is adequate. On the other hand, the testing procedures and methodologies are often very complex requiring extensive system knowledge and extremely well controlled testing procedures. Given the ever-increasing complexity of the ultrasound equipment and the intricacies of accurate equipment testing, quite frequently an important component to a quality program is the purchase of a system and transducer service contract.

With that said, there have been a series of tests designed to verify continuing performance of the ultrasound equipment. To perform these "performance" tests, test equipment such as test objects and test phantoms are often necessary. The use of test objects and test phantoms is an attempt to provide a constant reference frame so that a standard can be developed, and so that changes over time can be identified. It is important to note that although most test phantoms offer a stable means by which to "calibrate" and compare performance over time, the ability to accurately mimic the characteristics and complexities of tissues is limited. As a result, there is no way of guaranteeing that a specific result or metric with a test phantom necessarily corresponds to a measure of accuracy in a system on live patients.

2.2 Purpose of Testing

Test objects and phantoms are used for ultrasound system validation and performance testing. The testing can be performed by the ultrasound manufacturer, regulatory bodies, or within ultrasound laboratories. The purpose of these tests is:

- To assess performance differences between different ultrasound system designs
- To assess a system's performance and/or manufacturing
- To monitor system degradation over time
- To minimize artifacts

3. 2-D and Doppler Testing

3.1 Tested Parameters

It is helpful to dichotomize the testing equipment into two principal categories: 2-D imaging and Doppler based techniques. Recalling the Doppler effect, this distinction should be intuitive. For 2-D testing, static structures are adequate, but to test Doppler performance, the test equipment must provide or simulate movement. The following list includes the parameters generally tested using test objects for 2-D and Doppler techniques:

2-D Imaging:

1) Detail resolution
   - axial resolution
   - lateral resolution
   - elevation resolution

2) Contrast resolution

3) Penetration (sensitivity)

4) Range accuracy

Doppler:

1) Penetration (sensitivity)
   - PW spectral
   - CW spectral
   - Color Doppler

2) Range accuracy
   - PW spectral
   - Color Doppler

3) Peak or mean velocity accuracy
   - PW spectral
   - CW spectral
   - Color Doppler

4) Spectral Broadening
   - PW spectral

5) Lateral Resolution
   - Color Doppler

4. Doppler Testing and Phantoms

4.1 Types of Doppler Phantoms

Testing Doppler provides greater challenges than testing 2-D parameters. Since repeatable, calibrateable, and accurate movement must be generated to make a useful phantom, there are myriad problems to overcome. There are two families of Doppler testing equipment: flow based phantoms and non-flow based phantoms. Both types have advantages and disadvantages. We will begin by considering flow-based phantoms.

There is actually a third type of testing used principally by test and design engineers which bypasses the transducer and involves pure electronic signals. (This technique involves the use of a special input device that plugs in as if it were a transducer and electronically couples the system receive channels to an external electronic device, such as waveform generators, to generate phase varying signals.)

4.2 Flow Phantoms

4.2.1 Basic Design
In its simplest form, a flow phantom consists of a pump and fluid reservoir, a fluid constraining tube or conduit, a fluid, and a surrounding medium.

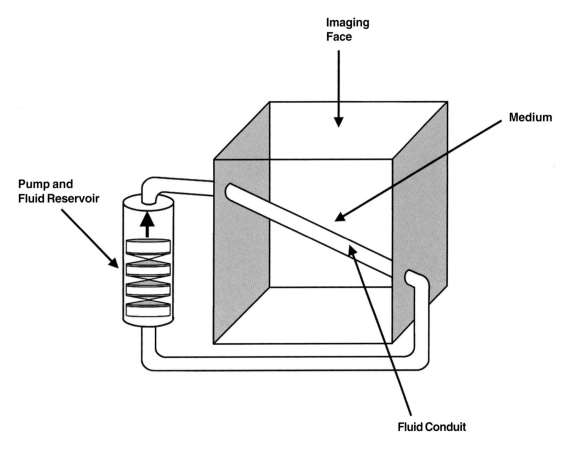

Fig. 1 **Flow Phantoms**

4.2.2 Blood Mimicking Fluids
Depending on the pumping mechanism, flow phantoms can provide either continuous or pulsatile flow. In either case, there are some real world difficulties to overcome to make Doppler flow phantoms work well. The first problem is how to create a fluid which mimics blood. Water cannot be used since ultrasound requires an acoustic impedance mismatch to cause reflections. Since water is homogenous, water creates virtually no reflection.

For research, there are times where human or animal blood is used. You can imagine the issues associated with using real blood. There are obvious issues of contamination, consistency over time (changes in blood viscosity), variations in blood lots (variation in hematocrit), accessibility, etc. Given the difficulties of using real blood, other fluids are much more commonly used. Since water cannot be used, quite frequently a suspension is created to increase the scattering properties. Problems still exist since over time the particles tend to precipitate out of solution, making the scattering property of the fluid variable over time. Additionally, air bubbles tend to develop in the fluid causing specular reflections which tend to saturate the Doppler circuitry and wall filters.

4.2.3 Other Potential Issues

Depending on the flow phantom design, other problems can exist such as: unwieldy size, weight, collapsing flow tubes (conduits), in-adherence of tubes to medium walls, and leaks. For all of these reasons, it is very difficult to develop a flow phantom which is consistent enough over time to develop a stable sensitivity reference.

4.2.4 Example of Flow Phantoms

The following pages contain examples of various types of flow phantoms and related products from multiple vendors. An attempt was made to include a variety of phantoms from multiple vendors so as to demonstrate the range of testing approaches. All italicized text comes directly from each specific manufacturer.

Fig. 2   **ATS Model 527 Doppler Flow Phantom**

Model 527 ATS
Doppler Flow Directional Discrimination Device

- *Directional Discrimination*
- *Flow Velocity*
- *Sensitivity at varying depths*
- *Maximum Penetration*
- *Location of Flow*

Product Description
Model 527 rubber-based tissue mimicking phantom from ATS is designed to test color Doppler flow imaging systems. This phantom monitors the ability of the system to discriminate the direction of flow in small vessels, of close proximity, at varying depths. The phantom contains four pairs of 2 mm flow channels. The edge-to-edge spacing between the flow channels within each pair progressively increases from 1 mm to 4 mm. If greater distances are desired, a combination of two flow channel pairs can be used. A fixed-angle scan surface maintains a constant angle between the sound beam and the test fluid flowing the phantom at 18° or 56° permitting continuous scanning at depths ranging from 3 to 17 cm.

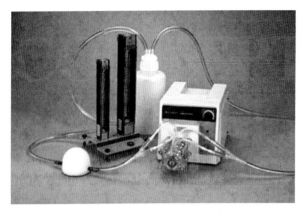

Fig. 3   **ATS Model 700 Doppler Flow Controller**

ATS Model 700
Doppler Flow Controller and Pumping Systems

Product Description
The Model 700 Doppler Flow Controller and Pumping System from ATS, when combined with an appropriate phantom provides an easy and accurate means of evaluating an ultrasound Doppler imaging system's ability to detect sensitivity at varying depths, maximum penetration, flow velocity, location and directional discrimination. Model 700 consists of a variable speed positive displacement pump, flow integrator, in-line flow meters, and a test fluid reservoir. The Model 700 is used with an appropriate phantom such as the ATS Doppler Flow Phantoms Models 523, 523A, 524, 525 and 527 and Model 707 Doppler Test Fluid. The System provides steady-state flow ranging from 20 to 950 ml/minute. Higher flow rates are available upon request. The speed of the pump is controlled by one knob. Two In-line flow meters continuously monitor the flow rate of the blood mimicking test fluid through the phantom during the test procedure. The large capacity test fluid reservoir insures the fluid pumped through the phantom will be free of air bubbles even after hours of continuous use.

Fig. 4   **CIRS Model 046 Blood Mimicking Fluid**

ATS Model 046

Blood Mimicking Fluid from ATS is intended for use in any flow phantom and with any type of pumping mechanism. It was formulated to simulate the acoustic and physical characteristics of blood, thus providing a stable and reliable fluid for Doppler studies and system evaluations.

The fluid is non-hazardous and is formulated to meet the requirements for recommended blood-mimicking fluid as described in the IEC 1685 draft specifications. The fluid is fully degassed prior to packaging to minimize noise from air bubbles. In addition the scatters are neutrally buoyant thus preventing clumping and settling of the particles. Each batch of fluid is certified for speed of sound, attenuation, density and viscosity traceable to NIST.

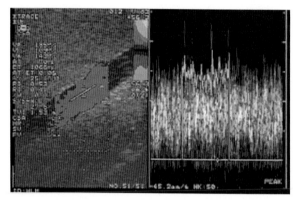

Fig. 5   **Color Flow and Spectral Doppler of Blood Mimicking Fluid**

Property	Human Blood (37°C)	Model 046 Blood Fluid
Viscosity (mPas)	3	4 ± 0.5
Velocity (ms⁻¹)	1583	1570 ± 30
Attenuation (dB cm MHz)	0.15	< 0.1
Backscatter (f⁴ m⁻¹ s⁻¹)	4×10^{31}	Not Measured
Fluid Properties	Non Newtonian	Newtonian

Fig. 6   **Properties of Blood Mimicking Fluid**

Dynatek Dalta EchoCal

The EchoCal series of velocity phantoms are simple, user-friendly calibration devices for ultrasound instruments. The principle of operation is the development of well-defined, accurate laminar flow through a tube of very precise dimensions. A flexible arm is provided to hold the ultrasound probe stationary. The fluid contains suspended particles which provide reflection of the ultrasound waves. The design has been tested and proven at the Laser Doppler Anemometry Laboratory at Memphis State University and several North American medical centers. In short, the EchoCal series of instruments are very helpful for ultrasonographer training and for troubleshooting today's complex and sensitive ultrasound systems.

Fig. 7   **Dynatek Dalta EchoCal Doppler Flow Phantom**

Dalta Laboratories developed these calibration phantoms to address some of the concerns of the FDA regarding the reliability of quantitative Doppler ultrasound data. The introduction of reference calibration phantoms and quality assurance protocols for the quantitative aspects of ultrasound will provide verification, and in turn, valid quantitative data. In conjunction with some of the nation's premiere cardiovascular flow dynamists, Delta Laboratories developed these phantoms, incorporating the same methodologies used in their heart valve performance and durability testing instrumentation. This patented pulsatile bellows technology produces laminar flow in a rigid environment is not susceptible to dimensional changes due to age, hydration, temperature or altitude. We can demonstrate precision and accuracy over hundreds of millions of cycles. Accuracy of velocity is verified within 2%.

GAMMEX-RMI Optimizer Doppler Flow System 1425A-05

This self-contained, dual-purpose system provides variable flow rates, vessel orientations and test objects. These features make the OPTIMIZER an excellent instrument for performing scanner selection, quality control testing, training and research. The OPTIMIZER consists of the flow system, test instrument and electronic flow controller. Together they provide a realistic test medium for assessing the following quality indicators: maximum signal penetration, channel isolation or directional discrimination, registration accuracy of duplex sample gates and congruency between B-mode and color flow images, flow rate readout accuracy for various angles, beam directions and operating modes. Attenuation coefficient: 0.5 ±0.05dB/cm/MHz.

Fig. 8 **Gamex OPTIMIZER Doppler Flow System**

4.3 Non-flow Phantoms

4.3.1 Eliminating Variable Reflectivity

Given the difficulties with creating a stable flow phantom, non-flow type Doppler phantoms were created. To create the necessary Doppler shifts, moving targets such as vibrating plates, moving belts, and moving strings are used. These phantoms eliminate some of the issues associated with stabilizing reflection variability over time but often introduce new challenges related to the signal strength.

4.3.2 String Phantoms (Moving Targets)

A string phantom is created using a motor, a motor controller, a pulley or series of pulleys, a string stretched across the pulley, and a water tank. The motor controller is programmed to move the pulleys in a specific manner. Since the string is attached to the pulleys, moving the pulleys causes the string to move. The Doppler sample volume is placed over the string so that the motion of the string causes a corresponding Doppler frequency shift. Since sound will not couple well through air, the string is immersed in a water bath, and the transducer surface placed in the water. Since the string velocity can be controlled very precisely, these phantoms are intended for peak velocity calibration primarily, as well as Doppler gate registration accuracy and spectral broadening. A variation of the string phantom is a moving or vibrating plate phantom. With a vibrating plate, the Doppler shift is created by insonating the moving plate or target.

4.3.3 Blossoming

Whereas repeatability is less of an issue with moving target phantoms, there is a significant problem introduced by using a reflector which varies so much from blood. Obviously, in comparison with blood, string and plate targets are extremely specular as reflectors. The result is that the reflections from the targets are much stronger than the normal signals processed by the Doppler circuit, often causing saturation of the electronics. When the electronics saturate, the signals often "bleed' into adjacent FFT bins during the signal processing phase. When signals artificially spread into adjacent bins, the resulting spectrum is spread, resulting in an artificially high peak velocity. This artifact is often called "blossoming."

Pegasus Lectures, Inc.

4.3.4 Need to Use Much Lower Gains and Transmit Power

As a result of blossoming, moving target Doppler phantoms often cause an overestimation in peak velocity. Additionally, since the signal is so strong, sensitivity is not well tested using a target phantom. To mitigate these problems the Doppler transmit and receiver gain must be turned down significantly below the normal use range. If standard transmit and receive levels are used, the peak velocity registered will be well beyond the expected velocity as determined by the true string velocity.

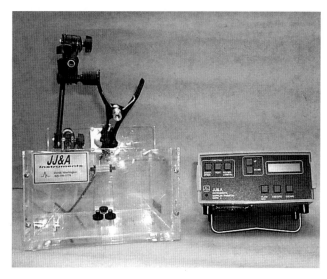

Fig. 9 **Doppler String Phantom**

JJ&A Instruments

The Mark 4 Doppler phantom is a very accurate device for testing Doppler ultrasound scanners. It is especially useful for checking sample volume registration, color registration, directional discrimination, and Doppler velocity accuracy.

The Mark 4 offers superior accuracy by using a string target that never changes (unlike suspended scatterers in fluid flow phantoms), and a crystal-controlled stepper motor. The motor speed is adjusted 1000 times per second, allowing realistic reproductions of human blood flow velocity patterns and a wide range of constant velocities.

The Mark 4 has been designed for ease of use. It can be set up quickly and easily with ordinary tap water, it is simple to use, and almost no maintenance is required. Ultrasound technologists, biomedical technicians, researchers, and manufacturers all rely on the Mark 4 for hassle-free, reliable testing.

Waveform Simulations:

- *Sine waves with peak speeds of 100, 150, and 200 cm/sec*
- *Triangle waves with peak speeds of 100, 150, and 200 cm/sec*
- *Stepped ramp wave with stops at 0, 20, 40, 60, 80, and 100 cm/sec*
- *Physiological waveforms including common carotid, femoral, aortic, pediatric umbilical, stenotic common carotid, pediatric renal, pediatric ductus arteriosus, pediatric middle cerebral artery, and pediatric descending thoracic aorta*
- *Flow Simulation Speeds: 10 to 200 cm/sec bi-directional flow*

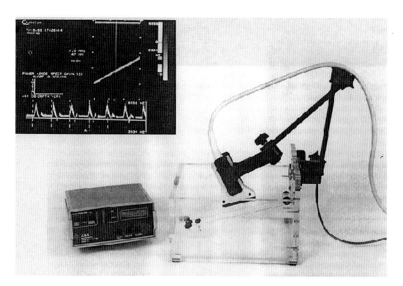

Fig. 10   **Use of Doppler String Phantom**

CIRS Model 043

The CIRS Model 043 Doppler String Phantom is an essential tool for people who work with Doppler Ultrasound. The crystal controlled motor accurately generates sixteen pre-programmed waveforms using advanced string target technology. Since the speed is adjusted 1000 times every second, you know it's precise and repeatable.

The Model 043 can be set for use with water or velocity-corrected fluid. If you're using water, it adjusts the string speed accordingly so the different speed of sound in water won't affect your tests. And unlike fluid-flow phantoms, the target never changes; you know what your test results should be every time.

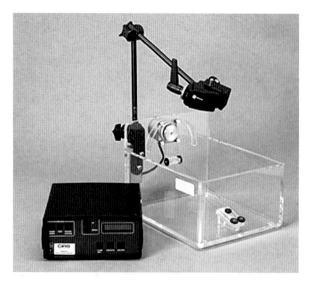

Fig. 11   **CIRS Model 043 Doppler String Phantom**

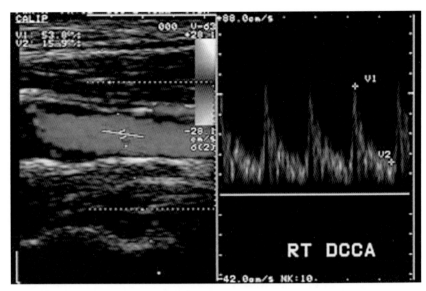

Fig. 12   Typical Carotid Blood Flow Simulated by CIRS Phantom

Waveforms Included:
Adult common carotid, stenotic carotid, femoral, aortic. Fetal middle cerebral artery, renal artery, umbilical artery. Pediatric descending thoracic artery, patent ductus arteriosus.

Test waveforms:
Sinewaves with peak speeds of 100, 150, and 200 cm/second. Triangle waves with peak speeds of 100, 150, and 200 cm/second. Stepped ramp wave with stops at 0, 20, 40, 60, 80, and 100 cm/sec.

Fluke Biomedical/Nuclear Associates 84-362 DSP-1 Sensitivity Phantom
The DSP-1 is a small, portable phantom that uses advanced phase-modulation technology to provide a constant flow simulation at 1 kHz. It enables the user to quantitatively test Doppler scanners for sensitivity, and it tests the entire ultrasound system, including the transmitter, transducer, beamformer, and receiver. Electronic signal injection techniques don't do this.

How it works:
The DSP-1 phantom produces Doppler signals that mimic blood-flow. In flowing blood, the ultrasound signal bounces off of the moving blood cells and returns to the transducer. The returning echo is shifted in pitch by the Doppler effect. The ultrasound equipment displays this pitch change by showing various colors on the display, creating a moving graph, or simply playing the audio out of a speaker.

In the DSP-1, the target is a roughened circular plate that is made to vibrate microscopically. The vibrating target is moving alternately toward and away from the ultrasound transducer. This vibrating action is equivalent to actual moving targets. The Doppler display of this vibrating target shows both positive and negative flow, since the target vibrates both toward and away from the transducer.

Chapter 11

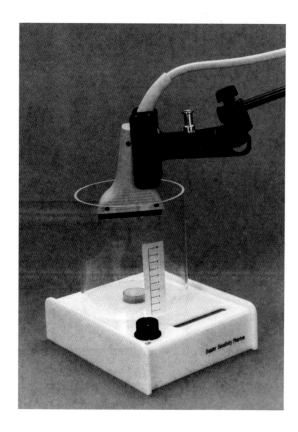

Fig. 13 **Nuclear Associates DSP-1 Doppler Sensitivity Phantom**

The DSP-1 therefore acts as a moving Doppler target without actually moving anything more than a few micro-inches. The result is a simple-to-operate, rugged phantom with essentially no moving parts.

The fundamental principle behind the DSP-1 is phase modulation of the ultrasound beam by the vibrating target plate. The total path length between the ultrasound transducer and the target plate is made to vary microscopically in a sinusoidal fashion. This changing phase of the returning signal can be shown mathematically to generate secondary signals, or pairs of sidebands symmetrically about the carrier frequency. Doppler ultrasound equipment cannot distinguish these phase modulation sidebands from classic Doppler shifts, so they are treated like a Doppler shift. This phenomenon can be seen qualitatively without a phantom by performing a carotid exam and having a patient talk at the same time. You will hear the voice in the Doppler audio because the voice is vibrating the tissues, causing phase modulation.

5. Imaging Phantoms and Test Objects

5.1 Detecting Performance Degradation

In addition to Doppler testing, there is a desire to test a system's imaging capability. The central concept is that testing should be performed periodically to ensure that the system performance has not degraded over time.

5.2 Test Repeatability

Imaging phantoms have been designed to test many imaging parameters. In terms of true quality assurance and equipment testing for imaging, the difficulties arise in the repeatability of the test. Let's presume that a system is to be tested bi-monthly to ensure that there is no loss of sensitivity. The perceived sensitivity will depend on many system controls, including but not limited to the:

- Transducer
- Positioning of transducer on phantom
- Transmit power
- Receiver gain
- Focus depth
- Post processing curves (compression/dynamic range)
- Ambient Light (lighting of the room)
- Monitor contrast setting

From test to test, if any of these controls are set differently, the perceived sensitivity will change, leading to the incorrect conclusion that the system performance has degraded. Therefore, for these quality tests to have merit, careful documentation of the testing procedure and strict adherence to the procedure is paramount. Care must be taken when testing equipment to make certain that the derived conclusion is based on actual system variation and not a change in procedure.

5.3 Testing Detail Resolution

Most of the imaging tests are easily understood from the descriptions of the test objects included. However, there are a few tests which require some explanation. For example, assume that you are imaging the pins in the configuration shown in the following figure. What type of resolution would be tested?

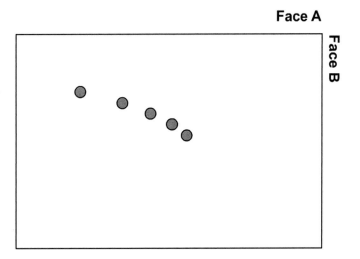

Fig. 14　**Phantom Pin Groups for Resolution Testing**

The correct answer is that you cannot determine what resolution you are testing unless you know on what face of the phantom the transducer is being placed. If the transducer were placed on face A, for the pin configuration given, lateral resolution would be tested. If the transducer were placed on face B, then axial resolution would be tested. Notice that with the transducer on Face A, the pins are uniformly spaced axially, but have varying separations laterally.

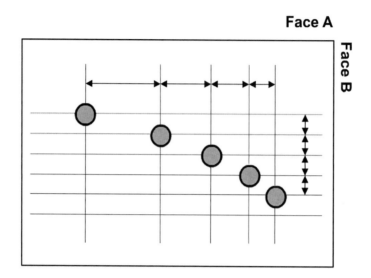

Fig. 15   **Determining "Tested" Resolution**

By placing the same transducer on face B, the pins would be uniformly spaced laterally, but vary in separation in the axial direction. In order to test detail resolution, there must be a variation in separation distance. If all the pins are the same distance apart, the system can either detect all of the pins or none of the pins. With varying separation distances, the resolution is determined as the smallest distance apart the system still detects two structures.

6. Commercially Available Imaging Phantoms

ATS Model 539 Multipurpose Phantom

- *Dead Zone or Ring-Down*
- *Vertical Measurement Calibration*
- *Horizontal Measurement Calibration*
- *Sensitivity/Penetration*
- *Functional Resolution*
- *Focal Zone*
- *Axial & Lateral Resolution*
- *Image Uniformity*
- *Gray Scale & Displayed Dynamic Range*

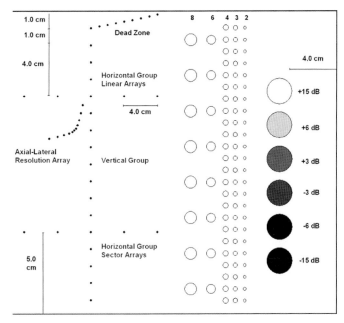

Fig. 16   **Target Drawing of ATS Model 539 Multipurpose Phantom**

Product Description

The Model 539 Multipurpose phantom is an easy, comprehensive means of evaluating imaging systems with an operating frequency range of 2.25 to 7.5 MHz. Phantom is designed with a combination of monofilament line targets for distance measurements and tissue mimicking target structures of varying sizes and contrasts. Cystic-like target structures are positioned in-line vertically, thereby permitting an entire target group to be displayed in one view. Due to the acoustic similarity of the background material and the target structures, artifacts caused by distortion, shadowing or enhancement have been eliminated. Six gray scale targets ranging in contrast from +15 to -15 dB are provided to evaluate the system's displayed dynamic range and gray scale processing performance.

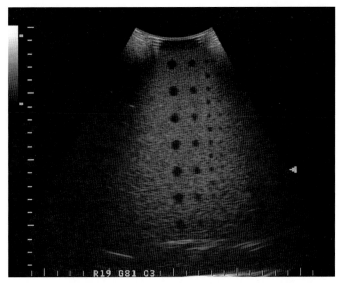

Fig. 17   **Curved Linear Image of ATS Multipurpose Phantom**

Notice that image was created using a curved linear transducer. Because of the curve of the surface, there is no contact with the phantom on the left and right edge of the transducer. Within these two regions there is image dropout. Within these two regions there is significant reverberation within the gel causing acoustic shadowing below. You should also notice that the first 7 cysts of 8 mm diameter are detected, the very bottom cyst is not. For the 4 mm cysts, the very top cyst is not detected because of insufficient lateral resolution. Furthermore, deeper than 12 cm, the ability to detect the 4 mm cysts deteriorates. For the top 5 cm, the 3 mm cysts are in the region of dropout caused by lack of contact. By 10 cm, the ability to detect the 3 mm cysts is pretty difficult, and the cyst certainly appears smaller than 3 mm. Only 1 of the 2 mm cysts is visible at the depth of about 8 cm.

CIRS

The CIRS series of ultrasound phantoms, unlike human subjects or random scannable materials, offers a reliable medium which contains specific, known test objects for repeatable qualitative assessment of ultrasound scanner performance over time.

This phantom is constructed from the patented solid elastic material, Zerdine®. Zerdine, unlike other phantom materials on the market, is not affected by changes in temperature. It can be subjected to boiling or freezing conditions without sustaining significant damage. Zerdine is also more elastic than other materials and allows more pressure to be applied to the scanning surface without subsequent damage to the material. At normal or room temperatures the Zerdine material found in the Model 040 will accurately simulate the ultrasound characteristics found in human liver tissue.

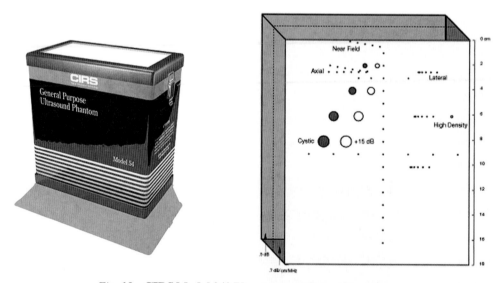

Fig. 18   **CIRS Model 040 Phantom and Target Drawing**

CIRS Model 040

The Model 040 was designed to allow for assessment of:

- *uniformity*
- *axial and lateral resolution*
- *depth calibration*
- *dead zone measurement*
- *registration within two different backgrounds of 0.5 and 0.7 dB/cm/MHz.*

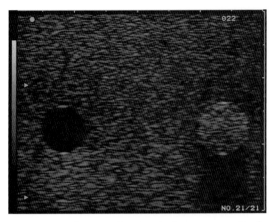

Fig. 19a   **Image of a Cystic Structure and a Mass in the CIRS Model 040 Phantom**

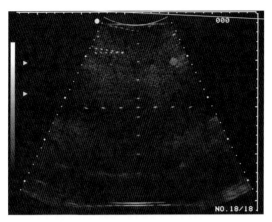

Fig. 19b   **Image of Phantom Displaying Various Pin Groups**

Figure 19a is an image of a cyst and mass. Notice that the mass demonstrates acoustic shadowing. In *Figure 19b*, the various pin groups are visualized. Notice that the "sideways V shaped" group of pins at a depth of approximately 3 cm is useful for visualizing axial resolution.

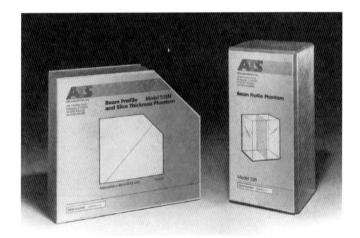

Fig. 20   **ATS Model 538 Beam Profile & Slice Thickness Phantoms**

ATS Model 538, Model 538N
Beam Profile & Slice Thickness Phantoms

Product Description
The phantoms contain a thin plane of echogenic material embedded in an anechoic rubber-based tissue-mimicking matrix. The scattering plane in the Model 538 is located in the center of and perpendicular to the scanning plane of the phantom. Model 538N has two scan planes. The scattering plane is oriented at 45° to one scan plane and perpendicular to the other. The beam profile is easily displayed at varying depths using either the Model 538 or Model 538N. The beam profile contains a great deal of information regarding the configuration of the sound beam as it propagates through the tissue-mimicking media. The beam profile clearly displays the near field, focal length, focal zone, beam width, side and grating lobes and beam divergence in the far field. In addition, amplitude variations in the near field are displayed as varying degrees of brightness versus the almost homogeneity of the amplitude in the far field.

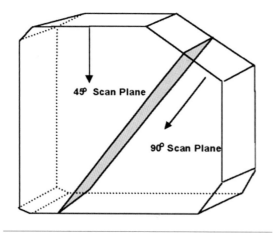

Fig. 21   **Geometry ATS Model 538N**

ATS Model 538N

The Model 538N provides a means of evaluating the slice thickness of an imaging system at varying depths. Slice thickness or elevational resolution, the third component of spatial resolution, displays reflections produced by structures in front of or behind the beam's main axis. The effect of changes in the slice thickness is identical to those seen with axial and lateral resolution. The thinner the slice thickness the better the resolution; as the slice thickness increases, the degree of spatial resolution decreases.

Tests Performed:

- *Beam Profile*
- *Slice Thickness (Model 538N only)*
- *Image Uniformity*
- *Tissue Harmonic Imaging Compatibility*

Fig. 22   **CIRS Model 047 Gray Scale Phantom**

CIRS Model 047
Gray Scale Phantoms

Introducing a new design using proven, patented materials to permit rapid visualization of Gray Scale resolution power at continuous depths from 1 to 12 cm. Model 047 is a single simple tool to assess resolution of masses varying in size, depth and contrast. The Model 047 is usable on all diagnostic ultrasound machines thus allowing user evaluation of Gray Scale sensitivity with a wide range of transducer frequencies. This phantom is an ideal training tool for learning optimum system setup and evaluating system performance. Masses may be viewed with either a circular or elliptical cross-section. The mass diameters were selected so the volume imaged would double as the diameter increased. The gray-scale levels were selected to achieve a doubling in signal intensity as you move from mass to mass. The anechoic masses comply with the ACR accreditation program.

Features:

- *21 Testing objects: Diameters: 2.4, 4, & 6.4 mm Contrast: Anechoic, -9, -6, -3, +3, +6, +9 dB*
- *Depth of test object varies continuously as phantom is scanned laterally*
- *Scatter controlled independently from attenuation*
- *Carry case included*

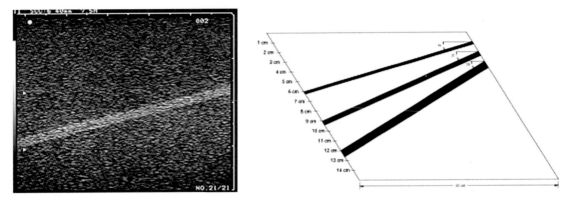

Fig. 23a **Longitudinal View and Target Drawing**

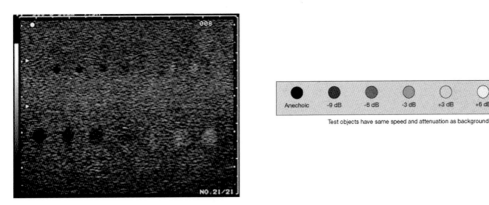

Fig. 23b **Transverse View and Target Drawing**

Notice that the -3 dB cyst and 3 dB mass are virtually indistinguishable from the surrounding tissue mimicking material. This image gives a relatively good idea of what a 3 dB noise figure looks like. Also notice that an increase from 3 db to 6 dB makes the signal easier to appreciate but still does not represent very good signal to noise. By 9 dB, the signal, although not pristine is at least immediately detectable with some degree of confidence.

Chapter 11

CIRS Model 555
3-D Spatial Measurement Capabilities

The Model 555 Set consists of two phantoms as described in the AIUM publication "Standard Methods for Calibration of 2-Dimensional and 3-Dimensional Spatial Measurement Capabilities of Pulse Echo Ultrasound Imaging Systems". These phantoms were designed to evaluate measurements taken on ultrasound systems using newer spatial encoding algorithms. This is especially important for the 3-D and 4-D ultrasound systems currently on the market.

Fig. 24 **CIRS Model 555 3-D Ultrasound Calibration Phantom**

Both phantoms are manufactured from the water-based polymer developed by CIRS called Zerdine®[1] and housed in rugged ABS containers that minimize desiccation. The background is calibrated to mimic the ultrasound characteristics of human liver tissue. Unlike other phantom materials Zerdine® is not damaged by changes in temperature.

The Model 055 is a volumetric target phantom and contains a small egg and a large egg. There are two scanning surfaces and the targets are off centered within the background material. Depending upon what side is scanned, the test objects are located at distances ranging from 2 to 6 cm from the scanning surface.

The Model 055A is a wire-target phantom that can be used to measure linear and curved dimensions as well as perimeters, volumes and surface areas. It may also be used to determine image uniformity and depth of penetration.

MATERIAL:
Zerdine®(1), solid elastic water-based polymer
Freezing Point: 0°C
Melting Point: above 100°C

ATTENUATION COEFFICIENT:
0.50 dB/cm/MHz ± .05 dB/cm/MHz

SPEED OF SOUND:
1540 m/s ± 6 m/s

CONTRAST:
Targets 9 dB ± 3 dB lower than background

DEPTH OF TARGETS:
2 cm to 6 cm from scanning surface

VOLUME OF TARGETS:
Small Egg: 6.7 cc
Large Egg: 65.0 cc

SCANNING MEMBRANE:
Saran-based

PHANTOM DIMENSIONS:
(nominal)
15 cm L x 15 cm W x 14.7 cm H

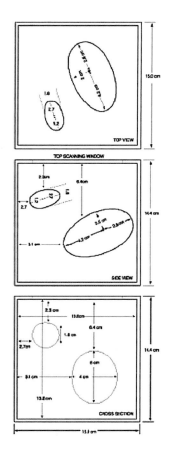

Fig. 25a **Target Drawing of CIRS Model 555**

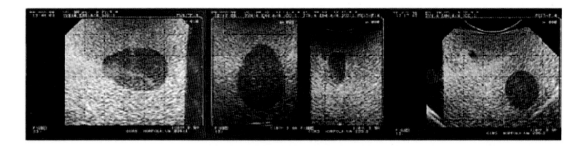

Fig. 25b **Images of CIRS Model 555**

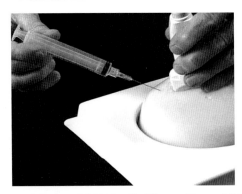

Fig. 26 **CIRS Model 052 Needle Biopsy (Breast) Phantom**

CIRS Model 052
Breast Phantom

The Model 052 accurately mimics the ultrasonic characteristics of tissues found in an average human breast. The size and shape of the phantom simulates that of an average patient in the supine position.

A special holding tray facilitates proper hand position during the training procedures.

Protected by a membrane, the phantom's flesh-like consistency, Zerdine®[1] simulates needle resistance. Each cystic mass may be aspirated once while each solid mass may be biopsied multiple times. Cyst material is stained green and solid masses are black for easy identification.

The Model 052 Ultrasound Needle Biopsy Phantom was developed by those skilled in the art of ultrasound guided needle biopsy procedures and is the ideal training device.

Features:

- *Improve eye-hand coordination*
- *Build confidence and reduce patient anxiety*
- *Test new equipment*
- *Experiment with new techniques*
- *Instruct others*
- *Contains cysts which can be aspirated*
- *Contains solids which can be biopsied*

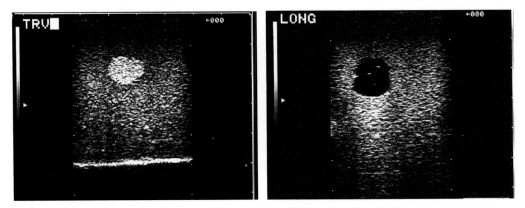

Fig. 27 **Image from CIRS Model 052**

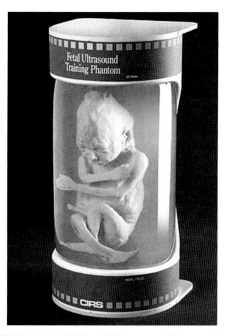

Fig. 28 **CIRS Model 068 Fetal Ultrasound Biometrics Phantom**

CIRS Model 068
Fetal Ultrasound Biometrics Phantom

The CIRS Model 068 Fetal Ultrasound Biometrics Phantom facilitates teaching and demonstration of fetal ultrasound examination techniques in a non-stressful situation. A tissue equivalent full fetal model is suspended in a non-echoic, amniotic fluid-like environment. The phantom is housed in a rotatable cylinder. A variety of fetal/transducer orientations can be achieved for more challenging examinations. Transabdominal measurements of biparietal diameter (BPD), anterior/posterior diameter (APD), femur length, abdominal circumference and crown to rump length can be taken.

All anatomies are based on published biometric data at normal fetal growth rates for a gestational age of 21 weeks[1]. This enables assessment of composite measurement techniques and biometric analysis programs common to most ultrasound scanners.

The phantom can also be used for 3D reconstructions, surface rendering and a variety of other applications. Optional carrying case is available.

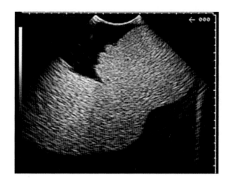 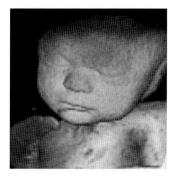 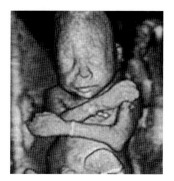

Fig. 29 **2-D and 3-D Views of Fetal Phantom**

Fig. 30 **ATS Interventional Arterial Phantoms**

ATS Models PVB-1, PVB-2 & PVB-3
Interventional Arterial Phantom

Tests Performed

- *Focal Zone*
- *Sensitivity*
- *Functional Resolution*
- *Contrast Resolution (PVB-3 only)*

Product Description

The PVB series of Interventional Arterial Phantoms are constructed of a tissue mimicking rubber-based material. The phantoms are housed in a chemical resistant, injection molded polypropylene shell to permit sterilization by means of autoclaving.

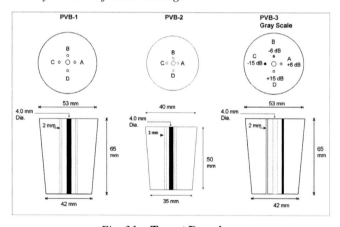

Fig. 31 **Target Drawings**

Models PVB-1 & PVB-2 *contain five cylindrical cavities. A 4 mm diameter cavity is located in the center of the phantom and four 2 mm cavities are positioned at 90° intervals around the central cavity. The edge to edge spacing of the four cavities relative to the central cavity are 1, 2, 3, and 4 mm.*

Model PVB-3 *contains five cylindrical cavities. A 4.0 mm diameter cavity is located in the center of the phantom and four 2 mm grayscale targets ranging from +15 to -15 dB relative to the background material are located at 90° intervals around the central cavity. The edge to edge spacing of the four 2 mm cavities relative to the central cavity is 4 mm. The PVB is designed to evaluate the acoustical*

Onda HIFU Phantom

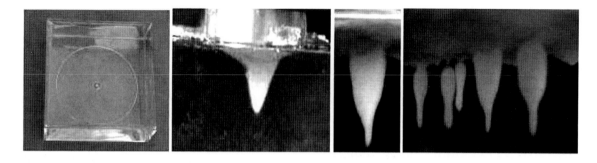

Fig. 32 **HIFU Testing and Onda Clear Phantom Gels**

For (High Intensity Focused Ultrasound) HIFU imaging, the idea is to generate high enough intensities so as to cause bioeffects to lesions. These ultrasound images clearly demonstrate that high intensities can clearly produce dramatic effects.

The complexity of testing HIFU devices in animal tissue is significantly reduced by using our propri-etary recording gels. Phantom gels are crystal clear synthetic gels that produce lesions of the same position, size and shape as those produced in real tissue when ultrasonic power is applied to the gel. The lesions appear as white three-dimensional solid profiles inside the clear gel and are stable for many weeks. The gels are shipped in clear plastic boxes with lids. The product is stable for several weeks at room temperature, and longer if refrigerated.

Applications for HIFU phantoms:

R&D
Many ultrasonic transducer parameters such as transducer geometry, frequency, and power profiles can be evaluated in a short amount of time without the problems caused by tissue variability. The progression of lesion growth, position, size and shape versus time can be recorded and evaluated.

Manufacturing Quality Control
Phantom gels can detect many defects in HIFU systems such as beam shape variations and alignment problems.

Transducer Performance Evaluation and Protocol development
For any medical procedure it is critical to detect even subtle changes in HIFU and other ultrasonic system performance before and after the procedure. One can use phantom gels to confirm ultrasonic systems, system protocol, and detector feedback loop performance.

Training
The use of these clear phantom gels in training can dramatically improve system operator perfor-mance by providing immediate visual feedback. Watching the lesion grow as power is applied is not possible using living tissue.

HIFU Phantom Material Properties

Density:	*1060 kg / m3*
Phase velocity:	*1600 m/s*
Attenuation Coefficient:	*0.6 dB/(cm-MHz)*
Specific Heat:	*3850 J/(kg-°K)*
Thermal Conductivity:	*0.55 W/(cm-°K)*
Optical:	*Turns permanently opaque when temperature reaches a threshold of 70 °C (this phenomenon results in the formation of tissue mimicking lesions when the phantom is exposed to high intensity ultrasound)*

7. Conceptual Questions Answers: Pg. 967

1) A string phantom is useful for measuring the following parameters: peak _____, spectral _____, depth _____, and gate size in PW _____.

2) A _____ phantom is not useful for determining Doppler sensitivity since the string target is such a strong reflector.

3) If a tissue mimicking phantom has multiple gray scale targets of varying contrast, what type of resolution can be tested?

4) If a tissue mimicking phantom has multiple gray scale targets with contrast levels of +15, +10, +2, -3, -6, and -14 dB, which two targets would be most likely to blend into the surrounding tissue mimicking material and not be visualized?

5) A tissue equivalent phantom attempts to mimic tissue's _____ and scattering characteristics.

6) The_____ _____ is the area at the top of the image which cannot produce an accurate image due to the ring down effect.

7) _____ down is when the transmit pulses in a _____ mode feeds back into the receiver causing bright ringing echoes obscuring the near _____ image.

8. Quality Assurance Statistics

8.1 As Part of the Quality Program

A part of every quality program is comparing the labs test results against a metric to assess lab performance. Ultimately, a laboratory must ensure that the results of their clinical testing correlate well with the results from other diagnostic exams. The starting point for this assessment is tracking the data through tables or patient logs. The information documented in these logs then become the data for statistical calculations which compare the laboratory "comparison test" against the metric test generally referred to as the "gold standard." There are many different statistical indices which can be used to assess the correlation of lab tests with other modalities such as the accuracy, sensitivity, specificity, and positive and negative predictive values. Throughout the next section, the specifics of these statistical indices, as well as the practical issues of how to calculate these parameters is discussed.

9. Q&A Statistics

Note: This material is generally covered on most credentialing exams, and extensively on vascular related exams.

9.1 The Values of Statistics:

It is often said that one can reach any desired conclusion using and manipulating statistics. If you know how to "spin" the numbers, you can support any claim and reach any conclusion which serves your purpose. Merely by changing the reference, statistics can lead to very different conclusions. Therefore, for statistics to have any real meaning, it is critical to clearly express the reference and/ or any assumptions. When this simple, common sense approach is followed, statistics regarding clinical testing can be valuable.

9.2 What is a Statistical Testing?

Statistical testing in medicine really involves two different tests: a reference test and a comparison test. The reference test is referred to as the gold standard. The comparison test is the procedure you desire to validate. A test becomes the gold standard when it becomes recognized as the most consistent and most accurate test for a particular disease. A comparison test is any other testing procedure, competing technology, or variation from the gold standard test.

To begin, statistical testing assumes that there is a relatively meaningful gold standard against which to compare. If a test is compared with a gold standard with some degree of error, then the results of that statistical test will reflect that error. For example, imagine that you have to correct an exam to see how many times a student answered correctly and how many times that student answered incorrectly for a given number of questions. The answer key for the exam is like the gold standard In essence, if there are errors in the answer key, then there will potentially be errors in the "corrected exam." In other words, the score will not necessarily be a true or accurate representation of the student's knowledge. Similarly, if the gold standard is not 100% accurate, then the statistical indices that specify the quality of the testing procedure will also not be completely accurate. We will further discuss the implications of an inaccurate gold standard later in this chapter.

10. Making Statistical Indices More Intuitive:

There are three things you must do if you want to develop an intuitive and practical understanding of statistical indices:

1. Realize that all indices start with a presumption that the gold standard is perfect.

2. Pay particular attention to the English of the statistical terminology.

3. Pay close attention to the labels and layout of any table of data.

As we learn about statistical indices, each of the these three points will be further detailed and discussed.

Chapter 11

10.1 Presume that the Gold Standard is Perfect, *Adhering to the "Golden" Rule.

The term "gold standard" sometimes misleads people. As already mentioned, there is no guarantee that any test that has been deemed the "gold standard" is perfect, or even very good. This fact seems inconsistent with the term "gold" for some people. However, you must understand that the term "gold" does not refer to a test being perfect, but rather the term refers to a test being "the best" at a given moment in time. In medicine, in reality, the gold standard may better be termed "the test that has had the most repeatable results to date which will be used as a reference for all new tests or competing technologies". Clearly, this terminology is cumbersome at best and the term "gold standard" is much easier to port around. Again you must realize that the gold standard test for a specific procedure today will eventually be replaced with a better "gold standard."

Note: To make statistical indices make sense, you will need to presume that the gold standard is perfect even if it is not. Since the "gold standard" is the best information we have to use as a reference, we will need to assume that this reference is perfect. Since this presumption will be referred to many times, this starting point assumption will be referred to as the "golden" rule.

10.1.1 The Golden Rule:

For the purposes of statistical indices, the assumption is that the gold standard is perfect.

As you will see, all statistical indices are relative to this assumption. Let's look at the first application of this rule.

10.1.2 The Meaning of the Words "True" and "False" with Respect to the Golden Rule

If the results of a test match the results of the gold standard (which by the golden rule we trust implicitly) then the test is said to be "true." In other words, truth is when you match the gold standard since we presume that the gold standard is perfect. To reiterate, when the test matches the gold standard it is presumed to be correct, or "true."

"True" is when the test results match the gold standard

Similarly, if the results of a test do not match the results of a gold standard (which again by the golden rule we implicitly trust) then the test is said to be "false."

"False" is when the test results do not match the gold standard

You will see further applications of the "golden" rule as we discuss the testing data in detail.

10.2 Pay Particular Attention to the English of the Statistical Terminology.

The second key to understanding statistical indices is to pay close attention to the language and English meanings. Trying to memorize the definition of each calculation is difficult and the definitions tend to evaporate from your memory over time. Quite frequently, you will see the calculations taught as a series of arrows overlapping a graph with no reference made to the true meaning or significance of the calculation. By really thinking about the connotation of each word, and using a little logic, you can learn how to calculate and interpret these indices much more easily without the pain of pure memorization.

Note: The approach usually taught for calculating statistical indices generally involves memorizing a series of circles and arrows overlaid on the table. There is no guarantee that the data will always be presented in the "conventional" format as is displayed in Figure 37. If the data is presented in any format other than the conventional format, the arrow approach becomes invalid unless you transpose the arrows with the data. In other words, the arrow approach is particularly troublesome when the data in the table is not presented in standard format, as may be the case on an exam. When you really understand statistical indices, and do not just memorize calculation technique, transposition of the data will not present a problem.

10.2.1 The Meaning of the Words "Positive" and "Negative"

Remember that both the comparison test and the gold standard test are attempting to predict the presence of disease. Therefore, if the result of a test is positive, it means that the test predicted the presence of disease. Similarly, if the test is negative, it means that the test predicted the absence of disease. Now if we take this simple English interpretation and combine it with our application of the golden rule, we get the following simple to understand terms:

Remember all tests are referenced to the gold standard.

True Positive **(TP)**:	The test is correct (T) because it matches the gold standard and the test is positive for disease (P).
True Negative **(TN)**:	The test is correct (T) because it matches the gold standard and the test is negative for disease (N).
False Positive **(FP)**:	The test is incorrect (F) because it does not match the gold standard and the test is positive for disease (P).
False Negative **(FN)**:	The test is incorrect (F) because it does not match the gold standard and the test is negative for disease (N).

10.3 Pay Close Attention to the Labels and Layout of any Table of Data.

When calculating statistical indices, it is common to format the data in a 2 x 2 table. Conventionally, the gold standard data is displayed in columns below the title "Gold Standard" and the comparison test data is displayed in rows next to the title of the comparison test. It is important to realize that the data can be presented in any format, forcing you to pay strict attention to the labels on the axes of the table. We will start by building up the table of data in the "conventional format."

11. Building the Table of Data

Let's begin by building up the table one piece at a time, as demonstrated in the graphs below. Notice that next to the title "Comparison Test" there is: a plus sign (+). As you would anticipate, the plus sign stands for the word positive. Therefore, every positive test for disease by the comparison test will be contained in this row.

Gold Standard

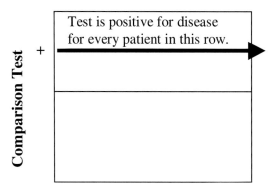

Fig. 33 **When the Test Predicts Disease**

In the table below notice that a minus sign has been added next to the comparison test. As you would anticipate, the negative sign stands for the test being negative for disease. Therefore, every negative test for disease by the comparison test will be contained in this row.

Gold Standard

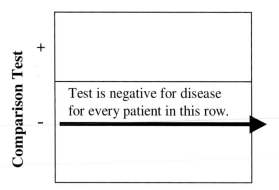

Fig. 34 **When the Test Predicts No Disease**

So far, these two partial tables (above) only represent the results of the test, but do not indicate how well the test matches the gold standard. We will now add symbols below the "gold standard" to create columns to use as a reference for the test results.

Gold Standard

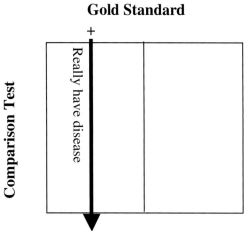

Fig. 35 **When the Gold Standard Predicts Disease**

Referring to *Figure 35*, since the plus sign indicates positive for disease, any entry in the column below the plus sign of the gold standard indicates that the gold standard was positive for disease. Since by the golden rule we always presume the gold standard is correct, we presume everyone in this column really does have disease.

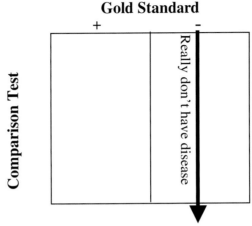

Fig. 36   **When the Gold Standard Predicts No Disease**

Similarly, any entry displayed in the column below the negative sign implies that the gold standard was negative for disease. Since we believe the gold standard, this means that anyone below the minus sign really does not have disease.

Now if we combine all four of these partial tables together, the "conventional" format is achieved (*Figure 37*). When combining these four partial tables, whenever the comparison test matches the gold standard, since we trust the gold standard, the test is called "true." In contrast, whenever the test results do not agree with the gold standard, the test is called "false." For example, notice that in the upper left quadrant, both the test and the gold standard predicted disease, thereby making the test a true positive (TP).

Gold Standard

	+	−
+	(TP) test correctly predicted disease	(FP) test incorrectly predicted disease
−	(FN) test incorrectly predicted no disease	(TN) test correctly predicted no disease

Comparison Test

Fig. 37   **Interpreting the Table**

12. Exercises: Interpreting the Statistical Table   Answers: Pg. 967-970

Use the general table of *Figure 37* to answer the following questions. Be sure that you can answer these questions since these concepts are commonly covered on credentialing exams.

1.   How many tests were performed in this study?

2.   For the patients tested, how many patients truly have disease?

3.   For the patients tested, how many patients truly do not have disease?

4.   How many times was the test positive for disease?

5.   How many times did the test correctly predict disease?

6.   How many times was the test negative for disease?

7.   How many times was the test correct when it predicted the absence of disease?

8.   How many times was the test correct overall?

9.   How many times was the test incorrect overall?

10.   What percentage of the time was the test correct overall?

11.   What percentage of the time was the test incorrect overall?

12.   What percentage of the patients tested have disease?

13.   What percentage of the patients tested do not have disease?

14.   A perfect test (relative to the gold standard) would have zeroes for which two values?

13. Statistical Parameters

Once the data have been classified according to true or false and positive or negative, there are a series of calculations which can be made. Each of these statistical parameters tells us something different about the quality of the testing procedure (relative to the gold standard).

Again, paying close attention to the true meaning of the names of each calculation can make life infinitely simpler. For example, you should learn the distinction between the words specificity, sensitivity, and accuracy. Let's look at the meaning of each of these words so as to determine how each of these parameters can be calculated mathematically.

13.1 Sensitivity

The word "sensitive" implies the ability to detect small parameters. Since the prevalence of disease should be less than the absence of disease (i.e. should be a small number) sensitivity refers to the ability of a test to detect disease. Now recalling that the quality of the test is made in reference to the gold standard (the golden rule) we can easily state that the sensitivity is the times the test correctly predicted disease divided by all of the times the disease really does exist, or

$$\text{Sensitivity} = \frac{TP}{TP + FN} \times 100\%$$

13.2 Specificity:

The word "specific" refers to the ability to "not paint everything with the same broad brush." Imagine that only one patient has disease but your test claims that every patient tested has disease. For the one patient who has disease, the test was certainly correct; however, the test was not very specific. In other words, the test did not do a good job of detecting how many people do not have disease. The specificity refers to the ability of a test to detect the absence of disease relative to the number of people who in reality do not have disease, or

$$\text{Specificity} = \frac{TN}{TN + FP} \times 100\%$$

13.3 Accuracy

The word accurate refers to how often something is correct overall. So the accuracy of a test is the percentage of times the test is correct, of course relative to the gold standard. Therefore the accuracy is all of the times the test is correct divided by all of the tests, or:

$$\text{Accuracy} = \frac{TP + TN}{TP + FN + TN + FP} \times 100\%$$

13.4 Positive Predictive Value

As the name suggests, the positive predictive value is a measure of how often the test is correct when positive for disease as a percentage of the total times the test is positive for disease, or

$$\text{Positive Predictive Value} = \frac{TP}{TP + FP} \times 100\%$$

(Notice how the calculation involves only "positive" terms.)

13.5 Negative Predictive Value

As the names suggests, the negative predictive values is a measure of how often the test is correct when negative for disease as a percentage of the total times the test is negative for disease, or

$$\text{Negative Predictive Value} = \frac{TN}{TN + FN} \times 100\%$$

(Notice how the calculation involves only "negative" terms.)

Note: The accuracy is an overall measure which includes both a measure of when the test was correct when positive for disease and when the test was correct when negative for disease. As a result, the accuracy must be between the sensitivity and the specificity. Also, the accuracy must be between the negative predictive value and the positive predictive value. Note that neither of these statements is the same as saying that the accuracy is the average of the sensitivity and specificity or that accuracy is the average of the negative and positive predictive values. This point will become clear in the next set of exercises.

14. Numerical Example

Let's use an example to demonstrate how to perform these calculations.

◊ **Example:** A series of tests was performed and compared with a gold standard test. The test under question resulted in:

- 120 predictions of no disease which agreed with the gold standard,
- 20 predictions of no disease which did not agree with the gold standard,
- 70 predictions of disease which agreed with the gold standard,
- 10 predictions of disease which did not agree with the gold standard.

What are the sensitivity, specificity, accuracy, positive predictive value, and negative predictive value? *(Again, use the standard English definitions to help.)*

Predictions of no disease when there is no disease is called a true negative, so: TN = 120.
Predictions of no disease when there is disease is called a false negative, so: FN = 20.
Predictions of disease when there is disease is called a true positive, so: TP = 70.
Predictions of disease when there is not disease is called a false positive, so: FP = 10.

Putting the data into the "standard" table format, the table becomes:

Gold Standard

	+	−
+	(TP) 70	(FP) 10
−	(FN) 20	(TN) 120

(Comparison Test)

Now recall that the sensitivity refers to how many times the test correctly predicted disease divided by all the times there truly is disease, so

$$\text{Sensitivity} = \frac{TP}{TP+FN} = \frac{70}{70+20} = \frac{70}{90} = \frac{7}{9} = 77.8\%$$

Now recall that specificity refers to how many times the test correctly predicted the absence of disease divided by the total number of times there was no disease, so

$$\text{Specificity} = \frac{TN}{TN + FP} = \frac{120}{120 + 10} = \frac{120}{130} = \frac{12}{13} = 92.3\%$$

Now recall that the accuracy is the total number of times the test was correct divided by the total number of tests, so

$$\text{Accuracy} = \frac{TP + TN}{TP + FN + TN + FP} = \frac{70 + 120}{70 + 20 + 120 + 10} = \frac{190}{220} = 86.4\%$$

Now recall that the positive predictive value is the number of time the test correctly predicted disease divided by the total number of positive predictions, so

$$\text{Positive Predictive Value} = \frac{TP}{TP + FP} = \frac{70}{70 + 10} = \frac{70}{80} - \frac{7}{8} = 87.5\%$$

Now recall that the negative predictive value is the number of time the test correctly predicted no disease divided by the total number of negative predictions:

$$\text{Negative Predictive Value} = \frac{TN}{TN + FN} = \frac{120}{120 + 20} = \frac{120}{140} = \frac{12}{14} = \frac{6}{7} = 85.7\%$$

(Notice that the accuracy is between the sensitivity and the specificity, but it is not the average of the sensitivity and the specificity. Similarly, the accuracy is between the positive predictive value and the negative predictive value, but is not the average of the two.)

15. Real World Understanding

To develop a more intuitive understanding of these statistical indices, a real world analogy is usually helpful. Let's say that you go for a series of tests because you are experiencing some ailment called "X-disease." Let's consider some different possible scenarios based on the resulting data for X-disease relative to a gold standard.

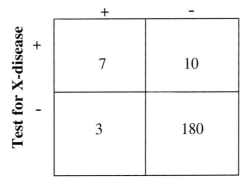

Gold Standard for X-disease

Scenario 1: The test for X-disease is negative. How confident should you be that you do not have X-disease?

> *Answer:*   *Pretty confident*

$$\text{The Negative Predictive Value} = \frac{TN}{TN + FN} = \frac{180}{180 + 3} = \frac{180}{183} = 98\%.$$

$$\text{The Specificity} = \frac{TN}{TN + FP} = \frac{180}{180 + 10} = \frac{18}{19} = 95\%.$$

Therefore, most of the time that the test is negative, the test is correct. Also, most of the time that X-disease is not present, the test results are correct.

Scenario 2: The test for X-disease is positive. How worried should you be that you really have X-disease?

> *Answer:*   *Somewhat worried but not convinced*

$$\text{The Positive Predictive Value} = \frac{TP}{TP + FP} = \frac{7}{7 + 10} = \frac{7}{17} = 41\%.$$

$$\text{The Sensitivity} = \frac{TP}{TP + FN} = \frac{7}{7 + 3} = \frac{7}{10} = 70\%.$$

From the sensitivity we know that the test is fair at detecting the presence of disease (70% of the time). However, when positive, the test is only correct 41% of the time. Therefore, a positive result has a fairly good probability of being incorrect.

Scenario 3: What can be said about the sensitivity and positive predictive value of this test for X-disease if the gold standard is poor?

> *Answer:*   *Nothing*

It is possible that the test is correct more times or fewer times relative to "truth." Therefore, the true sensitivity and positive predictive value could be very good, very bad, or change very little.

16. Exercises: Statistical Indices   Answers: Pg. 970-972

1. Calculate all 5 statistical indices for the following data:
   St. Bongo's Hospital compares the results of a new ultrasound test with the gold standard with results as follows: the test was positive for disease 24 times and matched the gold standard 20 times. The test matched the gold standard 94 times when negative for disease. Overall, 120 tests were performed.

2. Calculate all 5 statistical indices for the following data:
   Merky Municipal Hospital compares the results of their ultrasound test with the gold standard with results as follows: the test was incorrectly positive for disease 14 times and positive a total of 45 times. The test was negative for disease 220 times of which it did not match the gold standard 14 times.

KEY CONCEPTS — Quality Assurance

- Quality assurance has many components including lab protocols, record keeping, laboratory accreditation, individual certification, equipment testing, and statistical analysis of laboratory results for efficacy.

- There are many phantoms and test objects designed to test various system performance parameters.

- Ideally tests are performed routinely by qualified personnel, with results compared to past results, when possible, for identification of changes.

- Doppler testing is very challenging. There are a few different fundamental approaches to Doppler testing:
    - Flow phantoms
    - String phantoms
    - Vibrating plates or belts

- Imaging phantoms can include string targets, pins, cystic structures, and masses as well as tissue mimicking material.

- Tissue mimicking material is designed to create attenuation as well as yield the approximate propagation velocity of 1540 m/sec as expected in tissue.

- You should be aware of how different geometries of pin layouts could be used to test various system performance parameters such as lateral, axial, and elevation resolution.

- Specialized phantoms exist from multiple companies to test performance aspects of 3D imaging, intravascular imaging, and new ultrasound techniques such as high intensity focused ultrasound (HIFU).

- Statistics play a vital role in assuring quality patient testing.

- The reference for the quality of a test is the recognized "gold standard" procedure.

- Gold standards are not always correct; however, for statistical comparison, the assumption is that the gold standard is perfect.

- When a test matches the gold standard, the test is considered to be correct or "True".

- When a test does not match the gold standard, the test is considered to be incorrect, or "False".

- The terms "Positive" and "Negative" refer to whether the test indicated disease (positive) or the absence of disease (negative).

- The overall accuracy is the measure of the times the test was considered to be correct (all the "Trues") divided by all the tests performed:

$$\text{Accuracy} = \left(\frac{TP + TN}{TP + FN + TN + FP} \right).$$

- The sensitivity of a test is a measure of the test's ability to detect the presence of disease when disease exists:

$$\text{Sensitivity} = \left(\frac{TP}{TP + FN} \right)$$

- The specificity of a test is a measure of the test's ability to detect the absence of disease when no disease exists:

$$Specificity = \left(\frac{TN}{TN + FP} \right)$$

- The accuracy must be between the sensitivity and the specificity.

- The positive predictive value (PPV) is a measure of how many times the test is correct of all the times the test predicts disease:

$$PPV = \left(\frac{TP}{TP + FP} \right)$$

- The negative predictive value (NPV) is a measure of how many times the test is correct of all the times the test predicts no disease:

$$NPV = \left(\frac{TN}{TN + FN} \right)$$

- The accuracy must also be between the negative and positive predictive values.

Note: See Appendix N: Physical Units and Appendix O: Equations for additional review.

CHAPTER 12

Fluid Dynamics

1. Flow Analogy

1.1 Foreword on Flow

Many people have difficulty conceptualizing the parameters which govern flow. Learning the equations which predict the relationships between flow parameters usually seems daunting. Before you despair, there are two important points you should consider:

- You know much more about flow and hemodynamics than you realize.
- If viewed the correct way, much of what you need to know is relatively intuitive and interesting.

With these two points in mind, the following analogy was written to give you a way to conceptualize some of the flow parameters without first discussing the complexities of the equations and the circulatory system. From this analogy, the foundation will be constructed for a few of the fundamental equations that govern fluid dynamics.

Note: In addition to blood flow, vascular sonographers are expected to learn about electrical current flow. Since we cannot see the streaming of electrons down a current path, this conceptualization is generally more challenging than the conceptualization of fluid flow. Again, there is a saving grace:

- Electrical current flow and blood flow follow analogous rules.

Therefore, by learning the principles which govern flow, you will already have the foundation for understanding the basics of electrical current flow covered in Appendix A: Vascular Principles.

1.2 Flow Analogy

Pretend you are a child once again. You and a very large group of playmates are investigating the basement of an old, large, vacated building. At the base of one of the walls is a dark hole which was once covered by a grating which now lays on the floor. You, along with most of your friends, are afraid of the dark.

Unfortunately, for you and your friends there is one extremely powerful bully in the group who forces you into the tunnel to see where it goes. You proceed to crawl down the tunnel. The bully, unsatiated by making only you miserable, decides to keep forcing more and more of your playmates into the tunnel. The tunnel is very long and just wide enough to allow four of you to squeeze through at the same time.

At one point the tunnel narrows so that there is room only for one person at a time to pass through. Since the bully is pushing a constant stream of your friends into the tunnel behind you, all your friends are pushing you to get through the narrowing as fast as possible so that they don't get squashed.

As the tunnel returns to its normal width, you would like to continue traveling down the tunnel as a group again. As each of you gets pushed through the narrowing so fast, you can imagine that you will all be slightly discombobulated and that it will take a little effort to regroup and return to an orderly flow down the tunnel. Finally, you reach the end of the tunnel which dumps into the basement of a connecting building. As you get out of the tunnel, you realize that you are hot, sweaty, and tired.

1.3 Flow Analogy Exercises   Answers: Pg. 973-974

1)   The bully is analogous to which structure in the body?

    a) The arterial system
    b) The venous system
    c) The heart
    d) The liver

2)   Match the following:

    a) The bully   1. blood vessels
    b) The tunnel   2. heart
    c) You and your friends   3. stenosis
    d) Narrowing of tunnel   4. blood

3)   Volumetric flow was represented by

    a) The bully forcing people into the tunnel.
    b) The fact that all the children were warm and tired after exiting the tunnel.
    c) The speed with which children went down the tunnel.
    d) The number of children per time who went down the tunnel.

4)   Which of the following would represent a higher volumetric flow?

    a) twice as many children through the tunnel in twice the time
    b) the same number of children in more time
    c) more children in the same amount of time
    d) half as many children in half the time

5)   In question 4, which two choices represent the same flow?

    a) Choices a & b
    b) Choices a & d
    c) Choices b & d
    d) Choices b & c

6) The tunnel could best be described as

   a) the vessel or flow path.
   b) the resistance.
   c) the capacitance.
   d) pressure.

7) The bully at the entrance of the tunnel

   a) creates the pressure difference to cause the children to flow.
   b) creates the resistance to cause the children to flow.
   c) represents flow.
   d) none of the above.

8) You, like the other children, were afraid of the dark, and didn't want to make the difficult travel through the tunnel, yet you went. The reason you overcame your resistance to go down the tunnel was

   a) flow just naturally occurs.
   b) the bully created enough pressure to overcome the resistance.
   c) the bully created enough capacitance to overcome the resistance.
   d) the capacitance of the tunnel created flow to overcome the resistance.

9) The rate at which each of you traveled down the tunnel is termed the

   a) velocity.
   b) flow.
   c) volume.
   d) time.

10) Assume there are two tunnels identical in width, but one is 50 meters long and the other is 100 meters long. Which would you more readily travel and why?

   a) 50 meters because it offers greater resistance
   b) 100 meters because it offers greater resistance
   c) 100 meters because it offers less resistance
   d) 50 meters because it offers less resistance

11) Assume that the bully forces you to travel four abreast through the tunnel. Now assume tunnel A is 50 meters long and 4 feet wide while tunnel B is 50 meters long and 2 feet wide. Which tunnel will you choose and why?

   a) Tunnel A - greater resistance
   b) Tunnel B - greater resistance
   c) Tunnel A - less resistance
   d) Tunnel B - less resistance

12) You are still traveling 4 abreast through the tunnel. Tunnel A is 50 feet long and 2 feet wide, while Tunnel B is 100 feet long and 4 feet wide. Which tunnel would you choose and why?

a) Tunnel A - greater resistance
b) Tunnel B - greater resistances
c) Tunnel A - less resistance
d) Tunnel B - less resistance

13) Which statement best describes what happened at the narrowing in the tunnel?

a) The flow increased because of an increase in resistance.
b) The flow decreased because of an increase in resistance.
c) The velocity increased to maintain a constant flow through an increase in resistance.
d) The velocity decreased because of an increase in resistance, decreasing the flow.

14) At what area in the tunnel were you moving the fastest?

a) Just before the narrowing in the tunnel
b) Just as you were exiting the narrowing in the tunnel
c) In the broader section of the tunnel
d) The same everywhere within the tunnel

15) The best "description" of the "discombobulation" after exiting the "stenosed" area of the tunnel is

a) chaotic (turbulent) flow.
b) uniform (laminar) flow.
c) backwards (reverse) flow.
d) sticky (viscous) flow.

16) When you exited the tunnel, the bully no longer could pressure you, whereas before you entered the tunnel, he was able to exert great pressure. This difference in pressure which results in flow represents _____ and is called a pressure _____.

a) flow, increase
b) energy, increase
c) energy, gradient (change)
d) work, decrease

17) Which of the following is the best explanation of why you were hot and tired at the end of the tunnel?

a) The pressure gradient represents energy spent overcoming a resistance, and some of that energy gets converted to heat.
b) The flow creates energy which is spent overcoming a resistance.
c) The resistance represents energy spent to create flow.
d) The flow represents a pressure gradient.

Reviewing the Explanations
It is important that you read through the explanations to the flow analogy questions in Appendix H before continuing with this chapter. In the upcoming sections in which the equations are developed, we will be relying on the conclusions which are drawn from this analogy.

2. Fluid Dynamics

2.1 Fluid Dynamics: Flow and Related Terms
Fluid dynamics is the study of fluid flow through a flow system. The primary equations which predict the basic behavior of flow were developed by engineers, mathematicians, and physicists many years ago. In this chapter we will learn the principles and the mathematical equations which govern the idealized behavior of fluid flow. In Chapter 13, Hemodynamics, we will apply these principles and equations to blood flow.

As always, before we start developing equations, we must make sure we are all using the same language. Luckily, physicists and mathematicians generally use words which are also used in every-day language to describe physical phenomena. As a result, you probably already have some level of comfort with at least some of the following terms. On the other hand, if you currently misinterpret or misconceive the meaning of any of these words, you must correct the mistake now, before these misconceptions lead you to incorrect conclusions.

The following list of terms, representing the primary variables used in hemodynamics, will now be discussed in greater detail.

> power
> work
> energy
> potential energy
> kinetic energy
> pressure
> (volumetric) flow
> resistance
> capacitance
> compliance
> velocity
> viscosity

2.2 Fluid Dynamics: Definitions

Power:
The rate at which energy is transferred. Power describes how fast work is being performed. The unit for power is:

$$\left(Watts = \frac{Joules}{sec} \right).$$

Work:
The amount of energy transferred.
Work is the integration of the total power used to complete a job over time. The unit for work is Joules. As displayed below, the units help demonstrate the relationship between work and power.

Obviously work and power are related since:
$$Work = (average\ power) \times (total\ time)$$
Checking the units
$$Joules = \left(\frac{Joules}{second}\right) \times seconds.$$

Energy:
Energy is a conceptual quantity which includes many different physical forms such as mass energy, kinetic energy, potential energy, heat energy, radiation energy, etc. Energy has many different units depending on the type of energy. A fundamental law regarding energy is that energy is always conserved. This law implies that energy is never lost, only converted to another form.

Potential energy:
Potential energy represents energy that is stored which can be converted to other forms of energy. (A pressurized fluid in a reservoir, energy stored in a spring, or mass which exists at a specific height in the presence of gravity all represent potential energy.)

Kinetic energy:
Kinetic energy represents energy related to movement and is proportional to the velocity squared of the movement.

Pressure:
Pressure is a measure of force per unit area. (There are many different units for pressure as outlined in Chapter 2 and in Appendix N.) Pressure can be broken down into two different categories: static pressure and dynamic pressure. Static pressure is associated with potential energy and dynamic pressure is related to kinetic energy.

(Volumetric) Flow:
Volumetric flow is the volume of fluid per time which moves past a point. (liters/min or m³/sec, etc.) Frequently the term "volume" or "volumetric" is dropped and just the word "flow" is used.

Resistance:
The resistance is the ratio of the pressure drop across a vessel (or flow path) per volumetric flow. In essence, the resistance is a measure of the impediment that must be overcome for flow to occur.

Capacitance:
The capacitance is a measure of the ability to hold a change in volume per change in time or $\left(\frac{dV}{dt}\right)$ where V is the volume and t is the time.

Compliance:
The ratio of the change in volume to a change in pressure (dV/dP) where V is the volume and P is the pressure.

Velocity:
The speed with which a fluid moves in a specific direction (units of m/sec).

Viscosity (fluid):
The ratio of the shear stress to the shear rate of a fluid, or more simply stated, a measure of the resistance of a fluid to flow due to the attraction of the molecules.

2.3 Power, Work and Energy in Practical Terms

As already expressed, the physical parameters of work and power are related; however, there are some significant differences between these two terms. Power refers to the rate at which work is performed, whereas work refers to the total energy expended. Using analogies is perhaps the easiest way to make this distinction clear.

Let's say that your job is to move boxes from a warehouse onto a loading platform to later be transported by trucks around the country. Power refers to how many boxes per time you can move. How much work you do refers to how many total boxes you move. Imagine if you move 3 boxes per minute and you work for 60 minutes. Your power is 3 boxes/minute, but your work is 180 boxes moved. Now imagine that your co-worker can move 5 boxes per minute, but takes a 30 minute break every hour. Your co-worker has a higher power of 5 boxes/minute, but has a lower work of only 150 boxes.

The following two examples will further illustrate this distinction between power and work.

◊ **Example 1:** Person A stuffs envelops for mailing at a rate of 100 envelopes per hour for 1 hour. Person B stuffs envelopes at a rate of 10 envelopes per hour for 10 hours.

	Power	**Conversion**	**Work (energy)**
Person A	$100\dfrac{envelopes}{hour}$	$100\dfrac{envelopes}{hour} \times 1\ hour \Rightarrow$	$100\ envelopes$
Person B	$10\dfrac{envelopes}{hour}$	$10\dfrac{envelopes}{hour} \times 10\ hours \Rightarrow$	$100\ envelopes$

Person A has a higher power, but both people perform the same amount of work.

◊ **Example 2:** A 50 Watt light bulb is run for 100 hours. Your electric company will charge you for what amount of energy consumption?

$$50\ Watts \bullet 100\ hours = 5000\ Watt \bullet hours$$
$$= 5 \bullet 10^3\ \text{Watt} \bullet hours$$
$$= 5\ kW \bullet hrs$$

Note this is really an energy measurement since

$$50\ kW \bullet hours = 5 \bullet 10^3\ \frac{Joules}{sec} \bullet 1\ hour \bullet \frac{3600\ sec}{hour}$$
$$= 18 \bullet 10^6\ Joules$$
$$= 18\ MJoules$$

It is more convenient for the power company to express bills in terms of kW • hrs instead of Joules, since few people know the relationship between power and energy. However, 5 kW • hrs and 18 MJoules represent the same amount of energy consumption, as shown above.

The concepts of power and work are important to understanding hemodynamic problems that occur within the cardiovascular system. For example, let's say that there is a problem with the aortic valve such that it has a higher resistance to flow than normal. A higher resistance implies that it will take greater power to maintain the same volume of flow across the valve. Of course, if the power requirement is higher, the heart (left ventricle) will have to expend more energy to meet the higher power requirement. Unfortunately, unlike the workers in the above analogies, the heart can't take a break. The result is that over time, the increased work load will affect the left ventricular function.

2.4 Energy

Energy is a term that is commonly used in the world outside of fluid dynamics and hemodynamics. For how often the term is used, ironically, the term energy is rarely defined. Perhaps the reason energy is rarely defined is that the term "energy" really refers to a myriad of parameters grouped together because of their ability to perform work. As stated in the definitions, there are many different types of energy such as thermal, radiation, nuclear, kinetic, etc. Within hemodynamics, the driving force to propel blood is a change in energy. Flow can only occur from a higher to lower energy level. This should make sense if you consider water and a hill. Stationary water at the top of a hill represents more energy than the equivalent volume of stationary water at the bottom of a hill. Therefore, without adding another source of energy such as pressure from a pump, it is not likely for water to begin spontaneously flowing up the hill. Conversely, no additional energy source is needed to make water flow from the top of the hill to the bottom of the hill.

One of the central axioms in physics is that energy is always conserved. Simply stated, the conservation of energy theorem says you can neither create nor destroy energy, only change its form. Think of ultrasound imaging, electropotential energy is converted into acoustic (mechanical) energy which is transmitted into the body. As the acoustic energy waves travel through the body, attenuation through absorption, reflection, and refraction occurs. Absorption is primarily the conversion of the acoustic energy into heat energy. The reflected waves are converted back to electropotential energy by the transducer. Note that energy has been conserved. If you add up the energy which returns to the transducer, that which is reflected but not received, the energy refracted, and the amount of energy absorbed, you will get back the original amount of energy transmitted.

With respect to fluid flow, we will start with some assumptions that greatly simplify understanding the basic principles of flow. We will start with the assumption that there is never any energy lost to heat through friction of the fluid with the vessel walls, or through the shear forces associated with a moving viscous fluid. Whereas these assumptions are not true, the complexity of dealing with these real world energy transformations would make developing basic, intuitive equations very difficult. The fact that many assumptions are made (there are more coming) will not change the usefulness of the equations eventually derived. However, once the equations are created, we will need to reconsider the effects of these invalid assumptions, to more accurately predict the fluid hemodynamics of the cardiovascular system. In other words, for now don't worry about the fact that we have oversimplified reality; we will bring these complexities back in the next chapter, so as to make our assessments more accurate.

Figure 2 illustrates the basic principles of hydrostatic pressure.

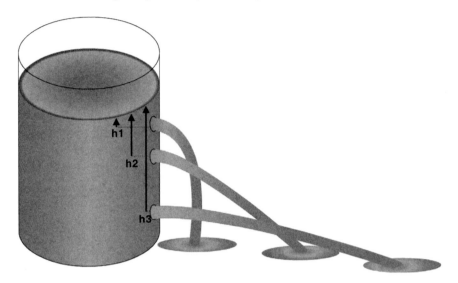

Fig. 2 **Hydrostatic Pressure**

Notice that there is a column of fluid of height h_1 above the top spigot, whereas there is a taller column of fluid of height h_2 above the middle spigot, and the tallest column of fluid h_3 above the bottom spigot. The hydrostatic pressure associated with the top spigot will therefore be the lowest, the hydrostatic pressure associated with the middle spigot will be intermediate, and the hydrostatic pressure for the bottom spigot will be the highest. This fact is demonstrated by the velocity (and hence distance) of the flow out of each spigot.

In the clinical world, the hydrostatic pressure is clearly associated with the height and positioning of the patient. When substituting for the approximate density of blood and the value for the acceleration due to gravity, the hydrostatic pressure is calculated to be approximately:

$$0.776 \frac{mmHg}{cm} = 1.97 \frac{mmHg}{inch} \approx 2 \frac{mmHg}{inch}.$$

Hydrostatic pressure will be further discussed in Chapter 13 in the venous section of hemodynamics.

2.7 Volumetric Flow (Q)
The "flow" or "volumetric flow" is defined as the amount or volume of a quantity which moves past a point per unit time.

◊   *Example:*   6 liters/min
                                    200 gals/hr
                                    10 people/day

The word flow is often misused in ultrasound. Frequently, when someone states that they used Doppler to measure the flow, what they really mean is that they used Doppler to measure the velocity of the flow. This distinction is very important since flow is a measure of volume per time (m^3/sec) whereas velocity is a measure of distance per time (m/sec). Further promoting this confusion is the fact that there is a mathematical relationship between flow and velocity (as expressed by the continuity equation).

Because this confusion exists with respect to the meaning of the word flow, I generally suggest that the word "volume" or "volumetric" be used in conjunction with the word flow. Since the word volume implies a quantity, using the word volumetric serves as a reminder of the distinction between flow and velocity.

2.8 Velocity (v)

The velocity is defined as the speed with which something is moving in a particular direction (distance/time).

As you will see from the flow equations, velocity, flow, and pressure are related. However, you can never assume that a higher velocity necessarily means more flow. Similarly, you cannot assume that a high flow represents a high velocity. Once the equations have been developed and discussed, these facts should be apparent.

2.9 Capacitance

2.9.1 Capacitance Defined

An often overlooked parameter of the cardiovascular system is the capacitance. The resistance and changes to resistance are frequently discussed, but the capacitance and the effects of capacitance on the hemodynamic system are commonly ignored.

The capacitance is defined as a change in volume per change in time, or:

$$\frac{\Delta V}{\Delta t} \left(or \left(\frac{dV}{dt} \right) using\ derivative\ notation \right).$$

where V represent the volume and t represents the time. As you will see, the capacitance is closely associated with the compliance. We will first strive to understand the meaning of capacitance before discussing the role of capacitance in the cardiovascular system. An understanding of capacitance is perhaps best achieved through analogies.

2.9.2 Understanding the Capacitance

Imagine that there is a very large barrel, and the question is, "Does this barrel have a large capacitance?" In all fairness, without more information this question cannot be answered, although the natural inclination would be to answer "Yes". If further information were given that indicates that the only opening to fill the barrel is a pin hole on the top lid, then the answer clearly becomes "No". Even though the receiving chamber has the ability to hold a large volume, the time to fill the volume through the small pinhole would be great. Therefore, even though the barrel can hold a large volume, a change in volume cannot be achieved in a short time, and hence the barrel has a low capacitance.

In comparison, if the filling hole is made larger, then the capacitance will increase. Ultimately, the highest capacitance is reached when the entire top of the barrel is removed and the barrel has the potential to be filled very rapidly, as demonstrated in *Figure 3*.

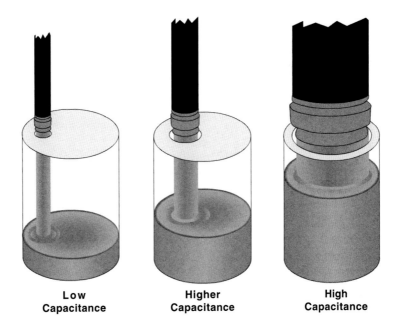

Low	**Higher**	**High**
Capacitance	**Capacitance**	**Capacitance**

Fig. 3   **Understanding Capacitance**

From these diagrams, you will notice that, even though the flow containers are rigid cylinders, the capacitance varies with the amount of filling. The initial capacitance may be high, but as the reservoir fills, the residual capacitance decreases until the reservoir is completely full and the capacitance goes to zero.

The role of the capacitance in the cardiac system will be discussed in Chapter 13.

2.10 Compliance

Like the capacitance, the compliance is related to the ability to hold a change in volume. However, whereas the capacitance is the change in volume per time, the compliance is the change in volume per pressure, or:

$$\frac{\Delta V}{\Delta P} \left(or \left(\frac{dV}{dP} \right) using\ derivative\ notation \right).$$

A high compliance implies that there is a large increase in volume for a small increase in pressure. For incompliant flow paths, there is only a slight increase in volume from a more significant increase in pressure.

2.11 Fluid Viscosity

Sir Isaac Newton described the viscosity of a fluid as the ratio of the shear stress to the shear rate. This complex terminology basically means that the fluid viscosity is a measure of the resistance to flow offered by a fluid. For liquids, this resistance is principally caused by short-range molecular cohesive forces. In essence, for a fluid, the viscosity is a measure of the "sticky" attraction of the molecules. The fluid viscosity tends to be heat dependent, such that the viscosity of a fluid decreases with increases in temperature.

◊ *Example:*

Very Viscous Fluids	Lower Viscosity Fluids
• cold motor oil	• hot motor oil
• molasses	• water
• maple syrup	• maple sugar water

As seen from the resistance equation, the resistance to flow is proportional to the fluid viscosity. The effects of fluid viscosity to flow will become more significant as we transition from our simple fluid models in this chapter to the more complex models of actual blood flow. For now, as already stated, the presumption is that there is no energy loss to heat due to frictional and viscous effects. In the next chapter, Hemodynamics, this artificial constraint will be removed.

2.12 Exercises: Flow and Related Definitions   Answers: Pg. 974-975

1. In a closed system, an increase in flow velocity results in an increase in _____ energy.

2. In a closed system, an increase in flow velocity results in a decrease in _____ energy.

3. Assuming a closed system with no energy losses to heat, a positive change in potential energy must equal the negative change in _____ energy.

4. Which of the following is not an appropriate unit for flow?

   a) $\dfrac{m^3}{sec}$

   b) $\dfrac{liters}{min}$

   c) $\dfrac{m}{sec}$

   d) $\dfrac{gallons}{day}$

   e) All are appropriate

5. Which of the following two fluid systems performed more work?

   System A: 10 liters pumped out in 10 minutes
   System B: 11 liters pumped out in 40 minutes

6.   In a lossless closed system, if the velocity of flow doubles the kinetic energy _____ .

7.   A change of 5 ml per mmHg is a measure of what flow parameter?

8.   A change of 5 ml per second is a measure of what flow parameter?

9.   Which system has a higher capacitance?

      System A: can receive 10 liters in 1 minute
      System B: can receive 2 liters in 10 minutes

10.   If energy can be lost to heat, fluid at a distal point (later in the flow path) will have _____ energy than/as the fluid at a proximal point, for a closed system.

      a) less
      b) more
      c) the same

3. Derivation of Equations

3.1 Introduction

Before developing the fluid dynamic equations, there are three important points that will facilitate a better and more intuitive understanding.

1)   The starting points for some of the equations are found in the answer section of the flow analogy. Make certain to review the analogy exercises and explanations.

2)   The fundamental fluid dynamic equation, Poiseuille's law, was originally determined empirically (from observation and experimentation rather than theory and mathematical rigor). Most treatments of hemodynamics begin by simply stating Poiseuille's equation and then manipulating the equation to derive the resistance equation, the simplified law of fluid dynamics of hemodynamics, and the volumetric flow equation. In this text, we will do exactly the opposite. Using observation, reasoning and mathematical relationships, we will develop the resistance equation, the simplified law of hemodynamics, and the volumetric flow equation. From these three equations we will express Poiseuille's law.

      The standard approach more clearly reflects how the equations were discovered, but the approach taken here will help develop a more intuitive understanding of the equations.

3)   The development of the equations will be based on intuitive understanding and will not be mathematically rigorous. There is value in mathematical rigor when proving the validity of mathematical expression, but this is not our goal. These equations have been long since validated and require no proof. Our goal is to understand how the equations can be applied and what each tells us about the flow of blood with varying hemodynamic situations.

3.2 The Resistance Equation

The conceptual foundation for the resistance equation was found by answering questions 10, 11 and 12 of the flow analogy. For the sake of clarity, similar scenarios will be repeated here to help develop the mathematical relationships between the physical parameters which determine the resistance to flow.

Scenario 1: (Varying Length)

Assume there are two pipelines through which the same volumetric flow of 10 liters/min is required. Which of these two pipelines, as illustrated in *Figure 4*, would require more energy, hence offering greater resistance?

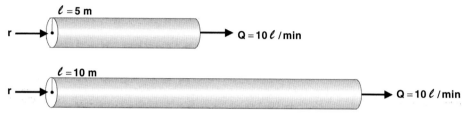

Fig. 4 **Effect of Length on Resistance**

Clearly the longer flow conduit will require more energy to transport the same volumetric flow. By definition, energy per volumetric flow is the resistance. Therefore as the length of the conduit increases (presuming the same radius and the same volumetric flow), the resistance increases. Mathematically this relationship is proportional, or:

$$R \propto \ell$$

(As the length increases, the resistance increases.)

Scenario 2: (Varying the Radius)

Assume there are two pipelines through which the same volumetric flow of 10 liters/min is required. Which of these two pipelines, as illustrated in *Figure 5,* would require more energy, hence offering greater resistance?

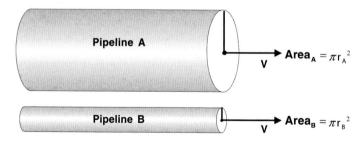

Fig. 5 **Effect of Radius (Area) on Resistance**

Clearly pipeline B will require more energy per volumetric flow (higher resistance) than pipeline A. Therefore, as the radius decreases, the resistance increases. Mathematically this relationship represents inverse proportionality, or:

$$R \propto \frac{1}{r}$$

(As the radius decreases, the resistance increases.)

Pegasus Lectures, Inc.

Scenario 3: (Varying Both the Length and the Radius)

Assume there are two pipelines through which the same volumetric flow of 10 liters/min is required. Which of these two pipelines, as illustrated in *Figure 6*, would require more energy, hence offering greater resistance?

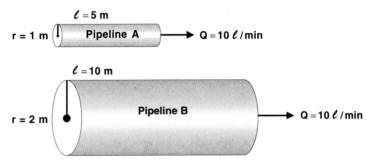

Fig. 6   **Dominance of Radius over Length to Resistance**

Notice that in this case, pipeline A is half the length of pipeline B and also has a radius half that of pipeline B. We have already seen from scenario 1 that a decrease in length results in a decrease in resistance. In this scenario however, even though pipeline B is longer by a factor of 2, pipeline A will require more energy per volumetric flow than pipeline B. In other words, this scenario demonstrates that changes in the radius affect the resistance faster than changes in the length affect resistance. As a result, the power of the radius in the inverse relationship is higher than the power of the length in the proportional relationship.

$$R \propto \frac{1}{r^{Power}}$$

The mathematics to demonstrate that power is really a fourth power requires much more effort than is warranted for our purposes, especially since the mathematics will not improve our intuitive understanding of the equation. Therefore we will simply state that resistance is related to the radius to the fourth power or

$$R \propto \frac{1}{r^4}$$

(Small changes in the radii produce absolutely enormous changes in the resistance.)

Scenario 4: (Varying Viscosity)

Let us again presume that there are two pipelines as depicted in *Figure 7*. Note that the pipelines are identical in both length and radius and that they have identical volumetric flows. However, pipeline A is transporting water and pipeline B is transporting honey.

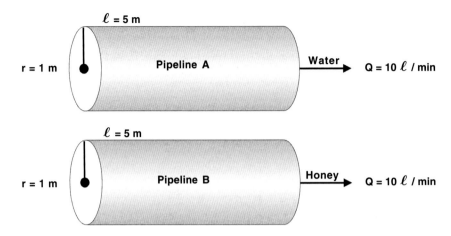

Fig. 7   **Effect of Viscosity on Resistance**

Even though the dimensions of the flow conduits are the same, pipeline B will require more energy to transport the same volumetric flow. Clearly there is another parameter related to the fluid itself, and not the flow path, which affects resistance. This other parameter is the viscosity, usually designated by the Greek letter η. As defined in Section 2.2, the viscosity is a measure of the 'sticky' attraction of the molecules within a fluid. By this definition honey would therefore be more viscous than water.

As viscosity increases the resistance also increases. Mathematically this is a proportional relationship, or:

$$R \propto \eta$$

(As the viscosity increases, the resistance increases.)

Combining the Relative Expressions:

Now that we have the mathematical relationship between the variables which determine the resistance, we can combine these relationships into one equation to create the resistance equation.

From the three relative relationships we have $R \propto \dfrac{\ell\eta}{r^4}$.

by introducing a few constants this expression becomes absolute; and the resistance equation is:

Resistance Equation:

$$R = \frac{8\ell\eta}{\pi r^4}$$

Note that this one equation expresses that $R \propto \ell$, $R \propto \eta$, $R \propto \dfrac{1}{r^4}$.

3.3 Volumetric Flow (continuity equation)

From the resistance equation, we now have a means of determining how much of an impediment to flow exists for a given flow situation. The next step is to determine the mathematical relationships that will allow us to measure the volumetric flow in terms of parameters we can either visualize or measure with ultrasound. As we did with the resistance equation, we will start by assessing various scenarios to develop mathematical relationships.

Scenario 1: (Varying Cross-sectional Area)

Assume there are two pipelines as depicted in *Figure 8*. Further presume that the flow velocity is the same in pipeline A and pipeline B ($V_A = V_B$).

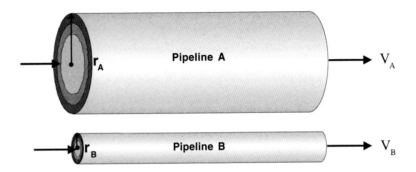

Fig. 8   **Effect of Cross-sectional Area on Volumetric Flow**

For the same velocity, clearly the larger cross-sectional area of pipeline A would permit a higher volumetric flow than pipeline B. Since we are assuming a round flow orifice, the cross-sectional area is calculated as:

$$area = \pi r^2.$$

Therefore, as the radius increases a little, the cross-sectional area increases more significantly (by the square of the change), causing a large increase in volumetric flow. Mathematically this relationship is written as proportionality or:

$$Q \propto area \text{ or } Q \propto r^2.$$

(As the area increases for a fixed velocity, the volumetric flow increases.)

Scenario 2: (Varying Mean Velocity)

Now let us assume that the two flow conduits are identical in cross-sectional area. However, in pipeline A, the average velocity is lower than the average velocity in pipeline B, as depicted in *Figure 9.*

Note: A bar over the top of a variable is generally used to express an average, so the average spatial velocity is denoted as $\bar{v}$.

Chapter 12

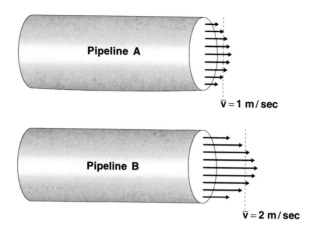

Fig. 9 **Effect of Velocity on Volumetric Flow**

Even though both vessels are identical in cross-sectional area, it is clear that pipeline B has a greater volumetric flow because of the higher average flow velocity. Mathematically, this relationship is proportionality or:

$$Q \propto \bar{v}.$$

(For a fixed cross-sectional area, an increase in average or mean velocity results in an increase in flow.)

Combining the Relationships

Now that we have the mathematical relationships relating to the volumetric flow with the mean velocity and with the cross-sectional area we can combine these relationships into one equation:

Continuity Equation:

$$Q = \bar{v} \bullet area.$$

This equation, which allows for the definition of the volumetric flow, is usually referred to as the continuity equation in the cardiac world. The term "continuity" is used since, for a closed system (a system with no inputs or outputs), all the flow through one region must equal all the flow through any other region of the flow system. The flow is continuous throughout the system, mathematically expressed as:

$$Q_a = Q_b.$$

3.4 Simplified Law of Hemodynamics

As already discussed in the definition Section (2.2), and from question 8 of the flow analogy, we know that flow only occurs from a higher to a lower energy state. Pressure exerted across a vessel wall is one form of energy. Therefore presuming the absence of other energy sources, we would anticipate that flow would occur from a higher pressure region to a lower pressure region. Clearly, a pressure gradient is required to get a volume of fluid to flow across a resistance pathway. Therefore we would expect there to be a physical relationship expressible mathematically between pressure change, resistance, and volumetric flow. We will use the following scenarios to determine the basic mathematical relationship between the related variables of pressure change, resistance and volumetric flow.

Scenario 1: (Same Volumetric Flow, Different Resistances)

Assume you need to pump the same volumetric flow of 10 liters/min down a pipe. Now presume you can choose which pipeline you prefer, as indicated in *Figure 10*.

Which of these two pipelines would require more energy to achieve the required volumetric flow?

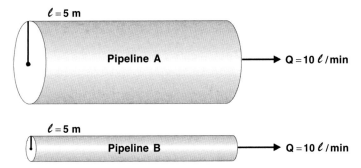

Fig. 10 **Effect of Resistance on the Pressure Gradient**

Clearly pipeline B will offer more resistance to flow than pipeline A since pipeline B is smaller. To overcome this increase in resistance requires a greater expense of energy. In other words a greater pressure drop (gradient) will occur with an increasing resistance. Mathematically this relationship is expressed as proportionality or:

$$\Delta P \propto R.$$

(An increase in resistance results in an increase in pressure drop for a fixed volumetric flow.)

Scenario 2

This time assume that you have two identical pipelines, but that pipe A requires 10 liters/min (a higher required volumetric flow) while pipe B requires only 1 liter/min (a lower volumetric flow). As indicated in *Figure 11*, which of the flow pipelines would require more energy to achieve the required volumetric flow?

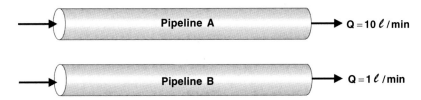

Fig. 11 **Effect of Volumetric Flow on the Pressure Gradient**

Transporting more volume across a resistive path will require a greater energy expenditure. Therefore, for a fixed resistance, an increase in volumetric flow results in an increase in the pressure gradient. Mathematically this relationship is again proportional or:

$$\Delta P \propto Q.$$

(For a fixed resistance, a higher flow (Q) results in an increase in the pressure gradient.)

Combining the Relative Expressions

Now that we have the fundamental relationship between pressure, volumetric flow, and resistance, we will combine these relationships together into one equation referred to as the simplified law of hemodynamics:

Simplified Law of Hemodynamics:

$$\Delta P = Q \bullet R.$$

(Notice that both relationships ($\Delta P \propto R$ and $\Delta P \propto Q$) are contained within this one equation.)

3.5 Poiseuille's Law

We have already developed the simplified law of hemodynamics or:

$$\Delta P = Q \bullet R.$$

Additionally, we have already developed the resistance equation:

$$R = \frac{8\ell\eta}{\pi r^4}.$$

By substituting the expression on the right side of the equal sign of the resistance equation into the simplified law we get:

$$\Delta P = Q \bullet \frac{8\ell\eta}{\pi r^4}.$$

If we rewrite this equation in terms of Q (multiply both sides of the equation by πr^4 and divide both sides of the equation " $8\ell\eta$ " by and simplify):

$$\frac{\pi r^4}{8\ell\eta}\Delta P = \frac{Q \bullet \cancel{8\ell\eta}}{\cancel{\pi r^4}} \bullet \frac{\cancel{\pi r^4}}{\cancel{8\ell\eta}}.$$

Rewriting the equation with constants in front, the equation becomes:

Poiseuille's Law:

$$Q = \frac{\pi \Delta P r^4}{8\ell\eta}.$$

This equation is known as Poiseuille's law. From this one equation we can see a clear relationship between the volumetric flow (Q), the pressure gradient (ΔP), the radius of the vessel (r), the length of the vessel (ℓ) and the viscosity of the fluid (η).

3.6 Simplifications Made for the Equation

It is important to realize that Poiseuille's law, and hence the simplified law of hemodynamics only holds true under specific conditions. Specifically, the assumptions necessary for Poiseuille's law to hold true are detailed below.

a) The flow conduit is a rigid cylindrical tube.
b) The flow is steady state, laminar flow.
c) The fluid is Newtonian.

The fact that vessels within the arterial and venous system are not rigid or cylindrical is evident. Also the fact that flow through the arterial system is pulsatile and not steady state is also evident. A Newtonian fluid is a fluid whose viscosity is variable only with changes in temperature, and does not vary with changing geometry. Water is an example of a Newtonian fluid. Unlike Newtonian fluids the viscosity of blood changes not just with changes in temperature but also with changes in hematocrit and vessel size. Therefore blood is not a Newtonian fluid. In other words, all of the requirements for Poiseuille's law to hold true are not met in hemodynamics.

The question naturally arises "What is the value of this equation given that none of the criteria are met?" The answer is twofold: first, under some hemodynamic situations the errors caused by not meeting these criteria are small enough that the law is still a fairly good prediction of behavior, and secondly, when the errors are much greater, the equation still gives an upper boundary and clearly indicates the direction and magnitude of the error. In other words when the equation doesn't hold close enough to true, we at least know what parameters need to be analyzed to improve our hemodynamic assessment. These points are the basis on which we apply the equations of fluid dynamics to blood flow (hemodynamics) in the next chapter.

4. Bernoulli's Equation and Energy

4.1 Conservation of Energy and an Apparent Contradiction
As discussed in Section 2, energy is always conserved. The central theorem is that energy remains constant, although it may be transformed into different forms. There is an apparent contradiction present, since on one hand we are stating that fluid will only flow from a higher energy to a lower energy state, and on the other hand we are stating that energy must be conserved, and therefore the energy must be the same everywhere in the system. For this reason, many people then state that flow only occurs from a higher to lower pressure. This approach works fine until you include the form of pressure associated with a static fluid column (hydrostatic pressure) in the pressure measurement. In the presence of hydrostatic pressure, it sometimes appears that fluid is moving from a lower overall pressure to a higher overall pressure (as occurs when blood flows from the aorta toward the ankle in a standing patient). At this point some find it more convenient to switch back to referring to energy as the driving force, returning to the original apparent contradiction.

Of course the conservation of energy theorem really does hold and this pressure/energy confusion is the result of the fact that there are many different types of energy, and all forms of energy present must be considered for the situation to make sense. The difficulty arises from the fact that energy is a very tough parameter to neatly and concisely define. Bernoulli's equation will become the tool that will help us express the various forms of energy and how these energy forms exist at different locations in the fluid flow path.

4.2 Bernoulli's Equation (simplified)
Bernoulli's equation is actually the conservation of energy theorem with an attempt to incorporate all of the forms of energy into one equation. The full-blown Bernoulli's equation, although appearing very formidable and imposing, states that for a closed system, all the energy at one location must equal all of the energy at another location. We will use the very simple flow model of *Figure 12* to start the equation discussion.

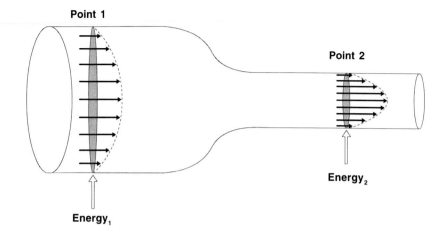

Fig. 12 **Bernoulli's Equation and the Conservation of Energy (Assume no Energy Loss)**

For simplification, let's begin with the presumption that there is no energy lost to heat caused by friction with the flow conduit walls, or in essence the frictional and viscous effects are close to zero. Afterwards, we will remove this artificial constraint. Also, we will presume that the diameter of the vessel is small enough so that even in the wider section, since the vessel is parallel to the ground, the hydrostatic pressure is essentially zero throughout the entire tube. We will also presume a rigid tube.

Assumptions:
1) rigid tube
2) non-viscous fluid
3) no surface friction
4) incompressible homogenous fluid
5) steady state (non-pulsatile) flow

Energy at Point 1
For a fluid moving at point 1 there are 2 types of energy, potential energy and kinetic energy. The total energy at point 1 is given by:

$$Total\ Energy_1 = KE_1 + PE_1.$$

The potential energy is related to the lateral pressure exerted on the vessel wall at point 1. The kinetic energy is related to the square of the mean velocity at point 1. We will use the following conventions to refer to the two types of energy at point 1:

$$Potential\ Energy: PE_1 = P_1$$
$$Kinetic\ Energy: KE_1 = \frac{1}{2}\rho v_1^2$$

So the total energy at point 1 can be written as:

$$Total\ Energy = P_1 + \frac{1}{2}\rho v_1^2$$

Energy at Point 2

At point 2, the energy can also be written as the sum of the potential kinetic energy at point 2, or:

$$Total\ Energy_2 = KE_2 + PE_2.$$

The potential energy is related to the lateral pressure exerted on the vessel wall at point 2. The kinetic energy is related to the square of the mean velocity at point 2. We will use the following conventions to refer to the two types of energy at point 2:

$$Potential\ Energy : PE_2 = P_2.$$

$$Kinetic\ Energy : KE_2 = \frac{1}{2}\rho v_2^{\ 2}.$$

So the total energy at point 2 can be written as:

$$Total\ Energy_2 = P_2 + \frac{1}{2}\rho v_2^{\ 2}.$$

Conservation of Energy Theorem Applied

Since there has been no energy lost to heat, and all of the fluid is still contained within the flow conduit (closed system), the total energy at point 2 must equal the total energy at point 1:

$$Total\ Energy\ 1 = Total\ Energy\ 2.$$

By substitution this expression can be rewritten as:

$$P_1 + \frac{1}{2}\rho v_1^{\ 2} = P_2 + \frac{1}{2}\rho v_2^{\ 2}.$$

Rewriting the Equation in Terms of a Change in Pressure (pressure gradient)

From the above equation, we can manipulate the equation to express the change in potential energy in terms of the kinetic energy conversion as follows:

$$P_1 - P_2 = \frac{1}{2}\rho v_2^{\ 2} - \frac{1}{2}\rho v_1^{\ 2}.$$

Grouping like terms, this expression can be simplified to:

$$P_1 - P_2 = \frac{1}{2}\rho\left(v_2^{\ 2} - v_1^{\ 2}\right).$$

And using the Greek letter delta to stand for the gradient, this expression can be equivalently written as:

$$P_1 - P_2 = \Delta P = \frac{1}{2}\rho\left(v_2^{\ 2} - v_1^{\ 2}\right).$$

4.3 Simplified Bernoulli and Modified Simplified Bernoulli Equation

By substituting for the normal density of blood ($\rho \approx 1.06 \times 10^3 \ kg/m^3$) with the velocity expressed using the units of m/sec, the simplified form of the Bernoulli equation becomes:

Simplified Bernoulli's Equation:

$$\Delta P(mmHg) \approx 4\left(v_2^{\ 2} - v_1^{\ 2}\right)$$

(where the velocity is in the units of m/sec).

A further simplification can be made if the distal velocity is significantly greater than the proximal velocity, or $v_2 \gg v_1$. In this case, the proximal velocity can be dropped from the equation with little error in the calculation of the pressure gradient, and the simplified modified form becomes:

Modified Bernoulli's Equation:

$$\Delta P(mmHg) \approx 4(v_2^{\ 2})$$

(where the velocity is in the units of m/sec).

4.4 Bernoulli's Equation with Hydrostatic Pressure Term

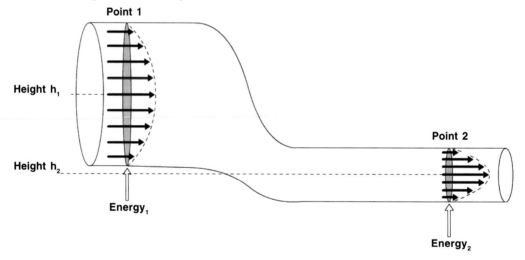

Fig. 13   **Bernoulli's Equation with Hydrostatic Pressure Term**

Notice in *Figure 13*, point 1 is at a different mean height than point 2. As a result there is a difference in hydrostatic pressure, related to the force of gravity. Therefore, the energy at point 1 and point 2 will both now be comprised of three terms, a potential energy term related to the lateral pressure on the flow conduit walls, the kinetic energy related to the square of the velocity of the flow, and the gravitational potential energy at each location.

$$\underbrace{P_1}_{\substack{\text{Pressure}\\\text{Potential}\\\text{at point 1}}} + \underbrace{\frac{1}{2}\rho v_1^{\ 2}}_{\substack{\text{Kienetic}\\\text{energy}\\\text{at point 1}}} + \underbrace{\rho g h_1}_{\substack{\text{Gravitational}\\\text{potential}\\\text{(hydrostatic pressure)}\\\text{at point 1}}} = \underbrace{P_2}_{\substack{\text{Pressure}\\\text{Potential}\\\text{at point 2}}} + \underbrace{\frac{1}{2}\rho v_2^{\ 2}}_{\substack{\text{Kinetic energy}\\\text{at point 2}}} + \underbrace{\rho g h_2}_{\substack{\text{Gravitational}\\\text{potential}\\\text{(hydrostatic pressure)}\\\text{at point 2}}}$$

Pegasus Lectures, Inc.

Once again, this equation can be rewritten in terms of a pressure gradient by manipulating the terms:

$$P_1 - P_2 = \frac{1}{2}\rho v_2^2 - \frac{1}{2}\rho v_1^2 + \rho g h_2 - \rho g h_1.$$

Grouping by like terms and simplifying yields the expression:

Bernoulli's Equation:

$$\Delta P = P_1 - P_2 = \frac{1}{2}\rho\left(v_2^2 - v_1^2\right) + \rho g\left(h_2 - h_1\right).$$

4.4 Bernoulli's Equation with Heat Term

Up to this point, our derivation of the Bernoulli equation has ignored the effects of frictional and viscous energy loss. For many hemodynamic situations, the energy losses associated with the friction and heat through major arteries is small enough to be insignificant. However, when flow traverses higher resistance vessels such as the arterioles or the stenotic arteries, the energy loss through friction and viscous effects can become appreciable. In these cases, the energy term cannot be ignored as we have to this point. As a result, we will add an energy term which represents energy dissipated as heat as the result of friction and viscous effects. If this term is added to the Bernoulli equation, we now have the expression:

$$\underbrace{P_1}_{\substack{\text{Pressure}\\\text{Potential}\\\text{at point 1}}} + \underbrace{\frac{1}{2}\rho v_1^2}_{\substack{\text{Kienetic}\\\text{energy}\\\text{at point 1}}} + \underbrace{\rho g h_1}_{\substack{\text{Gravitational}\\\text{potential}\\\text{(hydrostatic pressure)}\\\text{at point 1}}} = \underbrace{P_2}_{\substack{\text{Pressure}\\\text{Potential}\\\text{at point 2}}} + \underbrace{\frac{1}{2}\rho v_2^2}_{\substack{\text{Kinetic energy}\\\text{at point 2}}} + \underbrace{\rho g h_2}_{\substack{\text{Gravitational}\\\text{potential}\\\text{(hydrostatic pressure)}\\\text{at point 2}}} + \underbrace{Heat}_{\substack{\text{Energy dissipated}\\\text{as heat along}\\\text{flow conduit}}}.$$

We now have the full-blown Bernoulli's equation which takes into account the major energy sources interacting to create flow. By building this equation piece by piece, it is hoped that the formidable appearance of the equation is no longer a deterrent to understanding the premise behind the equation.

4.5 Understanding Bernoulli's Equation (An Airfoil and Lift)

In most general physics textbooks, an airfoil (airplane wing) is used to demonstrate an application of Bernoulli's principle. In reality, if we take a very non-mathematical approach to reviewing the principles of lift, we can gain great insight as to what happens when flow goes through a narrowing of a flow conduit.

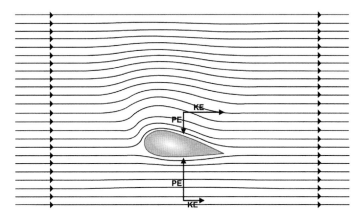

Fig. 14 **Applying Bernoulli's Equation and Lift**

Chapter 12

Notice that the distance across the top of the airfoil (wing) is longer than the distance underneath the wing. As a result, the flow across the top of the wing will have a higher velocity than the velocity below the wing. From the conservation of energy theorem, we know that if the kinetic energy (related to the velocity squared) has increased above the wing, then the potential energy must have decreased by the commensurate amount. The potential energy term is related to the pressure that is exerted in the direction of the wing. In other words, as the potential energy decreases, the force pushing the wing down also decreases.

Conversely, the lower velocity flow underneath the wing has less kinetic energy, implying that there is a greater potential energy. Again since the potential energy is related to the pressure exerted in the direction of the wing, there is a greater pressure pushing up on the wing. The net result is that there is a greater pressure pushing up on the wing than pressure pushing down on the wing, resulting in a net upward force, otherwise known as lift.

Clearly, if the velocity of the air traversing the wing is increased, the differential forces between the bottom and top of the wing increases, creating more lift (a greater difference in potential energy). In other words, traveling at a higher velocity produces more lift. Another means by which more lift can be generated is to increase the path length across the top of the wing, by adding an extension to the wing as is done with airplane wings by use of wing flaps. In other words, the greater the velocity increase, the more kinetic energy and the greater the drop in potential energy.

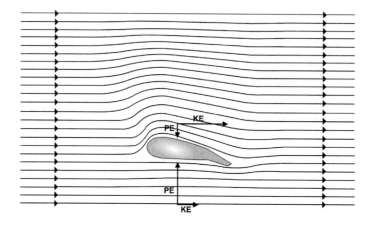

Fig. 15 **Use of an Aileron to Produce More Lift**

Although maybe not immediately apparent, the exact principle used to describe lift also describes fluid flowing through a narrow conduit. As was shown with *Figure 15*, as the cross-sectional area of the flow conduit decreases, the velocity increases. Since the energy must be conserved, the increase in kinetic energy associated with the higher velocity means that there must be a commensurate decrease in the potential energy which exerts pressure on the vessel walls. Therefore, higher velocity flow results in a decrease in pressure measured across the vessel walls. By measuring the velocity of the flow before and after the narrowing and plugging these values into Bernoulli's equation, we can calculate how much the kinetic energy has increased. Since we assume that there is no energy lost to heat, the increase in kinetic energy is exactly equal to the decrease in pressure across the walls. It is precisely for this reason that we refer to this change in energy as a pressure drop.

Pegasus Lectures, Inc.

5. Basics of Flow and Flow Diagrams

5.1 Simplifications and Assumptions for These Equations to be Employed

The equations that we have developed are based on many assumptions which are not consistent with blood flow in a patient. Specifically, these equations were based on the following assumptions:

1. The flow conduit is a rigid tube.
2. The surface of the tube is smooth with no irregularities.
3. The fluid is Newtonian (homogenous, constant viscosity).
4. The fluid is incompressible.
5. There is no energy lost to heat .
6. The flow is steady state (non-pulsatile).

As already stated in Section 3.6, it is clear that the above assumptions will not hold true in the body. Therefore, interpreting the results from applying these equations must take these inconsistent simplifications into account. In the following section, we will apply these equations in a simple flow model that, unlike actual blood vessels, does meet the required assumptions.

It is important to note that although this simple model does not perfectly mimic actual blood flow, the analysis of the model is still extremely helpful in developing an understanding of the fundamental relationships and basic principles of blood flow.

The added complexity associated with actual blood flow will be addressed thoroughly in the next chapter.

5.2 Flow Definitions

Steady flow: As the name suggests, steady flow is a constant volumetric flow.

Pulsatile flow: Volumetric flow which is dynamic with time. As a result of the dynamic pressure generated by the heart, blood flow is clearly pulsatile.

Laminar flow: When a fluid moves in a "well behaved" manner and in a uniform direction. Specifically flow is laminar when the fluid moves in concentric rings with no crossing of ring boundaries.

   a) **Plug flow:**
   A special type of laminar flow in which the velocity profile is relatively constant across the entire vessel. Plug flow usually results from an acceleration component such as entrance effects or early systole, as in the ascending branch of the aorta.

   b) **Parabolic flow:**
   A special type of laminar flow in which the velocity profile across the vessel is shaped like a parabola. Arterial flow in straight, unchanging arteries, absent of disease is typically parabolic. Venous flow is typically parabolic except at the junctures of smaller to larger veins where the flow is disturbed.

Disturbed flow: Disturbed flow is any deviation from laminar flow.

Turbulent flow: When a fluid does not move in a "well behaved" manner nor in a uniform direction. Turbulence is chaotic or random, disturbed flow which occurs distally to a stenosis or narrowing (exit effect).

Velocity: Recall that velocity was defined earlier as the rate at which something is moving in a particular direction and has units of $\frac{distance}{time}$.

Acceleration: Acceleration is the change of velocity over time. A positive acceleration means an increase in velocity. A negative acceleration is also referred to as a deceleration.

Entrance effects: The change in velocity profile which results when entering into a vessel of reduced diameter. Since there is a decrease in area, the velocity must increase (acceleration) to maintain constant flow. This acceleration results in a flattening of the velocity profile.

Exit effects: The change in velocity profile which results when exiting from a vessel of smaller diameter. Since there is an increase in area, the velocity must decrease (negative acceleration) to maintain constant flow. Inertial energy is dissipated by chaotic or turbulent flow.

Perhaps one of the easiest ways to develop an understanding of the significance of these terms is to analyze a flow conduit with changing dimensions. For this case, we will constrain our flow model to meet the assumptions that were made to develop the equations. Namely, the tube will be rigid, the tube walls will be regular and smooth, the fluid will be incompressible and homogenous, the flow will be steady state, and the energy losses through heat will be negligible.

5.3 Steady Flow Diagram in a Rigid Tube

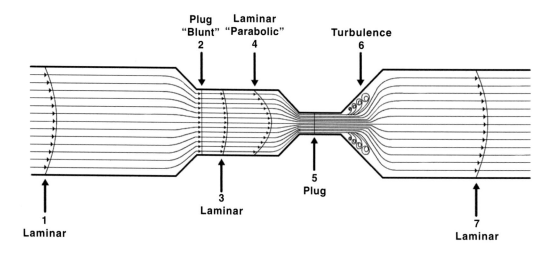

Fig. 16   **Flow Through a Rigid Tube**

The following descriptions of flow and flow regions refer to *Figure 16*.

Region

1)   Laminar Flow:

Concentric rings of flow through a wide segment of the vessel (parallel streamlines). Each "ring" of fluid flows orderly, not crossing or colliding with any other ring. There is not much frictional loss since very little of the fluid comes in contact with conduit walls.

2)   Plug Flow:

(An entrance or inlet effect.) According to the volumetric flow equation (continuity equations), to maintain constant volumetric flow, the velocity must increase because of the decrease in cross-sectional area. A change in velocity with respect to time is the definition of acceleration. As the fluid reaches region 2, there is acceleration to maintain flow. The acceleration results in a flattened velocity profile.

3 → 4) Parabolic Laminar to Steeper Parabolic Laminar:

Notice how the laminar flow is flattened in region 2 but more distally becomes a parabolic shape in region 3. Since the narrowed segment is long with respect to the diameter, more distally (region 4), a sharper parabolic flow velocity profile develops.

4 → 5) Parabolic Laminar to Plug Laminar:

Just as occurred at the transition from region 1 → 2, acceleration from region 4 → 5 flattens the velocity profile in order to maintain a constant volumetric flow (entrance effect).

5 → 6) Turbulence:

As the high velocity fluid exits the narrow diameter of region 5 to the larger diameter of region 6, there is a major change in flow constraints (exit effects). The flow no longer experiences as much of the constraining effects of the narrow walls, reducing the frictional effects. The core of the jet sprays into region 6 and then begins to decelerate. The outer edges of the flow see a low resistance path into the wider section, no longer constrained by the conduit walls. The flow direction therefore becomes somewhat chaotic and random. Since the overall resistance to flow decreases, the velocity decreases to maintain a constant flow.

6 → 7) Parabolic laminar flow:

Distal to the turbulence, the concentric rings of flow (parallel streamlines) are again developed and the flow has returned to the "well behaved" velocity profile.

5.4 Steady State Flow in a Curved Vessel

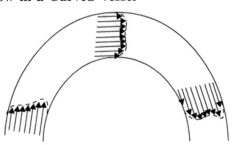

Fig. 17   **Flow in a Curved Vessel**

Note in *Figure 17* that the velocity profile across a curved flow conduit differs from the velocity profile in a straight segment. For the flow model given, notice that the velocity along the outer radius and the inner radius changes with location along a curve.

5.5 Flow Examples
The following images are direct examples of fluid dynamics principles. Video clips have been included on the Animation and Image Library CD for better appreciation of the flow and flow disturbances. The images and videos are courtesy of Flometrics of Solana Beach, California.

Fig. 18 **Recirculation and Turbulence at a Pump Inlet**

This pump exhibited poor efficiency from energy losses associated with turbulence. The turbulence occurs at the inlet of the pump where the expansion angle was too great resulting in flow disturbance and recirculation.

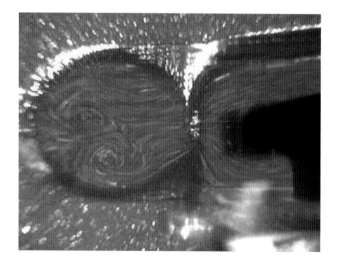

Fig. 19 **The Outlet of the Pump in Cross Section**

The dark object on the right is the pump impeller. In this case the pump outlet is too large, and this causes a double vortex in the pump outlet.

View Animation and Image Library CD

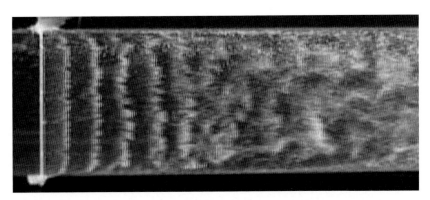

Fig. 20   **Turbulent Flow Developed in a Pipe Illustrated Through Hydrogen Bubble Generation**

Figure 20 demonstrates turbulent flow in a straight pipe. The technique used to visualize the flow patterns involves the generation of hydrogen bubbles. Electricity is pulsed in the wire which causes the water to dissociate (generating hydrogen bubbles). Another electrode generates oxygen elsewhere in the system. Salt is added to the water to make the water conductive. In this case the turbulence is evident downstream of the entrance effect. (The flow is from left to right.)

View Animation and Image Library CD

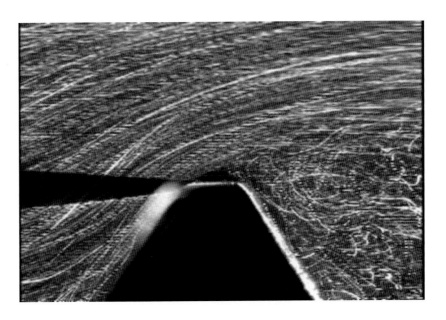

Fig. 21   **Flow Separation and Turbulence Caused by an Object in the Flow Path (a truncated pyramid)**

Chapter 12

Figure 21 is an extraordinary display of many fluid and physics principles. The flow is moving from left to right. As the flow encounters the truncated pyramid, there is acceleration due to the decrease in flow cross-sectional area. Distal to the pyramid there is a flow separation and turbulence as the flow cross-sectional area increases. Notice how chaotic the flow is in the distal flow region. This flow separation causes a pressure drop from the excess drag.

This figure was generated using a laser light. You should notice the bright reflection on the left side from the specular surface of the pyramid. On the right side, there is a wonderful example of refraction as the light travels at different velocities in the pyramid as in the fluid. The refraction causes a shadow (clearly visible on the right side of the picture).

Fig. 22   Slower Flow and Vortices Caused by an Object in the Flow Path (a truncated pyramid)

Figure 22 demonstrates the flow disturbance with slower flow. Notice that the turbulent region is occupied with vortices. As the high velocity flow exits the narrowed region, the fluid behind the pyramid becomes entrained. At the boundary of the flow separation, some of the higher velocity flow interacts with some of the lower velocity flow, and the fluids begin to swirl and travel in a swirling motion (vortices).

 **View Animation and Image Library CD**

6. Reynold's Number and Turbulence

6.1 Reynold's Number

Reynold's number is a dimensionless index which indicates the likelihood of turbulence occurring. A higher Reynold's number implies a greater likelihood of turbulence occurring.

Reynold's number is defined as the ratio between the inertial forces and the viscous forces as follows

$$R_e = \frac{inertial\ forces}{viscous\ forces} = \frac{\rho\ d\ \bar{v}}{\eta}$$

where:

$$\rho = density$$
$$d = vessel's\ diameter$$
$$\bar{v} = spatial\ mean\ velocity$$
$$\eta = viscosity.$$

Note that the terms in the numerator are associated with the inertial energy (related to the mass of fluid that is moving), and that the terms in the denominator are associated with the viscosity. When the inertial energy is great with respect to the constraining energy losses associated with a viscous fluid, the flow can become uncontrolled and random (turbulence). Therefore, an increase in fluid density, vessel diameter, and mean velocity all increase the likelihood of turbulence. It should make sense that a smaller diameter vessel would have a lower risk of turbulence since a fluid in a small vessel is tightly constrained by the energy losses to the walls and can't easily swirl and eddy.

Conversely, when the energy associated with the inertia is low with respect to the constraint to flow caused by the viscosity, the flow will be laminar, developing well behaved streamlines. This fact too should make sense since it is more difficult to get a "sticky" fluid to swirl and eddy.

Note: $R_e > 2,000$ (<u>usually</u>) results in turbulence.

For the fluid dynamic situation we have discussed, a Reynold's number below 2,000 usually results in laminar flow. As we will learn in the next chapter, turbulence can occur at much lower Reynold's numbers as more complex flow situations (relative to our simple well behaved model) are allowed.

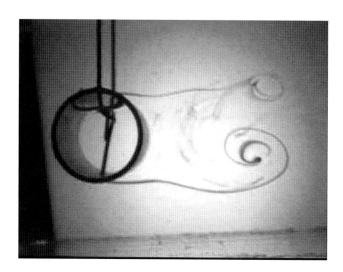

Fig. 23 Flow Over a Cylinder and a Low Reynold's Number

Figure 23 shows a cylinder in cross flow in a water tunnel. The velocity of the water is about 2 cm/sec over the cylinder with a diameter of 3 cm. The corresponding Reynolds number is about 500, such that the flow across the cylinder is relatively well behaved. To visualize the flow dilute food coloring is injected at the top and bottom of the cylinder.

Fig. 24 Flow over a Cylinder and a Higher Reynold's Number and Turbulence

Figure 24 shows the same cylinder as figure in cross flow in a water tunnel. The Reynolds number is about 5000. Notice from the colored distal flow profile that the flow pattern is very unsteady and oscillates up and down.

Fig. 25   **Introduction of a Flow Separator (Splitter) with High Reynold's Number**

In *Figure 25*, a splitter plate has been added downstream from the cylinder. Notice that the plate interacts with the distal flow, damping out the up and down oscillations evident in *Figure 24*, even though the Reynolds number is still about 5000.

Fig. 26   **Addition of a Second Flow Disturbance just Distal to the Cylinder with a High Reynold's Number.**

Figure 26 demonstrates the resulting flow from a second flow disturbing structure just distal to the large cylinder. In this case, the up and down oscillation of *Figure 24* is decreased but there is a fair amount of turbulence generated from the small distal cylinder. In this case, the Reynolds number is still about 5000.

View Animation and Image Library CD

Chapter 12

7. Exercises Answers: Pg. 975-976

1. For a fixed resistance, if the volumetric flow is doubled, how does the pressure gradient change?

2. For the given flow situation what is the velocity at point B?

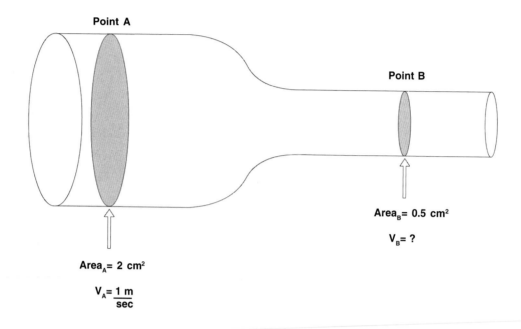

Point A

Point B

$Area_B = 0.5 \ cm^2$

$V_B = ?$

$Area_A = 2 \ cm^2$

$V_A = \dfrac{1 \ m}{sec}$

3. If the radius of a flow conduit doubles, how does the resistance change?

4. How much will the velocity have to increase to maintain the volumetric flow if the cross-sectional area is reduced by 50%?

5. What is the hydrostatic pressure for a fluid similar to blood at the bottom of a 2 foot column?

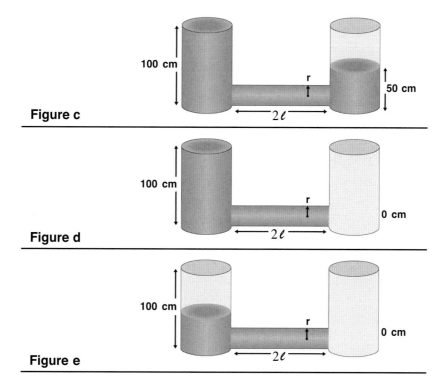

Reference Figure

Figure a

Figure b

6. a) If the volumetric flow for the reference figure is Q, what is the volumetric flow for figure a?

b) If the volumetric flow for the reference figure is Q, what is the volumetric flow for figure b?

Figure c

Figure d

Figure e

7. a) If the volumetric flow for the reference figure is Q, what is the volumetric flow for figure c?

b) If the volumetric flow for the reference figure is Q, what is the volumetric flow for figure d?

c) If the volumetric flow for the reference figure is Q, what is the volumetric flow for figure e?

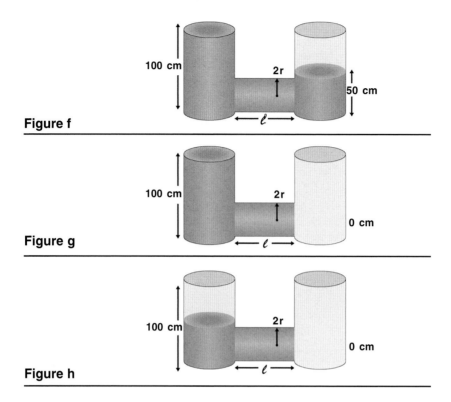

Figure f

Figure g

Figure h

8. a) If the resistance for the reference figure is R, what is the resistance for *Figure f*?
   b) If the volumetric flow for the reference figure is Q, what is the volumetric flow for *Figure f*?
   c) If the volumetric flow for the reference figure is Q, what is the volumetric flow for *Figure g*?
   d) If the volumetric flow for the reference figure is Q, what is the volumetric flow for *Figure h*?

9. If the resistance for the reference figure is R, what is the resistance for *Figure D*?

- There are many terms associated with fluid dynamics (and hemodynamics) with which you should be familiar. The starting point is to gain familiarity with terms like resistance, capacitance, pressure, velocity, volumetric flow, etc.

- Hydrostatic pressure within a fluid reservoir is the pressure that results from a column of fluid above. Hydrostatic pressure is related to the height of the column, the density of the fluid, and the force (gravity).

$$\rho = mgh$$

- For blood, the approximate hydrostatic pressure is 2 mmHg per inch.

- The capacitance is a measure of the ability to hold a change in volume per time.

- The resistance to flow is determined by the geometry of the flow path and the characteristics of the fluid.

- The resistance is proportional to the viscosity of the fluid, proportional to the length of the flow conduit, and inversely proportional to the radius of the flow conduit to the fourth power:

$$\left(R = \frac{8\ell\eta}{\pi r^4} \right)$$

- The simplified law of hemodynamics relates the pressure gradient with the volumetric flow and the resistance:

$$\Delta P = Q \bullet R$$

- The volumetric flow (continuity) equation relates the volumetric flow with the spatial average velocity and the cross-sectional area:

$$\left(Q = \bar{v} \times area \right)$$

- Poiseuille's law is really the same as the simplified law of hemodynamics with a substitution for R from the resistance equation:

$$\left(Q = \frac{\pi(\Delta P)r^4}{8\ell\eta} \right)$$

- One of the fundamental theorems of physics is that energy is conserved. This theorem becomes the foundation for the Bernoulli equation.

  ○ The pressure exerted across the vessel walls represents potential energy.

  ○ Kinetic energy is related to the velocity of the fluid flow. As the velocity increases, the kinetic energy increases as the square of the velocity (non-linearly).

  ○ The Bernoulli equation basically states that presuming no energy conversion to heat, in a closed system, the energy is conserved.

  ○ For flow through a narrowing, as the fluid accelerates to a higher velocity, there is an increase in kinetic energy. Since energy is conserved, this increase in kinetic energy is the result of a decrease in potential energy.

- ○ Since the pressure across the walls is related to the potential energy, a decrease in the potential energy represents a decrease in pressure across the walls.

- ○ Distally, if the flow conduit expands back to the original dimension, the velocity decelerates reducing kinetic energy. The reduction in kinetic energy implies an increase in potential energy (presuming no loss of energy to heat), and hence, a return of the pressure across the walls to the original value (pressure recovery).

- ○ The pressure drop at the location of a narrowing can therefore be determined by the kinetic energy difference between the location proximal and at the location of the narrowing:

$$\text{Bernoulli's equation: } \left(\Delta P = 4\left(v_2^2 - v_1^2\right) \right)$$

- ○ If the proximal velocity (v_1) is much less than the distal velocity (v_2), then the Bernoulli equation is simplified further to the commonly used form of

$$\text{Simplified Bernoulli's: } \left(\Delta P \approx 4v_2^2 \right)$$

- Laminar flow implies well-behaved concentric rings of flow through the cross-section of a flow conduit.

- Laminar flow develops a parabolic flow profile across the flow conduit diameter.

- Smaller cross-sectional areas result in steeper parabolic flow profiles.

- When flow enters into a narrowing, there is an acceleration which causes a flattening of the velocity profile called "plug" or "blunt" flow.

- At the exit of a smaller flow region to a larger flow region, there is commonly turbulence.

Note: See Appendix N: Physical Units and Appendix O: Equations for additional review.

CHAPTER 13

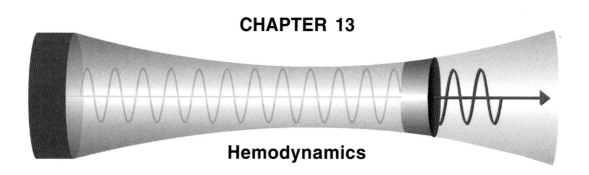

Hemodynamics

Introduction

The simplifications and assumptions made to derive basic fluid dynamic equations require re-examining before application in the much more complex situation of blood flow in a patient. In Chapter 12, Fluid Dynamics, major assumptions were made either explicitly or implicitly which clearly do not hold for blood flow. A few of the most obvious differences from our simplified model are: multiple branching vessels in parallel and series combinations, pulsatile flow, elastic vessels, and a viscous fluid. As a result of these new complexities not addressed by our fluid model, the equations developed can serve only as a foundation for interpreting the cardiovascular system, but by themselves, will not always adequately describe the specific behaviors of hemodynamics.

The starting point must therefore be to re-familiarize ourselves with the main components of the cardiovascular system; making certain to understand the principal function of each system component. The next step will be to address each simplification made in Chapter 12 and determine the effect of these complexities with respect to each system component (subsystem). Once we understand how each subsystem of the cardiovascular system is working, we can then integrate our knowledge of each subsystem to develop a comprehensive understanding of the healthy cardiovascular system at rest, as one closed system.

Once an intuitive understanding of a healthy system has been developed, the complexities of exercise and compensatory changes will be introduced. Further complexities will then be introduced by comparing a compromised (diseased) system at rest and a compromised system under exercise. Finally, the state of significant disease will be discussed with respect to the fluid dynamic equations.

The latter part of the chapter is devoted to how spectral Doppler is used to assess these hemodynamic parameters. This approach forces some repetition of material, but leads to a more intuitive and thorough understanding by discussing the practical aspects of Doppler assessment of hemodynamic parameters after already having learned about the hemodynamic parameters.

1. Removing Some of the Simplifications

While developing the equations for fluid dynamics we made a series of assumptions and simplifications, which most certainly are not true in the case of blood flow in a live patient. We must analyze each of these assumptions to determine when our equations will be adequate for predicting flow conditions, and when we must realize that our equations will be far from predictive.

1.1 The Assumption: Steady State Flow

The driving pressure for blood flow is highly pulsatile. The normal pulse pressure waveform in the aorta has a rapid acceleration, a gradual decrease to the dicrotic notch, a slight increase in pressure as the aortic valve closes, and then a gradual decline throughout diastole (discussed in Vol. II, Appendix B). Clearly, this driving pressure waveform is far removed from our assumption in the last chapter in which we assumed steady state flow.

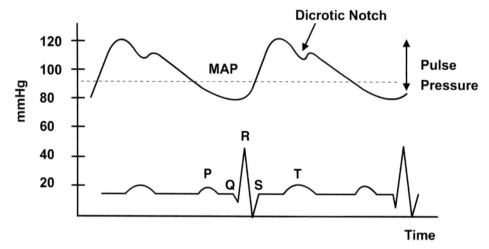

Fig. 1 **EKG and Pressure Waveform**

The fact that the pressure is dynamic introduces a plethora of changes which affect flow. The most obvious effect of pulsatile flow is a flow velocity which varies significantly during the cardiac cycle. Understanding how the velocity varies is critical since the velocity is the principal parameter measured by Doppler that we use to interpret changes in hemodynamics. In addition to this time variant velocity signal, the other resulting changes with pulsatility are contingent on the interaction of many parameters, including the cardiac output, the pulse pressure, the mean arterial pressure, the peripheral resistance, the venovasomotor tone, the compliance of the aorta and major arteries, and the presence or absence of disease. To truly understand the impact of pulsatile instead of steady-state flow, we will need to assess each branch of the arterial system piece-by-piece. This assessment is covered in Section 3.

2. The Assumption: Rigid Flow Conduits

To develop the fluid dynamic equations, the assumption was made that the flow conduits are rigid tubes. In contrast, healthy arteries and veins are relatively elastic.

2.1 Elastic Arteries

The elasticity of the arterial system is important for the following reasons:

1) The elasticity of the aorta allows the aorta to be capacitive.
2) The capacitance of the aorta allows energy to be stored in the walls of the aorta to provide the energy to propel blood during diastole.
3) Run off from the capacitive aorta and major arteries through the resistive arterioles and capillaries reduces the pulsatility of the flow (providing more continuous flow at the periphery and improving the efficiency of the heart).

Although the capacitance of the aorta and major arteries is critical to the proper functioning of the arterial system, the arterial system is known as the "resistive" component of the cardiovascular system. Later in this chapter we will learn the significance of having high resistance at the level of the arterioles and to a lesser extent, at the capillaries.

2.2 The Impact on Poiseuille's Law

In terms of the equations, the principal effect of the wall elasticity is that the simple linear relationship between pressure and volume as dictated by Poiseuille's law (and the simplified law of hemodynamics) does not hold true. In other words, although Poiseuille's law dictates that for a fixed resistance, the change in pressure is proportional to the change in volumetric flow, or $\Delta P \propto Q$, in actuality, the relationship is non-linear. Although this perturbation of the equation may be initially upsetting for those who prefer the simplicity of linear relationships, the non-linear behavior is actually somewhat intuitive in the context of real life situations. Perhaps more importantly, this non-linear relationship is a big factor in the ability of the human body to compensate for exercise.

To understand the non-linear relationship, we must consider what happens when a pressure is applied to an elastic vessel. As the pressure increases, the force on the walls increases, causing the walls to stretch. Since the increase occurs in a radial direction, there is an increase in the overall cross-sectional area of the vessel. Of course, this cross-sectional area increase is integrated (added) over the length of the dilated vessel, resulting in significantly greater volume. Therefore, it should not be too surprising that the relationship between increasing pressure and total volume is non-linear.

2.2.2 Compliance

Additionally, you should consider that this rapid rate of increase of volume with pressure for an elastic vessel has limits. As the walls distend more and more, the elasticity begins to decrease. This situation is often likened to an analogous situation in which a rubber band is stretched or when a balloon is inflated. After a certain amount of stretch of the rubber band, or inflation of the balloon, the tension increases and neither the rubber band nor the balloon exhibit much further elasticity. With greater distension of the vessel walls, as further elasticity begins to decrease, a greater pressure will be required to affect a similar change in cross-sectional area of the vessel. Therefore, with significant distension of the vessel walls, the compliance of the vessel (and the capacitance of the vessel) increases at a decreasing rate. *Figure 2* will help demonstrate this point.

The following curve demonstrates the volume-pressure relationship for a compliant, healthy vessel. You should notice that there is a large range over which small increases in pressure result in a fairly large increase in volume percentage. However, you will also notice that at both the lower and upper end of the curve, the rate of change of volume with pressure is slower than in the middle segment. At the lower end of the curve, there is an initial pressure necessary just to fill the vessel (the static filling pressure). Until this filling pressure is overcome, an increase in pressure results in a slower percentage increase in volume. Once this filling pressure has been exceeded, the pressure volume relationship increases at a relatively constant rate over a wide range. As the vessel walls become significantly stretched, the ability to hold an increase in volume begins to decrease (both the capacitance and the compliance decrease rapidly). As shown at the upper end of the curve, as the compliance begins to decrease rapidly, significantly greater pressure is necessary to achieve a percentage change in volume.

2.2.3 Pressure Volume Relationship of a Compliant Vessel

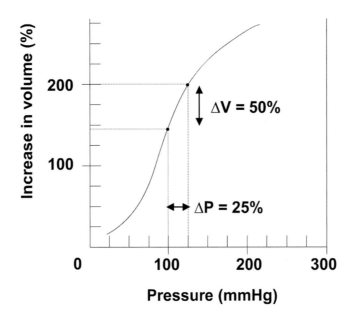

Fig. 2 **Pressure Volume Relationship for a Compliant Vessel**

Redrawn from Berne, R.M., and Levy, M.N., Cardiovascular Physiology, Mosby 1992

Reading this graph:
As with all graphs of data, the first thing you should do is look at the axes of the graph to understand the data presented. Notice that although the graph looks linear over a large range of data in the middle, the vertical axis represents percent increase in volume, not volume. From this graph, as indicated by the dotted lines, a 25% increase in pressure results in a little more than a 50% increase in volume. If the relationship were linear, the 25% increase in pressure would result in a 25% increase in pressure.

2.2.4 Pressure Volume Relationship of a Incompliant Vessel

For the compliant vessel we have just seen the rate of change of volume with pressure is faster than the linear relationship that Poiseuille's law predicts. This increase in volume with respect to pressure can be helpful when the body is attempting to meet a higher metabolic demand as occurs in exercise. Unlike for the compliant vessel, the non-linear relationship for the non-compliant vessel changes in the wrong direction. The following graph compares the pressure volume relationship for both the healthy compliant vessel and a much less compliant vessel. In contrast with the compliant vessel, notice the slower rate of change (the flatness of the curve) for a non-compliant vessel. Obviously, how much slower the rate of change (how much flatter the curve) becomes is dependent on the degree of incompliance. For the curve given, the same 25% increase in pressure results in less than 7% percent increase in volume. In this case, the increase of volume with pressure is clearly less than at a linear rate. The significance of this condition will become more apparent as we discuss the compensatory mechanisms for exercise.

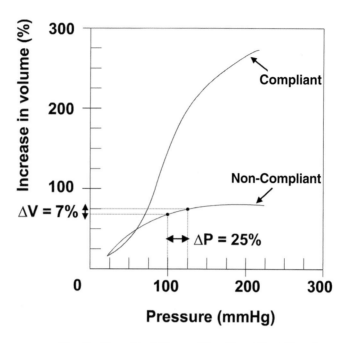

Fig. 3   **Compliant Versus Non-Compliant Vessel**

Redrawn from Berne, R.M., and Levy, M.N., Cardiovascular Physiology, Mosby 1992

2.2.5 Elastic Veins

The venous system is referred to as the "capacitive" component of the cardiovascular system. At rest, approximately 65% of the blood volume resides in the veins. In contrast to the capacitance of the major arteries of the arterial side of the cardiovascular system, the elasticity of the venous system is important for the following reasons:

1) Since the venous pressure gradient with respect to the right atrium is small and is time variant (changes with movement and respiration), the capacitance of the veins creates a reservoir where blood can reside until an adequate gradient exists for return.

2) The capacitance of the venous system serves as a reservoir from which to draw under blood loss situations such as hemorrhage, or under increased volumetric demand such as occurs with exercise. (An increased volume of blood is stored in the vascular beds of the skin and liver.)

2.3 The Assumption: Single Flow Conduit

2.3.1 Regulation of Flow

Although never explicitly stated, there was a tacit assumption made in Chapter 12; specifically, the flow paths discussed were always restricted to the simple case of a single flow conduit. For hemodynamics, the flow path is considerably more complex, including a network of vessels all varying in diameter, length and interconnections. These complex networks are critical to regulate volume of flow to organs with different and varying metabolic demands. As we will see later in this chapter by varying the resistances of the various paths, blood can be shunted to regions with higher metabolic demands from regions less critical and or with lower metabolic demands.

2.3.2 Multiple Vessels: Series and Parallel Combinations

When a flow path consists of more than one vessel, the resulting resistance of the overall complex flow path can be termed the "effective resistance," and depends on the specifics of the vessel interconnections. There are two different ways in which vessels can be interconnected: series or parallel. As the names suggest, a "series" connection implies that the output of one vessel flows into the input of another vessel. In comparison, a parallel arrangement implies that there are multiple vessels with shared inputs and with shared outputs.

2.3.2.1 Series Combinations

When two vessels are in series, the effective resistance is simply the sum of each of the individual vessel resistances. This fact should be somewhat intuitive since each segment of the path represents another resistance which must be overcome for flow to occur. If one segment is highly resistive and the next has low resistance, then it should be intuitive that the effective resistance will be close to the resistance of the high resistance segment. The following diagram illustrates the effective resistance of two vessels in series.

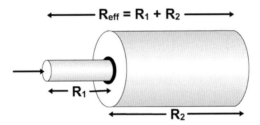

Fig. 4   **Effective Resistance of Vessels in Series**

2.3.2.2 Parallel Combinations

When two vessels are in parallel, the effective resistance is slightly more complex. Having multiple vessels in parallel actually reduces the effective resistance. This fact should be intuitive since the more paths for flow to reach a destination, the lower the impediment to flow and the lower the resistance. For parallel combinations the inverse effective resistance is calculated by adding the inverse of each parallel resistance as specified in the following diagram.

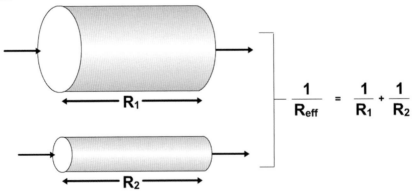

Fig. 5   **Effective Resistance of Parallel Vessels**

Note: The proximal and distal connections necessary to make these vessels truly "parallel" are intentionally omitted so as to demonstrate only parallel resistance, thereby not having to add in the series resistances of the two connecting vessel sections.

2.3.3 Combinations and Effective Resistance

The series and parallel combinations just demonstrated are still very simple in comparison to the networks that exist in the body. It is not necessary to calculate the effective resistance for every combination possible. Instead, to develop an intuition as to how the body can regulate resistance by the complex arrangement of vessels of varying diameters and lengths, we will consider a few simple cases and then extrapolate those results in order to understand more complex networks.

◊   **Example 1:**   Compare the resistance of one long vessel of length "4L" with the effective resistance of four shorter vessels in series each with the same diameter as the long comparison vessel, and each with a length of "L".

Recall that resistance is proportional to the length.

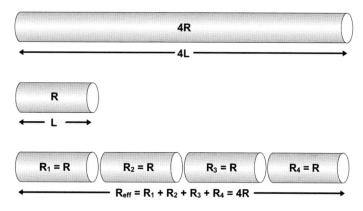

Fig. 6   **Example of Series Resistance**

So in this simple case, not surprisingly, we see that the effective resistance of four shorter segments all of equal length and diameter is equivalent to the resistance of a vessel with the same diameter and four times the length.

◊   **Example 2:**   Compare the resistance of one vessel of length L with the effective resistance of four vessels in parallel, each with the same length and diameter as the comparison vessel. $(R=R_1=R_2=R_3=R_4)$

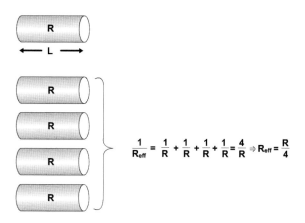

Fig. 7   **Example of Parallel Resistance**

◊ **Example 3:** Compare the resistance of one vessel of radius 4r with the effective resistance of four vessels in parallel, each with a radius of r and the same length as the large radius comparison vessel. $(R=R_1=R_2=R_3=R_4)$

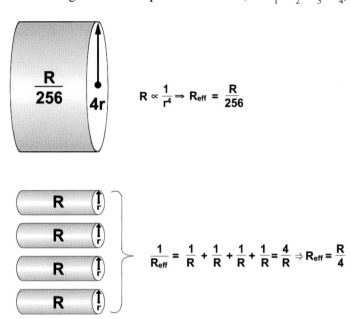

$$R \propto \frac{1}{r^4} \Rightarrow R_{eff} = \frac{R}{256}$$

$$\frac{1}{R_{eff}} = \frac{1}{R} + \frac{1}{R} + \frac{1}{R} + \frac{1}{R} = \frac{4}{R} \Rightarrow R_{eff} = \frac{R}{4}$$

Fig. 8 **Example of Parallel Resistance vs. Larger Radius Vessel**

This example is critical for understanding hemodynamics. To start, the resistance of the large vessel is only 1/256 the resistance of an individual smaller vessel. This fact should be clear from Chapter 12 in which we learned that the resistance is inversely related to the radius to the fourth power. It is critical to understand that having one vessel of four times the radius (r) does not result in the same resistance as having four vessels in parallel of radius (r). This fact should become more obvious if you compare the total cross-sectional areas of the two situations given.

For the large vessel, the area is:
$$Area = \pi(4r)^2 = 16\pi r^2.$$

For the four smaller vessels, the total area is:
$$Area = \pi(r)^2 + \pi(r)^2 + \pi(r)^2 + \pi(r)^2 = 4\pi r^2.$$

Therefore, it should make sense that the non-linear relationship between the radius and the area will have a non-linear effect on the effective resistance as well. Since the area of the larger radius vessel is four times greater than the parallel combination of four smaller radii vessels, the resistance of the larger vessel is significantly less.

◊   ***Example 4:***   Let us now consider the effective resistance of a parallel network in series with a proximal feeding vessel and distal runoff vessel. For this case, as indicated in the *Figure 9*, we will assume that the four parallel vessel are of identical radii and length. The effective resistance of this network is as demonstrated in the diagram.

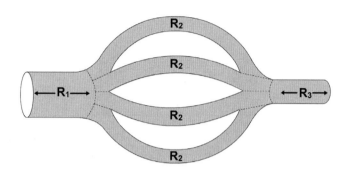

Fig. 9   **Resistance of a Parallel Series Network**

$$R_{eff} = (R_1) + (Parallel\ combination\ of\ R_2) + R_3$$

Parallel combination of R_2 is calculated by:

$$\frac{1}{R_2\ (Parallel)} = \frac{1}{R_2} + \frac{1}{R_2} + \frac{1}{R_2} + \frac{1}{R_2}$$

$$so\ \ \frac{1}{R_2\ (Parallel)} = \frac{4}{R_2}$$

$$therefore\ R_2\ (Parallel) = \frac{R_2}{4}$$

Substituing for parallel calculation of R_2
in equation for $R_{eff,}$ results in:

$$R_{eff} = R_1 + \frac{R_2}{4} + R_3.$$

2.3.4 Extrapolating these Results to Complex Networks

You should note from this diagram that the effective resistance is really the same as the serial resistance of the inflow vessel, the parallel combination network, and the outflow vessel. Whereas the resistance of the parallel network can be made relatively low either by increasing the diameter of one or more of the parallel vessels, by increasing the total number of parallel vessels, or any combination thereof, the effective or overall resistance can only be low if the proximal and distal series resistances are both low. Since resistances in series add, a serial resistance is always higher than any individual resistance in the series. Since parallel combinations add inversely, the parallel combination of any resistances decreases the effective resistance relative to each individual component. You can now start to imagine how complex networks of parallel and series combinations control effective resistances to various organs so as to shunt blood based on volumetric demand.

2.4 The Assumption: Conservation of Energy and No Energy Loss to Heat

2.4.1 General Heat Loss

The fundamental theorem that energy is conserved was greatly simplified by assuming that no energy in the system was converted and lost to heat. As a result of this simplification, we were able to equate the sum of the kinetic and potential energy at one location within the system to the sum of the kinetic and potential energy at any other location in the system. This was precisely the model that was used to create Bernoulli's equation.

2.4.2 Impact on Bernoulli's Equation and Calculating Pressure Gradients

It must be remembered that the simplified Bernoulli's equation used to determine the pressure gradient across a lesion assumed no energy lost to heat. For many cases, this simplification does not render our measurements excessively inaccurate since the application of Bernoulli's equation in the body is always over very short distances within a vessel. The presumption is therefore that not enough energy can be converted to heat over the short distances of the relatively large vessels.

However, as we will see from assessing some of the other assumptions, there are flow situations in which the energy loss to heat through frictional and viscous effects is not minimal and must be taken into account to accurately assess severity.

How much energy is converted to heat is impacted by many parameters including the vessel diameter, volumetric flow, fluid viscosity, fluid velocity, endothelial surface smoothness, and geometric perturbations to flow such as "sharp" corners or kinks. This "loss" of energy is precisely why there is a need for a beating heart.

It is the job of the right ventricle to provide enough energy to overcome the energy losses across the pulmonary bed, and the left ventricle's job to produce enough energy to overcome the energy losses which occur from flowing across the total peripheral resistance.

Because there are many factors which impact the energy conversion to heat, we will need to assess each parameter individually. Since there is almost always an interaction between each of these parameters, there will be a need for some redundancy in the explanations and discussions.

2.4.3 The Assumption: Smooth Straight Vessels

Friction is a resistive force which impedes flow. Overcoming friction requires energy, which ultimately is converted to heat. For normal healthy vessels, the endothelial lining is relatively smooth with respect to the characteristics of blood and especially true with respect to the plasma component of the blood. As a result, although there are certainly frictional losses, the losses are generally small enough so as to be masked in the other numerous error sources affecting our measurement accuracy. However, this does not imply that frictional energy losses with the vessel wall are always negligible.

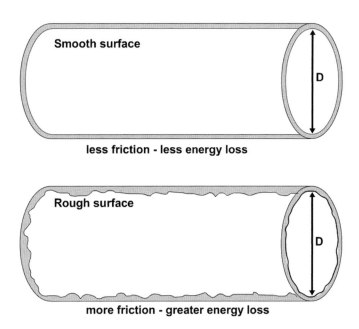

Fig. 10   **Surface Smoothness and Frictional Loss**

The condition under which frictional energy losses could increase enough to be significant are easy to identify but hard to quantify. All of the following parameters (in no particular order) will increase frictional energy losses:

1) Rougher vessel surface characteristics
2) Sharper angles including bends, kinks, twists, and branches
3) Higher "viscosity" blood (higher hematocrit)
4) Higher volumetric flow
5) Increased velocity

When these sources of energy loss are not recognized, the assessment of severity generally tends to be underestimated. As the percentage of energy converted to heat increases, clearly our equations based on the assumption of no heat loss become less indicative of reality.

2.4.4 The Assumption: Large Vessels
In Chapter 12, although never explicitly stated, there was a tacit assumption that the vessels were relatively large. This assumption was hidden in the overall assumption that the viscous and frictional energy losses to heat were negligible and could be ignored. This assumption is also clearly violated in the normal state of blood flow to smaller vessels at the periphery, as well as in the presence of disease in the larger vessels.

The following diagram is perhaps one of the most instructive diagrams to understanding energy loss through frictional and viscous effects. Although the diagram itself simplifies the true continuum of flow velocities across a cross-sectional area of a vessel by quantizing the flow into discrete concentric rings, the basic principles relayed are still accurate and illustrative of a very complex boundary condition which results in unmeasured energy loss. As the rings are drawn progressively "thinner," the discretization error decreases, thereby more closely modeling the true continuum of flow velocities across a vessel. In the limit, as the rings become infinitely thin, the model converges to the true flow distribution. Therefore, we can use an imprecise model to develop the concepts and then mentally make the results converge to a realistic estimate of the true behavior.

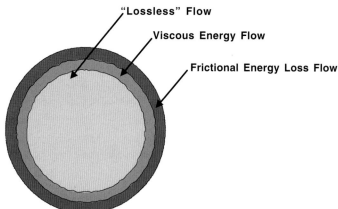

Fig. 11 **"Discretized" Energy Losses**

For the pictured vessel in *Figure 11*, imagine that the outer ring represents the volume of fluid that loses energy to friction by direct or virtually direct contact with the vessel walls. (As discussed earlier, how much energy is lost is dependent on many parameters.) Now imagine that the next inner layer represents the fluid that is losing energy to friction by sheering against the slowly moving fluid along the walls (viscous effects). (The amount of energy lost to viscous effects is also dependent on many parameters including principally the apparent viscosity of the blood). The large inner disc represents the flow that traverses the vessel without significant energy losses as a result of friction.

Clearly, in progressing toward the center of the vessel, each "ring" of flow progressively "sees" less and less effect of the energy losses associated with the vessel wall. In fact, it is precisely this interaction that is responsible for determining the parabolic flow profile present in the well behaved flow situation of laminar flow. As already mentioned, although this is a simplification, we can still use this model as a reference for varying vessel diameters to determine what the relative effects of diameter will be on energy loss and velocity profile.

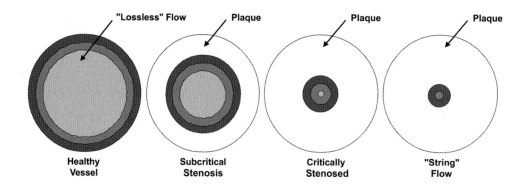

Fig. 12 **Energy Losses with Varying Stages of Disease**

Referring to *Figure 12*, assume that there are four vessels of different lumen diameters, but each vessel is required to maintain the same volumetric flow. Again, the outer layer represents the region of fluid losing energy to friction with the vessel walls. The next inner layer represents the "layer" of fluid losing energy to the drag created by the viscous attraction of the concentric rings of flow. Finally, the inner layer represents the percentage of fluid that progresses through the vessel with minimal boundary effects.

Referring to *Figure 13*, notice that since the boundary layers have remained approximately the same in thickness, the resulting unaffected flow percentages vary significantly. For the vessel with the largest lumen, vessel A, a very large percentage of the total flow through the vessel does not experience boundary layer losses. For the second largest lumen, vessel B, notice that the total cross-sectional percentage is much smaller. As a result, to achieve the same volumetric flow as in vessel A, the velocity in the center of the vessel will need to be much higher, thereby creating a steeper velocity profile across the vessel.

For the even smaller vessel lumen, C, a critical point has been reached. Almost all of the fluid through this vessel's cross-sectional area is losing energy to frictional and viscous effects, resulting in a very small percentage of blood traveling through the center unaffected. As a result, the velocity in the center will be extremely high. This situation is the critical point at which volumetric flow will not be preserved.

In the smallest vessel lumen, vessel D, all of the flow going through the vessel is "seeing" the effects of the vessel frictional and viscous energy losses. This case is often referred to as "string flow" since there is a very narrow "string" of flow traveling at low velocities. As a result, the energy losses are so great that there will not be enough energy in the system to maintain the volumetric flow. This flow profile, "string flow", is the precursor to vessel occlusion.

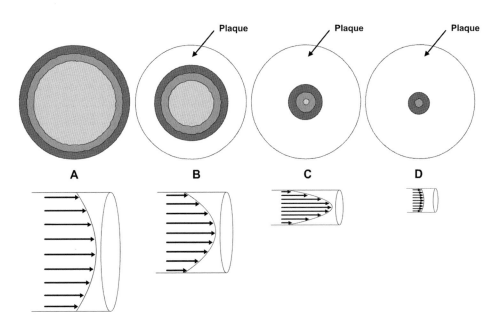

Fig. 13 **Velocity Profiles with Varying Stages of Disease**

2.4.5 The Assumption: Newtonian Fluid (and Blood Viscosity)

We assumed that the fluid in our model was Newtonian meaning that the fluid was homogenous and the viscosity variable only with changes in temperature, but constant with change in flow geometry. In reality, blood is not a Newtonian fluid, since the "viscosity" of blood changes with both changes in temperature and changes in the flow geometry. To develop an appreciation of why blood is non-Newtonian, we will begin by considering the components which constitute blood.

Whole blood consists of formed elements and plasma. The formed elements include red blood cells (RBCs) or erythrocytes, and white blood cells (WBCs) or leukocytes and platelets. Plasma consists of mostly water with a mix of proteins such as albumins and other solutes. The hematocrit is the percentage of whole blood occupied by formed elements, typically ranging from 37 to 54%. It is precisely because of this complex composition of blood, and the interaction of the constituent components that blood is not a Newtonian fluid. From the description of blood as non-homogenous, it is clear that the viscosity of blood also varies with varying hematocrit.

As a general rule, the "viscosity" of the blood decreases about 50% with a 50% decrease in hematocrit. Also, the blood viscosity increases about 5% per degree decrease in temperature. For very small diameter vessels, the apparent viscosity of blood also decreases as the vessel diameter decreases. This effect is the result of the blood composition changing distribution when flowing in high resistance vessels. In essence, the formed elements tend to congregate in the center stream decreasing interaction with the vessel walls. The plasma which has a lower "viscosity" than whole blood tends to flow along the surface of the vessel walls. This redistribution of blood components thereby decreases the energy lost to frictional effects (shear stress), further decreasing the viscosity. As a result, the term "apparent viscosity" is frequently used to refer to the resistance blood offers to flowing. As already mentioned in Section 2, more viscous energy losses result than are accounted for by the Bernoulli equation.

2.4.6 The Assumption: No Turbulence (and Reynold's Number)

The equation developed by Jean Poiseuille relating the volumetric flow with the pressure gradient was predicated on laminar flow profiles. In the presence of turbulence, there are greater energy losses that are not addressed. Whereas the pressure gradient is expressed as proportional to the volumetric flow by Poiseuille's law (and the simplified law), in the presence of turbulence, the pressure gradient is related non-linearly and is more accurately approximated by a square relationship. In other words, in the presence of significant turbulence, the pressure drop measured by the simplified Bernoulli's equation will underestimate the true energy loss.

3. Pressure, Flow, and Resistance in the Cardiovascular System (The Simplified Law)

3.1 Overview

It is always instructive to begin with a simple understanding of the overall objective of a system, even if greatly simplified. The fundamental purpose of the cardiovascular system is to meet the metabolic demand of all end organs in the body by supplying adequate oxygenated blood volume (perfusion) and return for removal of wastes and re-oxygenation. To perform this function, the cardiovascular system is actually comprised of many "subsystems", each which has distinct properties and distinct roles. Specifically, at the very highest level, the cardiovascular system consists of a pumping system (left-sided heart), the arterial system, the venous system, the right-sided heart, and the lungs. Of course it is possible to also consider other interacting subsystems such as sympathetic and parasympathetic regulation, but these topics are outside the scope and purpose of this text.

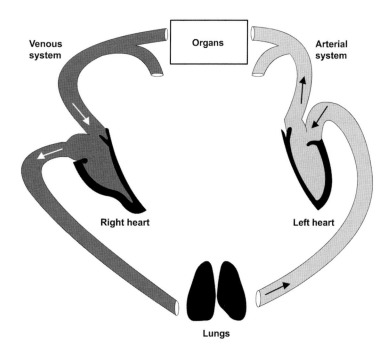

Fig. 14 **Cardiovascular System**

Notice that this system is really two pumps in parallel with a series connection. In other words, the left and right heart really act as two distinct pumps running side–by-side, with the output of each pumping system eventually becoming the input of the other pumping system. Presuming an intact, healthy system, over short periods of time, the volume within the system is fixed, with no new input or output. As a result, this type of system which cannot change its volume is referred to as a "closed" system. Of course, over longer periods of time, the volume can vary with fluid absorption (and dehydration) and blood cell production.

3.2 Left Heart
The left heart is discussed in Vol. II, Appendix B: Cardiovascular Principles, but for the purpose of continuity, a brief preview is included here.

The function of the left heart is to provide the energy necessary to overcome the peripheral resistance so as to perfuse the end organs. As blood enters the left ventricle, there is a gradual increase in pressure until the phase of isovolumic contraction occurs. With the valves closed, the contraction of the left ventricle (LV) rapidly increases the pressure, eventually increasing the pressure beyond the residual pressure in the aorta. With a pressure gradient across the aortic valve, the aortic valve opens allowing blood to flow into the aorta. It is important to note that although blood is flowing into the aorta, in the early stage, with contraction, the pressure in the LV is still increasing faster than the rate of pressure increase in the aorta, maintaining forward flow. Eventually, as the volume increases in the aorta and decreases in the ventricle, the forward flow decreases and then reverses. During the flow reversal, the aortic valve closes. At this point the arterial system is now responsible for propelling the blood forward to the periphery.

3.3 The Arterial System

3.3.1 Flow and Pressure in the Aorta

Even though blood is flowing out of the aorta into the large arteries, the rate of inflow from the high pressure LV is higher than the outflow rate into the large arteries, leading to volume increase in the aorta. Therefore, as forward flow is ejected into the aorta, the pressure in the aorta begins to increase, mirroring the pressure in the left ventricle. The rate at which the volume increases with respect to the change in pressure is defined as the aortic compliance. The rate at which the volume changes per time, is termed the capacitance. As discussed earlier, the capacitance is generally related to the compliance such that a greater compliance results in a greater capacitance. Presuming a healthy, compliant aorta, it is the capacitance which determines how much volume can be stored in the aorta for expulsion in the diastolic phase.

As the volume in the aorta begins to rise, the vessel walls are stretched, increasing the tension in the vessel walls, decreasing the residual compliance. As more and more volume is added, the rate of pressure increase is faster and faster with less and less volume added. Eventually, the pressure in the aorta begins to rise faster than the pressure in the LV, slowing the forward flow and eventually leading to the flow reversal responsible for closure for the aortic valve. The increase in volume into the aorta is also critical since some of the energy is stored in tension (potential energy) in the vessel walls. This energy helps propel the blood flow forward during diastole once the aortic valve is closed. Therefore, the compliance and capacitance are critical for appropriate functioning of both the left-sided heart and the arterial system.

3.3.2 Arterial Vessel Sizes

Figure 15 shows the relative sizes of the vessels which comprise the cardiovascular system. On the arterial side notice how the vessel radii progressively reduce from the large radius of the aorta to the very small radii of the capillaries.

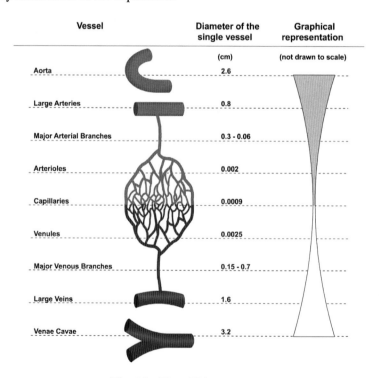

Vessel		Diameter of the single vessel	Graphical representation
		(cm)	(not drawn to scale)
Aorta		2.6	
Large Arteries		0.8	
Major Arterial Branches		0.3 - 0.06	
Arterioles		0.002	
Capillaries		0.0009	
Venules		0.0025	
Major Venous Branches		0.15 - 0.7	
Large Veins		1.6	
Venae Cavae		3.2	

Fig. 15 **Vessel Diameters**

Pegasus Lectures, Inc.

To determine how the pressure will change across the various levels of the arterial system, we will need to consider the effective resistances of each level.

3.3.3 Resistance in the Arterial System

As we have already learned, the total effective resistance of a series combination of vessels is a simple addition of the individual resistances. For blood flow in the body, the effective resistance is really the series combination of many parallel resistive systems. This fact is illustrated in *Figure 16*.

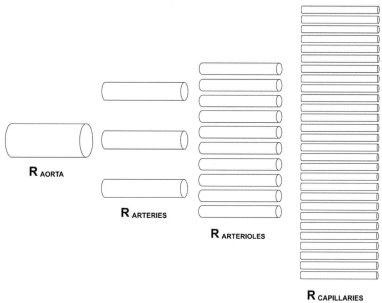

Fig. 16   **Complex Resistance Network of the Arterial System**

Notice how the effective resistance of the entire arterial system is really the series resistance of the resistance of the aorta, the effective resistance of the arteries, the effective resistance of the arterioles and the effective resistance of the capillaries. However, since there are multiple arteries in parallel, the effective resistance at the level of the arteries is determined inversely as the sum of each individual artery. Similarly, the effective resistance of the arterioles and of the capillaries is calculated as the parallel combination of each individual arteriole and the parallel combination of each individual capillary, respectively.

3.3.4 Volumetric Demand and Vascular Bed Resistance

So far, we have discussed the effective resistance as a control mechanism to meet the requirement of the system as a whole. Since not all end organs have the same demand, the cardiac output must be distributed in nonuniform percentages. The control of volume shunting is through the relative resistances of the vascular beds feeding each organ. Organs with high volumetric demands, such as the brain, have low resistance vascular beds. Organs with low volumetric demands, like the face and scalp, have higher resistance beds.

3.3.5 Effective Resistances in the Arterial System

Making some assumptions about the size and numbers of vessels in parallel, the relative effective resistance of the entire cardiovascular system was calculated and plotted in the following graphs. The resistances were referenced to the resistance of the aorta, so that a value of 1 implies that the effective resistance is equal to the resistance of the aorta. A value less than 1 implies that the resistance is less than the resistance of the aorta. Clearly, a value greater than 1 implies a resistance higher than the aorta. You will note that the data for the graph in *Figure 17* is the same as the data in *Figure 18*, but *Figure 17* is a linear display whereas *Figure 18* is a logarithmic display.

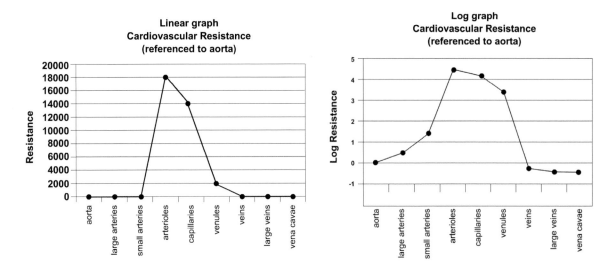

Fig. 17 **Relative Resistances (linear display)**   *Fig. 18* **Relative Resistances (log display)**

3.3.6 Flow and Pressure in the Arteries

The overall resistance changes very little from the low resistance aorta to the large arteries. Although this may seem counter-intuitive since the radius of the aorta is fairly large in comparison to the large arteries, you must realize that there are multiple large arteries in parallel such that the total flow is distributed. As a result, the effective resistance is still low, and there is little if any pressure drop recorded across the major arteries.

3.3.7 Flow and Pressure in the Arterioles

At the level of the arterioles, the radius is significantly decreased relative to the arteries, causing a significant increase in resistance for each individual arteriole. Although there are significantly more arterioles than major arteries (as in Example 3, illustrated by *Figure 8*), the parallel combination of these arterioles still results in a much higher resistance than the resistance of the aorta or the effective resistance of the large arteries (about 18,000 times higher). As a result of this extremely high resistance, the arterioles are referred to as the resistive component of the cardiovascular system. Because of this high effective resistance, there is a significant pressure drop across the arterioles.

3.3.8 Flow and Pressure in the Capillaries

As seen in *Figure 17*, like the arterioles, the capillaries are also highly resistive. The parallel resistance of the capillaries is lower than the effective resistance of the arterioles but still significantly higher than the resistance of the aorta or the effective resistance of the arteries. As a result, there is a further dramatic decrease in the pressure with flow across the capillaries.

3.4 Venous System

3.4.1 Relative Vessel Sizes

Referring to *Figure 15,* notice how the radius progressively increases from the very small caliber venules to the very large radius vena cava. Although the basic behavior appears to mirror the relative change in vessel sizes on the arterial side (just in reverse direction) there is one critical difference; the pressure on the venous side is significantly less than the pressure on the arterial side, and hence, there can be no significant pressure drop across the smaller caliber venules as occurs across the arterioles.

3.4.2 Resistance of the Venules

Referring to the relative resistance plots of *Figure 17* and *Figure 18,* it is clear that the effective resistance of the venules is much lower than the resistance of the arterioles and capillaries, but still relatively high with respect to the resistance for the aorta. As just mentioned, this fact is important since the pressure on the venous side is already much lower than the pressure on the arterial side. If the effective resistance of the arterioles were too high at the level of the venules, there would not be enough energy in the system to overcome the total peripheral resistance.

3.4.3 Resistance of the Veins and the Vena Cava

Again referring to *Figures 17 and 18,* once the flow proceeds from the venules into the veins and the vena cava, the effective resistances drop precipitously, dropping below the resistance of the aorta. This dramatic decrease in resistance is critical since there is very little pressure left to drive the fluid back to the right atrium. In essence, even a little resistance becomes problematic since the pressure in the venous system is so low.

3.5 Right Heart

The right heart is discussed in Vol. II, Appendix B: Cardiovascular Principles, but as with the left heart, for purpose of continuity, a brief preview is included here.

The function of the right heart is to provide the energy necessary to overcome the resistance of the pulmonary bed so as to oxygenate the oxygen depleted blood. As blood enters the right atrium through the vena cava, the pressure is very low. During the filling phase of the right atrium, the tricuspid valve to the right ventricle is closed. As the volume increases in the normal right atrium, the pressure increases and eventually exceeds the pressure in the relaxed right ventricle. As a result of the pressure gradient, the tricuspid valve is pushed open and rapid flow from the right atrium to the right ventricle occurs. With electrical stimulation, the atrium contracts, providing what is commonly referred to as the "atrial kick."

Eventually, the increasing pressure in the ventricle exceeds the decreasing pressure in the atrium and backflow occurs which results in tricuspid valve closure. During the ventricular filling phase, it is important to note that since the pressure in the right ventricle is below the residual pressure in the pulmonary artery, the pulmonic valve (between the right ventricle and the pulmonary artery) is closed. With ventricular contraction, with both the tricuspid valve and the pulmonic valve closed, the pressure in the ventricle increases rapidly (isovolumic contraction).

Once the pressure rises above the residual pressure in the pulmonary artery, the pulmonic valve is opened and rapid flow from the right ventricle into the pulmonary artery occurs. Just as occurs with the aorta, with increasing volume into the pulmonary artery, the pressure in the pulmonary artery eventually exceeds the pressure in the right ventricle and flow reversal occurs resulting in the closing of the pulmonic valve.

3.6 The Lungs

The transport mechanism for oxygen (O_2) to blood is the mechanical process of diffusion. Diffusion occurs from a higher O_2 concentration to a lower O_2 concentration. The blood returned to the right side of the heart is oxygen depleted and hence, has a low O_2 concentration. The pulmonary artery eventually branches down to the pulmonary capillaries which surround alveoli. In a healthy person the O_2 concentration in the alveoli is higher than the concentration in the blood, so that the oxygen diffuses through the membrane separating the air from the blood.

3.7 Return to the Left-Sided Heart

Oxygenated blood flow from the pulmonary bed is returned to the left atrium via the pulmonary veins. As with the right-sided system, even as the volume increases in the left atrium, the pressure increase is not too dramatic since the normal atrium is highly capacitive. Once the pressure in the left atrium does exceed the pressure in the relaxed left ventricle, the mitral valve opens and rapid filling of the ventricle occurs. At this point, the cycle (as described above) repeats.

4. The Healthy Cardiovascular System as a Whole

4.1 Velocity Versus Cross-Sectional Area

One of the most striking features of the cardiovascular system is how the velocity can decelerate from close to 1 m/sec at the aorta down to approximately 1 mm/sec at the level of the capillaries, and then accelerate back to close to 1 m/sec in the vena cavae. The mechanism that controls this acceleration and deceleration is predicted by the continuity equation. Since the cardiovascular system is closed, we know that all of the volume through the capillaries is the same as the volume through the aorta (cardiac output). Therefore, we can set up a simple relationship between the velocity and area of the aorta with the total cross-sectional area of the capillaries to determine the velocity of the flow through the capillaries.

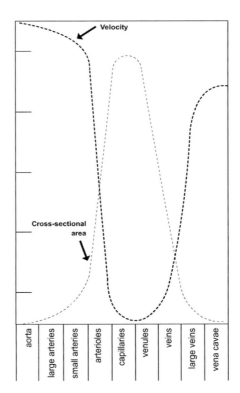

Fig. 19
**Velocity Versus Total
Cross-Sectional Area**

$$Q_{Ao} = Q_{cap}$$

$$v_{Ao} \times area_{Ao} = v_{cap} \times area_{cap}$$

Assuming the aortic area to be approximately 4 cm², the aortic velocity to be about 1 m/sec, and the velocity at the capillaries to be about 1 mm/sec, the total cross-sectional area of the capillaries is calculated as:

$$\frac{v_{Ao} \times area_{Ao}}{v_{cap}} = \frac{1\frac{m}{sec} \times 4\ cm^2}{0.001\frac{m}{sec}} = area_{cap}$$

and the total cross-sectional area of the capillaries is:

$$area_{cap} = 4,000\ cm^2.$$

Of course, as the blood flows across the venous system, the opposite situation occurs such that the total cross-sectional area reduces and the velocity accelerates back to the right atrium. Since the vena cavae has a slightly larger cross-sectional area than the aorta, we would then expect the velocity in the vena cavae to be slightly lower than the velocity in the aorta.

4.2 Pressure Changes Across the Arterial System

4.2.1 Overview
Referring to *Figure 20*, you should notice some dramatic characteristics of the pressure wave-form across the cardiovascular system:

1) The pulse pressure increases slightly from the aorta to the small arteries (the mean changes very little).
2) The pulsatility is highly damped at the level of the arterioles.
3) A very rapid pressure drop occurs at the arterioles.
4) There is still a significant pressure drop across the capillaries.
5) The pressures in the venous side are very low and relatively "steady-state."

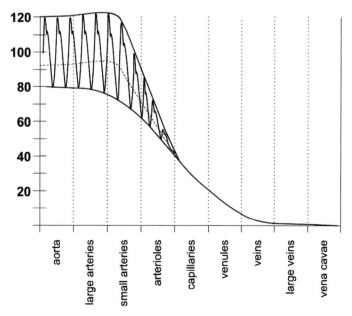

Fig. 20   **Pressure Through the CV Systems**

4.2.2 Increasing Pulse Pressure

Recall that the resistance is inversely related to the radius to the fourth power. Since the radii of healthy large arteries (and even the proximal end of healthy small arteries) are large, the resistance is very low. From the simplified law, we know that a low resistance results in very little pressure loss. In fact, in some patients the pulse pressure actually increases progressing from the aorta through the large arteries (*Figure 20*).

This increase in pulse pressure is perfectly normal although it does not always occur. As rapid ejection of blood occurs into the aorta, a pressure wave propagates down the arterial tree. The amplitude of the pressure wave depends on many parameters including the left ventricular stroke volume, the compliance of the aorta, the peripheral resistance, and the compliance of the arterial walls. In general, an increase in stroke volume, and an increase in peripheral resistance will result in a higher amplitude wave. Conversely, an increase in the compliance of the aorta, or an increase in the compliance of the arterial walls results in a decrease in the pressure amplitude. It should not be surprising that if a larger volume is ejected, a larger pressure waveform results. To understand how the compliance affects the pressure amplitude we must consider how the compliance changes within the normal arterial system.

Recall that a healthy aorta is very compliant so as to accept the high stroke volume of the left ventricle. In the more distal arteries, since the vessel walls are less compliant than the aorta, when a large volume is injected, the pressure rises more rapidly across the vessel walls. The result is a slight increase in the peak pressure. From the conservation of energy theorem (and Bernoulli's equation) we know that the slight increase in radial pressure across the wall came from a slight decrease in the kinetic energy. With age, the compliance of the vessel walls decreases, increasing systemic peak and pulse pressures.

An interesting note is that the changing arterial stiffness actually plays another role. As we learned in Chapter 2, waves travel faster as the stiffness increases. Therefore, since the stiffness of the arterial walls increases with distance from the aorta, the pressure wave accelerates as it travels from the aorta toward the periphery. The gradual increasing taper of resistance acts similarly to the idea of an impedance matching technique. Imagine if the arteries leading to the highly resistive arterioles were very compliant. At the juncture from the small arteries to the arterioles there would be a very large pressure wave reflection, decreasing the arterial efficiency. Instead, by gradually decreasing the capacitance, no large mismatch occurs and the reflected wave amplitude is reduced. An important note: Doppler waveforms, Doppler spectrums, and pulse volume recordings (PVRs), do not measure pressure. There is often confusion regarding this point since both velocity, as measured by Doppler, and pulse volume, as measured by PVRs, are related to pressure and changes in pressure. A higher peak pressure in a particular arterial segment does not necessarily imply a higher peak velocity in that arterial segment relative to another segment. The pressure is only one of the variables that determines velocity. Similarly, a high peak pressure in a particular arterial segment does not necessarily imply a higher volume in that segment relative to other arterial segments. Again the pressure is only one of the variables that determines volume.

4.2.3 Decrease in Pulsatility and Pressure Drop

At the level of the capillaries, metabolic exchange occurs through the mechanical process of diffusion. As a mechanical process, diffusion requires adequate time for nutrient and waste exchange across cell membranes. By increasing the total cross-sectional area, the velocity is decreased so as to accommodate exchange. Additionally, high pressure cannot be tolerated in the small capillaries so the pressure must be decreased. The resistance of the arterioles is the primary mechanism for controlling this pressure. From an efficiency standpoint, it would be best to allow diffusion to occur continuously, and not just at peak pressure times. The high resistance of the arterioles also meets this need by damping the pulse pressure. This concept is less foreign to you than you might think. If you put your "resistive hand" on something that is vibrating, the vibrations become damped, decreasing the peaks.

4.2.4 Pressure Drop Across the Capillaries
Since the capillaries must be small to accommodate the intimate contact necessary for diffusion, the resistance of each individual capillary is very high. Collectively, the large total cross-sectional area makes it possible to maintain the volumetric flow without increasing the velocity (a fundamental necessity for diffusion to occur). As the blood flows across the resistive capillaries, there is, not surprisingly, a further decrease in pressure.

4.2.5 Pressures in the Venous Side are Low
The fact that the venous pressures are low is the theme of the very next topic, so please continue reading.

4.3 The Venous System

4.3.1 Dichotomizing the Cardiovascular System
Although the cardiovascular system is one closed system, it is instructive to consider it as two subsystems in series. To this point, the focus has been on the arterial subsystem and the ability to meet metabolic demand. No less important is the role of the venous system. Adequate volume must be returned to the right-sided heart for oxygenation and for the left-sided heart to have volume to pump. The major parameters affecting the venous subsystem are:

1) The heart's pumping action and dynamic pressure
2) Venous capacitance
3) Hydrostatic pressure
4) Calf muscle pump
5) Transthoracic and abdominal pressure related changes (gradients) resulting from inspiration/expiration
6) Venous resistance and transmural pressure

We will now discuss each parameter in some detail.

4.3.2 Venous Pressure
Referring to *Figure 20*, you will notice that the dynamic pressure continues to decrease, transitioning from the capillaries to the venules to the veins. At the extremities, typical venous pressures are approximately 15 mmHg. For a healthy individual, the pressure in the right atrium varies cyclically, and commonly has a mean between 2 mmHg and 8 mmHg. Typical venous pressures and right atrial pressures when considered together imply that there is only about 10 mmHg dynamic pressure to drive venous return. As a result, the resistance, the capacitance, and the muscular control of the venous system will be very different than the corresponding parameters for the arterial side.

4.3.3 Venous Capacitance and Circulatory Pressure

The venous system is referred to as the "high capacitance" element of the cardiovascular (CV) system. We have already seen that the capacitance of the aorta, and to a decreasing extent the major arteries, plays a major role in arterial blood flow. Progressing from the high capacitance aorta, through the main arteries, to the arterioles, the capacitance significantly decreases. Transitioning from the arterial to the venous side, the capacitance increases significantly such that at rest, approximately 65% to 70% of the blood volume resides in the venous system (veins and venules). This capacitance is critical for two reasons:

- The capacitance of the venous system acts as a reservoir to supply volume under higher demand.
- Control of venovasomotor tone (changing the capacitance) becomes the principal regulator of mean arterial pressure.

Increased venovasomotor tone results in a decrease in capacitance. Since there is a large volume of blood in the veins, the venoconstriction acts as a pump, decreasing the "stored" volume. The decrease in volume stored in the veins results in an increase of volume returned to the heart, leading to an increase in cardiac output. The pressure volume relationship dictates that an increase in cardiac volume results in an increase in systemic pressure. Therefore, increasing the venovasomotor tone results in an increase in the mean circulatory pressure. In other words, the capacitance of the venous system provides a mechanism to control mean circulatory pressure.

4.3.4 Hydrostatic Pressure

When discussing Bernoulli's equation, we developed a simplified form, but also discussed a more complete form which included the concept of hydrostatic pressure. In Chapter 12, we learned that the hydrostatic pressure is related to the height of the fluid column, the density of the fluid, and the force of gravity. For blood, the hydrostatic pressure is approximately 2 mmHg per inch. For a standing patient, the hydrostatic pressure is lowest at the top of the head and maximal at the feet. If the patient lies down, the "column" of blood throughout the body is at approximately the same height throughout the body and the hydrostatic pressure goes to zero. To assist in overcoming the effects of gravity on venous return from the legs, an ingenious pumping system exists, discussed in the next section.

Referring to *Figure 21*, clearly, for a standing patient, the hydrostatic pressure is 0 mmHg at the top of the head and highest at the feet. The hydrostatic pressure in the right atrium is clearly higher than 0 mmHg but lower than the pressure in the feet. However, we will artificially choose the right atrium (RA) as the "reference" for hydrostatic pressure and claim that the pressure at the level of the right atrium is 0 mmHg. For this convention to make physical sense, the pressure in the head must be lower than 0 (negative), while the pressure below the atrium is still positive, just not as large a positive number. This convention makes pressure measurements more convenient so that central pressures do not need to be adjusted for a patient's height. The other benefit is that in the sitting position, the brachial artery is approximately at the same level as the RA. Therefore, by making the RA the reference for hydrostatic pressure, pressures in the brachial artery (which have the same hydrostatic pressure as the RA) can be used to approximate systemic pressures.

The following table gives the blood volume distribution in the cardiovascular system of a patient at rest.

- 65-70% in the veins and venules
- 10-12% in the systemic arteries
- 5% in the heart
- 5% in the pulmonary veins
- 5% in the systemic capillaries
- 4% in pulmonary capillaries
- 3% in pulmonary arteries

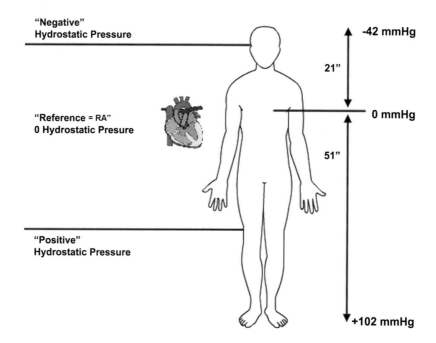

Fig. 21 **Reference for Hydrostatic Pressure**

Hydrostatic pressure will increase with distance (height). Recall that in the supine position the dynamic venous pressure at the level of the ankles is approximately 15 mmHg. Changing to an upright position will add approximately 102 mmHg of hydrostatic pressure (for a six-foot tall person) yielding a total venous pressure of approximately 117 mmHg. For quick calculations you can assume that every inch is equivalent to almost 2 mmHg (*Figure 21*).

4.3.5 The Calf Muscle Pump
Venous return from the legs in a prone position requires less energy than from a standing position. This should be clear since venous return while standing requires overcoming hydrostatic (gravitational) pressures. Since we can't always be lying down, the calf muscle pump mechanism aids in venous return. The calf muscle pump mechanism consists of

- Deep and superficial veins of the lower legs
- Contracting leg muscles
- Fascial compartments (venous sinusoids)
- Venous valves

Muscular contraction compresses the intramuscular veins and surrounding superficial veins, raising venous pressure and facilitating blood flow cephalad toward the heart. The venous valves close, preventing retrograde flow. The presence of venous valves segments the venous flow into short columns, which diminish the effect of hydrostatic pressure. In patients with venous insufficiency, incompetent valves permit blood to reflux down the leg, filling the veins and limiting the amount of blood propelled toward the heart with each muscular contraction. As venous hypertension increases, the calf muscle pump is unable to adequately empty the veins to reduce the venous pressure to the normal state, thereby increasing the rate of edema formation in the lower extremities.

We will consider venous return in three different states:

1) **At rest (prone or supine position)**
   As already stated, less energy is required for venous return in the prone position than standing. Flow will persist from the legs to the right atrium as long as the pressure continually decreases from the legs to the atrium. As discussed in the upcoming Section 4.3.6, intra-abdominal pressure changes occur with respiration. As this pressure increases, volumetric flow will decrease. If the intra-abdominal pressure exceeds venous pressure in the legs, flow will cease. As expiration decreases intra-abdominal pressure, venous flow will again increase.

2) **Muscle contraction**
   As the muscle contracts, the increased tissue pressures act to reduce venous capacitance. The veins therefore act like blood reservoirs, increasing and decreasing holding volume. With muscle contraction, the increase in pressure causes the valves to open, allowing blood to flow toward the right atrium. With closure, the valves act as a check valve, restricting venous reflux in response to gravity.

3) **Muscle relaxation**
   Muscle relaxation decreases the intravascular pressure, thereby decreasing venous flow.

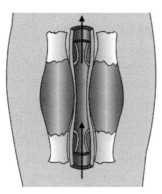   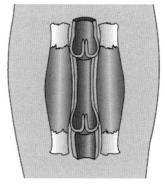

Muscular Contraction   Muscular Relaxation

Fig. 22   **The Calf Muscle Pump**

4.3.6 Respiration Related Changes

Venous return is affected by pressure changes which result from inspiration and expiration. Intrathoracic and intra-abdominal pressure changes occur as the diaphragm distends and contracts to aid in inspiration and expiration. The normal lower extremity venous signal decreases with inspiration and increases with expiration.

During inspiration: Diaphragm descends
Increased intra-abdominal pressure
Decreased intrathoracic pressure
Inferior vena cava is compressed
Venous flow from legs is impeded
Increase in flow from the abdomen to the thorax
Increase in flow from the upper extremities to the thorax

During expiration: Diaphragm rises
Decreased intra-abdominal pressure
Increased intrathoracic pressure
Pressure on vena cava is released
Blood in legs flows cephalad to fill veins
Decrease in flow from the abdomen to the thorax
Decrease in flow from the upper extremities to the thorax

4.3.7 Venous Resistance and Transmural Pressure

In general, the walls of venous vessels are much thinner and far more elastic than the arterial vessels. (This is a simplified explanation of why veins are very distensible and possess a great capacity to hold large volumes of blood). As we already know, if the veins expand, resistance to flow decreases. Since the vessels are very elastic they can increase diameter by an increase in intravascular pressure, or decrease diameter by an increase in surrounding tissue pressure. The difference between the intravascular pressure and the surrounding tissue pressure is known as the transmural (across the "vessel" wall) pressure.

The transmural pressure is always referenced from the inside of the vessel through the vessel wall. Therefore, when the intravascular pressure exceeds the surrounding tissue pressure, the transmural pressure increases, implying that the vessel distends. When the tissue pressure exceeds the intravascular pressure, the transmural pressure is considered low, and the vessel "collapses" into a "flattened" or "dumbbell" shape. *Figures 23 and 24* demonstrate high and low transmural pressure.

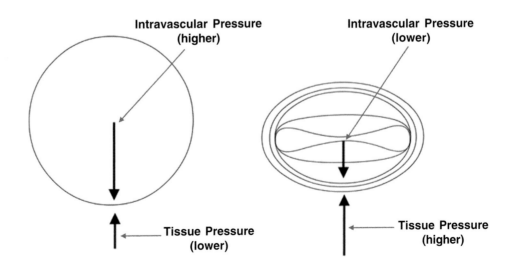

Intravascular Pressure (higher)

Intravascular Pressure (lower)

Tissue Pressure (lower)

Tissue Pressure (higher)

Fig. 23 **High Transmural Pressure**   *Fig. 24* **Low Transmural Pressure**

The concept of transmural pressure is important for at least two reasons. First, in the presence of artificially induced low transmural pressure, venous signals will disappear. As a result, you must be very careful when performing a venous study not to allow patient positioning or muscle tension to cause a low transmural pressure. Second, a blood pressure cuff measurement essentially creates a negative transmural pressure and a calibrated increase of the transmural pressure to detect the intravascular pressure.

Note: The important point to remember is that the reference point for a transmural pressure measurement is the inside of the vessel looking out. In other words, if the pressure inside is higher than the pressure outside the vessel, the transmural pressure is considered to be positive. This reference was arbitrary. However, the vascular field standardized by referencing from the inside out, so you must remember this fact.

4.3.8 When Things Go Wrong: Effects of Edema

Most venous thrombi are small and have little physiologic impact. However, when venous obstruction is more extensive, peripheral venous pressure increases, which can lead to venous congestion and peripheral edema. In the presence of venous obstruction the venous resistance increases. The severity of elevation in venous resistance depends on the location and length of the obstructed venous segment as well as the number of veins involved and the presence and/or development of collateral vessels. The elevation of venous resistance (venous hypertension) can be caused by venous obstruction, venous reflux, or a combination of both. Normally, pressure in the capillaries exceeds that in the veins and venules. In the presence of chronic venous insufficiency the capillary venous pressure increases, disrupting the balance of intravascular and interstitial fluid and osmotic pressure. Fluid passes through the capillary walls at an increased rate and edema occurs. The increased capillary permeability and increased intravascular pressure in the capillaries permits protein-rich fluids and red blood cells to transfer into the subcutaneous tissues causing fibrosis and hyperpigmentation. Venous stasis changes such as hyperpigmentation, induration, and ulceration are generally concentrated on the medial aspect of lower leg just above and posterior to the medial malleolus.

Causes of peripheral edema may include:

- Increased intravascular pressure in the capillaries
- Decreased plasma proteins
- Lymphatic obstruction
- Increased capillary permeability

Poor transference of metabolites and metabolic waste products between capillaries and cells can result in:

- Chronic impairment to skin perfusion
- Stasis dermatitis
- Ulcerations

5. The Subcritical Diseased Cardiovascular System at Rest

5.1 Asymptomatic Patients

It is possible for a patient to have diseased vasculature and still be asymptomatic. Given that we now understand many of the parameters of the hemodynamic system, we can easily understand how disease can be present with potentially no signs present. The simple answer is compensation.

The cardiovascular system has a tremendous compensatory ability. For a healthy system under exercise, the cardiac output will typically increase from about 5 liters/minute to as much as 20 liters/minute for a trained athlete. There are many mechanisms involved in compensating for induced stresses on the system, whether the stress is an increased volumetric demand due to exercise or a pressure loss associated with disease. In the presence of disease, it is possible that the energy losses for normal metabolic demand are minimal enough such that no significant hemodynamic change occurs.

With progressive worsening, it is still possible that no symptoms may occur, as long as there is adequate compensation in the system such that the metabolic demand is met (adequate perfusion). It is only when the compensatory mechanisms are not able to meet the metabolic demand that symptoms are commonly experienced. To understand how this works, we will return to our simplified equations and our understanding of hemodynamics. Let's presume that there is a low percentage stenosis in a large artery as depicted in *Figure 25* below. Under normal situations, there should be no pressure drop across the artery because of the extremely low resistance. (Recall that from the simplified law: $\Delta P = Q \cdot R$, so for a very low resistance there is very little pressure change.) In this case, even though there is a narrowing in the large vessel, since the residual radius is still very large, the resistance remains very low. Furthermore, since the cross-sectional area is still very large, the velocity will not change appreciably. As a result, very little energy is converted to kinetic energy, and very little energy is lost to frictional and viscous effects, such that the pressure gradient will be negligible.

If there is negligible pressure loss across the stenosis, then the total energy in the system distal to the stenosis remains approximately equal to the energy proximal to the stenosis. If the total energy in the system is little changed, then the distal vascular beds will be adequately perfused and the patient will be asymptomatic

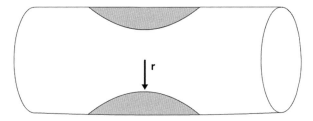

Fig. 25   **Residual Radius with Disease**

With increasing percentage stenosis, as the radius and area decrease, the velocity increases so that the volumetric flow is maintained, as predicted by the continuity equation $Q = \bar{v} \times area$. In other words, if the area decreases, the average velocity must increase to maintain the same volumetric flow. As already discussed, an increase in velocity represents an increase in the kinetic energy and a decrease in the potential energy. Since the ideal conditions assumed in the fluid dynamics chapter are not met, the increase in kinetic energy indicates that there will be greater frictional and viscous losses to heat than occurs in the lower kinetic energy state of a healthy vessel. As a result, the total energy distal to the stenosis will be lower than normal, requiring the system to compensate to still meet the metabolic demand. The diagram of *Figure 26*, depicts how there would be inadequate perfusion pressure if there were no compensatory changes for the pressure loss associated with arterial vessel disease.

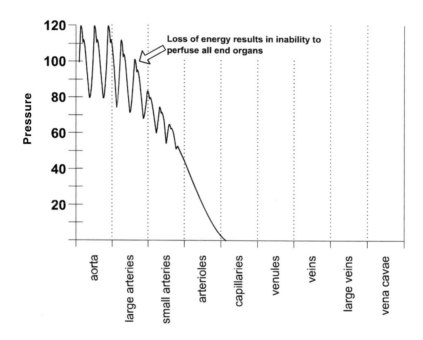

Fig. 26   **Diseased Arteries (If There Were No Arteriole Compensation)**

Fortunately *Figure 26* does not represent reality, for most patients.

When disease is present in the large arteries, the overall pressure in the large arteries is lower than normal, and the arterioles will dilate, decreasing the effective resistance. The decrease in resistance of the normally highly resistive arterioles allows for the same volume of flow as in a healthy vascular system, with less associated pressure loss. In essence, the muscular control of the arterioles is the principal mechanism to regulate the effective resistance. By regulating the resistance of the arterioles, the overall serial resistance remains constant, even in the presence of increased resistance in the normally low resistance large vessels. The arteriole compensation therefore effectively lowers the energy losses adequately to still perfuse the end organ, and the patient remains asymptomatic. *Figure 27* demonstrates how the decrease in pressure across the arteriole from arteriole vasodilation compensates for the proximal pressure loss.

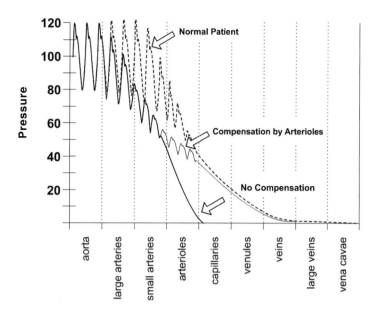

Fig. 27   **Normal versus Diseased Arteries with Adequate Compensation**

The following diagram of *Figure 28* demonstrates why patients with severe peripheral arterial disease who have already progressed through maximal vasodilation experience rest pain. As indicated, even though the arterioles vasodilate, there is inadequate compensation for the proximal energy losses.

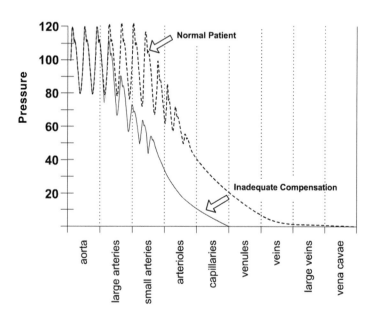

Fig. 28   **Normal versus Diseased Arteries with Inadequate Compensation**

5.2 Asymptomatic Patients with Exercise (Unmasking a Subcritical Stenosis)

Under normal metabolic demand, since the end organ was adequately perfused with the patient at rest, the patient remained asymptomatic. Even though there was disease present, the energy losses in providing the volumetric flow to meet the normal metabolic demand were either negligible, or still small enough to be adequately compensated by the arteriole vasodilation.

In the state of exercise, the metabolic demand significantly increases, leading to an increase in volumetric flow. The volumetric flow increases potentially as much as fourfold or even more. In a healthy patient, the increase in demand is met through a whole series of changes such as increased heart rate, increased stroke volume, slight increase in pressure, preferential shunting away from noncritical organs, arteriole dilation, collateral capillaries, and venous constriction. In combination, these compensation mechanisms are able to meet the significantly increased demand, such that the patient does not experience symptoms of pain. However, in the presence of subcritical disease, the onset of exercise often results in pain commonly referred to as claudication, thereby exposing the presence of disease.

To understand the reasons for the associated pain with exercise, we must again refer back to our simplified equations. According to the simplified law of hemodynamics, for a fixed resistance, an increase in flow volume results in an increase in kinetic energy. Under normal situations, since the arteries are very large, and relatively compliant, any increase in energy loss which results from an increased flow volume could be compensated by the arterioles. This situation is depicted in *Figure 29*.

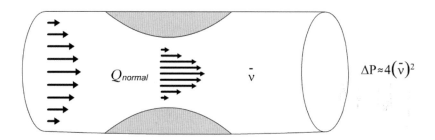

Fig. 29 **Pressure Gradient with Normal Volumetric Demand**

In the presence of disease in the artery, the increased demand results in a significant increase in velocity and kinetic energy. As depicted in *Figure 30*, the fourfold increase in volumetric flow results in a fourfold increase in the mean velocity and a sixteen –fold increase in the kinetic energy term, presuming the full volume is maintained. This increased velocity causes much greater energy losses and potentially very turbulent distal flow. The Bernoulli equation presumed that all of the increased kinetic energy would be converted back to potential energy since the friction, viscosity, and turbulence were ignored. In contrast, the real-world situation leads to significant energy losses from these frictional terms such that the arterioles are not able to adequately compensate and the increased metabolic demand cannot be met.

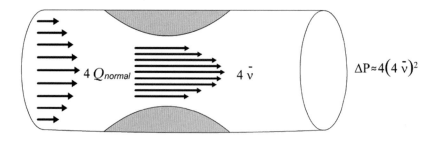

Fig. 30 **Sixteen-fold Increase in Pressure Gradient with Four-fold Increase in Volume**

When the increased demand is not met, a state of ischemia develops which ultimately leads to pain, otherwise referred to as claudication. Since the pain is intense, the patient is usually forced to cease activity, returning volumetric flow back to baseline. After a period of time, the ischemic tissue is re-perfused and the pain diminishes and then completely abates. This explains why, in differentiating vascular claudication from neurogenic or musculoskeletal claudication, the following criteria must be met:

1) Pain (usually muscle cramps in the thigh, buttock or calf) presents after walking a *predictable* distance
2) Pain is relieved by resting a *predictable* period of time
3) The symptoms are *reproducible*

5.3 Symptomatic Patients and Critical Stenoses

The process of unmasking a stenosis is necessary for patients who are asymptomatic at rest. In comparison, if the stenosis becomes more severe, the patient will begin to show persistent signs of disease. In these cases, the problem is quite clear, the disease has become severe enough that even under the normal metabolic demands, there is not enough compensation in the system to compensate for the energy losses across so significant a lesion.

Figure 31 depicts the transitional stage from maintained volumetric flow to decreased volumetric flow. In the presence of significant narrowing, the velocity in the center stream is very high, but the majority of the flow is traveling at a much lower velocity. With progression of disease, the volumetric flow and velocity decrease precipitously resulting in a condition referred to as "string" flow, as there is only a "string" of flow making it through the highly resistive narrowing (as discussed in Section 2.4.4).

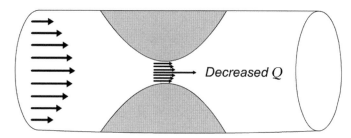

Fig. 31 **Flow Profile for Transitional Stage from Maintained Volumetric Flow**

Any further narrowing past this point results in a precipitous drop in the peak velocity, and clearly insufficient volumetric flow. The following graph depicts how the velocity varies with the percent reduction in cross-sectional area for a large vessel.

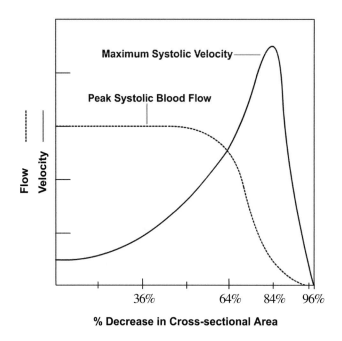

Fig. 32 **Velocity and Flow Changes with Percentage Stenosis**

As is easily imagined, in these critical states of disease, ischemia of the end organ is persistent, eventually leading to tissue necrosis unless collateral flow is developed. It is important to realize that even when there is adequate perfusion through collateralization, the resistance through the collateral pathway is always higher than the resistance through the normal, healthy pathway.

6. Spectral Doppler as a Means of Assessing Hemodynamics

Our assessment of the hemodynamic parameters is generally achieved through application and interpretation of spectral Doppler. In Chapter 7, we learned the fundamentals of spectral Doppler. To fully understand hemodynamic assessment by Doppler techniques, we will need to combine our Doppler understanding with our understanding of the hemodynamics.

6.1 What Doppler Tells Us

As we learned in Chapter 7, spectral Doppler presents the range of frequency shifts measured from the flow system. Given that we know the angle between the insonifying beam and the flow, the frequency shifts can then be displayed as velocities through application of the Doppler equation and our knowledge of basic trigonometry. For a Doppler spectrum, the vertical axis represents increasing frequency shifts towards and away from the transducer, or equivalently, through the Doppler equation, increasing velocity toward and away from the transducer. Since the transmitting of Doppler lines is repeated for a period of at least a cardiac cycle, the variation of the Doppler spectrum with time is presented on the horizontal axis. Since blood flow is pulsatile and/or phasic, we expect that the Doppler signal will be pulsatile and/or phasic. Additionally, the "third" axis of the Doppler display corresponds to signal strength, or amplitude. The amplitude of the Doppler spectrum is related to the reflected signal strength. For a fixed location in a patient, in a relative manner, the varying spectral signal intensities are generally related to the number of reflecting red blood cells, such that greater concentrations of red blood cells result in greater reflectivity.

6.2 Returning to the Hemodynamic Equations

Perhaps the most essential issue to understand is how the spectral Doppler velocities, timing, and amplitude information from spectral Doppler can be related to the hemodynamic situations indicating health or disease severity.

In developing an understanding of hemodynamics, the starting point is to understand that pressure drives flow. Since pressure drives flow, clearly pressure must be one of the principal determinants of the velocity, the time variance of the velocity, and the velocity distribution as registered in spectral Doppler. Not surprisingly, we will need to return to our basic fluid equations to develop the relationship between the pressure in the system and the velocity in the system as measured by Doppler.

6.3 Characteristics of the Spectrum

6.3.1 Systolic Acceleration and Pressure

6.3.1.1 Doppler Acceleration for a Healthy Large Vessel

The sharp upstroke of a normal pressure waveform represents the rapid rise in pressure during systole. From the simplified law, a rapid increase in pressure should result in a rapid increase in volume, for a relatively fixed resistance. The following three steps will illustrate how a rapid acceleration in pressure is visualized as a rapid change in velocity on a Doppler spectrum.

Step 1: Relate pressure change with volume change.

$$\Delta P = Q \times R$$

So as the pressure increases, the volume increases.

Fig. 33   **Pressure Waveform**

By the volumetric flow equation, a rapid increase in volumetric flow, results in a rapid increase in velocity assuming a relatively fixed flow cross-sectional area.

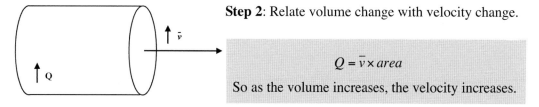

Step 2: Relate volume change with velocity change.

$$Q = \bar{v} \times area$$

So as the volume increases, the velocity increases.

Fig. 34   **Volume and Velocity Relationship**

Since the vertical axis of Doppler represents velocity and the horizontal axis represents time, the slope of the Doppler spectrum represents the rate of change in velocity per time, otherwise referred to as the "acceleration." Hence, for normal flow situations, a rapid increase in pressure should result in a rapid acceleration. You should note that the change in time that it takes for the velocity to go from its minimum at the end of the diastolic flow phase to the peak systole is referred to as the risetime.

Step 3: Measuring the change in velocity with respect to time (acceleration)

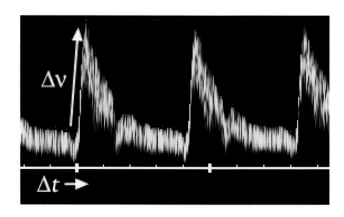

Fig. 35 **Measuring Acceleration**

From *Figure 35*, the acceleration equals the change in velocity divided by the change in time, or:

$$acceleration = \frac{\Delta v}{\Delta t}$$

The risetime, is the change in time, or simply, Δt. Measurement of the acceleration time or rise time at the level of the common femoral artery has been commonly used as a quantitative diagnostic tool to aid in differentiating inflow (aortiliac) from outflow (femoropopliteal) disease. In general, for a healthy femoral artery, a normal risetime is considered to be less than 122 msec.

6.3.1.2 Doppler Risetime for a Diseased Vessel

The acceleration of the Doppler spectrum will decrease with a proximal flow reducing stenosis. This decrease in acceleration is clearly the consequence of an inability for the volume to rapidly increase across the increased resistance of the stenosis. Since the volume of flow does not increase rapidly, the velocity does not increase rapidly, resulting in less acceleration. The decrease in acceleration is visualized as a longer time to reach the peak velocity, or in other words, a longer risetime. A risetime of greater than 144 msec is usually indicative of a flow limiting proximal stenosis. Acceleration time is not prolonged with disease distal to the level of probe insonation.

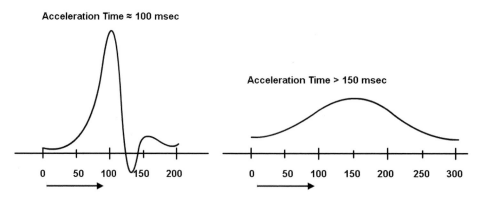

Fig. 36 **Longer Risetime and Proximal Disease**

6.3.2 The Spectral Window

6.3.2.1 Presence in Healthy Vessel

Figure 37 displays the Doppler spectrum for blood flow in a normal common carotid artery. For this spectrum, the sample volume was relatively small (1.5 mm) and was placed in the center stream of the flow. Since the flow is laminar, the flow accelerates and decelerates without creating eddies or swirling flow patterns. Since the sample volume is centrally placed in a large vessel where the frictional and viscous affects are least pronounced, the highest velocities in the vessel are recorded, of course varying with the changing pressure throughout the cardiac cycle. By its central placement in a large vessel, the sample volume does not include the low and zero velocity flow along the walls of the vessel. All of the velocities recorded in systole are relatively high, creating a region of no signal at the lower velocities closer to the baseband. This region of signal absence is called the spectral window. The spectral window is indicated by the white arrows in *Figure 37*.

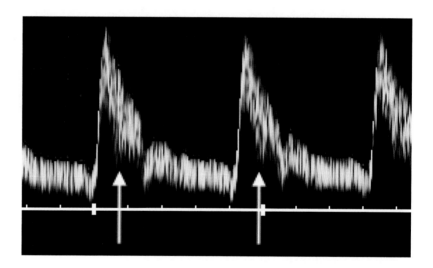

Fig. 37   **Spectral Window**

6.3.2.2 Absence in Diseased Vessel

As previously discussed, in the presence of turbulence, the velocity varies significantly, resulting in an entire range of frequency shifts. Unlike the laminar example we have just discussed, in addition to the narrowband of frequency shifts about the peak velocity, there is an entire range of frequency shifts continuing all the way down to the baseline, and depending on angle, potentially even extending in the opposite direction. As a result, when performing Doppler in the presence of turbulence, the spectral window is not present.

Figure 38 demonstrates the turbulence that occurred in a right renal artery stenosis. Note that there is no spectral window in systole, and that there is a component of flow in the reverse direction (below the baseline).

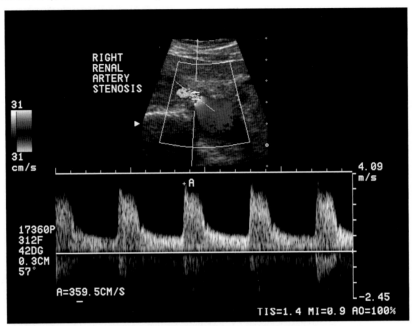

Fig. 38 **Spectral Display of Turbulence**

6.3.2.3 Absence of the Spectral Window in a Healthy Vessel

There are many reasons which can cause the absence of a spectral window besides flow disturbance, including:

- CW Doppler (instead of PW Doppler)
- A large PW sample volume (gate size) relative to the vessel size (small vessels rarely display a spectral window)
- The sample volume too close to the vessel wall (including in the elevation direction)
- Overgaining of the spectrum
- Flow angle close to 90 degrees
- Spectral broadening artifact

From this list, it is obvious that the absence of the spectral window does not necessarily imply a hemodynamic state of turbulence. Therefore, caution must be used when interpreting based on the absence of the spectral window. Conversely, when a spectral window does exist, it is evident that there is laminar flow.

6.3.3 Systolic Acceleration and Velocity Distribution

The velocity distribution of the flow is affected by the acceleration, deceleration, friction with the vessel walls, and the viscous effects within the fluid as well as the changes in the vessel geometry and the volumetric flow. For the spectrum in *Figure 37*, you should also notice that during the early phase of systolic upstroke, the spectrum demonstrates decreased spectral broadening associated with the acceleration. As mentioned in Section 5.4 of Chapter 12, acceleration leads to a flattening of the velocity profile. A flatter velocity profile implies that there is a narrower distribution of velocities and hence a narrower (less broadened) spectral signal.

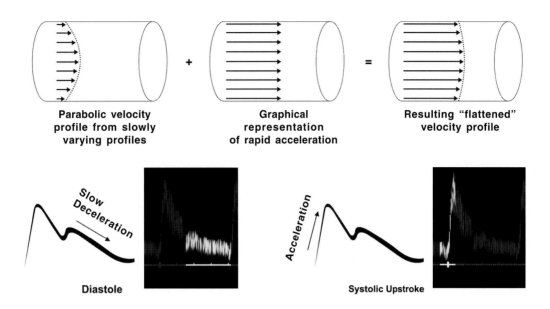

Fig. 39 **Relating Pressure Characteristics with Spectral Characteristics**

You should also notice that as the acceleration diminishes and then reverses, the signal becomes broader. In cases in which the deceleration is significant and the distal resistance is relatively high, it is possible to get flow reversal along the walls of the vessel. This situation is demonstrated in the following figure.

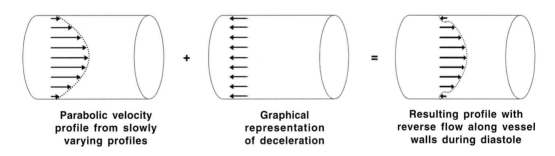

Fig. 40 **Diastolic Flow Profile**

6.3.4 Flow Reversal and Phasicity

6.3.4.1 Normal Flow Reversal

A short reversal of flow during the latter stage of systole or early stage of diastole can occur in a patient with normal vasculature. When normal, the flow reversal is brief and occurs as the result of the reflected pressure wave from the higher distal resistance, given that the more proximal vessels are compliant. As discussed earlier in the chapter, for a healthy patient the distal resistance is higher for lower volumetric demand organs than higher volumetric demand organs. Therefore, in arteries feeding a normally high resistance bed, the short duration phase reversal is considered normal.

6.3.4.2 Abnormal Flow Reversal

There are many situations which can result in a flow reversal, but the basic mechanism is almost always the same. From the flow equations, we know that flow will always go from a higher to lower energy state.

◊ *Example 1:* The Vertebral Steal

In subclavian steal syndrome ("vertebral steal"), high-grade stenosis or occlusion is present in the proximal subclavian or brachiocephalic artery (before the vertebral artery junction). Since inadequate volume is sent through the subclavian artery, the arterioles of the affected arm and associated beds vasodilate. Since the ipsilateral vertebral artery is on the distal side of the disease, the low resistance of the arm initially causes flow during diastole to reverse to perfuse the arm. Physiologically this occurs because the resistance to flow across the subclavian stenosis exceeds the resistance to flow to the arm through the indirect pathways of the head, such as the circle of Willis. Since volume is being "stolen" from the head, there is frequently a compensatory volume increase on the contralateral side or other ipsilated vessels. As the severity of disease worsens, the vasodilation of the upper extremity arterioles will eventually cause holodiastolic flow reversal so as to meet the volumetric demand of the upper extremity.

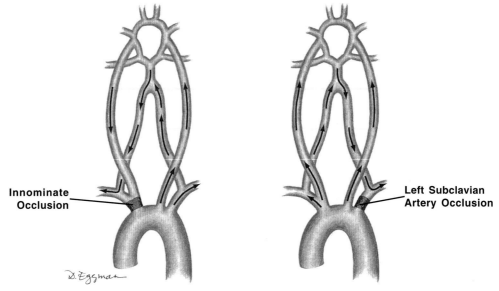

Innominate Occlusion

Left Subclavian Artery Occlusion

Fig. 41 **Vertebral Steal**

◊ *Example 2:* Aortic Insufficiency

Once the stroke volume is ejected into the aorta, the aortic valve is supposed to remain closed, offering an effectively infinite resistance to backflow into the left ventricle. In the presence of aortic insufficiency (abbreviated as AI or sometimes referred to as aortic regurgitation (AR), the valve leaflets do not close properly). As the AI progresses in severity, the valvular leak offers a relatively low resistance path to the left ventricle. Once the ventricle has gone through isovolumic relaxation, the pressure in the ventricle is much lower than the pressure in the aorta. With a normal aortic valve, this pressure gradient is inconsequential. However, with the low resistance path through the insufficient valve, this pressure gradient can result in significant flow from the aorta back into the ventricle.

Figure 49 is an image of blood flow in a silicone rubber model of a carotid artery through the bifurcation. The silicone rubber produces model arteries with realistic compliance, curvature, and excellent visibility. By supplying variable pressure waveforms, pulsatile flow can be achieved. The flow within the artery is visualized using a proprietary technique similar to the laser sheet light technique. In this case, the flow separation is evident even in the still image. The higher volumetric percentage into the upper artery (mimicking the lower resistance ICA) is evident from the appearance of more uniform flow lines. For appreciation of the hemodynamic changes that occur at the bifurcation, a video has been included on the Animation and Image Library CD.

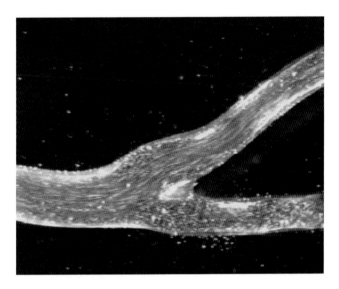

Fig. 49 **Flow Through a Carotid Artery and Bifurcation**

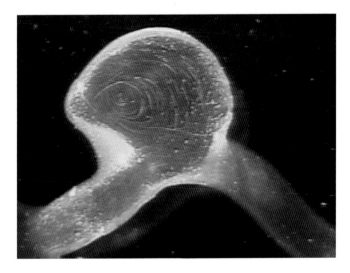

Fig. 50 **Flow in an Aneurysm**

 **View Animation and Image Library CD**

- Hemodynamics is the extension of fluid dynamics to blood flow.

- The equations in fluid dynamics become the foundation for discussing hemodynamics.

- In the development of the fluid equations many assumptions were made to produce ideal situations.

- To understand hemodynamics with respect to the fluid equations, it is important to understand what assumptions that were made do not hold true and how these changes from simpler, ideal situations impact the flow of blood.

- The elasticity of vessel walls indicates that the capacitance will serve as a more important factor in blood flow than in the rigid tube models used in the fluid dynamics development.

- You should understand how overall resistance is affected by multiple flow paths.

  - When vessels are in series, the resistances of the individual vessels add (overall resistance increases).

$$R_{series} = R_1 + R_2 + \cdots + R_n$$

  - When vessels are in parallel, the reciprocal of the overall resistance equals the sum of the reciprocal of each individual resistance (overall resistance decreases).

$$\frac{1}{R_{parallel}} = \frac{1}{R_1} + \frac{1}{R_2} + \cdots + \frac{1}{R_n}$$

- For blood flow, energy is lost to frictional and viscous effects.

- All of the following parameters increase the amount of energy lost to heat:
  - Smaller cross-sectional area
  - Rougher surface
  - Increased velocity
  - Higher viscosity

- Blood is a non-Newtonian fluid which means that the viscosity of blood changes with the flow geometry, not just with temperature.

- Progressing from the left ventricle to the arterioles, the capacitance decreases and the resistance increases.

- The arterioles are the "resistive" element of the cardiovascular system and are principally responsible for the regulation of blood volume.

- The venous system is highly capacitive. At rest, approximately 65% of the blood volume is contained in the venous system.

- As predicted by the continuity equation (volumetric flow equation), the velocity of the blood and the cross-sectional area have an inverse relationship.

  - As the total cross-sectional area increases (from aorta to capillaries), the velocity decreases.

- As the total cross-sectional area decreases (from venules to the vena cava), the velocity increases.

- Hydrostatic pressure can affect pressure measurements (about 2 mmHg per inch).

- The right atrium was chosen as the arbitrary reference for hydrostatic pressure, "making" pressures in the head negative and pressures at the feet less positive (in the standing position).

- When lying down the hydrostatic pressure goes to zero.

- The calf muscle pump aids in venous return through the use of venous valves which restrict reflux.

- Respiration affects venous return. Since venous pressures are relatively low, changes in pressure in the thorax and abdomen result in changes in venous return to the right heart.

- During inspiration, the pressure increases in the abdomen and decreases in the thorax, increasing venous return from the abdomen to the right atrium but decreasing blood return from the legs to the abdomen.

- During expiration, the pressure decreases in the abdomen and increases in the thorax, decreasing venous return from the abdomen to the right atrium but increasing blood return from the legs to the abdomen.

- Transmural pressure is a measure of the relative pressure difference from the pressure within the vessel (intravascular pressure) to the pressure outside the vessel (tissue pressure).

- Transmural pressure is always referenced from the inside of the vessel to the outside of the vessel.

- A high transmural pressure results in a distended vein whereas a low transmural pressure results in a collapsed vein.

- The concept of transmural pressure can also be applied to arteries (the basic premise of a blood pressure measurement) but is more complex because of the muscular banding of the arteries (referred to as hoop stress).

- Flow across large, healthy vessels results in very little pressure decrease.

- With the existence of diameter reducing disease, the pressure drop with flow increases as predicted by the simplified law.

- Vasodilation of the arterioles compensates for pressure loss across proximal disease.

- If the stenosis becomes significant enough, and/or the volumetric demand is increased, the energy losses may become more significant than can be compensated for by the arterioles. At this point the patient becomes symptomatic.

- Spectral Doppler is used to measure velocity information and is then related to the flow conditions through Bernoulli's equation.

- Higher velocities imply greater kinetic energy and hence, greater energy losses to friction and viscous effects.

- Analysis of spectral Doppler always must entail consideration of the proximal and distal flow conditions and parameters since local flow is affected by both.

Note: See the Abbreviations: Physical Units and Equations Appendices for additional review.

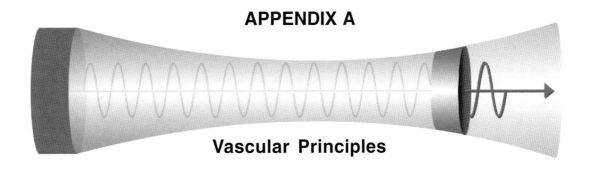

APPENDIX A

Vascular Principles

Introduction

Vascular principles is really a collective title for myriad topics. Within the category of vascular principles are included venous testing procedures, arterial testing procedures, pressure measurement techniques, ankle to brachial and related indices, patient positioning, transcranial imaging and Doppler, transcutaneous oximetry, and arteriovenous fistula. As a result of this broad categorization, unlike the other chapters in this book with one central theme, this appendix must therefore focus on many different techniques. As a result, a slightly different style has been adopted to adequately cover so many topics without converting this one section into an entire book of its own. Furthermore, this appendix is intended to compliment but not replace a book on vascular technology.

Some of the vascular principles still covered on the credentialing exams are related to testing procedures which are no longer commonly performed. There are two approaches one can take with regards to this "older" material. One approach is to learn only what is necessary to successfully complete credentialing exams since these tests are performed less and less frequently. The other approach is to realize that the value of understanding many of the earlier vascular tests is not knowing the exact procedures, but rather understanding the principles underlying the tests and how each relates to hemodynamics and the compensatory mechanisms of the body. Given the detailed development of the fluid dynamics and hemodynamics of Chapters 12 and 13, it is anticipated that references to specific concepts already learned in these previous chapters will allow for a very pointed approach in this appendix.

1. Electrical Principles

We are all familiar with electrical appliances, tools, measuring devices, heating devices, and medical devices. Each of these devices performs a task at the expense of energy. That energy is provided through a current flow created by a voltage difference (energy gradient) applied to the device. In essence, if you don't plug them in, they don't consume energy and they also do nothing. We will now define the quantities which give these devices the capacity to function. You should notice the strong similarities between the parameters described for electricity and the analogous terms for blood flow discussed in Chapters 12 and 13.

1.1 Ohm's Law
You have already learned that a pressure gradient is equivalent to the flow multiplied by the resistance or:

$$\Delta P = Q \bullet R$$

For electrical current flow (electricity), the equivalent equation is referred to as Ohm's law:

$$Ohm's\ Law:\ \Delta E = I \bullet R \text{ or } \Delta V = I \bullet R$$

where: UNITS
$\Delta E = \Delta V$ = change in voltage (electromotive force)   Volts
I = electrical current   Amperes
R = electrical resistance (impedance)   Ohms

From this equation it should be evident that a change in voltage for electricity is analogous to a change in pressure for fluid flow. Similarly, the electrical current is analogous to the volumetric flow (fluid current). Finally, the electrical resistance is equivalent to the hydraulic resistance.

Voltage (Volts): analogous to pressure for blood flow
Voltage is the difference in electric potential energy that drives an electrical current to flow from a high potential to a low potential.

Current (Amperes): analogous to blood flow
Current is a stream of electrons which moves along a conductor (a conductive pathway is usually metal in circuit design) from a high potential to a low potential.

Resistance (Ohms): analogous to hydraulic (flow) resistance
Electrical resistance is a measure of how much impedance a current path offers to electron flow. A high resistance requires a very high energy difference to get current to flow. If the resistance is low, current can easily flow, therefore a smaller energy difference (voltage) is required.

1.2 Power
Recall from Chapter 11 that power is a measure of the rate at which work is performed. For electricity, the power is calculated by multiplying the voltage by the current, or:

$$Power = \Delta V \bullet I$$

The unit for electrical power is Watts: (volts · Amps = Watts = Joules/second).

Since from Ohm's Law we know that $\Delta V = I \bullet R$, we can rewrite the equation in terms of the

current, I, as $\dfrac{\Delta V}{R} = I$. Substitution for the current in the power equation yields:

$$Power = \Delta V \bullet I = \Delta V \bullet \frac{\Delta V}{R} = \frac{(\Delta V)^2}{R}.$$

Hence, we see that electrical power is proportional to the amplitude of the electrical signal squared, just as we learned that the acoustic power is proportional to the amplitude of the acoustic pressure squared.

Pegasus Lectures, Inc.

Recall:

Power: The rate at which work is being performed (Watts).

Energy: The total amount of power used (Joules) to complete a job which is equivalent to the (average power) · (time).

1.3 Why Electrical Principles Matter to Vascular Principles

Many of the medical devices commonly used are now electrical. In addition, many of the signals monitored are either electrical or easily converted into electrical signals. It is therefore beneficial to have a basic understanding of some of the underlying electrical principles. The specific reason that electrical principles were required knowledge for vascular testing is related to a form of plethysmography called impedance plethysmography. Impedance plethysmography is based on the application of Ohm's law. Ohm's law is also utilized in strain-gauge plethysmography. Both of these techniques are discussed later in this appendix.

Additionally, electrical principles are valuable for understanding muscle contraction. Within the body, electrical charges result from changing concentrations of charged ions such as sodium ions (Na^+). These changes in concentrations produce electrical impulses which result in muscle contractions. An electrocardiogram (ECG) is a display of the electrical signals as they travel along conductive pathways within the heart causing myocardial contraction.

2. Relating Electrical Signals to Physical Parameters

There are three basic concerns when measuring small electrical signals:

1. Displaying information
2. Calibration for quantification
3. Electrical coupling (AC versus DC coupling)

2.1 Information Display

There are two common means by which electrical signals are presented for interpretation, display on a monitor such as a CRT (or newer monitor technologies such as LCD, etc), and strip chart.

2.1.1 The Cathode Ray Tube (CRT)

In Chapter 6 we discussed the standard U.S. format monitor and characteristics. For many years, the Cathode Ray Tube (CRT) has been one of the most readily employed devices for display of electrical signals. Some common examples are television screens, computer screens, video monitors and oscilloscopes. The basic principle is that an electron beam proportional to the signal is steered across a phosphorescent screen. The areas that receive the most energy from the electron beam phosphoresce or glow brightest. The beam is scanned over the entire screen in a rapid sequence, fast enough to appear (generally) as a continuous display.

2.1.2 Strip Chart

The most often used device for recording measured electrical signals or biologically related electrical signals has been the strip chart recorder. With a strip chart recorder, a stylus (writing implement) deflects proportionally to the signal voltage while a piece of paper scrolls by at a constant known rate. The result is a record of changing voltage versus calibrated time.

2.1.3 Calibration of a strip chart

A strip chart recorder can be easily calibrated. By applying a known voltage, the deflection of the stylus can be compared against a standard and adjusted. For example, if 100 mV represents 1 inch of deflection, 2.5 inches of deflection represents 250 mV. In earlier days, calibration of strip chart recorders was manual. The user would push a calibrate button and then turn a Vernier dial until the appropriate deflection occurred with the test signal. Most strip chart based equipment now self-calibrates when powered on.

In the last few years digital storage has started to diminish the number of strip charts produced. Instead, the digital waveform over time is stored and can be replayed as when it was displayed in real time. However, strip chart recorders still exist and are commonly used to record pressure waveforms and EKGs.

To make any electrical measurements the test equipment must be electrically coupled to the signal being measured. For EKG signals, the signal is already electrical. If the signal is not already electrical, such as with detecting audible sound or pressure, some form of transducer is necessary.

3. Two-Wire vs. Four-Wire Measurements and Calibration

Measuring physiological signals can be difficult because usually these signals are very small. As a result, the transducer or (sensor) might actually interfere with the small signals being measured, obviously an undesirable situation. Since two-wire devices involve placing the sensor in the direct path of the signal to be measured, two-wire approaches are rarely used. Instead, a four-wire approach is used. Recall that flow always follows a path of least resistance, so current flow will always choose a path with lower resistance. Compare the two-wire and the four-wire situation below.

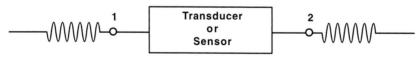

Fig. 1 **Two-wire System**

- Current flows through the sensor, so the sensor's impedance affects the measurement.
- The interaction between the measuring device and the signal being measured makes calibration of two-wire devices very difficult.

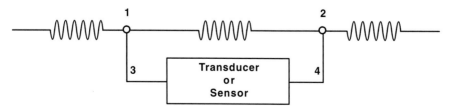

Fig. 2 **High impedance (resistance) to current flow.**
(Four-wire system)

- Very little current flows through the sensor since it has a very high resistance. The signal is therefore less affected by the measurement technique.
- Four-wire devices are easily calibrated.
- Almost all test-measuring devices are now designed to be four-wire devices

3.1 AC vs. DC Coupling

3.1.1 AC (alternating current) electricity is what you get from your standard wall plug. Alternating current means that the electrical charges change (alternate) direction periodically. As a result, the voltage will change rapidly from positive to negative, and back again. In the U.S., the rate of change in polarity is 60 Hz (60 times per second).

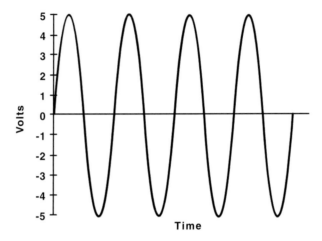

Fig. 3 **Alternating Current**

3.1.2 Direct Current is the type of electrical current you get from a battery. The current does not change direction or amplitude, thereby creating a constant voltage.

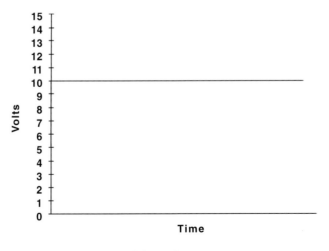

Fig. 4 **Direct Current**

Sometimes, AC and DC voltages are combined.

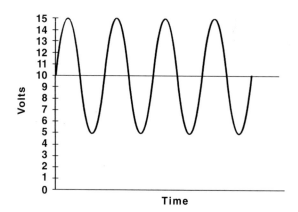

Fig. 5   **AC Signal with a DC Bias**

3.1.3 Choosing the Appropriate Coupling for Indirect Arterial and Venous Testing
Often with indirect arterial and venous testing the user must select the type of electrical coupling for the testing device. As technology advances, this user intervention is becoming less frequent. However, since there is still some of the older equipment in existence, it is important that you understand choosing the appropriate coupling.

AC coupling

AC coupling means that you have coupled the test equipment to the test signal so that only the AC component of the signal is presented. This means that you can only see signals which vary relatively quickly over time. In other words, the slowly varying component of the signal, the DC component, is eliminated.

DC coupling

With DC coupling, both slowly and quickly varying signals are presented. If there is a large DC component, since AC and DC signals can combine, the signal might get too large for the dynamic range of the display device. The result is that the signal tracing pegs to the maximum possible value, or "disappears."

- Would you expect to use AC or DC coupling for quickly changing arterial flow?

  You must use AC coupling for an arterial signal, or the signal tracing may peg at the maximum value, or "disappear" off the screen or strip chart.

- Would you expect to use AC or DC coupling for slowly varying venous flow?

  You must use DC coupling for a venous study, or there will be no display of a slowly varying signal, or a flat-line signal. In other words, even though there is a venous signal, incorrectly using an AC coupling can lead to the incorrect conclusion that there is no signal present.

Note: Although in general coupling for arterial signals should be AC and venous signals should be DC, a quickly varying venous signal would also require an AC coupling. As a result, you must consider if the signal is changing quickly or not for the appropriate coupling, not just if the signal is arterial or venous.

4. Plethysmography

Plethysmography is actually a category of methods which records change in pressures or volume. Much of the work done by plethysmography has been replaced by newer techniques such as B-mode scanning and Doppler scanning. However, plethysmography is still sometimes used and its methods are instructive in how the vascular system functions.

4.1 Displacement (pneumatic cuff) Plethysmography:
Air-filled plethysmography/ Pulse volume recording (PVR)

A pneumatic cuff is placed around the limb or digit to be evaluated. The cuff is inflated to a low pressure (approximately 65 mmHg). Volume changes in the limb create a pressure change which is converted to an analog recording. Significant stenosis or occlusion of a major artery will be reflected by diminished waveform amplitude and dampening of the waveform contour. In general, displacement plethysmography is difficult to calibrate because of varying patient limb sizes.

4.2 Strain-gauge Plethysmography
Strain-gauge plethysmography consists of fine-bore silicone rubber tubes filled with a liquid-metal alloy (usually mercury). The electrical resistance of these metal filled tubes is proportional to the tube's length. The gauge is wrapped around the limb or digit being evaluated. As the limb expands or contracts, the length of the gauge changes correspondingly, resulting in a varying electrical resistance. Through Ohm's Law, the varying electrical resistance over time can be displayed as a varying voltage waveform which is representative of the volume and hence, pressure changes within the segment under observation. The strain-gauge system, unlike the displacement system is easily calibrated. Strain-gauge plethysmography can be used for both arterial and venous testing.

4.3 Impedance Plethysmography (IPG)
Aluminum strip electrodes are placed circumferentially around the limb. A low-level current measures the relative change in impedance, allowing for measurement of the relative change in blood volume (used primarily for venous disease). Since blood is a relatively good conductor of electrical current, as the volume of blood within a limb fluctuates, the electrical resistance within the limb fluctuates. Through Ohm's Law, the low level current across the resistance of the limb produces a voltage. By measuring and displaying the voltage changes, the change to resistance, and hence blood volume, is detected. The four-wire method is most commonly used as the two-wire method cannot easily be calibrated, and is therefore less accurate.

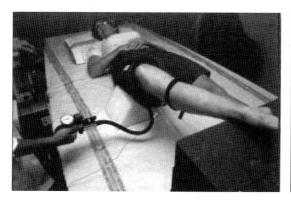

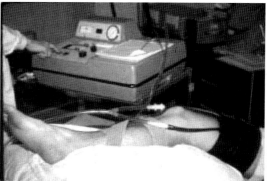

Fig. 6 **Strain-gauge Plethysmography**   *Fig. 7* **Impedance Plethysmography**

4.4 Inflow and Outflow Studies

Deep vein thrombosis causes obstruction in the venous system, decreasing the capacity of the veins to fill with blood as well as decreasing venous emptying. Venous inflow/outflow studies induce a temporary venous occlusion in order to measure the vein's flow. The venous capacitance and venous outflow are both decreased in the presence of a major obstruction in the deep veins.

4.4.1 Venous Capacitance/Venous Outflow (VC/VO)

Strain gauge plethysmography and impedance plethysmography are both types of inflow/outflow studies. It is important to note that strain gauge and impedance plethysmography are only sensitive to obstruction above the level of the knee. These tests are also not sensitive to partially occlusive thrombus.

Maximum venous capacitance (MVC)

The ability of the veins to fill with blood during a period in which the venous outflow is halted (approximately 2 min).

Maximum venous outflow (MVO)

The amount of venous emptying that occurs when the occluding cuff is deflated.

Venous outflow/Venous capacitance (VO/VC)

Measured values of venous outflow and capacitance are plotted on a grid.

Procedure:

For strain gauge or impedance plethysmography used for the detection of deep vein thrombosis, a thigh cuff should be inflated to 50 mmHg for a period of approximately 2 minutes. Immediately upon release of the cuff the outflow curve is recorded. MVC and MVO values are calculated to evaluate the ability of the veins to fill with blood and how quickly the limb empties with rapid cuff deflation.

Interpretation:

Normal – The tracing should fall to baseline within 3 seconds of cuff deflation. Without obstruction the veins are able to accommodate the increase in blood volume caused by the cuff inflation and are able to empty quickly following cuff deflation.

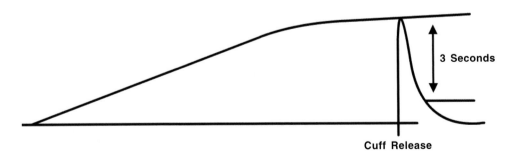

Fig. 8 **Normal IPG Tracing**

Abnormal – The time for the tracing to fall to baseline is greater than 3 seconds. Venous obstruction (intrinsic or extrinsic) causes diminished limb volume increase and a slower outflow.

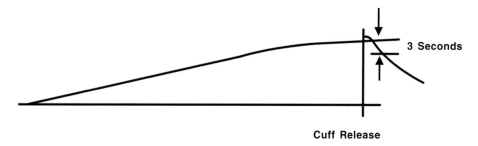

Fig. 9 **Abnormal IPG Tracing**

4.5 Photoplethysmography

Photoplethysmography (as the name suggests) uses light produced from an infrared light-emitting diode and a photosensor to detect changes in blood volume. Infrared light is generally used since its wavelength is shorter than visible light, increasing reflectivity from red blood cells. As the blood volume changes from systole to diastole, the amount of absorption and therefore, reflection changes. Blood attenuates light in proportion to its content in the tissue. The change in reflectivity is then recorded and represents volume changes. Since the infrared light cannot penetrate very deeply, PPG is generally used for cutaneous blood flow and superficial vessels. The waveform shape represents the arterial inflow and venous outflow of the capillary system.

4.5.1 Venous Reflux Testing

Capabilities:
- Evaluates the presence and severity of venous insufficiency

Limitations:
- Contraindicated in patients with deep vein thrombosis.
- Improper placement of PPG sensor will result in inaccurate data

Patient Positioning:
- The patient is placed in a sitting with legs dangling.
- Care should be taken to avoid pressure against the popliteal fossa (extrinsic pressure on the popliteal vein).

Fig. 10 **Patient Positioning - Venous Reflux Testing**

Procedure:

PPG sensors are placed approximately 5-10 cm above the medial malleolus. The patient performs dorsiflexion maneuvers or manual calf compressions are performed. Tracings are generated during calf exercises to determine the venous refill time (VRT).

If the study is normal (VRT > 20 sec) the exam is complete. If the results are abnormal (VRT < 20 sec), the test is repeated and a tourniquet is applied to isolate the level of incompetency.

Interpretation:

Normal - Venous refill time (VRT) > 20 seconds

Abnormal - Venous refill time (VRT) < 20 seconds

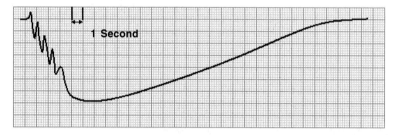

Normal PPG Venous Tracing

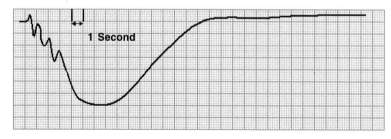

Abnormal PPG Venous Tracing

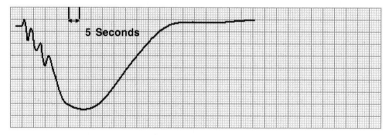

Fig. 11 **PPG Venous Tracings**

Is the third PPG tracing normal or abnormal? (Hint: note calibration)

Note: This last graph uses a different time base than the presumed 1 second per division. In this case, the VRT is greater than 20 seconds so this tracing represents a normal VRT.

Tourniquet application:

Tourniquet applied above knee - If an abnormal VRT converts to normal (> 20 sec), this is an indication of greater saphenous incompetence.

Tourniquet applied below knee - If an abnormal VRT converts to normal (> 20 sec), this is an indication of lesser saphenous incompetence.

VRT < 20 sec with and without tourniquet indicates incompetence of the deep and superficial systems.

Referenced from Peterson, L.; "Venous Insufficiency Testing", the Journal of Vascular Technology, Vol. XII, pp. 110-112, April, 1998.

4.5.2 Arterial Testing with Photoplethysmography

Capabilities:
- In conjunction with segmental pressures, aids in documenting the presence, level and severity of arterial occlusive disease.
- Helps in differentiating between vascular and non-vascular symptoms.
- Allows a method of follow-up for progression of disease, medical therapy, and surgical or interventional procedures.

Limitations:
- Determines volume changes: therefore, is unable to give information regarding a specific vessel.
- Unable to discriminate between collateral flow and primary arterial flow.
- Waveforms are affected by room temperature, basal state, and medications.
- Open wounds or severe trophic changes may limit sensor placement.
- Digits with low pressures (< 20 mmHg) may not generate a waveform.

Potential sources of technical error:
- PPG sensors unable to adhere to skin (thick, dry skin)
- Inconsistent ambient room temperature
- Nicotine/caffeine use
- Medications, ie. vasoconstrictors/vasodilators
- Voluntary or involuntary movement or tremor

Procedure (PPG):
- Place patient in a supine position.
- Affix the PPG sensor to the skin with double-sided tape. If also obtaining digit pressures, place cuff on digit prior to sensor placement.
- Adjust plethysmographic equipment to obtain an optimal arterial waveform. Analog recorded waveforms are generally recorded at a chart speed of 25 mm/sec.
- After obtaining waveform tracings, digit pressure may be taken. Pressure waveforms with the PPG sensor are recorded with a chart speed of 5 mm/sec. A digit cuff (2.5 cm) is placed at the base of the digit and inflated until the waveform disappears. The pressure is decreased slowly until the waveform reappears, indicating the digit systolic pressure.

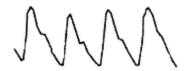

Fig. 12a   **Normal pulse contour** - steep systolic up-slope, narrow systolic peak and a dicrotic notch on the downslope.

Fig. 12b   **Mildly obstructive contour** - loss of dicrotic notch, slight bowing of the downslope away from the baseline, slight delay in systolic up-stroke.

Fig. 12c   **Moderately obstructive contour** - same changes seen in mild obstruction with the addition of a delay in the upstroke and appearance of a rounded peak.

Fig. 12d   **Severe obstruction** - low amplitude pulse contour with marked broadening of the contour.

Fig. 12e   **Advanced arterial insufficiency** - absent contour pulsations associated with rest pain, tissue loss and/or gangrene.

Fig. 12f   **Vasoconstricted contour** - variable tracing characteristics: low amplitude, loss of dicrotic notch, contour broadening and rounded peak. Differentiated from arterial obstructive disease by reversal to normal characteristics with vasodilation (warming, reactive hyperemia, medication).

Fig. 12a   **"Peaked pulse" contour** - pointed peak waveform with an anacrotic notch on the upslope and dicrotic notch high on the downslope.

5. Pressure Measurements

Pressure information is extremely useful for diagnosis. As such there are many different methods by which to obtain pressure information. Excluding the invasive approach of catheterization, pressure information is usually obtained by use of a sphygmomanometer. A sphygmomanometer consists of a cuff surrounding an inflatable air bladder, which is inflated by a small bulb and deflated by a small air release valve. The pressure of the cuff can be monitored by reading an attached mercury or aneroid manometer (an instrument to measure pressure).

5.1 Methods of Pressure Measurements

5.1.1 Palpatory method

After flow has been occluded, there will be no pulse distal to the occlusion. As the cuff pressure is lowered, the pulse will return. The palpatory method relies on finger sensitivity of the tester to feel the returning pulse. When a pulse is felt, the cuff pressure is recorded from the manometer. Obviously, there is considerable subjectivity with this method. Therefore, the palpatory method is not a recommended method of routinely obtaining pressure measurements.

5.1.2 Ausculatory method

By using a stethoscope, it is possible to determine the peak systolic and end diastolic pressure. The auscultatory method relies on Korotokov sounds to indicate the return of flow. In the procedure, we discussed how the cuff was inflated until arterial occlusion occurs. As the cuff pressure is released just below peak systolic pressure, blood flow begins to squirt through. Distal to the cuff occlusion a "stationary" pool of blood has collected. The blood which squirts through collides with this pool causing a vibration and turbulence, creating "Korotokov" sounds. Eventually, the cuff pressure drops below end diastolic pressure and flow returns to normal such that these sounds disappear. By recording the cuff pressure at which Korotokov sounds commence and conclude, peak systolic and end diastolic pressures are known.

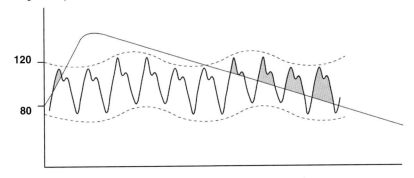

Fig. 13 **Auscultory Method of Pressure Measurement (Korotokov Sounds)**

5.1.3 Flow Meter (Doppler)

In some segments or with certain disease states, Korotokov sounds may be difficult or impossible to detect. The same basic procedure is followed except some "flow meter" device such as Doppler or plethysmography is used distal to the cuff occlusion to determine at what cuff pressure systolic flow returns.

Specifically, the cuff is placed around the segment in which the systolic pressure is to be measured. A Doppler signal is identified distal to the level of the cuff. (For specific cuff and Doppler placement for LE and UE segmental pressures see Sections 6.1 and .6.2.) The cuff bladder is inflated manually or by a pumping mechanism, increasing cuff pressure. Eventually, the cuff pressure will exceed the intravascular pressure of the artery (supra-systolic) under measure, causing occlusion. The air release valve is then opened allowing a gradual decrease in cuff pressure of approximately 2-3 mmHg/sec. When the cuff pressure drops just below the peak systolic pressure, a little flow will escape the cuff occlusion. Initially, blood will only squirt through in peak-systole, when the intravascular pressure exceeds cuff pressure. As the cuff pressure continues to drop, flow under the cuff will become more and more regular with the cardiac cycle. Eventually, the cuff pressure drops below end diastolic pressure and the flow returns to normal.

Note: The pressure measured is at the level of the artery (arteries) underlying the cuff, not the vessel from which the Doppler signal was obtained.

5.2 The Correct Cuff Size

Studies have been performed which demonstrate that using an inappropriate cuff size will result in inaccurate pressure measurements:

cuff too narrow	$\Rightarrow$	*overestimation of pressure*
cuff too wide	$\Rightarrow$	*underestimation of pressure*

The AHA recommends:

> *width* = *1.2 * segment diameter*
> *or*
> *20% wider than the segment diameter*
>
> *length* ≥ *2 * width*

Note that $1.2 \cdot$ diameter is the same as 0.4 * circumference because:

$$Circumference = \pi * d$$

Let x = the percentage of the circumference equivalent to 1.2d

$$1.2d = x * (\pi * d)$$

$$x = \frac{1.2}{\pi} \approx 0.4$$

$$width = 1.2 * diameter = 0.4 * circumference$$

6. Arterial Pressure Measurements

6.1 Lower Extremity Segmental Pressures

Capabilities:
- Documents the presence, level, and severity of arterial occlusive disease
- Provides a method of follow-up for progression of disease, to monitor medical therapy, and evaluate surgical or interventional procedures
- Differentiates vascular symptoms from neurologic or musculoskeletal disorders

Patient Positioning:
For lower extremity evaluation the patient must be supine with the extremities at the same level as the heart. The head may be slightly elevated with the patient's head resting on a pillow. If the patient is unable to lie in a supine position, he/she may be moved to an alternate position such as the lateral decubitus position. It is important that the extremities remain at the same level as the heart. The patient's legs may be slightly externally rotated to facilitate proper Doppler placement and insonation.

Technical Considerations:
- Important: Allow a 10-15 minute rest period prior to beginning the procedure to stabilize the systolic pressure. Pressures in patients with arterial occlusive disease may drop precipitously after minimal exercise.
- Provide a consistent and comfortable ambient room temperature.
- Pressure measurements should be taken at the same level as the heart. If the patient is not supine, hydrostatic pressure will produce erroneous blood pressure measurements. Example: if pressures are obtained while the patient is in a sitting position, the lower extremity systolic pressures will be elevated. If the extremity is elevated above the level of the heart, erroneously low pressure readings will be generated.
- Cuffs should be of appropriate size to encircle the limb circumference. Take care not to position the bladder or connector of the cuff over bony structures.

Appropriate cuff size:
- Bladder size 12 X 40 cm - (brachial, below knee, ankle)
- Bladder size 12 X 54 cm - (high thigh, above knee)
- May use 10 X 40 cm bladder at the brachial and ankle levels

Segmental Pressures: Four Cuff vs Three Cuff Method:
- **Three Cuff Method**
  A three cuff method may be used with a 19 X 40 cm bladder at the thigh level. This method does not allow for differentiation of proximal and distal thigh pressures. One advantage of the three cuff method is that the thigh pressure obtained is generally more accurate due to the artificial pressure elevation generated by the four cuff method.

- **Four Cuff Method**
  With the four cuff method of segmental pressures, cuffs are applied to the following segments: high thigh, above knee, below knee, and ankle. Although the four cuff method introduces an artifactual elevation of the high thigh measurement due to limb size discrepancy, the four cuff method is generally preferred by most laboratories as it allows for differentiation of superficial femoral artery obstruction.

Procedure: Segmental Pressures

Apply blood pressure cuffs at the brachial, high thigh, above knee, below knee and ankle levels. Obtain bilateral brachial pressures and then begin lower extremity pressures at the level of the ankle, moving proximally. Use the best signal of the posterior tibial, dorsalis pedis, or peroneal arteries to obtain pressures. If the distal signals are weak or absent, AK pressures may be obtained using the popliteal artery. Remember, the systolic pressure being measured is the pressure in the artery (arteries) underlying the cuff, not at the level of the Doppler.

If pressures need to be repeated, wait approximately one minute before re-inflating the cuff to allow for normalization of flow.

Interpretation:
Ankle/Brachial Indices (ABI's)

The ankle/brachial indices are calculated for each leg by dividing the highest ankle pressure (DP, PT, or peroneal) by the highest brachial systolic pressure.

$$Ankle\,/\,Brachial\ Index\ (ABI) = \frac{highest\ ankle\ pressure\ (PT, DP, peroneal)}{highest\ brachial\ systolic\ pressure}$$

> 1.00	=	Within normal limits (except with calcified vessels)
0.90 - 1.00	=	Asymptomatic - minimal arterial obstruction
0.50 - 0.90	=	Claudication range
< 0.50	=	Impending tissue loss/gangrene

Pressure Gradients

- A gradient of 20 mmHg or greater between brachial pressures suggests innominate, subclavian, axillary, or brachial artery obstruction on the side with the lower brachial pressure.
- The proximal high thigh (HT) pressure should be at least 20-30 mmHg higher than the brachial pressure. A low high-thigh pressure is suggestive of inflow disease. Superficial femoral artery disease coupled with a stenosis or occlusion of the profunda femoris artery may also result in a low high-thigh pressure.
- Normally, the pressure gradient between adjacent levels of measurement of the leg should be no greater than 20 mmHg:

> High thigh (HT) - Above knee (AK)
> Above knee (AK) - Below knee (BK)
> Below knee (BK) - Ankle

- Limb to limb pressures at the same level should not exceed 20 mmHg.

Abnormal Gradient	Suggested Level of Disease
HT - brachial	Aortoiliac, SFA/profunda
HT - AK	SFA, SFA/profunda
AK - BK	distal SFA, popliteal
BK - ankle	tibioperoneal

Diabetic patients may exhibit arterial medial wall calcification of the arteries making the arteries difficult to compress or incompressible with pressures > 200 mmHg. The arterial segmental pressures are artificially elevated in the presence of medial wall calcification.

Note: Some laboratories report pressure gradients of up to 30 mmHg between cuff segments as normal. This criterion is also acceptable. Each laboratory must validate their diagnostic criteria by comparison to angiography and/or surgery.

High - Thigh Index (HTI)

Normally, with the four cuff measurement method, the high thigh pressure should exceed the higher brachial pressure by at least 30 mmHg. When the high thigh pressure measurement is low, the iliac artery is indicated as the site of obstruction.

$$High-Thigh\ Index(HTI) = \frac{high-thigh\ pressure}{highest\ brachial\ pressure}$$

> 1.2 = Normal
0.8 - 1.2 = suggests aortoiliac stenosis
< 0.8 = suggests iliac occlusion

Toe/Brachial Index (TBI)

$$Toe/Brachial\ Index(TBI) = \frac{toe\ pressure}{highest\ brachial\ pressure}$$

$\geq$ 0.70 = Normal FBI

Referenced from Gerlock, Giyanani, & Krebs. Applications of Non-invasive Vascular Techniques. W.B. Saunders Company, 1988.

6.2 Upper Extremity Arterial Pressures

Technical Considerations:
- Cuffs should be of appropriate size to encircle the limb circumference.
- Take care not to position the bladder of the cuff over bony structures, i.e. the elbow.

Procedure:
- Place blood pressure cuffs over the muscular portion of the arm and forearm bilaterally.
- Use the radial and ulnar arteries to obtain systolic pressures of the arm. The brachial artery may be used to obtain the upper arm pressure.

Appropriate cuff size:
- Bladder size 12 X 40 cm for upper arm (brachial)
- Bladder size 10 X 40 cm for forearm
- May use 10 X 40 cm bladder on upper arm if the patient is thin
- Use the radial and ulnar arteries to obtain systolic pressures of the arm. The brachial artery may be used to obtain the upper arm pressure.

Potential sources of technical error:
- Improper cuff placement
- Compression of the radial or ulnar arteries by excessive pressure

Interpretation:
- A gradient of 20 mmHg or more between brachial pressures suggests innominate, subclavian, axillary, or brachial artery obstruction on the side with the lower brachial pressure.
- Normally, the forearm pressure should be equal to or slightly higher than the brachial pressure.
- A gradient of 10-20 mmHg is suggestive of:
  - brachial artery obstruction distal to the cuff
  - obstruction in both the radial and ulnar arteries
  - obstruction in a single forearm artery (decreased pressure)
- The radial and ulnar pressures should be within 5-10 mmHg.
- A pressure gradient > 10 mmHg suggests obstruction in the vessel with the lower pressures.

Finger/Brachial Index (FBI)

$$Finger\ /\ Brachial\ Index(FBI) = \frac{finger\ systolic\ pressure}{ipsilateral\ brachial\ systolic\ pressure}$$

0.8 - 1.0 = Normal FBI

Decreased digit pressures are indicative of the following:
- radial or ulnar obstructive disease
- incomplete deep and/or superficial palmar arch
- digital artery obstructive disease

7. Reactive Hyperemia

Reactive hyperemia literally means "more blood in response to an action." Whenever tissue becomes ischemic because of a temporary stenosis or occlusion, the body responds by increasing blood flow to reinstate adequate perfusion and meet the "built up demand."

Reactive hyperemia studies can be performed when a patient cannot be stressed or exercised to measure the ability of a patient's vessels to vasodilate after a period of induced vasodilation and ischemia. The technique involves placing a pneumatic cuff around the thigh and inflating to a pressure 20-30 mmHg above the highest brachial pressure. This pressure is maintained for 3 to 5 minutes and then released.

The ankle pressure changes on release of the cuff are similar to post exercise findings. A mild drop (17-34%) may occur in normal patients. A single level obstruction demonstrates an approximate 50% drop in ankle pressure while multilevel obstructions demonstrate a greater than 50% drop following reactive hyperemia testing.

8. Skin Temperature and Skin Changes

Skin color changes:
- **Pallor elevation** - patient's legs become pale in color with elevation. The arterial system cannot pump adequate blood into the capillary system against gravity through the arterial blockages.
- **Dependent rubor** - a deep red color occurs due to blood pooling in the arterioles.

Capillary filling

Capillary filling is a crude method of assessing arterial blood flow characterized by pressing on an area on the toes or sole of the foot and assessing the time for the blanched area to return to a pink color.

Trophic changes: Trophic changes are skin changes that are indicative of arterial insufficiency.
- Hair loss over toes and dorsum of foot
- Thin, shiny, smooth or scaly skin
- Thickened, brittle toenails

Cyanosis: Cyanosis is a dusky, bluish discoloration of the skin
- Localized cyanosis - indicative of a local area of decreased circulation
- Generalized cyanosis - overall decreased perfusion; i.e. CHF, advanced respiratory disease

Temperature changes:
- Symmetrical coolness - vasoconstriction
- Asymmetrical coolness - arterial insufficiency

9. Occlusion Pressures

Pressure necessary to occlude superficial veins is obviously less than pressure necessary for deep venous occlusion. Similarly, a significantly higher pressure is necessary to overcome the high transmural pressure of an arterial vessel.
- Superficial venous occlusion - approximately 10-20 mmHg
- Deep venous occlusion - approximately 40-70 mmHg
- Arterial occlusion - approximately 30 mmHg > systolic pressure

Since small pressures can cause venous occlusion, proper care must be taken in patient positioning for testing. Artifact can easily be introduced by incorrectly positioning a limb under test. For lower extremity testing, the proper position entails positioning the knee in a slightly flexed position with the leg rotated externally. It is important to maintain a relaxed muscle position since muscle tension can change tissue pressures, affecting the transmural pressure. By placing the examination table at approximately 30 degrees, intravascular pressure is increased through an increase in hydrostatic pressure. For examinations such as venous reflux testing with photoplethysmography where the patient is positioned in a sitting position, care should be taken to avoid pressure against the popliteal fossa, causing extrinsic compression of the popliteal vein.

10. Oculoplethysmography (OPG)

The OPG is used to measure the systolic pressure in the ophthalmic artery by obtaining an indirect measurement of the pulse delay within the ophthalmic artery. Since the ophthalmic artery is a branch of the internal carotid artery, a delay in the pulse as compared to the ipsilateral external carotid artery, or as compared to the contralateral side, would suggest a significant obstruction within the internal carotid artery. OPG pressure measurements are achieved by attaching a small suction cup on the sclera of both eyes. A vacuum is then produced, distorting the eye shape until the ophthalmic artery blood supply is occluded. The vacuum pressure is then slowly released and the pressure at which pulsatile flow returns to the ophthalmic artery is recorded. The OPG works by measuring changes in the volume of the eye during arterial pulsations. The pulse in the ear is often measured simultaneously as a measure of the external carotid artery flow.

Capabilities:
- Monitors direction of flow in some of the terminal branches of the ICA.
- Aids in detecting a hemodynamically significant obstruction of the ICA.

Limitations:
- Only indicates hemodynamically significant stenoses.
- Cannot differentiate severe stenosis from occlusion.
- Not sensitive to non-obstructive lesions, i.e. ulceration, plaque hemorrhage.
- Procedure cannot be performed on patients with the following contraindications:
  - History of retinal detachment
  - History of glaucoma
  - Recent (past 6 months) eye surgery
  - Allergy to local anesthetics
  - Involuntary or voluntary movement may make it difficult to generate a reliable tracing

Procedure:
- The patient is placed in a supine position.
- Bilateral systolic blood pressures are recorded.
- Suction eyecups are applied to the anesthetized sclera (lateral aspect of the eye). Explain to patient that they will experience momentary loss of vision when the vacuum is applied.
- Baseline analog pulse recordings are generated.
- A vacuum of 300 mmHg or 500 mmHg is applied to the ocular globe. Patients with a systolic blood pressure < 140 mmHg generally require only a 300 mmHg pressure applied. Patients with a systolic blood pressure > 140 mmHg may need 500 mmHg vacuum.
- As the vacuum is increased, the intraocular pressure increases. When the intraocular pressure exceeds the ophthalmic artery pressure, the pulse recordings fall to baseline.
- After reaching the 300 or 500 mmHg vacuum, the vacuum is slowly reduced and the return of the arterial ocular pulsations is recorded bilaterally. Systolic ophthalmic arterial pressure is calculated from the analog recordings. The ocular recordings and systolic arterial blood pressures are compared.

Interpretation:
- Normal: < 5 mmHg difference between the two ophthalmic systolic pressures.
- Abnormal: > 5 mmHg pressure difference between the two ophthalmic systolic pressures.

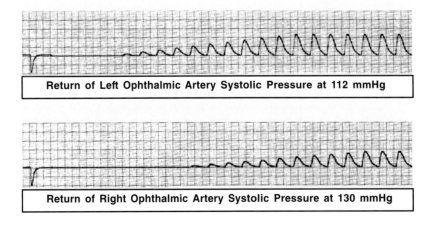

Return of Left Ophthalmic Artery Systolic Pressure at 112 mmHg

Return of Right Ophthalmic Artery Systolic Pressure at 130 mmHg

Fig. 14   **OPG Tracing from a Patient with a Left ICA Occlusion**

11. Miscellaneous

11.1 Arteriovenous Fistula

An arteriovenous fistula is an abnormal communication between the arteries and venous systems. The etiology may be congenital or acquired (traumatic). Characteristic flow includes increased arterial diastolic flow and pulsatility of the venous flow. Often there is venous dilation around the fistula with distal arterial ischemia. The magnitude of these physiologic changes depends on the size and location of the communication.

11.2 Autogenous Arteriovenous Fistulae

Creating an arteriovenous fistula is a method of achieving long term vascular access for hemodialysis. There are various anastomotic approaches to surgically connect the artery and the vein. The direction of blood flow in the artery and vein proximal to the connection is normal. The arterial flow is shunted into a vein, bypassing the normal arteriole-capillary-venule flow. This creates a fall in peripheral vascular resistance. An increase in cardiac output compensates for the fall in peripheral vascular resistance by causing increased flow through the fistula. Venous outflow is also increased with the creation of the AV fistula although a significant increase in central venous pressure usually does not occur due to the large capacity of the veins.

11.3 Pseudoaneurysm

A pseudoaneurysm (false aneurysm) is created by the perforation of the intima and media and is generally contained by a thin layer of adventitia or thrombus. A communication is created between the main arterial lumen and a sac that is formed by the leaking blood. Flow between the sac and the arterial lumen with each cardiac cycle creates characteristic "to and fro" motion.

12. Transcutaneous Oximetry

All of the testing methods we have previously discussed measure the hemodynamic consequences of peripheral vascular disease. Transcutaneous oxygen tension measurements ($tcPo_2$) are used to measure the metabolic demand of the tissue. The $tcPo_2$ values are a function of cutaneous blood flow, metabolic activity, oxyhemoglobin and oxygen diffusion of the tissue. Changes in $tcPo_2$ are usually not seen with moderate arterial disease unless uncovered by conditions of stress. The $tcPo_2$ levels fall as the level of oxygen reaching the tissue is decreased.

Common areas of measurement:
- dorsum of foot
- anteromedial calf (approximately 10 cm below patella)
- thigh (approximately 10 cm above patella)
- chest (sub-clavicular region)

Interpretation:
- Normal $tcPo_2$ levels: approximately 60 mmHg
- In general a level of 55 mmHg is considered normal regardless of patient age. Normally, there usually is a mild decrease in $tcPo_2$ from the leg to the foot (5-6 mmHg). Also noted is a decrease in $tcPo_2$ values with increasing age.
- Patients with claudication may have normal or near normal resting values. Changes in $tcPo_2$ values

are not seen as long as the body's autoregulatory capacity is capable of preserving a normal level of peripheral blood flow. Claudicating patients that develop collateral vessels create a mechanism of alternate blood flow to continue providing an adequate level of peripheral blood flow at rest.

The tcPo$_2$ measurements are more sensitive in cases of advanced ischemia. It is only in patients where the autoregulatory capacity is exhausted that we see a decrease in the tcPo$_2$ values. In patients with advanced arterial insufficiency the arterial inflow is so severely restricted that the amount of oxygen available to be delivered to the tissue is exceeded by the metabolic requirements, yielding inadequate oxygen available for diffusion to the skin tissue. Patients with advanced limb-threatening arterial ischemia generally exhibit tcPo$_2$ values of less than 20 mmHg at the foot level.

13. Transcranial Doppler

13.1 General

Transcranial Doppler is a noninvasive technique to assess the major cerebral arteries through natural cranial windows. There are three natural acoustic windows: the transtemporal, transorbital and transforaminal windows. Although an imaging transducer may be used, a "blind" Doppler usually allows for a more complete assessment of the course of the intracranial vessels. Transcranial Doppler is a learned skill by which the technologist must learn to identify the intracranial vessels through intracranial anatomy, flow direction, vessel depth and the audible Doppler signal. The technologist aligns the ultrasound beam axially to the blood vessels to obtain the lowest angle possible. By audible assessment the highest pitch (velocity) and strongest signal (amplitude) is identified.

When insonating the intracranial vessels the following technical parameters must be used:

- 2 MHz (or lower frequency) pulsed wave Doppler with spectral analysis
- Large sample volume (greater than 1 cm)
- Bi-directional Doppler

13.2 Identifying Vessels

Since the identification of the intracranial vessels is primarily based on vessel anatomy, flow direction and sample volume depth it is imperative that the technologist understands the following parameters:

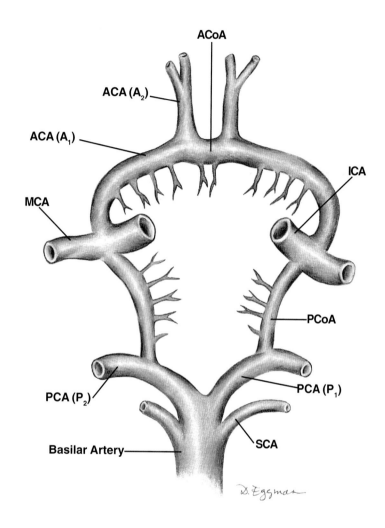

Fig. 15   **Circle of Willis**

Normal Circle of Willis

ACA (A$_1$) - Anterior Cerebral Artery (pre-communicating segment)
ACA (A$_2$) - Anterior Cerebral Artery (post-communicating segment)
ACoA – Anterior Communicating Artery
MCA - Middle Cerebral Artery
ICA - Internal Carotid Artery
PCA (P$_1$) – Posterior Cerebral Artery (pre-communicating segment)
PCA (P$_2$) – Posterior Cerebral Artery (post-communicating segment)
PCoA – Posterior Communicating Artery
SCA – Superior Cerebellar Artery

Window	Vessels Evaluated	Direction	Depth (mm)
Transtemporal:	MCA	Toward	30-60
	MCA/ACA bifurcation	Bi-directional	55-65
	ACA (A1)	Away	60-80
	PCA (P1)	Toward	60-70
	PCA (P2)	Away	60-70
	Terminal ICA	Toward	55-65
	ACoA*		
	PCoA*		
	(*May be identified if carrying collateral flow)		
Transorbital:	Ophthalmic artery	Toward	40-60
	Carotid siphon:		
	Supraglenoid	Away	60-80
	Genu	Bidirectional	60-80
	Parasellar	Toward	60-60
Transforaminal:	Vertebral artery	Away	60-90
	Basilar artery	Away	80-120

13.3 Technical Limitations:

- Absent or small temporal windows (often found in postmenopausal women – age, race, and gender all affect windows)
- Hyperostosis (increase in skull density and thickness, predominantly found in women)
- Weak signals from attenuation through bone (> 17 dB one way)
- Improper identification of acoustic window
- Anatomic variations (incomplete Circle of Willis, hypertrophy or absent vessels, congenital abnormalities)
- Signal exceeds Nyquist limits (aliasing)
- Large sample volume
- Unknown Doppler angle
- Collateral flow misinterpreted as stenosis

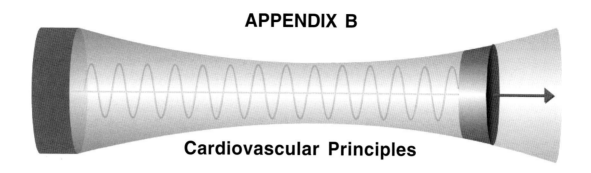

APPENDIX B

Cardiovascular Principles

Introduction

Like vascular principles, cardiovascular principles is really a collective title for myriad topics. Within the category of cardiovascular principles are included basic heart anatomy, basic embryology, congenital defects, cardiac physiology, cardiac evaluation methods, and principles of cardiac hemodynamics. As with Appendix A: Vascular Principles, because of this broad categorization there is not one central theme to this chapter. As a result, a slightly different style has been adopted to adequately cover so many topics without converting this one section into an entire book of its own. Furthermore, this appendix is intended to compliment but not replace a book on cardiovascular technology.

1. The Circulatory System

The circulatory system is driven by the heart. The heart is actually two pumps attached in series. The right side of the heart is responsible for providing blood to the pulmonary bed for oxygenation. The left side is responsible for profusing the systemic side. Understanding how the heart acts as a pump is important for understanding electrical, volume, and pressure function and problems. We will begin by quickly reviewing the major system components.

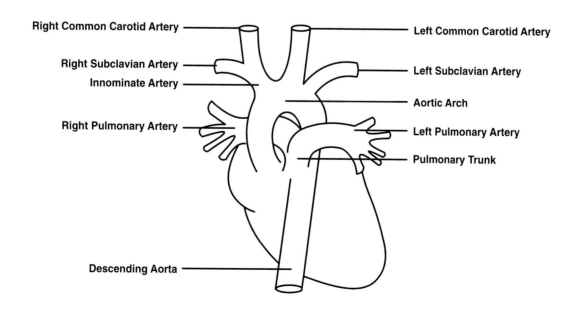

Fig. 1 **The Heart and Large Vessels**

1.1 Pulmonary vs. Systemic Circulatory Components

The function of the heart is intricately tied and affected by all of the circulatory system. It is beneficial to quickly review the major components and their principal functionality.

Pulmonary	**Systemic**
pulmonary artery	aorta
arteries	arteries
capillaries	arterioles
veins	capillaries
	venules
	veins
	vena cava

1.2 Pulmonary vs. Systemic Circulation

Pulmonary	**Systemic**
low pressure	high pressure
low resistance	high resistance
RV wall is thin	LV wall is thick
low O_2 content	high O_2 content

1.3 Arteries

The arteries are divided histologically into three layers:

Intima: Monolayer of endothelial cells innermost layer.

Media: Relatively thick layer containing smooth muscle cells, collagen and elastin. (The intima and media are separated by the internal elastic membrane.)

Adventitia: Consists of fibroblasts, collagen, and elastic tissue. The adventitia provides overall strength and structure for the vessel. (The external elastic membrane separates the media from the adventitia.)

Vaso Vasorum: Small blood vessels that penetrate the outer wall of the artery.

Note: The intima and the inner portion of the media receive nutrients by diffusion from the arterial lumen. The outer portion of the media and the adventitia are provided with nutrients by the vaso vasorum.

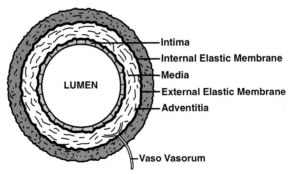

Fig. 2 **Layers of an Artery**

Understanding the structure of the arteries is important for understanding the functional behavior of the aorta and the resistive control mechanism performed by the arterioles.

1.4 Veins
Similar to the arterial wall, the venous wall is composed of three discrete layers.

Intima: Innermost layer, single layer of endothelial cell. In larger veins a subendothelial layer of supportive tissue is identified.

Media: Composed primarily of smooth muscle. Provides support and some resistance to dilatation.

The histologic composition of the media is the major difference between arteries and veins. The media in arteries is much thicker which accounts for the firm character of the artery as well as the minimal distensibility of the artery.

Adventitia: Thin layer of connective tissue, outermost layer.

1.5 Comparison of Arteries and Veins

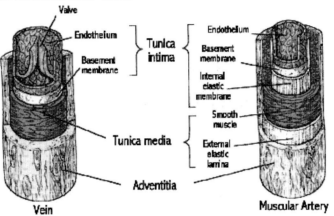

Fig. 3 **Comparison of Arteries and Veins**

1.6 Comparison of Arterioles and Capillaries

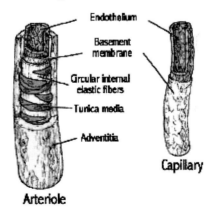

Fig. 4 **Comparison of Arterioles and Capillaries**

Illustrations of Comparison of Arteries and Veins and Comparison of Arterioles and Capillaries: Human Anatomy and Physiology, Third Edition; Spence AP, Mason EB, Copyright 1987 by the Benjamin/Cummings Publishing Company, Reprinted with permission of Pearson Education, Inc.

Often the physical structure of the veins is ignored; and the veins are thought of as strictly passive conduits for blood flow. This assumption is completely incorrect. Whereas the veins tend to be much less rigid than arteries, there is an ability for venous constriction. Normally, the majority of the blood is maintained within the venous structure (approximately 65%). When greater cardiac output is necessary, the veins are able to constrict, significantly decreasing their capacitance. When the constriction occurs there is generally a relatively large bolus of venous return. Additionally, muscle contraction around the capacitive veins also helps increase venous return.

2. Muscle Contraction and the Sodium Ion Pump

2.1 Positive and Negative Potentials

Muscle contraction is caused by an electro-chemical stimulus. In general, muscle contraction is caused by a specific sequence of chemical events which result in electrical changes. Specifically, changes in the concentration of sodium ions (Na+) causes changes in the electrical potential voltage. A sodium ion is a cation and has a positive charge. If there is a higher concentration of sodium ions within the cell membrane rather than external to the cell membrane, there is a voltage "potential" difference across the cell membrane, and the cell membrane is said to have a positive potential. Conversely, if the concentration of Na+ is higher externally the potential is negative. The reference for whether or not a potential is positive or negative is based on the charge external to the cell relative to the charge within the cell. This convention was arbitrary but is now the standard reference.

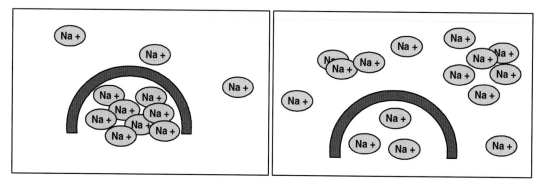

POSITIVE POTENTIAL   **NEGATIVE POTENTIAL**

Fig. 5 **Sodium Ion Concentration and Potential**

When a muscle cell is at rest, there is a greater concentration of ions external to the cell membrane and hence, a negative polarization called the "resting" potential. The resting potential is typically -90 mV. For a muscle to contract, a stimulus is needed to disturb the resting potential and excite the cell. The stimulus is caused by allowing some of the sodium ions from the higher external concentration to pass through the cell membrane.

2.2 Action Potentials

If the stimulus changes the potential beyond a threshold potential, the process becomes self-generating. The membrane allows for a rush of sodium ions to enter the cell, thereby significantly changing the polarization of the cell until the concentration of ions is higher within the cell. The cell is now positively polarized. Typically, the voltage peaks at about +40 mV. This rapid change in polarization is called an "action potential".

If, however, the initial stimulus does not exceed the threshold potential, there is no continuation of ion transfer and there is no action potential.

2.3 Repolarization

After a cell has been depolarized, the cell rapidly pumps the sodium ions through the cell membrane to the exterior of the cell, again returning to the resting potential of approximately -90 mV. This process is called repolarization.

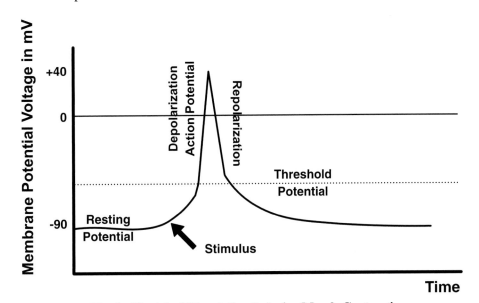

Fig. 6   **Electrical Stimulation Inducing Muscle Contraction**

2.4. The Depolarization Wave

The depolarization of a muscle cell membrane causes the muscle to contract. As an individual cell is depolarized by its action potential, a depolarizing wave begins to propagate to all surrounding cell membranes. The result is a "domino effect" by which all of the muscle cells are stimulated to create a muscle contraction.

2.5. The Refractory Period

Once a cell reaches its action potential, a stimulus is not able to activate the cell membrane until it has returned to a potential below the threshold voltage. This period of time during which a cell cannot be reactivated is called the absolute refractory period. Once the cell membrane has returned to a potential below the threshold, the cell can be stimulated but requires a larger stimulus than when the cell is at its resting potential. This period of time is called the relative refractory period. Once the cell returns to its resting potential, the cell can again be reactivated by a stimulus greater than the threshold voltage. The refractory period is extremely important in that it restricts an individual cell from remaining in a constant state of stimulation, and does not allow an action potential wave to return in the direction from which it came.

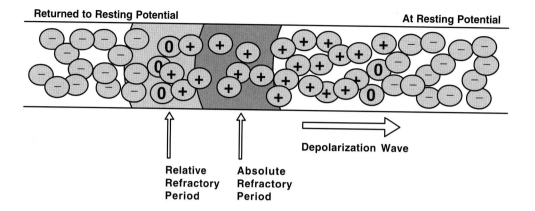

Fig. 7 **Traveling Depolarization Wave and Refractory Period**

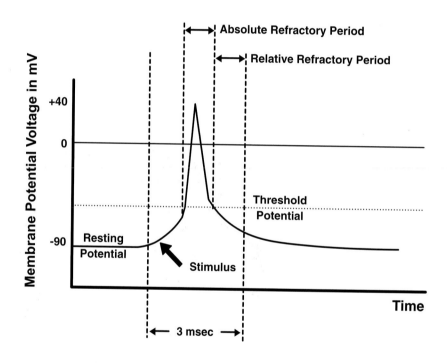

Fig. 8 **Electrical Potential and the Refractory Period**

3. Cardiac Muscle Contraction

3.1 Differences Between Skeletal and Cardiac Muscle

Like skeletal muscle, cardiac muscle contraction is stimulated to contraction by changes in concentration of the sodium ion across the cell membranes. However, there are some very important differences between cardiac muscle and skeletal muscle. Cardiac muscle has:

- a longer refractory period
- self-stimulating action potential (automaticity)
- a high-speed electrical conductive path

We will now consider the importance of each of these differences.

3.2 Extended Refractory Period

Recall that the refractory period for general muscle is about 3 msec. The absolute refractory period for myocardium is approximately 250 msec and the relative refractory period is approximately another 50 msec. By taking the reciprocal of the absolute refractory period, the maximum heart rate can be determined. A 250 msec period corresponds to a maximum heart rate of:

$$\frac{1}{250 \text{ msec}} = 0.004 \text{ kHz} = 4 \frac{\text{beats}}{\text{second}} = 4 \frac{\text{beats}}{\text{second}} * 60 \frac{\text{seconds}}{\text{minute}} = 240 \frac{\text{beats}}{\text{minute}}$$

The extended refractory period is critical for heart muscle so that the heart can act as an efficient pump. A too fast heart rate would not provide sufficient filling time, and hence, would create a very inefficient pump. Imagine if the refractory period for myocardial muscle were the same as for skeletal muscle. The polarization wave could potentially reactivate the heart muscle at almost 2000 beats per minute -- clearly not an acceptable rate.

3.3 Automaticity

Unlike skeletal muscle, cardiac muscle is able to depolarize without an external stimulus. This self-generating action potential is called "automaticity". Once the cell membrane of a myocardial cell is repolarized to its resting potential, the cell membrane is "leaky" to sodium ions. As a result depolarization begins immediately but slowly. As the sodium ions continue to leak across the membrane, the sodium ion concentration within the myocardial cells increases until the membrane potential reaches the threshold potential. Once the threshold potential is reached the cell is activated to rapid depolarization (action potential). Hence, because of the "leaky" membrane, myocardial cells are capable of self-activating without an external depolarizing wave.

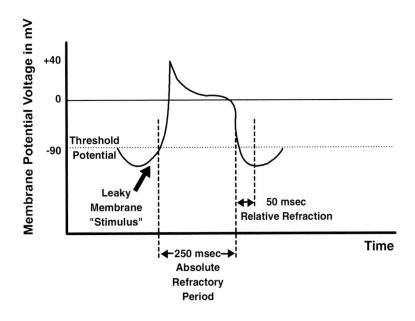

Fig. 9   **Electrical Potential for Heart Muscle**

The rate at which a cell depolarizes and repolarizes without an "external" stimulus is called the natural rate of the cell. However, an external action potential wave can stimulate the cell at a rate faster than the natural rate, as long as the cell is out of the refractory period. As demonstrated in the figure below H3 represents the natural rate of the cell. Both H2 and H1 demonstrate a faster heart rate which result from a depolarization wave stimulating the cell.

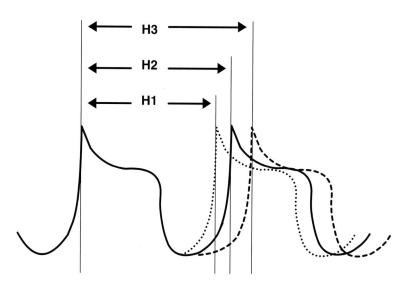

Fig. 10 **Varying Heart Rates**

3.4 High Speed Electrical Pathway

For a heart beat to create a useful pumping action, the contraction must take place in a very specific sequence. For skeletal muscle, the action potential travels from cell to cell at a uniform rate. In order to achieve the appropriate contraction sequence, the heart has high-speed electrical pathways to conduct the depolarization wave. The following sequence represents the normal electrical conduction pathway:

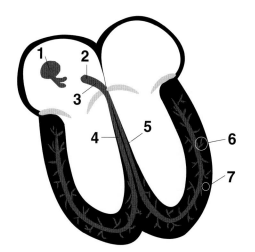

1	Sino-atrial Node (SA)	70 - 100 BPM
2	Atrio-ventricular Node (AV)	60 BPM
3	Bundle of His	50 – 55 BPM
4	Left Bundle Branch	50 – 55 BPM
5	Right Bundle Branch	50 – 55 BPM
6	Purkinje Fibers	40 – 45 BPM
7	Myocardium	30 –35 BPM

Fig. 11 **Pacing Locations and Cardiac Rates**

4. Electrical Signals: The EKG

An EKG (or ECG) is used to measure the electrical activity of the heart. When a depolarization wave travels towards a positive lead of the EKG, the deflected wave is positive or upward. If the depolarizing wave goes towards the negative lead, or equivalently away from the positive lead, the deflection is downward or negative. The following waveform represents a normal EKG waveform.

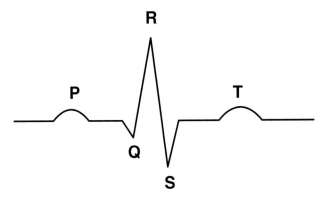

Fig. 12 **Normal EKG Waveform**

4.1 Phases of an EKG

It is important to understand how to interpret the basics of the electrical tracing displayed by an EKG.

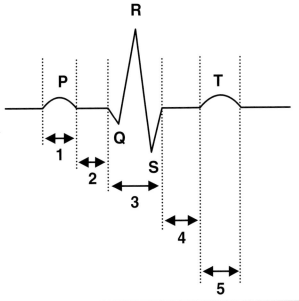

1	P - Wave	Atrial Depolarization
2	P -R Segment	Delay of Depolarizing Wave in AV Node
3	QRS Complex	Ventricular Depolarization
4	S-T Segment	Refractory Period
5	T - Wave	Ventricular Repolarization

Fig. 13 **Phases of an EKG Waveform**

The P Wave is the result of the depolarization wave stimulating the atria. Shortly after the electrical stimulus, the mechanical contraction of the two atria occurs. There is a delay in the action potential wave at the AV node. This delay is important to allow time for the blood to flow into the ventricles through the AV valves (mitral and tricuspid). The QRS complex represents the electrical activity which depolarizes the ventricles. Shortly after the depolarization of the ventricles, ventricular contraction occurs. The S-T segment represents the refractory period. During this period blood is ejected through the two semi-lunar valves (pulmonary and aortic). The T-Wave represents ventricular repolarization. Repolarization of the ventricles occurs from the epicardium towards the endocardium. This means that even though the repolarization wave makes the myocardium more negative, the deflection is positive since it is going away from the positive lead.

4.2 Interpreting Timing and the Heart Rate

EKG's are presented on a calibrated strip of graph paper or a calibrated graph on a monitor. The smallest square is 1 mm by 1 mm. The vertical axis is a measure of the strength of the electrical potential (voltage) and is measured in milli-Volts. The horizontal axis represents time. Each square represents 0.04 seconds. Major divisions are marked every 5 squares as shown on the two figures below.

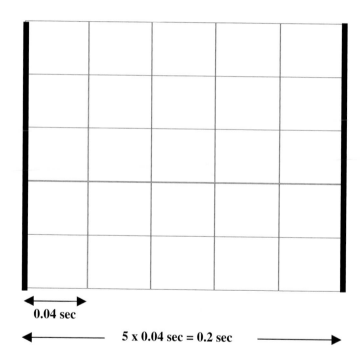

Fig. 14   **Strip Chart Timing**

With the knowledge that each individual square is equivalent to 0.04 seconds, the number of beats per minute (the heart rate) can be easily calculated as indicated by the following table.

$$1 \text{ major division} = \frac{1}{0.2 \text{ sec}} * 60 \frac{\text{seconds}}{\text{minute}} = 300 \frac{\text{beats}}{\text{minute}}$$

$$2 \text{ major divisions} = \frac{1}{0.4 \text{ sec}} * 60 \frac{\text{seconds}}{\text{minute}} = 150 \frac{\text{beats}}{\text{minute}}$$

$$3 \text{ major divisions} = \frac{1}{0.6 \text{ sec}} * 60 \frac{\text{seconds}}{\text{minute}} = 100 \frac{\text{beats}}{\text{minute}}$$

$$4 \text{ major divisions} = \frac{1}{0.8 \text{ sec}} * 60 \frac{\text{seconds}}{\text{minute}} = 75 \frac{\text{beats}}{\text{minute}}$$

$$5 \text{ major divisions} = \frac{1}{1 \text{ sec}} * 60 \frac{\text{seconds}}{\text{minute}} = 60 \frac{\text{beats}}{\text{minute}}$$

$$6 \text{ major divisions} = \frac{1}{1.2 \text{ sec}} * 60 \frac{\text{seconds}}{\text{minute}} = 50 \frac{\text{beats}}{\text{minute}}$$

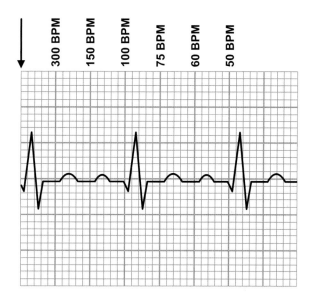

Fig. 15   **Calculating the Heart Rate from an EKG Tracing**

The above example shows an EKG waveform which repeats every three major divisions, representing a heart rate of 100 beats per minute.

An extensive treatment of EKG interpretation is beyond the scope of these materials. We highly recommend Dubin's <u>Rapid Interpretation of EKG's.</u>

5. Pressure and Volume

As already discussed, the electrical conduction of the action potential is very specific and sequential within the heart. The result is a very specific timing and sequencing of contractions. The result of these contractions is a periodic pressure waveform and a corresponding change in blood volume. Since nearly everyone is familiar with blood pressure measurements, we will start with the aortic pressure and work back through the left ventricle and left atrium to the pulmonary veins. Then we will discuss the parallel situation of the right-sided system from the pulmonic artery to the right ventricle to the right atrium to the vena cava.

5.1 A few Fundamental Concepts

To understand the time variant pressure and volume curves, it is useful to review a few fundamental concepts.

5.1.1 The Simplified Law of Hemodynamics

The simplified law of hemodynamics ($\Delta P = Q * R$) expresses the fact that blood flows from a higher pressure to a lower pressure. In other words, it takes a pressure gradient to cause fluid to flow across a resistive path. When the pressure within one chamber increases beyond the pressure of the adjacent chamber, the valve opens and the blood flows from the higher pressure to the lower pressure. The result is clearly an increase in pressure in the chamber into which the blood has moved.

5.1.2 Mechanical Events Lag Electrical Events

A second important concept is that mechanical events always lag electrical events. In other words, a mechanical event stimulated by an electrical event never occurs simultaneously with the electrical event.

5.1.3 Isovolumic Contraction

A third important concept is related to the relative incompressibility of a fluid. The prefix "iso" means the same. So the word isovolumic means the same volume. When a volume of fluid is compressed within a closed chamber, the volume of fluid stays relatively constant, but the pressure will significantly increase.

5.1.4 The Continuity Equation

The fourth important concept is demonstrated by the volumetric flow equation (Continuity Equation): $Q = \bar{v} * A$. This equation stresses that for a closed system the volume of fluid flowing out of the left side of the heart must equal the volume of fluid returning to the right side of the heart. This equation also allows for a calculation of the blood velocity. If there is an adequate pressure to overcome the resistance, the blood flow velocity will be determined by the relative cross-sectional areas. Going from a large chamber through a narrowing, such as a valve, will cause an increase in velocity to maintain the volumetric flow.

5.2 Aortic Arterial Pressure

5.2.1 The Pulse Pressure
With the four concepts just reviewed, we can begin looking at the aortic pressure. Typical aortic pressure is approximately 120 mmHg/80 mmHg. In other words, the peak systolic pressure is 120 mmHg, and the end diastolic pressure is 80 mmHg. The Pulse Pressure (PP) is defined as the difference between the peak systolic and end diastolic pressures. In this case the pulse pressure is 40 mmHg.

$$PP = \text{Peak Systolic - End Diastolic Pressure}$$

For this example: PP = 120 mmHg - 80 mmHg = 40 mmHg

5.2.2 The Mean Arterial Pressure (MAP)
The mean arterial pressure (MAP) would be 93 mmHg. This calculation is performed as follows:

$$MAP = \text{End Diastolic Pressure} + \frac{1}{3}(\text{Pulse Pressure}) = \frac{\text{Systolic} + 2*\text{End Diastolic}}{3}$$

For this example: $MAP = 80 \text{ mmHg} + \frac{1}{3}(40 \text{ mmHg}) = 93 \text{ mmHg}$

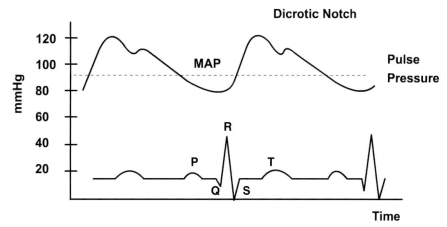

Fig. 16   **Aortic Pressure Waveform and EKG Tracing**

The calculation of the mean arterial pressure confuses many people since they think of averages as adding two numbers and dividing by two. If the pulse pressure wave were a symmetric square wave or sine wave this average would be correct. In reality, the mean pulse pressure should be the integral of the pressure over the time of a cardiac cycle. In other words, if you were to add the pressure at each point in time and then divide by the total number of pressure values used, the true mean pressure would be calculated. As an approximation, the pulse pressure waveform is most closely modeled by a triangle. From calculus, we learn that there is an equivalent area in one third of the base as the top two thirds of a triangle. This is demonstrated graphically in the figure below.

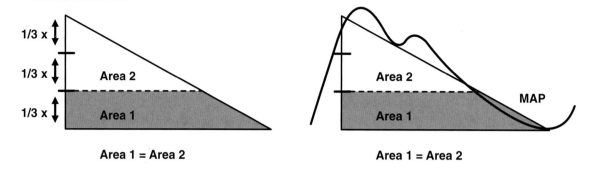

Fig. 17 **Estimation of the MAP by Equal Areas of a Triangle**

Therefore, a relatively accurate estimate of the mean pressure is achieved by the simple calculation of: $\text{MAP} = \text{End Diastolic Pressure} + \frac{1}{3}(\text{Pulse Pressure})$.

5.3 Isovolumic Contraction

The peak systolic pressure is clearly developed by the left ventricle. As the ventricle contracts, the pressure within the ventricle increases. This period is called "isovolumic contraction". Once the pressure within the ventricle exceeds the pressure in the aorta, the aortic valve is forced open. Blood flow begins from the higher pressure ventricle into the lower pressure aorta. The pressure then begins to rise within the aorta.

5.4 Compliance of the Aorta

The compliance of the aorta is very important since the entire volume of blood obviously cannot be instantaneously delivered to the periphery. As a result, the aorta stretches to hold the volume causing an increase in pressure. The amount of volume change per time is known as the capacitance.

5.5 Physiologic Back-flow and Valve Closure

Eventually, the pressure within the aorta exceeds the pressure within the emptying left ventricle. This reversal of the pressure gradient causes a momentary reversal of blood flow (physiologic backflow). This flow reversal causes the aortic valve to close. Once the valve closes there is a slight increase in pressure within the aorta as the momentum of backflow is converted to pressure across the aortic walls as the flow encounters the closed valve. This pressure change is reflected within the pulse pressure waveform and is known as the dicrotic notch. Over time, the pressure within the aorta decreases as the pressure within the aorta drives the blood across the distal resistance.

The end diastolic value and the shape of the pulse pressure waveform are all affected by the following parameters:

    1) The peak systolic pressure
    2) Peripheral resistance
    3) The capacitance of the aorta

5.6 Left Ventricular Pressure

5.6.1 Passive Filling

The pressure waveform within the left ventricle is obviously affected by both the inflow and outflow of blood as well as the ventricular contraction. During the diastolic phase, passive filling from the left atrium causes the pressure to increase slightly. The majority of the blood volume is passed from the atrium to the ventricle through passive filling. As the pressure in the ventricle rises close to the pressure within the atrium, the filling slows. Typically, this pressure is on the order of 10 mmHg or less.

5.6.2 Atrial Kick and Ventricular Contraction

After the electro-mechanical time delay from the P-Wave, atrial systole occurs. The contraction of the atrium ejects the final 20% of the volume. As ventricular systole occurs as a result of the depolarization wave represented in the QRS complex of the EKG, ventricular contraction begins. With the beginning of ventricular contraction, the pressure in the ventricle rises quickly to exceed the pressure within the atrium causing the mitral valve to snap closed.

5.6.3 Isovolumic Contraction

At this point the aortic valve is still closed. Since both valves are closed, the contraction of the ventricle (isovolumic contraction) causes a dramatic increase in the pressure. When the pressure within the ventricle exceeds the pressure within the aorta, the aortic valve opens allowing blood flow to exit the chamber. As already discussed, the pressure begins to rise within the aorta until the aortic valve is forced closed by a flow reversal. With the relaxation of the ventricle, "isovolumic relaxation", the pressure decreases. When the pressure within the ventricle is lower than the pressure of the left atrium, the mitral valve reopens and the cycle of passive filling begins again.

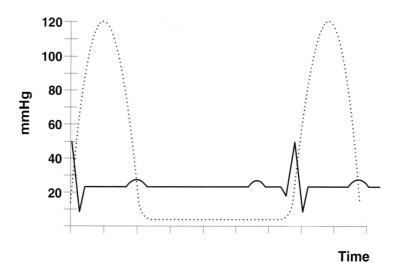

Fig. 17   **Left Ventricular Pressure Curve**

5.7 Left Atrial Pressure

The pressure within the left atrium is clearly a function of the pressure and inflow of the pulmonic veins, the outflow into the left ventricle, and atrial contraction. The pressure within the left atrium generally is below 10 mmHg. Clearly a low left atrial pressure is desired so that there can be oxygenated volumetric flow from the pulmonary bed. The pressure in the atrium begins to increase during ventricular systole as the mitral valve is closed and blood is returning from the pulmonic veins. In the atrial pressure waveform, this phase is identified as the "v" wave. Once the isovolumic relaxation reduces the ventricular pressure below the pressure within the atrium, the mitral valve opens, and passive filling begins from the atrium into the ventricle. With the opening of the mitral valve there is a sudden decrease in atrial pressure. As diastole continues, there is still returning blood flow from the pulmonic veins so that the pressure continues to slowly rise in both the atrium and the ventricle. When atrial systole occurs (the a-wave), there is a quick increase in atrial pressure which is responsible for a slight increase in ventricular filling, often referred to as the "atrial kick." As ventricular pressure begins to increase with ventricular contraction, the ventricular pressure quickly exceeds the pressure within the atrium, forcing the mitral valve closed. The increased pressure within the ventricle causes the mitral valve to push slightly back into the atrium causing a sharp increase in atrial pressure demonstrated as the "c wave."

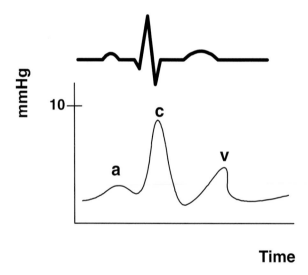

Fig. 18   **Left Atrial Pressure**

6. The Complete Cardiac Cycle

It is useful to put all of these diagrams together to get the full picture of how all of the electrical events, pressure waveforms, and volume waveforms relate. You should be able to explain all of the aspects of the timing of each waveform.

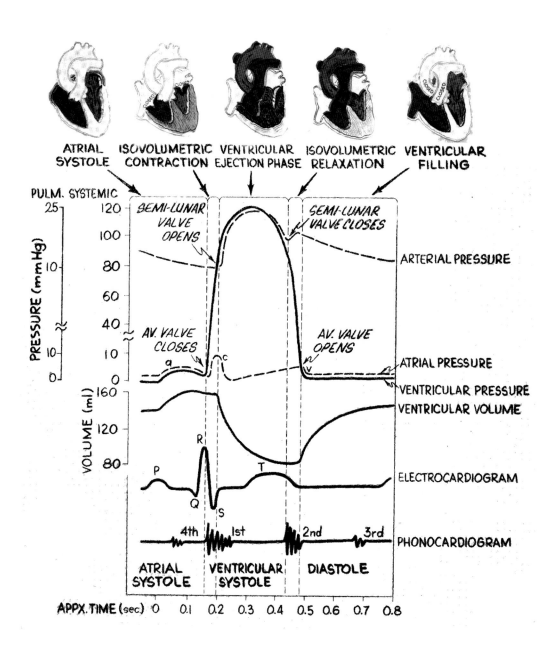

Fig. 19   **The Cardiac Cycle**

Reprinted with permission from Hewlett Packard: Basic Concepts of Cardiovascular Physiology by Michael Rudd

7. The Right Side and the Cardiac Cycle

Once the cardiac cycle for the left side of the heart is understood, the cardiac cycle for the right side of the heart is also easily understood. The principal difference between the left and right side is that the right side operates at a much lower pressure. Whereas the peak systolic pressure is typically around 120 mmHg on the left side, the peak systolic pressure is typically 25 mmHg on the right side. This lower pressure requirement should make sense since the function of the right side is to feed the pulmonary bed for oxygenation, whereas the left side needs to feed the entire systemic side.

8. Efficiency and Heart Performance

With the understanding of how the heart acts as a pump, it is valuable to consider the important related parameters which define its proper functioning and efficiency.

8.1 Stroke Volume
The stroke volume is the amount of blood ejected from the heart on a beat-by-beat basis. The unit is volume per beat or liters/beat. The stroke volume is equal to the difference in the ventricular volume between end diastole and end systole, or:

$$\text{Stroke Volume}\left(\frac{\text{liters}}{\text{beat}}\right) = \text{End Diastolic Volume}\left(\frac{\text{liters}}{\text{beat}}\right) - \text{End Systolic Volume}\left(\frac{\text{beats}}{\text{minute}}\right)$$

8.2 Cardiac Output
The cardiac output is a measure of the volumetric flow, or volume of blood per time that the heart pumps. The unit for cardiac output is volume per time, or liters/minute. The cardiac output can be calculated as the stroke volume times the heart rate, or:

$$\text{Cardiac Output}\left(\frac{\text{liters}}{\text{minute}}\right) = \text{Stroke Volume}\left(\frac{\text{liters}}{\text{beat}}\right) * \text{Heart Rate}\left(\frac{\text{beats}}{\text{minute}}\right)$$

8.3 Ejection Fraction
As the name indicates, the ejection fraction tells the percentage of blood volume ejected per beat. The ejection fraction is given by:

$$\text{Ejection Fraction }(\%) = \left(\frac{\text{SV}}{\text{EDV}}\right) * 100\%$$

8.4 Cardiac Index
The cardiac index is a method for normalizing the cardiac output relative to the size of the patient. The cardiac index is simply the cardiac output divided by the body surface area (BSA) of the patient, or:

$$\text{Cardiac Index}\left(\frac{\text{liters}}{\text{m}^2 * \text{minutes}}\right) = \frac{\text{Cardiac Output}\left(\frac{\text{liters}}{\text{minute}}\right)}{\text{BSA}\left(\text{m}^2\right)}$$

8.5 Mitral Regurgitant Fraction
The mitral regurgitant fraction is simply the difference in the ventricular inflow and outflow volume normalized by the inflow volume, or:

$$\text{Mitral RF}(\%) = \frac{(\text{mitral SV} - \text{aortic SV})}{\text{mitral SV}} * 100\%$$

Pegasus Lectures, Inc.

9. Frank-Starling's Law

The volumetric demand on the heart as a pump is variable. The demand at rest can be significantly less than in a state of exercise. For an adult male at rest, the cardiac output is typically about 5 liters per minute. For a trained athlete, with exercise, the cardiac output can increase to 20 liters per minute or more. The ability to be responsive and meet this variable demand is a very important characteristic of the heart. Starling's Law describes the mechanism by which the myocardium is able to function so as to meet the variable demand. In essence, Starling's Law states that the greater the amount of myocardial tension or stretch, the stronger the muscle contraction. In other words, the greater the volume returned to the heart, the greater the volume the normal heart is able to pump.

9.1 Cardiac Reserve and the Normal Heart

From *Figure 20*, notice that the normal heart typically operates at a very low point along the cardiac function curve as indicated by the line labeled "at rest". The difference between the cardiac output or volume at rest and the cardiac output or volume the heart is capable of pumping during stress (exercise) is called the cardiac reserve. Also notice that the rest point is in a relatively steep sloped portion of the curve. This means that as the myocardial tension increases, the output volume increases at a significant rate. Notice also that as the curve progresses the slope decreases. Operating along this flattened portion of the curve is significantly less efficient. At this point, an increase in tension does not result in a matched increase in output. At this point, the interaction between the actin and myosin fibers is no longer optimum so that the myocardium is not able to contract with the same increasing (the curve "flattens") force.

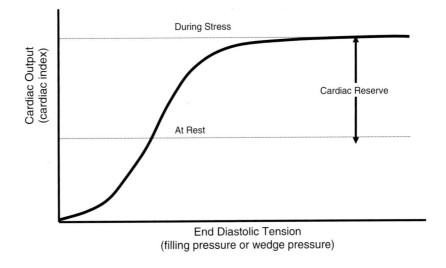

Fig. 20   **Starling's Curve (Cardiac Function Curve) for Normal Myocardium**

9.2 Damage and Loss of Reserve

Damage to the myocardium causes the curve to flatten and lower relative to the curve for healthy myocardium. Damaged myocardium is not able to contract as forcefully, thereby decreasing the pumping efficiency. In the figure below, notice how much less cardiac reserve there is for the damaged myocardium. This heart has very little ability to meet an increase in volumetric demand. Notice how the curve becomes very flat and then reverses. If the volumetric demand is such that the heart is operating at this flat portion, the heart is in heart failure.

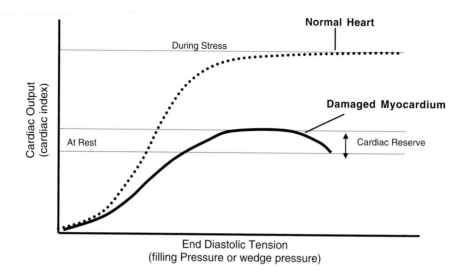

Fig. 21   **Starling's Curve (Cardiac Function Curve for Damaged Myocardium)**

It is also instructive to consider the functioning of the cardiac cycle through a pressure volume curve. As the name suggests, a pressure volume curve plots pressure versus volume over a cardiac cycle. A pressure volume curve can be drawn for each of the four chambers. We will focus on the left ventricle since it has to achieve the highest pressure to supply the systemic side.

10. Pressure Volume Curves

The pressure volume curve is actually bounded by two separate curves: the diastolic pressure curve and the isovolumic systolic pressure curve.

10.1 Diastolic Pressure Curve

The diastolic pressure curve demonstrates how the pressure increases with increasing volume without ventricular contraction. The diastolic pressure curve is essentially the compliance curve of the ventricle. Referring to *Figure 22*, note how this curve is initially relatively flat with increasing volumes. This flatness implies that the chamber is able to expand and hold a large volume without a significant pressure increase (a very high capacitance). Once the ventricular volume exceeds 150 ml, the pressure begins to rise at an accelerated rate. This increase in pressure results as the myofibrils reach their stretch limit and the restriction caused by the pericardium (decreasing compliance and decreasing capacitance).

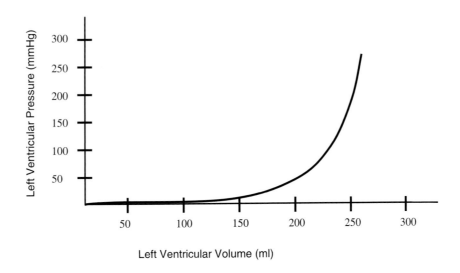

Fig. 22 **Diastolic Pressure Curve**

10.2 Isovolumic Systolic Pressure Curve

The isovolumic systolic pressure curve displays the pressure curve which results for various volumes of blood under ventricular contraction, with the restriction that no blood is allowed to be ejected. Note how different the systolic pressure curve is from the diastolic pressure curve. Notice how non-linear the process of contraction is. (If the process were linear, both curves would have the same basic shape just a more rapid slope under contraction.) The fact that the pressure rises very non-linearly with increasing volume is, of course, another expression of the Frank-Starling Law discussed already. Note also that once the volume rises above 150 ml, the pressure curve flattens and actually begins to decrease. At this point the myocardium has stretched to the limit at which it can no longer generate greater contractility.

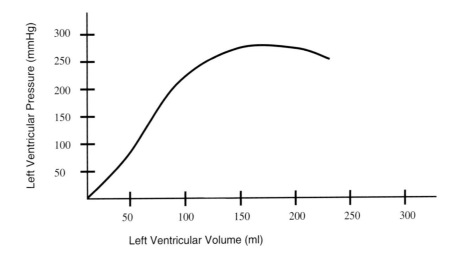

Fig. 23 **Isovolumic Systolic Pressure Curve**

10.3 Pressure Volume Loop

The pressure volume relationship over the cardiac cycle can now be added to the combined pressure curve as shown in *Figure 24*.

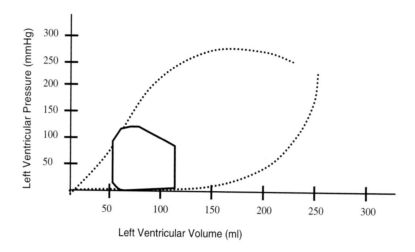

Fig. 24 **Pressure Volume Loop**

10.4 Understanding the Pressure Volume Loop

Using the diagram of *Figure 25*, we will analyze the pressure volume relationship.

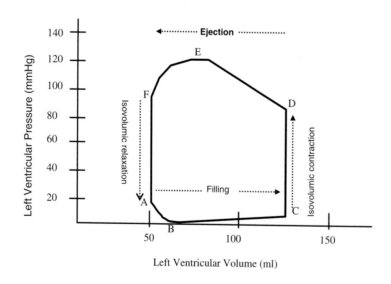

Fig. 25 **Pressure Volume Loop**

Pegasus Lectures, Inc.

A → B

At point A on the curve, the mitral valve opens and rapid filling of the ventricle begins. The pressure continues to drop even though there is a rapid inflow of blood because of the continuing relaxation of the left ventricle.

B → C

The time period from B to C represents the "resting" phase of diastole. During this time there is continued filling of the ventricle. Noticed that the pressure is initially very close to 0 mmHg and only increases to about 10 mmHg or less. The curve from B to C follows the diastolic pressure curve discussed in Section 10.1 and depicted in Figure 22. As discussed earlier, the rise in pressure is dictated by the compliance of the ventricle.

C → D

The short time period from C to D represents isovolumic contraction. At this point both the mitral and aortic valves are closed. The pressure increases dramatically until the pressure within the ventricle exceeds the pressure within the aorta.

D → E

Note that at point D the pressure within the left ventricle just exceeds the pressure within the aorta so that the aortic valve opens. As the aortic valve opens there is a rapid decrease in volume within the left ventricle as the blood flows into the aorta. The pressure continues to rise from point D to point E even though there is a dramatic decrease in volume. This continuing pressure increase is the result of continued ventricular contraction. Also notice that although the pressure continues to increase, it increases much more slowly than during the isovolumic contraction phase.

E → F

From point E to point F there is a continued but slowing decrease in volume in the left ventricle. Notice that there is still about 50 ml of blood in the ventricle at the end of the ejection phase. Note that the stroke volume is represented by the change in volume from point D to point F on the curve.

F → A

Point F represents the beginning of diastole. At point F the pressure within the aorta exceeds the pressure within the ventricle. The higher pressure within the aorta causes a reversal in blood flow back towards the ventricle. This flow reversal causes the aortic valve to snap shut. (Recall the discussion about the diacritic notch) The time period from F to A represents isovolumic relaxation. During this phase the ventricle relaxes, dramatically decreasing the ventricular pressure while maintaining the same volume (isovolumic). At point A, the mitral valve opens and rapid filling begins again to restart the cardiac cycle.

10.5 Preload and Preload Effects

The preload is related to the volume within the ventricle at the end of diastolic filling. From the diastolic pressure curve it is clear that a greater preload results in greater myocardial tension. From the Frank-Starling's Law we know that a greater muscle tension results in a more forceful contraction.

Some conditions which increase preload are:
1. Regurgitation
2. Ventricular Septal Defects
3. Atrial Septal Defects
4. Fluid Overload

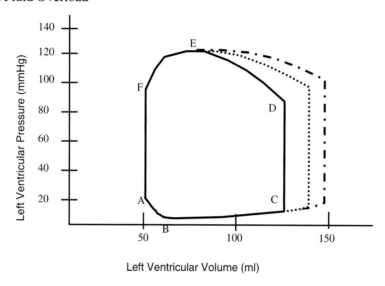

Fig. 26 **Pressure Volume Loop - The Effects of Increase Preload**

Notice that increased preload results in a greater stroke volume. Also note that the peak systolic pressure is unchanged since the afterload has remained unchanged.

10.6 Afterload and Afterload Effects
The afterload is essentially the resistance against which the ventricle must pump. A greater afterload will cause an increase in systolic pressure.

Some conditions which increase afterload are:
1. Hypertension
2. Aortic Stenosis
3. Pulmonic Stenosis

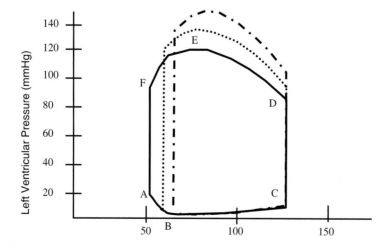

Fig. 27 **Pressure Volume Loop - The Effects of Increased Afterload**

Notice how an increased afterload increases the peak systolic pressure. An increase in afterload implies that the pressure within the aorta is greater. As a result, the pressure has to increase to a higher point during isovolumic contraction before the aortic valve opens. Also notice that the stroke volume decreases. This decrease in stroke volume is the result of having to overcome a higher resistance as a result of the increased afterload. Also note that in this case there is a higher residual blood volume in diastole, implying that the ejection fraction has decreased.

10.7 The Effects of Increased Contractility

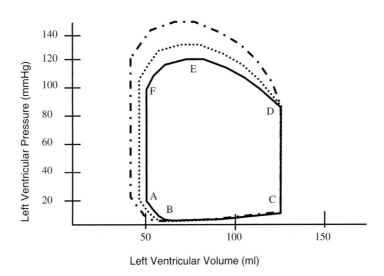

Fig. 28   **Pressure Volume Loop - The Effects of Increased Contractility**

With increased contractility, given that there is no change in preload or afterload conditions, there is an increase in both the peak systolic pressure and the stroke volume. Since the preload has not changed, the only way in which there can be a higher stroke volume is by increasing the ejection fraction. In other words, there is a lower residual volume in the ventricle during diastole.

11. Pressure and Volume Overload

11.1 Pressure Overload
To compensate for increased pressure, chamber wall thickness will increase. The wall thickening will affect both compliance and contractility thereby reducing filling and ejection.

Pressure Overload $\Rightarrow$ (Aortic stenosis, pulmonic stenosis)

11.2 Volume Overload
To compensate for increased volume, chamber volume must increase through an increase in chamber radius and a compensatory wall thickening. Since both the wall thickness and chamber radius increase, the ratio of the two remains constant. Diastolic pressure increases with increases in end diastolic volume; however, there is no significant increase in mass index.

Volume Overload $\Rightarrow$ (Aortic regurgitation, pulmonic regurgitation, mitral regurgitation, tricuspid regurgitation)

12. Fetal Heart Development

12.1 Early Development of the Heart

The heart begins as a network of cells, from which two longitudinal heart cords (also called cardiogenic cords) are formed about 18 or 19 days after fertilization. On about day 20, the heart cords develop canals, forming heart tubes (also called endocardial heart tubes). On days 21 and 22 the heart tubes fuse, forming a single median endocardial heart tube (*Figures 29* and *30*). Immediately following, the endocardial heart tube elongates; dilations and constrictions develop, forming first the bulbus cordis, ventricle, and atrium, and then the truncus arteriosus and sinus venosus (*Figure 31*). At this time (day 22), the sinus venosus develops left and right horns, the venous end of the heart is established as the pacemaker, heart contractions resembling peristaltic waves begin in the sinus venosus, and on about day 28 coordinated contractions of the heart begin to pump blood in one direction only.

Each horn of the sinus venosus receives an umbilical vein from the chorion (primitive placenta), a vitelline vein from the yolk sac, and a common cardinal vein from the embryo itself (*Figure 32*). Eventually, the left horn forms the coronary sinus and the right horn becomes incorporated into the wall of the right atrium.

Growth is rapid, and because the heart tube is anchored at both ends within the pericardium, by day 25 the tube bends back upon itself, forming first a U shape and then an S shape. The tube develops alternate dilations and constrictions along with further bending until it begins to resemble the fully developed heart (*Figure 33*). During the first weeks of embryonic growth, the heart is about nine times as large in proportion to the whole body as it is in the adult. Also, its position is higher in the thorax than the permanent position it will assume later.

12.2 Partitioning of the Heart

On about day 25, partitioning of the atrioventricular orifice, atrium and ventricle begins; it is completed about 10 to 20 days later (*Figure 34*). Most of the wall of the left atrium develops from the pulmonary vein, and as mentioned above, the right horn of the sinus venosus becomes incorporated into the wall of the right atrium. By about day 28, the heart wall has formed its three layers (endocardium, pericardium, epicardium). At about day 32, the interatrial septum forms, dividing the single atrium into left and right atria. An opening in the septum, the foramen ovale, closes at birth. The partitioning of the single ventricle into left and right ventricles begins with the formation of an upward fold in the floor of the ventricle, called the interventricular septum (*Figure 34*), and is completed by about day 48. The development of the atrioventricular valves, chordae tendinea, and papillary muscles proceeds from about the fifth week until the fifth month. The external form of the heart continues to develop from about day 28 to day 60.

12.2.1 Early Embryonic Development Of The Heart

Figures 29 and *30*: The primitive heart tubes fuse together and form a single endocardial heart tube during days 21 and 22 after fertilization; ventral views.

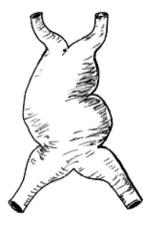

Figure 31: On about day 22 or 23, the first major structures form, and the heart tube begins to bend and twist; ventral view.

Figure 32: On about day 25, the tube has formed an S-shape.

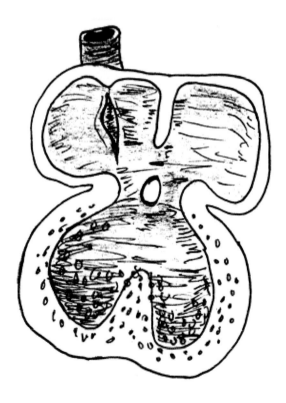

Figure 33: At about 32 days, the interior partitions can be seen clearly in this frontal section.

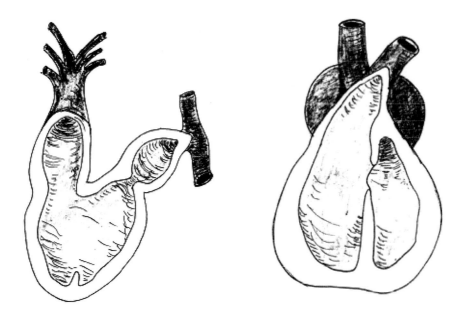

Figure 34: A frontal view at about 5 weeks shows the remaining three pairs of aortic arches.

Figure 35: A frontal section at 6 weeks shows the aorta and pulmonary trunk after the bulbus cordis, has been incorporated into the ventricles to become the infundibulum.

The text for Section 12 were reprinted with permission by McGraw-Hill:
Carola, Harley, & Noback. Human Anatomy & Physiology. McGraw-Hill, 2nd ed. 1992. pp 610-612.

13. Factors Affecting Jet Size

Regurgitant jets through valves occur between two chambers at different pressures when there is a mal-coaptation of the valve leaflets. For the atrioventricular valves (mitral and tricuspid), regurgitant jets occur during systole. For the semi-lunar valves (aortic and pulmonic), regurgitation occurs during diastole. An approach to assessing regurgitation severity entails measuring the jet size. From the equations discussed in Chapter 12 and Chapter 13 on fluid dynamics and hemodynamics, it should be clear that the jet size is affected by many parameters including, but not necessarily directly related to severity including:

- flow volume
- size and geometric aspects of the orifice
- the size and geometry of the receiving chamber
- other inflow
- pressure difference between chambers

14. Shunts

A shunt is a communication between the left and right sides of the circulation. Shunts generally cause volume overload, with subsequent dilation of the affected cardiac chambers. Intracardiac shunts include ventricular and atrial septal defects (VSDs and ASDs). Because of the higher pressures on the left side, most shunts are from left to right. With very large ventricular defects in the presence of significant pulmonary vascular resistance, bi-directional shunting with a predominant right to left component can occur leading to cyanosis. The most common extracardiac shunt is patent ductus arteriosus.

15. Pulmonary Disease

The most common cause of right ventricular failure is pressure overload resulting from elevated pulmonary artery pressure referred to as pulmonary hypertension. The most common cause of pulmonary hypertension leading to right heat failure is left heart failure. With left heart disease, the increase in left atrial filling pressure is translated back to the right heart through the pulmonary vasculature. As described by Frank Starling's law, the increase afterload results in right heart failure. Almost any severe pulmonary disease such as chronic obstructive pulmonary disease (COPD) can lead to pulmonary hypertension and ultimately right heart failure. When right heart disease occurs from pulmonary hypertension as a result of a primary pulmonary disease, it is termed cor pulmonale.

16. Pericardial Disease

16.1 Pericardial Effusion
Pericardial effusion is one of the most common presentations of pericardial disease. With pericardial effusion, fluid accumulates in the pericardial sac between the anterior right ventricular wall and the chest wall and between the posterior left ventricular wall and the posterior pericardium, creating an echo free space between the epicardium and the pericardium. Patients with a large pericardial effusion exhibit exaggerated movement of the heart, particularly of the anterior right ventricular wall. Often the anterior and posterior walls move in the same direction; paradoxical wall motion. The heart is surrounded by fluid and, with the exaggerated wall motion, is often described as "swinging heart." EKG changes such as alteration of the QRS complex may be noted as the position of the heart changes with the excessive motion of the heart. Tamponade occurs with very significant pericardial effusion which progresses to the point that the intrapericardial pressure becomes elevated resulting in impaired ventricular diastolic filling, low cardiac output (especially during inspiration) and equalization of intracardiac pressures. Hallmark signs of tamponade include presystolic collapse of the right atrium and right ventricular diastolic collapse, caused when the intrapericardial pressure exceeds the pressure within the cardiac chambers. Additional signs of tamponade include reduced left ventricular posterior wall excursion, left atrial diastolic collapse, left ventricular diastolic collapse, inspiratory movement of the interventricular septum towards the LV and inspiratory movement of the interatrial septum toward the left atrium, "swinging heart" motion, dilated inferior vena cava and/or superior vena cava. Also noted is marked respiratory variation of Doppler signals.

16.2 Pericarditis
Pericarditis is an inflammation of the pericardium which leads to thickening of the pericardium. As the pericardium becomes increasingly thickened and fibrotic it restricts the diastolic filling of the heart. Classic signs of constrictive pericarditis include early, rapid diastolic expansion with sudden cessation of left ventricular filling, interventricular and interatrial bulge to the left with inspiration, dilated IVC and hepatic veins with lack of respiratory variation.

Respiratory Variation of Doppler Peak Velocities with Constrictive Pericarditis

Valve	Inspiration	Expiration
MV	decrease (>25%)	increase (>25%)
TV	increase	decrease
AV	decrease	increase
PV	increase	decrease

Respiratory Variation of Pulmonary Venous Flow with Constrictive Pericarditis

Component	Inspiration	Expiration
D wave	increase	decrease
A wave	decrease	increase
	s/o ration of >65%	

Abnormal hepatic venous flow demonstrated with constrictive pericarditis includes a marked decrease or reversal of forward diastolic flow in expiration and a prominent atrial reversal flow in expiration.

17. Stress Testing

17.1 Detection of coronary artery Disease (CAD)

Stress testing is used primarily to identify the presence of coronary artery disease (CAD). CAD is arteriosclerosis of the inner lining of the coronary arteries.

Symptoms of CAD include:
1. chest pain (angina pectoris) from inadequate blood flow to the heart
2. heart attack (acute myocardial infarction)
3. sudden death, due to a fatal rhythm disturbance

Risk factors for CAD include:
1. family history of CAD
2. an abnormal serum cholesterol profile
3. cigarette smoking
4. hypertension
5. diabetes mellitus

17.2 The Premise of a Stress Test

The premise of a stress test is to increase metabolic demand of the "stressed" myocardium to determine if there is adequate perfusion via the coronary arteries. By increasing the demand, the presence of flow limiting blockages can be identified by various symptoms, changes in electrical activity (EKG), changes in pressure, and changes in heart wall motion. There are two basic methods of stress testing: exercise and physiologic. Exercise testing is usually performed on a treadmill or a stationary bicycle. Physiologic testing entails the use of a chemical stimulant to induce cardiac stress and is useful for patients who are unable to exercise.

17.3 Exercise Cardiac Stress Test

For exercise stress test on a treadmill, the patient exercises according to a standardized protocol, with progressive increases in the speed and elevation of the treadmill (typically changing at three minute intervals). During the exercise period, the patient's electrocardiogram (EKG), heart rate, heart rhythm, and blood pressure are continuously monitored as well as the overall condition of the patient observed. Changes in EKG, heart rate, and blood pressure are observed as indication of the presence of CAD. There are many possible causes of false positive tests which may result in further testing including radionuclide test or a stress echocardiography.

17.4 Stress Echocardiography

During stress echocardiography, imaging of the heart occurs at rest prior to stress and at the peak of exercise. With exercise, the increase in oxygen demand should result in increased left ventricular contraction. In the presence of coronary artery disease, the associated wall segments are inadequately perfused resulting in reduced contractility relative to adequately perfused segments.

17.5 Physiologic Stress Testing

When patients are unable to exercise maximally for stress testing, pharmacological stress can be induced. During a physiologic stress test, a drug such as dobutamine is administered to stimulate the heart to mimic the physiologic effects of exercise. While the drug is being administered, echocardiography or radionuclide imaging is simultaneously performed.

17.6 Indications

The following is a list of indications for stress testing:
- Diagnosis of chest pain
- Severity and prognosis of CAD
- Post MI rehab
- Evaluate arrhythmias
- Screen high risk / asymptomatic patients

17.7 Stress Testing: Interpretation

The following is a list of the primary changes used for interpretation of the presence of CAD from a stress test.
- ST segment depression
- ST segment elevation
- Decreased duration of exercise
- Hypotension
- Arrhythmias

18. Maneuvers altering Physiology

Various maneuvers are used to enhance the presence of cardiac murmurs under auscultation. The following table lists some of the maneuvers and the associated physiologic responses.

Maneuver	Physiologic Response
Standing	⇓ venous return, SV & CO
Squating	⇑ venous return, SV & CO
Handgrip	⇑ HR, CO & arterial pressure
Valsalva	⇓ venous return, SV & CO
Situps	⇑ HR, CO & SV
Amyl Nitrite	⇓ peripheral resistance & ⇑ HR, CO & SV

We will consider a few of these maneuvers to better understand how they might be used in clinical testing. For example, when a patient transitions from the recumbent to the standing position, there is a decrease in venous return which therefore leads to a reduction in stroke volume and a compensatory increase in heart rate. Since the stroke volume is decreased, this positional change results in a lessening of all murmurs except for mitral valve prolapse and hypertrophic cardiomyopathy. In contrast to transitioning from recumbent to standing, transitioning from standing to squatting results in an increase in venous return. The increase in venous return results in an increase in the stroke volume and cardiac output. The result is an increase in most murmurs except for mitral valve prolapse and hypertrophic cardiomyopathy, which decrease.

19. Control Mechanisms

There are many factors which contribute to the control of heart function including preload, afterload, contractility, and the autonomic nervous system (sympathetic and parasympathetic). We have already discussed the effects of preload, afterload, and contractility. We will now consider the role of the autonomic nervous system.

19.1 The Sympathetic Nervous System
Sympathetic nerve fibers innervate the entire heart almost evenly distributed. In addition to the stimulation through the nerve fibers, the sympathetic nervous system can exert influence over the heart through catecholamines, adrenaline, and noradrenaline circulating in the blood. Sympathetic stimulation increases heart activity such that three specific effects can be distinguished:
- an increase in heart rate
- increase in contractility
- an acceleration of the atrioventricular (AV) conduction

19.2 The Parasympathetic Nervous System
The parasympathetic system plays a minor role in the regulation of circulation. Specifically, the parasympathetic system can affect heart rate via the parasympathetic fibers carried to the heart in the vagus nerve. Parasympathetic stimulation causes:
- a marked decrease in heart rate
- a slight decrease in contractility
- and a slight decrease in AV conduction

Appendix C • Developing a Test Taking Strategy

Many people find taking exams almost as daunting as learning the actual material on which they will be tested. This section is designed to help improve your test taking skills, with some specific approaches for multiple choice exams. Realize that it is important to customize these strategy suggestions to your own strengths and weaknesses and to practice these strategies well before you take the actual exam. Your strategy should become second nature to you, so that while you are taking an actual exam you can concentrate on the subject, not the exam logistics.

Much of exam anxiety comes from unfamiliarity with:
1. The exam objective
2. The exam structure
3. The testing logistics
4. The exam material (conceptual and practical understanding)
5. The test question formats
6. The test answer formats
7. Logic and reasoning skills
8. The testing time pressure
9. The ability to remain focused

Section 1: The Exam Objective

The objective of the credentialing exams is to test for minimum level competency in utilizing ultrasound in a clinical environment. There are many applications and modalities of ultrasound, all of which require knowledge of many aspects of the physics. Ultimately, the purpose is to ensure quality patient care.

If you think about that objective, it will help you anticipate the focus of many of the exam questions. What aspects of the ultrasound physics and instrumentation are within your control? What are the limitations of ultrasound? What are the limitations of the instrumentation? How do you achieve the best possible results using this equipment? What generates artifacts, and how can these artifacts be both detrimental and beneficial to the diagnosis? How do you minimize artifacts which mask the needed information, and how do you interpret the artifacts which can be beneficial? What increases the risk of harm to your patients?

If you cannot answer these questions, you are not ready to take the exam. The ability to answer these questions requires a thorough conceptual understanding of the physics principles relating to waves, sound propagation, attenuation, instrumentation, artifacts, and bioeffects.

Note: Although this section was written to assist candidates preparing for the ultrasound physics credentialing exams, these strategies are easily applied to all specialty exams.

Section 2: The Exam Structure

The following table outlines the Ultrasound Credentialing Exams currently offered. Although this information is current as of the text print date, examination structure may be modified by the credentialing organizations. If you desire specific exam information or would like to request an application. Volume II, Appendix J contains contact information for each of the credentialing organizations.

	ARDMS							CCI				ARRT		
Credential	UPI	RDMS	CPI	RDCS	VPI	RVT	RPVI	RCS		RVS		ARRT(S)	ARRT(VS)	ARRT(BS)
Exam(s)	UPI	Abdomen Breast OB/GYN Neurosonology	CPI	Adult Echo Fetal Echo Pediatric Echo	VPI	Vascular Technology	PVI	Cardiovascular Science Examination	Non-invasive Echo Registry	Cardiovascular Science Examination	Non-invasive Vascular Registry	Sonography	Vascular Sonography	Breast Sonography
# Questions (multiple choice)	120	170	120	150	120	170	201	130	140	130	150	250	160	185
Length (# of hours)	2	3	2	3	2	3	4	2.5	2.5	2.5	3	4.5	3.25	3.5
Computer format	Yes	Yes	Yes	Yes	Yes	Yes	Yes	Yes	Yes	Yes	Yes	Yes	Yes	Yes
Each question of equal value	Yes	Yes	Yes	Yes	Yes	Yes	Yes	Yes	Yes	Yes	Yes	Yes	Yes	Yes
No deductions for incorrect response	Yes	Yes	Yes	Yes	Yes	Yes	Yes	Yes	Yes	Yes	Yes	Yes	Yes	Yes
Passing Score	65-75%							70%				scaled score of 75%		

ARDMS	American Registry for Diagnostic Medical Sonography
ARRT	American Registry of Radiologic Technology
CCI	Cardiovascular Credentialing International
CPI	Cardiovascular Principles and Instrumentation Examination
UPI	Ultrasound Physics and Instrumentation Examination
VPI	Vascular Physical Principles and Instrumentation Examination
RCS	Registered Cardiac Sonographer
RVS	Registered Vascular Sonographer
RDCS	Registered Diagnostic Cardiac Sonographer
RDMS	Registered Diagnostic Medical Sonographer
RVT	Registered Vascular Technologist
PVI	Physicians' Vascular Interpretation Examination
RPVI	Registered Physician in Vascular Testing

Section 3: The Testing Logistics

Almost all credentialing exams are now offered on computer. In order to minimize the risk of failure due to unfamiliarity with how to logistically take the exam on computer, you are generally given a practice session of up to fifteen minutes before the exam commences. When you are acclimated with how to use the mouse, advance to the next question, record answers, and mark answers to which you want to return; you can begin the exam. Should your fifteen minutes expire before you acknowledge your readiness to commence, you will be prompted as to your readiness to begin.

Pegasus Lectures, Inc. now offers practice exams on CD-ROM which allow you to practice taking the certification exams in the actual exam computer format. For more information on the Exam Simulation CD ROM's contact:

Pegasus Lectures, Inc.
PO Box 157
Forney, TX 75126
Tel: 972-564-3056
Fax: 972-552-9186
Email: PegasusLectures@aol.com
Web: www.PegasusLectures.com

Section 4: The Exam Material (conceptual and practical understanding)

Most people struggle with really learning the material. Memorization of equations and facts is a very poor substitute. When you look at the facts and equations you are expected to know, consider whether you can relate the facts and variables to what is physically occurring between the ultrasound wave and the tissue (medium)? Can you explain why the fact or equation has bearing on your study, the interpretation, and ultimately, the well being of the patient? If you can, then you are ready to take the exam. If you cannot, you now know your goal for this independent learning program.

Section 5: The Test Question Formats

Have you ever considered the different formats for multiple choice questions? There are many ways of categorizing question types, or formats. We will categorize the question types as follows:

1. The No Look
2. The Peek
3. The Look

By recognizing and learning how to respond to these question "types" you will save time and energy and minimize confusion.

1. *The No Look*
The "No Look" question type is the type of question which can be answered from the question alone, without first looking at the choices given. There are some very good reasons for not looking at the choices before answering this type of question.

➢ Of the choices given only one is correct. Why put a whole bunch of incorrect information into your head before you make a response? This will only confuse you.

➢ By first answering the question, you reduce the question into a simple matter of matching, instead of solving and matching. As a result, you will have less to remember between choices, taking less time and minimizing energy expense.

➢ The distracters do just that – distract your attention from the correct response.

Approach:

For most people, the best approach to answering the "No Look" type question is to answer the question before looking at the answers. Especially with technical questions, the information in the choices will begin to overload the normal thought process.

➢ Don't view the choices
➢ On your scratch paper, write down what information is given
➢ Make use of key words
➢ Write down the information or facts that you know
➢ Derive your answer
➢ Determine what units, if any, the answer should be in
➢ Check to see if any of the choices match your answer

Examples: (No Look)

· Given a spatial pulse length of 5 mm, what is the radial resolution?
· If the frequency increases, the wavelength will...

2. ***The Peek***

The "Peek" question type is the type of question which can be answered from reading the question and only peeking at the choices given. After peeking at the choices, this question type essentially becomes a "No Look" type question, and the approach should be the same as for the "No Look" type.

Approach

➢ Briefly peek at the choices
➢ Now follow the approach for the "No Look" type question

Example: (Peek)

· Which of the following sequences is in order?

3. ***The Look***

The "Look" question type is the type of question which leaves you no choice, to answer the question you must look at the choices given.

Approach

"Look" questions are generally straightforward. Look at each choice and decide on its validity before looking at the next choice. On your scratch paper, eliminate obviously incorrect choices before reading the next choice. Choices about which you are uncertain, should be indicated with some distinctive mark of your choosing. (One possibility is a "?".) This method will save you from having to reread all five choices if you are not completely certain among a few

Pegasus Lectures, Inc.

choices. (In our seminars we include a section on "making good use of your scratch paper".)

Example: (Look)
· Which of the following statements is correct?
· Of the following, which does not belong?

Section 6: The Test Answer Formats

Just as with the question types, the answer choices can be categorized many ways. We will break the answer choices into four types as follows:

1. **Not a true statement**
   Example: As the frequency increases the penetration increases.

2. **Half true, half not true**
   Example: Since resolution improves with increasing frequency, using a higher frequency will significantly improve image quality at deep imaging depths.

3. **True but irrelevant to the question**
   Example: Why is backing material used in ultrasound transducers?

   a) because lateral resolution improves with a narrower beamwidth.

4. **Completely true and relevant**
   (This is the one to shoot for!!)

Section 7: Logic and Reasoning Skills

There are many tools from logic and reasoning which are invaluable for taking multiple choice exams. Although it is not reasonable to teach an entire course of logic and reasoning in this section, we can give you a few helpful hints.

1. The end of many questions is part of the answer. If you ignore this fact, you will suffer the consequences!

   ➤ If the voltage is decreased by a factor of 2, the intensity is decreased by:
   (The first part of the answer is: the intensity is decreased by. Note that the word decreased already implies a negative number, so logically, your choice cannot be a negative number.)

2. Use keywords to dissect a problem.

   ➤ Which of the following sequences is in the correct **increasing** order?
   (The use of the word increasing suggests that there may be sequences in the correct order which are decreasing and hence, not the right answer.)

   ➤ The **best** reason why the focus of a transducer is shallow is:
   (The use of the word best specifies that there may be more than one choice which could be correct, however, one of the correct responses is better than the other correct re-

sponses. The best "correct response" is the one which gives the most specific and/or the most comprehensive information.)

3. Look for words of inversion or exclusion.

   ➤ Which of the following statements is **not** true about …
   (The use of the word not inverts the answer – for this question, the correct response is a false statement.)
   ➤ All of the following are true **except**
   (The use of the word except excludes choices – for this question the correct response is also a false statement. This type of question is very useful, since four choices are correct, and contain information which may help solve other questions.)
   Some examples of words which exclude, restrict or invert are: not, opposite, except, decreasing, only, most, least, etc.

4. Look for choices which are unrelated.
   (Many times choices that are given are true but unrelated to the question. These questions typically catch people who have memorized, and not really learned the material. These people recognize the statement as true, but do not realize that it is unrelated to the question being asked. Don't just memorize!)

5. Look for choices which are only partly true.
   (For a choice to be correct it must be completely true, not only partly true.)

6. Look for answers which are more complete, more specific or encompassing.
   (Often there is more than one choice which is correct, however, one choice is better because it gives a more complete or specific answer. Make sure you read all of the choices before answering!)

7. Look for mutually exclusive answers.
   Two statements are mutually exclusive if stating one directly excludes the other. It is important to recognize mutually exclusive answers and then determine whether the two mutually exclusive choices are related to the question. Let's look at some examples:

   ➤ Early humans believed ships could fall off of the earth because they took as fact that:
      A) the earth is flat.
      B) the earth is round.
      C) gravity could fail
      D) gods became angry and knocked people off.
      E) etc…

   (Note: The earth is flat implies that the earth is not round, and vice versa. In other words choices A and B are mutually exclusive. In this example, these choices are related to the problem, so we know that the answer must be one of the two choices.)

   ➤ One of the reasons that helped fuel the legend of vampires is:

A) the earth is flat
B) the earth is round
C) the inability to scientifically determine actual point of death
D) etc...

(Note: Although choices A and B are mutually exclusive, these two choices are unrelated to the problem and therefore can both be eliminated.)

8. Relate the choices to the exam objective.
(Make certain that your answer makes sense relative to the exam objective. For example, one of the fundamental objectives of the exam is to guarantee patient safety. Therefore, you will never answer a question which says performing needless scans, using more power than is necessary, or scanning for more time than is clinically necessary is acceptable.)

Section 8: The Testing Time Pressure

Students who know the material conceptually and develop a testing strategy rarely have time difficulties. Quite simply, once you know the material and approach the exam logically and systematically, the time allotted is more than adequate. Still, the fact that the exam is timed usually induces some amount of stress. The best way to make certain that the time aspect of the exam does not become an issue is to practice taking exams under the same time constraints.

Section 9: The Ability to Remain Focused

The ability to remain focused for long periods of time (oh, say about 120 - 180 minutes) is an acquired skill. Most people find it difficult and exhausting to stay focused on one subject matter for more than 15 minutes. The best way to develop this skill is to really understand the material and practice applying the material. Many people ignore the fatigue and focusing factor when preparing for an exam. As you take the practice exams, it is strongly suggested that you take the time constraints seriously, and learn how you will respond after trying to remain focused for such a long period of time. Try to clear your mind of extraneous thoughts. It is natural to find yourself periodically straying into the oblivion with your thoughts. You do not need to scold yourself, nor should you just allow yourself to mentally wander. Instead, try taking a quick mental break to relax your mind and then refocus. For most people, a 30 second relaxation period is all it takes. Many people are afraid to allow themselves the 30 second break, believing that they are wasting precious time. Quite simply, if your mind is frazzled, those 30 seconds might be the most usefully spent time during the exam. Besides, if you have practiced taking the exam, and have really learned the material, you will not be worried about using a few minutes spread throughout the exam to rest and recover.

Appendix C

Sample Questions

1. If the relative output power of an ultrasound instrument is calibrated in decibels and the operator increases the output by 20 dB, the beam intensity is increased by
    A. five percent.
    B. two times.
    C. twenty times.
    D. one hundred times.
    E. one million times.

Question Type: No Look
Keywords: intensity, increases
Rephrased question: Increasing the output by 20 dB, increases the beam intensity by

Solving the problem:

$$20 \, dB = 10 * \log_{10} \left(\frac{P_f}{P_i} \right)$$

$$2 = 10 * \log_{10} \left(\frac{P_f}{P_i} \right)$$

$$10^2 = \left(\frac{P_f}{P_i} \right)$$

$$100 = \left(\frac{P_f}{P_i} \right)$$

So the intensity, which is proportional to the power, is increased by a factor of 100, or one hundred times **(Choice D)**.

2. Assuming a fixed frequency, what happens if the diameter of an unfocused circular transducer is increased?
    A. The distance to the far field is reduced.
    B. The beamwidth in the near field is reduced.
    C. The beamwidth in the far field is reduced.
    D. The ultrasonic wavelength is increased.
    E. The sensitivity is reduced.

Question Type: No Look
Keywords: diameter, increased
Rephrased question: Increasing the crystal diameter causes

$$NZL_{(mm)} \approx \frac{D^2_{(mm)} * f_{(MHz)}}{6}$$

$$NZL_{(mm)} \propto D^2_{(mm)}$$

Increasing the diameter creates a much deeper focus, and hence, a narrower beamwidth in the relative far field.

Now find the choice which matches your answer.

Choice A is the opposite of what happens

Choice B is the opposite of what happens

Choice C is true

Choice D is unrelated. The wavelength is determined by the frequency and the propagation speed, neither of which change with transducer diameter.

Choice E is most likely the opposite of what occurs, a larger diameter crystal is effectively a larger antenna, and therefore usually more sensitive (BUT NOT ALWAYS).

3. Which one of the following sets of properties of a test object or a phantom is MOST relevant when assessing depth calibration accuracy?
   A. Reflector spacing and reflector reflection coefficient
   B. Attenuation in the medium and speed of sound in the medium
   C. Reflector spacing and ultrasonic attenuation in the medium
   D. Reflector reflection coefficient and ultrasonic attenuation in the medium
   E. Reflector spacing and speed of sound in the medium

Question Type:	Peek
Keywords:	most, depth, calibration, accuracy
Central concept:	Depth calibration has to do with signals arriving at correct time relative to transmit. This depends on the depth of the reflector and the propagation speed.

Now find the choice which matches your answer.

Choice A is half true, half not. Reflector spacing refers to depth, but the reflection coefficient determines echo amplitude, not propagation speed.

Choice B is half true, half not. Attenuation determines signal strength, not depth.

Choice C is also half true, half not. Again attenuation determines signal strength.

Choice D is completely false.

Choice E is correct.

4. From a safety standpoint, which one of the following methods is BEST?

    A. Low transmitter output and high receiver gain
    B. High transmitter output and low receiver gain
    C. High near gain and low far gain
    D. Low near gain and high far gain
    E. High reject and high transmitter output

Question Type: Peek

Keywords: safety, BEST (Implies more than one choice may be correct!)

Central concept: Patient safety depends on minimizing risk by limiting transmit power, mini mizing scan times, and not performing needless scans. By peeking, we know that this question is asking how the instrument controls should be set. Increasing gain does not increase risk to the patient, whereas increasing output power does.

Now find the choice which matches your answer.

    Choice A is true. Check other choices to be certain there is no better choice.
    Choice B is not consistent with minimizing risk because of high transmit power.
    Choice C is ridiculous!
    Choice D is generally true, but states nothing about the transmit power.
    Choice E is also not consistent with minimizing risk, since there is a high output power.

(Note: Scanning a difficult patient will force you to use higher transmit power and high receiver gain. Since we are not given any information which suggests a very difficult patient, and none of the other answers better relate to the question of patient safety, **the answer is clearly choice A.**)

5. Which one of the following instruments is a component that stores digital echo signal information?

    A.   Demodulator
    B.   Receiver
    C.   Video monitor
    D.   Logarithmic amplifier
    E.   Scan converter

Question Type: No Look

Keywords: stores, digital, signal

Central concept: There are effectively two instruments for storing digital data: the scan converter, or an external digital storage device such as an optical disk or floppy disk.

Now find the choice which matches your answer.

Choice E is a direct match!

6. The dynamic range of the receiver of an ultrasound instrument refers to the

    A. ability of the receiver to track a rapidly moving structure.
    B. range of echo signal frequencies that can be processed without distortion.
    C. speed with which the receiver recovers following the excitation pulse to the transducer.
    D. depth range in tissue over which moving echoes can be received.
    E. range of echo signal amplitudes that can be processed without distortion.

Question Type: No Look
Keywords: dynamic range, receiver
Central concept: The term dynamic range refers to a ratio of a maximum to a minimum of any quantity. You can talk about the dynamic range of an eye, the video display, a receiver or a bank account balance. It is critical to note the key word "receiver". The dynamic range of the receiver is the ratio of the maximum signal (or strongest signal) to the minimum signal (weakest signal) the receiver can faithfully detect.

Now find the choice which matches your answer.

    Choice A is completely unrelated. This distracter is for those people who have not learned the definition of dynamic range and guess based on the alternate meaning of the word dynamic as meaning movement.
    Choice B is a tough distracter. Although it is possible to speak of the receiver frequency input dynamic range, it is not common. We would generally refer to this as the receiver bandwidth.
    Choice C is completely unrelated. The time to recover from an excitation pulse is called the ring down, and creates a "dead zone."
    Choice D is just nonsense.
    Choice E is true. A distorted signal has been corrupted so that it no longer accurately repre sents the actual signal. Stating the "range of echo signal amplitudes that can be pro cessed without distortion," is equivalent to saying "the ratio of the maximum to mini mum signals which can be received accurately, or faithfully detected."

7. Which one of the following statements is TRUE about a single pulse of ultrasound from a trans-ducer?

    A. It contains a range of frequencies.
    B. It contains sound at the nominal frequency of the transducer only.
    C. It contains sound at the center frequency of the transducer only.
    D. The shorter the pulse the narrower the bandwidth.
    E. Sound energy is continuously transmitted.

Question Type: No Look
Keywords: true, single pulse
Central concept: The relationship between frequency and time is reciprocal. Short periods of time represent large frequency ranges. This is one reason why a backing material is used for a transducer. The backing material shortens the ring time (pulse duration), thereby increasing the bandwidth (range of frequencies over which a transducer can operate). A short pulse also creates a short spatial pulse length, improving longitudinal resolution.

Now find the choice which matches your answer.

> **Choice A is true.** Check other choices to be certain there is no better choice.
> Choice B is not true. (Note that choices A and B are mutually exclusive.)
> Choice C is not true. (Note that A and C are also mutually exclusive)
> Choice D is the opposite of reality. Shorter time implies greater frequency range.
> Choice E is a ridiculous answer to complete the required number of choices.

8. Increasing the gain of pulse echo instruments results in higher echoes displayed in A-mode. This is due to

    A. increased amount of sound emitted by the transducer
    B. increased amount of sound reflected
    C. increased efficiency of transducer conversion of sound into electricity
    D. increased amplification in the receiver
    E. decreased amplification in the receiver

Question Type: No Look
Keywords: increasing gain, higher echoes in A- mode
Central concept: Increasing the receiver gain increases the amount of amplification of the signal after it has already returned from the body. Increasing receiver gain increases the display brightness.

Now find the choice which matches your answer.

> Choice A describes an increase in transmit power, not receive gain.
> Choice B describes an increase in reflected energy. Receiver gain occurs after the signal is received from the patient, making this choice ridiculous.
> Choice C is completely unrelated. Receiver gain does not affect the efficiency of a transducer design.
> **Choice D is true.**
> Choice E is false. (Note that choices D and E are mutually exclusive and related, so one of these two answers would have to be correct.)

9. A sound wave leaves its source and travels through air. The speed of sound in air is 330 m/sec. One second later, an echo returns to the source. At what distance from the source is the reflector that produced the echo?

    A. 1540 meters
    B. 770 meters
    C. 660 meters
    D. 330 meters
    E. 165 meters

Chapter 7 Doppler

Answers: Pg. 977-981

1. Give the Doppler equation. Define each term.

2. From the equation determine all possible changes which would increase the detected Doppler shift (ex. if v increases, f_{dop} increases).

3. Rewrite the Doppler equation as v =

4. For a fixed blood velocity, if you increase the transmit frequency, what happens to the Doppler shift?

5. In the Doppler equation which factors are known, which are assumed, which are detected, and which term is calculated?

6. If the target is moving towards the detector, the wave fronts are _____ yielding a _____ Doppler shift.

   a) decompressed, positive
   b) compressed, negative
   c) decompressed, negative
   d) compressed, positive

7. In color flow Doppler flash artifact can be caused by
   a) high amplitude, low velocity changes such as motion of the transducer and motion from breathing.
   b) low amplitude, high velocity changes such as motion of the transducer and motion from breathing.
   c) thermal changes in the transducer.
   d) cavitation of tissue and gel.

8. If for a specific blood velocity the Doppler shift is 2 kHz, what would the Doppler shift be if you doubled the transmit frequency?

9. A negative Doppler shift means
   a) a negative blood flow velocity
   b) relative flow away from the transducer
   c) a decrease in amplitude
   d) aliasing

10. What percentage of the Doppler shift is detected at an insonification angle of:
    a) 0°
    b) 30^0
    c) 45^0
    d) 60^0
    e) 90^0
    f) 180^0

11. The typical range for Doppler shifts is + 10 kHz to -10 kHz, however, it is very common to far exceed these frequencies. Which scenario below would most likely demonstrate much higher shifts?
    a) 90^0 angle to flow, just distal to a severe stenosis, 5 MHz transducer
    b) 90^0 angle to flow, just distal to a severe stenosis, 10 MHz transducer
    c) 0^0 angle to flow, just proximal to a severe stenosis, 10 MHz transducer
    d) 0^0 angle to flow, just distal to a severe stenosis, 10 MHz transducer

12. For superficial imaging, high frequency Doppler yields higher amplitude signals. As the depth increases, lower frequency Doppler yields higher amplitude signals. Explain this phenomenon (make sure to include Rayleigh scattering and frequency effects in your explanation).

13. Knowing the blood velocity is useful since, from _____ equation, a pressure gradient can be determined.

14. Assume that the lowest wall filter setting on an ultrasound machine is 60 Hz. If, for a given transducer, the blood velocity you desire to quantify is below this cutoff, what can you do?

15. Explain what purpose wall filters serve.

16. Which mode must support the greatest signal dynamic range

    a)   B-mode (2D)
    b)   Color Doppler
    c)   PW spectral Doppler
    d)   CW spectral Doppler

17. The Nyquist criterion states that to detect a frequency of 2 kHz you must sample at a frequency of at least _____.

18. The resulting artifact from violating Nyquist is called _____.

19. For PW (and color Doppler), Nyquist dictates that to detect a Doppler shift of 3 kHz the _____ must be at least 6 kHz.

20. Since continuous wave Doppler effectively has an infinite PRF (transmitting continuously), the maximum detectable velocity is much _____ than for PW and is only restricted by the A/D sample rate. *(greater than / less than)*

21. The analog Doppler signal is analog to digital converted to allow for
    a)   spectral analysis.
    b)   wall filtering.
    c)   amplification and compression.
    d)   demodulation.

22. Spectral analysis is most generally performed by a mathematical function called an _____ or Fast _____ _____, which separates the composite frequency shifts into frequency bins for measurement.

23. Give the major advantage of PW and the major advantage of CW.

24. It is impossible to do CW Doppler with one crystal so "single crystal" transducers are actually split into two half segments which can either be run as two separate crystals or one whole crystal. Explain why it is not possible to do CW Doppler with only one crystal.

25. As you image deeper the maximum PRF decreases restricting the maximum unaliased velocities detectable. Explain why the PRF decreases with depth.

26. What is the blood velocity if the detected Doppler shift is 2 kHz, the insonification angle is 60°, the transmit frequency is 3.08 MHz, and soft tissue is assumed.

27. What do the three axes of a Doppler spectrum display?
    a) horizontal =

    b) vertical =

    c) imaginary =

28. Most color flow techniques use the Doppler effect, however, no FFT is performed since color sectors use multiple lines requiring too much calculation time and no convenient way of displaying the data. Instead of spectral analysis, color Doppler uses a correlation algorithm which yields

   a) a maximum velocity estimator.
   b) a mean velocity estimator.
   c) a modal velocity estimator.
   d) a completely unrelated velocity but pretty colors.

29. As you increase the sample volume size in PW Doppler, you will most likely see

   a) more spectral spread.
   b) a major change in the mean velocity.
   c) less spectral spread.
   d) a lower amplitude Doppler signal.

30. A good approach to minimizing the artifact of spectral broadening is

   a) to always use insonification angles of 60^0 or less.
   b) to always use insonification angles of 60^0 or more.
   c) to always make sure that the display is not overgained.
   d) a and c.
   e) b and c.

Chapter 8 Artifacts

Answers: Pg. 982-984

1. For the figure below, draw the sound paths which create each of the artifactual structures labeled "A", "B", "C", and "D".

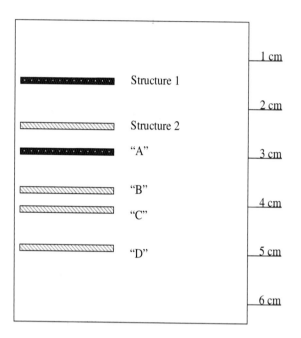

2. Most imaging artifacts are caused by _____ reflection. Since this type of reflection is highly _____ dependent, using a different imaging window or changing the steering is a good way of identifying whether there is an aspect of an image which is artifactual.

3. Multi-path artifact results in an artifactual structure appearing _____ than reality.

4. If the propagation speed through a structure is 1100 m/sec, distal to that structure, other structures will appear too _____.

5. "Ghost" arteries often appear when imaging an artery relatively superficial and just anterior to a strong _____ reflector. The "ghost" arteries are often classified as an example of _____ artifact although in reality they are caused by reverberation artifact.

6. _____ artifact causes an artificial image symmetric about the "mirroring" surface.

7. _____ results posterior to a region where there is greater than normal attenuation.

8. _____ often occurs from the edges of cysts, blood vessels, and bones because of _____.

9. Total internal reflection occurs at the _____ angle.

---

10.   The reciprocal artifact of shadowing is called _____ .

11.   All of the following will decrease the likelihood of aliasing in spectral Doppler EXCEPT
        a)   decreasing the Doppler gate depth
        b)   using CW Doppler
        c)   using a lower operating frequency
        d)   shifting the Doppler baseline
        e)   increasing the Doppler scale

        Explain:

12.   Which of the following Doppler scenarios would have the greatest risk of exhibiting range ambiguity artifact?
        a)   PW sample volume at 3 cm deep, phased array
        b)   PW sample volume at 3 cm deep, mechanical
        c)   PW sample volume at 6 cm deep, phased array
        d)   PW sample volume at 6 cm deep, mechanical

        Explain:

13.   Spectral _____ is caused by poor I and Q channel separation and is exacerbated by high _____ power and high receiver gain.

14.   The law which governs the amount of refraction is called _____ law.

15.   Which of the following Doppler changes would decrease the amount of spectral spread in a Doppler spectrum?

        a)   Using a smaller insonification angle.
        b)   Using a large linear transducer.
        c)   Imaging at a shallower depth.
        d)   Using a higher transmit power.
        e)   Using a higher receiver gain.

        Explain:

Chapter 9 Bioeffects

Answers: Pg. 985-986

1. The two principle mechanisms for creating bioeffects are _____ and _____.

2. Thermal bioeffects are highly dependent on the _____ factor as well as whether or not the modality is _____ or non-_____ .

3. Mechanical bioeffects are dominated by the peak _____ pressure.

4. _____ bioeffects dictate that scan times should be minimized so that heat does not "build up."

5. The modality which generally has the greatest risk of thermal bioeffects is _____, since the _____ factor is 1.

6. The intensity measurement which best indicates the risk of thermal bioeffects is the _____.

7. The modality which generally has the lowest risk of thermal bioeffects is _____ .

8. The modality which generally has the greatest risk of mechanical bioeffects is _____ .

9. Transient _____ is the form of "mechanical damage" which occurs when the mechanical index is too high.

10. The risk of mechanical bioeffects dictates that the minimum _____ power necessary to achieve good clinical results should be used.

11. The AIUM fundamental statement about the safety of diagnostic ultrasound states that "ultrasound is a very safe modality and to date there have been no confirmed _____ _____ by exposure to intensities typical of present ultrasound equipment."

12. There have been no confirmed bioeffects for unfocused-beam intensities below _____, for focused-beam intensities below _____, or when the thermal index value is below _____ .

13. For common intensities what does each of the following abbreviations stand for:

   a) SP:

   b) SA:

   c) TP:

   d) TA:

   e) PA:

   f) I_m:

14. The pulse average (PA) = $\dfrac{\text{total energy in pulse}}{\text{pulse time (duration)}}$

   The Duty Cycle = $\dfrac{\text{pulse duration}}{\text{total time (PRP)}}$

   So if you multiply the PA by the duty cycle, which intensity do you get?

15. Beam uniformity coefficient = $\dfrac{\text{spatial peak}}{\text{spatial average}}$

   so SA · (beam uniformity coefficient) = _____

16. What is the beam uniformity coefficient if the I_{SPTA} is 100 mW/cm² and the I_{SATA} is 25 mW/cm²?

17. What is the I_{SATA} given an I_{SPTA} of 100 mW/cm² and a beam uniformity coefficient of 2?

18. Given an I_{SATA} of 20 mW/cm², what is the I_{SAPA} if duty factor is 10%?

Chapter 11 Quality Assurance

Answers: Pg. 987-988

1.   A Doppler string phantom can be used to test all of the following EXCEPT:
        a)   peak velocity
        b)   gate registration accuracy
        c)   Doppler sensitivity
        d)   spectral characteristics

        Explain your reasoning:

2.   _____ _____ use complex fluids to mimic the properties of _____. Since, over time, the concentration of the particles in the fluid changes, there is difficulty in making repeatable measurements.

3.   The string of a Doppler flow phantom creates a very strong specular reflection that generally causes the artifact of _____. The result is that the peak velocities are generally significantly overestimated unless the transmit power and receiver are significantly reduced.

4.   For the multi-purpose phantom, the monofilament line targets are used for

        _____ _____.

5.   Which of the following test objects within a tissue mimicking phantom would most likely be indistinguishable from the background?
        a)   -6 dB
        b)   -3 dB
        c)   +2 dB
        d)   +6 dB
        e)   +15 dB

6.   The pin group very close to the surface of the imaging phantom can be used to test the
        _____ _____, or ring down distance.

7.   The AIUM standard 100 mm test object does not have _____ mimicking properties.

8.   Viewing a group of pins which vary in separation distance in depth can be used to test
        _____ resolution.

9.   The _____ is a percentage which must be between the sensitivity and the specificity.

10.   In comparison with a gold standard test, a testing procedure produces the following results: fifty-three patients have disease when the gold standard also found disease. Four patients are found with disease when the gold standard found no disease. One hundred and thirty patients are found with no disease when the gold standard also found no disease. Thirteen patients are found without disease when the gold standard found disease. Calculate the sensitivity, specificity, accuracy, positive predictive value, and the negative predictive value.

      a)   sensitivity

      b)   specificity

      c)   accuracy

      d)   positive predictive value

      e)   negative predictive value

Chapter 12 Fluid Dynamics Supplemental Exercises

Answers: Pg. 989-991

1.   Power has units of _____ which is the same as energy per_____, or Joules per _____.

2.   _____ energy is proportional to height.

3.   _____ energy is proportional to the velocity squared.

4.   Doubling the velocity of the flow results in a change in the kinetic energy by a factor of____.

5.   The unit for volumetric is_____.

6.   The equation for volumetric flow is:

7.   If a vessel radius triples, the resistance_____ by a factor of 81.

8.   Calculate the average spatial velocity at point B for the diagram below.

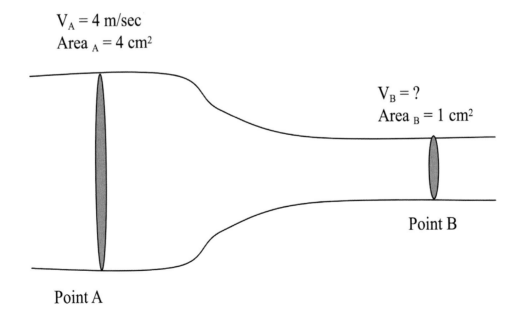

$V_A = 4$ m/sec
Area $_A = 4$ cm²

$V_B = ?$
Area $_B = 1$ cm²

Point B

Point A

9. If a vessel is stenosed such that the residual diameter is 25%, the resistance will increase by a factor of _____.

10. If the viscosity of the blood were to double, the resistance would _____.

11. The parameter which dominates the resistance is the vessel _____.

12. For a fixed resistance, doubling the flow will have what effect on the pressure gradient?

13. If a vessel vasodilates such that the new radius is twice the original radius, how much more blood volume can be supplied for the same pressure gradient?

14. With a(n) _____ in distal resistance, the _____ _____ flow component decreases.

15. After temporary ischemia, there is a short-term increase in _____ to re-perfuse the tissue. This response is called _____ _____.

16. Starting with the simplified law of hemodynamics, develop Poiseuille's law.

17. As the cross-sectional area of a flow path decreases, the likelihood of turbulence within that region _____.

18. _____ causes a "plug", or "blunt" flow profile.

19. When the Reynold's number is greater than _____, turbulence typically results.

20. A 25% radius reduction is equivalent to a _____% reduction in area.

21. A 10% reduction in radius is equivalent to a _____% residual diameter.

22. A 50% reduction in radius is equivalent to a _____% residual lumen area.

23. A 10% reduction in diameter results in an increase in resistance of _____%.

Chapter 13 Hemodynamics

Answers: Pg. 992

1. The venous system is highly _____ .

2. _____ _____ is the measure of the difference between the intravascular pressure and the tissue pressure.

3. When the intravascular pressure within a vein is greater than the surrounding tissue pressure, there is high _____ pressure and the veins will be distended.

4. A blood pressure measurement is made from the radial artery during a surgery. The patient is lying such that the radial artery is below the right atrium by about 10 inches. The measured blood pressure should be higher/lower due to _____ pressure by about _____ mmHg than if the radial artery were at the level of the right atrium.

5. _____ pressure increases with increasing height.

6. When recumbent, venous return is aided by _____ effects.

7. In the standing position, venous return is aided by the _____ _____ _____ .

8. Hydrostatic pressure is referenced to the _____ _____ and, in the standing position, is considered _____ in the head and positive in the feet.

9. In the supine position, the dynamic pressure at the level of the ankle is about _____ mmHg.

10. With _____ the diaphragm descends increasing intra-abdominal pressure, _____ venous flow from the legs to the abdomen but _____ venous return from the abdomen to the right atrium.

11. The viscosity of normal blood is _____ pascals.

12. The _____ are the resistive component of the arterial system.

Answers: Pg. 993-994

1. _____ equals the average power per time multiplied by time.

2. Using 120 Volts with a resistance of 1 kW, what would be the current?

3. The output of a stripchart recorder can be calibrated and should be _____ to the input signal.

4. _____ _____ comes from a battery, _____ current comes from wall outlets.

5. _____-_____ measurement devices are preferable to two-wire devices since a _____-_____ device can be calibrated and affects the signal less.

6. Using _____ coupling for a slowly varying signal may result in no signal detected.

7. If a signal "pegs" the display, the reason may be that _____ coupling was used when _____ coupling should have been used.

8. For a normal venous outflow study the waveform tracing should fall back to baseline within _____ seconds of cuff deflation.

9. In photoplethysmography a slightly slower upstroke, a disappearance of the dichroitic notch, and a slight bowing of the downslope away from the baseline would be classified as _____ _____.

10. For OPG, a difference between the two ophthalmic systolic pressures of more than _____ mmHg is considered abnormal.

11. Making a pressure measurement using a Doppler flow meter, the pressure measured is at the level of the _____, not at the level of the Doppler signal insonation.

12.   If the diameter of an arm is 10 cm, the appropriate cuff width should be at least _____ cm.

13.   An ABI greater than _____ is considered normal.

14.   With significant disease in the legs, the ankle pressure should _____, _____ the ABI.

15.   Calculate the right and left ABI given the following pressure measurements:

Right DP = 90 mmHg   Left DP = 120 mmHg
Right PT = 86 mmHg   Left PT = 118 mmHg
Right brachial = 120 mmHg   Left brachial = 110 mmHg

Right ABI =   Left ABI =

16.   What is the appropriate cuff occlusion pressure range for the deep venous system?

17.   Transcranial Doppler should be performed using which of the following conditions?

a)   PW, 4 MHz, gate size = 1 mm
b)   CW, 2 MHz
c)   PW, 2 MHz, gate size = 4 mm
d)   CW, 4 MHz
e)   PW, 2 MHz, gate size = 12 mm

18.   Using a trans-temporal window, if the transcranial spectrum from a depth of 70 mm is away from the transducer, the vessel insonated is either the _____ or the _____.

19.   Doppler signals from transcranial Doppler through a trans-temporal window are often very weak. The primary reason that these signals are generally weak is that the attenuation through bone is greater than _____ dB one-way.

20.   A normal HTI is greater than _____ .

21.   If the current through a 12 Volt device is 0.5 Amps, what is the resistance?

Appendix B: Cardiovascular Principles

Answers: Pg. 995-997

1.   Sodium ions are _____ charged.

2.   When there is a greater concentration of sodium ions external to the cell membrane there is a _____ potential.

3.   At rest, the "resting potential" is typically _____ mV.

4.   By pumping some of the sodium ions into the cell through the cell membrane, the potential changes. When the potential surpasses a _____, the process becomes self-generating and there is a rush of ions into the cell.

5.   The rapid change in polarization which occurs with the "rush" of sodium ions into the cell is called an _____ _____ and typically peaks at a voltage of _____ mV.

6.   During the process of _____, the cell rapidly pumps sodium ions out of the muscle cells until the "resting" potential is again reached.

7.   The period of time during which a cell cannot be stimulated by another stimulus is called the _____ _____.

8.   During the _____ _____ period, a greater stimulus is needed to depolarize a cell than when a cell is at its resting potential.

9.   Cardiac muscle has three unique characteristics relative to skeletal muscle:

      a)
      b)
      c)

10.   Calculate how many times per minute skeletal muscle can contract given that the refractory period is approximately 3 msec.

11.   What is the refractory period for cardiac muscle?

12.   Using the refractory period for cardiac muscle, determine the maximum number of cardiac muscle cell contractions per minute.

13.   Explain why it is so important that the refractory period for cardiac muscle is so much longer than the refractory period for skeletal muscle.

14.   The natural pacing rate of the AV-node is around _____ BPM.

15.   The _____ _____ have a natural pacing rate of 40-45 BPM.

16.   Draw and label an EKG tracing over a cardiac cycle making sure to label and describe the electrical event responsible for each wave characteristic.

17.   EKG's are plotted such that each minor division is _____ seconds and every major division represents five times the minor division, or _____ seconds.

18.   An EKG waveform that repeats every fourth major division has a rate of _____ BPM.

19.   The pulse pressure equals the difference between the _____ _____ pressure and the _____ _____ pressure.

20.   Calculate the MAP if the peak systolic pressure is 130 mmHg and the end diastolic pressure is 100 mmHg.

21.   The pressure in the ventricle rises dramatically during the phase called _____ _____. During this phase, the ventricle is contracting and all valves are _____ so that the volume remains _____ but the pressure increases.

22.   The _____ _____ occurs when the pressure in the aorta exceeds the pressure in the left ventricle causing a flow _____ which causes the _____ valve to close.

23.   Peak systolic pressure on the right side of the heart is typically _____ mmHg.

24.   Give the equation for the cardiac output in terms of the stroke volume:

        Cardiac Output =

25.   To calculate the cardiac index, what other information is necessary in addition to the cardiac output?

26.   With respect to cardiac loading, an increase in _____ can result in an increased stroke volume.

27.   With respect to cardiac loading, an increase in _____ can result in an increased peak systolic pressure.

28.   Aortic stenosis can cause pressure _____.

29.   Most VSD's and ASD's shunt left to right and cause right ventricle and right atrium _____ and may result in pulmonary _____.

30.   For normal patients the pressure in the left ventricle during passive filling increases within the range of:
        a)   0 - 10 mmHg
        b)   0 - 100 mmHg
        c)   20 - 100 mmHg
        d)   80 - 100 mmHg
        e)   20 - 30 mmHg

        Explain:

Answers. Pg. 943-953

1. Ultrasound is defined as
   a) 2 MHz - 10 MHz
   b) 20 Hz - 20 kHz
   c) greater than 20 kHz
   d) less than 20 kHz

2. The difference between sound waves and ultrasound waves is
   a) sound has lower frequencies than ultrasound
   b) ultrasound has higher frequency than sound
   c) no difference, ultrasound is defined as sound above human hearing
   d) ultrasound is a longitudinal wave and sound is a transverse wave.

3. The effects of ultrasound on live tissue are called
   a) absorption
   b) biological effects
   c) acoustic variables
   d) cavitation

4. The frequencies generally used for diagnostic ultrasound are
   a) 1,000 Hz to 10,000 Hz
   b) 1 MHz to 100 MHz
   c) 20 Hz to 20 kHz
   d) 2,000,000 Hz to 10 MHz

5. Soft tissue does not actually exist, but is an approximate average tissue composition. The assumed propagation velocity of sound in soft tissue is
   a) 1540 cm/sec
   b) 1560 cm/sec
   c) 1.54 m/sec
   d) 154,000 cm/sec

6. All of the following are acceptable units for frequency except
   a) 1/sec
   b) Hz
   c) times per day
   d) 3 days

7. The range of periods used for diagnostic ultrasound is
   a) 0.05 sec - 0.05 msec
   b) depends on the medium
   c) 0.5 µsec - 0.1 µsec
   d) 1 mm - 10 mm

8. How far can ultrasound travel in air in 5 seconds?
   a) 5 sec x 1540 m/sec = 7700 m
   b) 1540 m
   c) 331 m
   d) 5 sec x 331 m/sec = 1,655 m = approximately 1 mile

9. Match column b to column a

a		**b**		**Answer**
1	G	a	10^{-2}	1) _____
2	c	b	10^{1}	2) _____
3	da	c	10^{-6}	3) _____
4	k	d	10^{9}	4) _____
5	m	e	10^{-3}	5) _____
6	M	f	10^{3}	6) _____
7	n	g	10^{-9}	7) _____
8	μ	h	10^{6}	8) _____

10. If the diameter of a cyst increases by a factor of two, the area
    a) increases by a factor of two
    b) decreases by a factor of two
    c) increases by a factor of four
    d) cannot be determined since don't know initial area

11. Match column b to column a (more than one will apply)

a		**b**	
1)	circumference	a)	ft^3
2)	area	b)	ml
3)	volume	c)	mm
		d)	cm^2
		e)	gallons
		f)	cm
		g)	cm^3

12. A perimeter measurement is a measure of
    a) distance
    b) area
    c) volume
    d) pressure

13. If the frequency is 5 MHz, the period is
    a) 10 MHz
    b) 0.2 μsec
    c) 5 MHz/(1540 m/sec)
    d) cannot be determined without knowing propagation velocity

14. Transducer A operates at 2 MHz. Transducer B operates with a 0.5 μsec period. In a given patient which transducer will produce a sound wave of shorter wavelength?
    a) transducer A
    b) transducer B
    c) neither
    d) cannot be determined

15. Estimate the propagation velocity within a medium if the frequency is 2.5 MHz and the wavelength is 1.6 mm.
    a) 4000 m/sec
    b) 1560 m/sec
    c) 4000 m
    d) 0.64 m/sec

16. If the propagation velocity in a medium is 3000 m/sec, the medium is
    a) probably more dense than water
    b) probably stiffer than soft tissue
    c) probably stiffer than bone
    d) cannot be determined without knowing the frequency

17. Match column b to column a

	a		b
l)	frequency	a)	time
2)	period	b)	1 / time
3)	wavelength (λ)	c)	distance
4)	amplitude	d)	magnitude

18. Column a lists measurable quantities for both CW and PW. Column b lists measurable quantities related to PW. Match column b to column a according to similarity.

	a		**b**
1)	frequency	a)	amplitude
2)	period	b)	pulse duration
3)	wavelength	c)	spatial pulse length
4)	amplitude	d)	PRF

19. The pulse duration is the time for a pulse to occur and equals the
    a) (period) • (wavelength)
    b) (wavelength) • (# of cycles per pulse)
    c) (period) • (# of cycles per pulse)
    d) (frequency) • (wavelength)

20. The spatial pulse length is equal to the # of cycles per pulse multiplied by the wavelength and does NOT depend on which of the following
    a) frequency
    b) propagation velocity
    c) amplitude
    d) period

21. What is the duty factor if the pulse duration is 2 μsec and the PRF is 10 kHz?
    a) 1%
    b) 2%
    c) 20%
    d) 102 msec

22. Sound is a
    a) electromagnetic, longitudinal wave
    b) longitudinal, mechanical wave
    c) mechanical, transverse wave
    d) electromagnetic, transverse wave

23. Which of the following does not hold true for all waves?
    a) need a medium — Electromagnette
    b) transport energy
    c) cyclical variations
    d) none of the above

24. If an infrasound wave is traveling from left to right, the motion of the particles within the medium can be described as
    a) left to right and right to left
    b) left to right only
    c) up and down
    d) there is no particle motion

25. If a transverse wave is traveling east to west the particles within the medium are displaced
    a) north and south
    b) east and west
    c) depends on the medium
    d) west

26. The principal difference between electromagnetic waves and mechanical waves is
    a) electromagnetic waves can work in a vacuum
    b) electromagnetic waves cannot work in a vacuum
    c) mechanical waves require energy
    d) electromagnetic waves do not transport energy

27. Leaving all parameters fixed but increasing the frequency will
    a) increase the period and decrease the wavelength
    b) decrease the period and decrease the wavelength
    c) decrease the period and increase the wavelength
    d) decrease the period and leave the wavelength unchanged

28. Detail resolution will change with changes in any of the following EXCEPT
    a) increased frequency
    b) decreased SPL
    c) focus
    d) frame rate

29. Temporal resolution is related to all the following EXCEPT
    a) higher propagation velocity
    b) more lines per frame
    c) swept gain profile (TGC profile)
    d) imaging at shallower depths

30. Which of the following is not an acoustic variable?
    a) pressure
    b) propagation speed
    c) temperature
    d) density

31. If the maximum value of an acoustic variable is 10 and the mean is 3, the amplitude is
    a) 10
    b) 3
    c) 7
    d) 13

32. If in problem 31 the maximum value is increased from 10 to 17, the increase in intensity is
    a) twice as much
    b) half as much
    c) cannot be determined
    d) four times as much

33. If particle displacement caused by an acoustic wave is ± 6 nm, the amplitude is
    a) 6 nm
    b) 12 nm
    c) 3 nm
    d) -6 nm

34. The frequency of ultrasound
    a) changes with changes in the medium
    b) increases with stiffness
    c) increases with density
    d) is determined by the pulser and/or the transducer

35. The period of ultrasound
    a) changes with changes in the medium
    b) increases with stiffness
    c) increases with density
    d) is determined by the pulser and/or the transducer

36. The wavelength of ultrasound
    a) changes with changes in the medium
    b) increases with decreasing propagation velocity
    c) changes with spatial pulse length
    d) none of the above

37. The attenuation of 10 MHz ultrasound in soft tissue at a depth of 6 cm is
    a) 10 dB
    b) 10 dB/cm
    c) 30 dB
    d) 0.5 dB/(cm – MHz)

38. The attenuation of 10 MHz ultrasound in muscle at a depth of 6 cm is
    a) 10 dB
    b) 60 dB
    c) 30 dB
    d) 0.5 dB/(cm-MHz)

39. All of the following are related except
    a) frequency
    b) intensity
    c) power
    d) amplitude
    e) beam area

40. Refraction is the amount a wave direction is altered at an interface and
    a) changes with propagation velocity and density
    b) changes with propagation velocities and angle of incidence
    c) is determined by the acoustic impedance
    d) rarely occurs in ultrasound because of the frequencies used

41. For normal incidence, the percentage of transmission can be determined by the difference in
    a) angle to interface and propagation velocities
    b) densities and propagation velocities
    c) the amount of refraction (Snell's Law)
    d) there is no transmission for normal incidence

42. Which of the following is dependent on frequency?
    a) propagation velocity
    b) attenuation
    c) stiffness
    d) impedance
    e) acoustic transit time

43. Spectral analysis is the process of
    a) separating a signal into its frequency components for quantification
    b) assuring accuracy of peak velocity measurements
    c) filtering out low frequency signals
    d) increasing dynamic range based on frequency content

44. Axial resolution is determined by
    a) beamwidth
    b) beamwidth/2
    c) spatial pulse length
    d) SPL/2

45. Radial resolution is determined by
   a) beamwidth
   b) beamwidth/2
   c) spatial pulse length
   d) SPL/2

46. Lateral, azimuthal, or transverse resolution is determined by
   a) twice the bandwidth
   b) the bandwidth
   c) the beamwidth
   d) SPL/2
   e) beamwidth/2

47. An increase in amplitude by a factor of 10 is equivalent to how many dB?
   a) +10 dB
   b) -10 dB
   c) +20 dB
   d) -20 dB

48. An increase in power by a factor of 10 is equivalent to how many dB?
   a) +10 dB
   b) -10 dB
   c) +20 dB
   d) -20 dB

49. A decrease in intensity by a factor of 10 is equivalent to how many dB?
   a) +10 dB
   b) -10 dB
   c) -20 dB
   d) -20 dB

50. Using a 5 MHz transducer, what percentage of a 0.1 Watt/cm² beam is reflected at a normal interface 6 cm deep with propagation velocities of 1500 m/sec and 1600 m/sec?
   a) 10%
   b) 100%
   c) 0%
   d) no way of knowing

51. If medium 1 has an acoustic impedance one half that of medium 2, what percentage of the beam is reflected?
   a) 99%
   b) 11 %
   c) 50%
   d) 33%

52. If the power is decreased by a factor of two and all beam dimensions unaltered, the intensity is changed by
   a) 6 dB
   b) 3 dB
   c) -3 dB
   d) -6 dB
   e) -2 dB

53. If a gain in amplitude of 100 equals 40 dB and a gain of 13.7 equals 22.7 dB, a gain of 1,370 equals
   a) (40 + 22.7) dB
   b) (40 - 22.7) dB
   c) (40 x 22.7) dB
   d) (40/22.7) dB

54. If a transducer moves toward a target at 1 m/sec and a target moves toward the transducer at 1 m/sec, the velocity registered by the Doppler effect would be
   a) 1 m/sec
   b) -1 m/sec
   c) 2 m/sec
   d) -2 m/sec
   e) 0 m/sec

55. If a transducer moves toward a target at 1 m/sec and a target moves away from the transducer at 1 m/sec, the velocity registered by the Doppler effect would be
   a) 1 m/sec
   b) -1 m/sec
   c) 2 m/sec
   d) -2 m/sec
   e) 0 m/sec

56. Switching to a higher frequency transducer to quantify a regurgitant jet or stenotic flow will result in
   a) a higher Doppler frequency shift
   b) a lower Doppler frequency shift
   c) the same Doppler frequency shift
   d) a different velocity measurement

57. The wall filters in Doppler are _____ filters which reduce the_____ of _____ frequency signals.
   a) low pass, amplitude, low
   b) low pass, velocity, high
   c) high pass, amplitude, low
   d) high pass, velocity, low

58. Which of the following will not increase the Doppler shifted frequency?
   a) a higher propagation velocity
   b) using a higher transmit frequency
   c) a faster target velocity
   d) insonifying at 10° instead of 30°

59. Insonifying a blood vessel 4 cm deep, assuming soft tissue, what is the maximum detectable frequency shift?
   a) 1 MHz
   b) 10 kHz
   c) 15 kHz
   d) 20 Hz

60. Imaging with a maximum depth set at 10 cm using a narrowed color Doppler sector of 100 lines, with a packet size of 8, what is the frame rate?
   a) 10 MHz
   b) 10 seconds
   c) 10 Hz
   d) 80 Hz

61. Which binary representation is equivalent to the number 18?
   a) 10001
   b) 10010
   c) 0011
   d) 110010
   e) 10011

62. A digital scan converter is
   a) part of a transducer
   b) part of a receiver
   c) a computer memory
   d) what performs an FFT (Fast Fourier Transform)

63. For an unfocused disc shaped transducer, which of the following designs would give the shortest near zone length?
   a) diameter = 10 mm, freq. = 10 MHz
   b) diameter = 5 mm, freq. = 10 MHz
   c) diameter = 10 mm, freq. = 5 MHz
   d) diameter = 5 mm, freq. = 5 MHz

64. If the power of a beam is increased by 10% and the beam area is increased by 10%, then the intensity
   a) increases by 10%
   b) increases by 1%
   c) decreases by 10%
   d) remains the same

65. If the amplitude of a beam is doubled and the cross-sectional beam area is halved, then the intensity is
   a) eight times larger
   b) the same
   c) four times larger
   d) twice as large
   e) half the original

Appendix E

66. No Doppler shift is recorded when the insonification angle is
   a) 0°
   b) 90°
   c) 45°
   d) 180°

67. What determines the initial intensity of an ultrasound beam?
   a) the medium
   b) the source
   c) the spatial pulse length
   d) all of the above

68. Propagation velocity
   a) increases with density and decreases with stiffness
   b) increases with density and decreases with compressibility
   c) decreases with density and increases with compressibility
   d) decreases with density and decreases with compressibility

69. A 6-bit memory can represent how many shades of gray
   a) 32
   b) 64
   c) 16
   d) 12

70. Compensation is used for
   a) removing the high frequency transmit components of the echo
   b) temperature adjustments so as not to burn the patient
   c) normalizing gain differences due to attenuation
   d) creating time delays to focus and steer the transducer

71. The standard for U.S. television has been a frame rate of _____ and _____ lines per frame
   a) 60 Hz, 60
   b) 30 Hz, 60
   c) 60 Hz, 525
   d) 30 Hz, 525

72. Match the medium of column b with propagation velocity in column a

a		**b**
a) 4080 m/sec	1)	air
b) 1560 m/sec	2)	bone
c) 1540 m/sec	3)	lung
d) 1495 m/sec	4)	water
e) 1440 m/sec	5)	fat
f) 500 m/sec	6)	blood
g) 331 m/sec	7)	soft tissue

73. As the _____ increases, the _____ decreases, making the surface of most structures within the body appear rougher, thereby increasing the amount of _____.
    a) period, wavelength, reflection
    b) frequency, wavelength, reflection
    c) frequency, wavelength, scattering
    d) period, wavelength, reflection

74. With normal incidence, the amount of refraction is determined by
    a) the acoustic impedance mismatch
    b) the propagation velocity change
    c) the propagation velocity change and the incident angle
    d) none of the above, there is no refraction with normal incidence

75. Light, such as sunlight, consists of a spectrum of frequencies. The wavelength of blue light is approximately 475 nm and the wavelength of red light is approximately 660 nm in air. The fact that the sky looks blue and not red demonstrates that
    a) scattering increases with increased frequency
    b) scattering decreases with increased frequency
    c) refraction changes significantly with frequency
    d) none of the above

76. If the density and propagation velocity of medium 1 are both 1/10 the density and propagation velocity of medium 2, then the amount of reflection will be approximately
    a) 96%
    b) 60%
    c) 50%
    d) 0%
    e) 1%

77. The reasons why diagnostic ultrasound ranges the frequencies of 2 MHz - 12 MHz (not including intravascular) is that the low end is restricted by _____ and the high end is restricted by _____ .
    a) power, power
    b) power, electronics
    c) resolution, electronics
    d) resolution, penetration

78. The _____ effect is used by transducers to convert _____ energy into _____ energy and _____ energy into _____ energy.
    a) Doppler, acoustic, mechanical, mechanical, spectrum
    b) electromagnetic, electromagnetic, acoustic, acoustic, mechanical
    c) piezoelectric, electropotential, acoustic, acoustic, electropotential
    d) piezoelectric, electropotential, voltage, acoustic, mechanical

79. A matching layer or layers in transducer construction is used to _____ while a backing material is used to _____.
    a) lessen impedance mismatch, dampen the spatial pulse length
    b) lessen impedance mismatch, increase transducer sensitivity
    c) increase impedance mismatch, dampen spatial pulse length
    d) improve lateral resolution, improve axial resolution

80. In CW mode, if the drive frequency is 5 MHz and the crystal thickness is doubled, the transmit frequency will
    a) double
    b) quadruple
    c) halve
    d) remain unchanged

81. If you double the crystal diameter the frequency of operation in the PW mode will
    a) double
    b) quadruple
    c) halve
    d) remain unchanged

82. In pulsed mode, doubling the crystal thickness will _____ the frequency.
    a) double
    b) quadruple
    c) halve
    d) not change

83. Using a backing material shortens the spatial pulse length and
    a) improves sensitivity
    b) decreases transducer bandwidth
    c) increases transducer bandwidth and improves sensitivity
    d) increases transducer bandwidth and decreases sensitivity

84. For the unfocused transducer, the best approximation of the beamwidth at a distance twice the near zone length from the transducer face is
    a) equal to the aperture
    b) 1/2 the aperture
    c) twice the aperture
    d) cannot be determined

85. What is the principle called which states that all points on a wavefront can be treated as point sources producing spherical secondary wavelets whose tangential surface predicts the new position of the wave over time? (From this principle, the laws of reflection and refraction can be determined.)
    a) Snell's principle
    b) Huygen's principle
    c) Heisenberg's uncertainty principle
    d) Rayleigh's principle

86. Which of the following cannot be used to help focus a beam in the far field?
    a) lens
    b) electronics
    c) curved elements
    d) mirrors
    e) all of the above cannot

87. If the spatial pulse length is 5 mm, then the lateral resolution is
   a) 5 mm
   b) 10 mm
   c) 2.5 mm
   d) >1.0 mm
   e) cannot be determined

88. If the spatial pulse length is 5 mm, then the axial resolution is
   a) 5 mm
   b) 10 mm
   c) 2.5 mm
   d) 1.0 mm
   e) can not be determined

89. A shorter pulse duration
   a) increases the bandwidth of a transducer
   b) decreases the bandwidth of a transducer
   c) does not affect the bandwidth of a transducer
   d) can increase or decrease the bandwidth of a transducer

90. Which of the following transducer designs can change focus in both the lateral and elevation planes?
   a) 1-D phased sector
   b) all 1-D phased arrays
   c) linear sequential
   d) blind transducer
   e) annular array

91. To have multiple transmit focuses a system must shoot _____ acoustic liner to create a single display _____, _____ the frame rate, but possibly improving _____ resolution.
   a) two, frame, decreasing, lateral
   b) multiple, line, decreasing, lateral
   c) multiple, line, decreasing, axial
   d) multiple, line, increasing, axial

92. Arrange the following intensities from highest to lowest.
   a) I_{SPTA}
   b) I_{SATA}
   c) I_{SPTP}
   d) I_{SPPA}

93. Dynamic range means
   a) the ratio of the minimum to the maximum of quantity
   b) the ratio of the maximum to the minimum of a quantity
   c) the ratio of the maximum to the mean of a quantity
   d) the ratio of the maximum to the mode of a quantity

94. Which of the following modes has time on one axis and depth on another?
    a) A-mode
    b) B-mode
    c) C-mode
    d) M-mode
    e) Spectral Doppler

95. Of the following, all of the following are generally advantages of phased systems over mechanical systems except
    a) variable transmit focuses
    b) better temporal resolution
    c) higher PRF's
    d) multiple receive focuses

96. To evaluate rapidly moving structures, good _____ resolution is necessary.
    a) detail
    b) temporal
    c) display
    d) none of the above

97. Which intensity (SPTA) is most reasonable for diagnostic ultrasound?
    a) 1.8 mW/cm²
    b) 200 mW/cm²
    c) 1.8 W/cm²
    d) 1 kW/cm²

98. Color Doppler provides
    a) peak velocities
    b) mean velocities
    c) modal velocities
    d) laminar flow velocities

99. Regarding thermal bioeffects, the AIUM has determined that a maximum temperature rise of _____ above normal physiological levels may be used in clinical examinations without reservation.
    a) 0° C
    b) 1° C
    c) 10° C
    d) 15° F

100. The AIUM's conclusion involving in vivo mammalian bioeffects states that there have been "no independently confirmed significant biological effects in mammalian tissues exposed in vivo to unfocused ultrasound with intensities below _____ or to focused ultrasound with intensities below _____".
    a) 0.1 mW/cm², 1 W/cm²
    b) 0. 1 mW/cm², 100 mW/cm²
    c) 100 mW/cm², 1 W/cm²
    d) 1 W/cm², 25 W/cm²

101. A hydrophone is used to measure
    a) water levels
    b) water energy
    c) acoustic energy in a water bath
    d) electrical energy

102. Nylon lines within a test object are used to test
    a) detail resolution
    b) temporal resolution
    c) refraction
    d) all of the above

103. Attenuation over depth is corrected by
    a) discretion
    b) digitization
    c) rejection
    d) compensation

104. For which of the following insonification angles will the Doppler shift be greatest?
    a) 45°
    b) 10°
    c) 90°
    d) 180°

105. Which of the following modes has the worst temporal resolution?
    a) B-scanning
    b) m-mode
    c) B-mode (2D)
    d) Colorflow

106. Which of the following modes has the worst temporal resolution?
    a) colorflow
    b) B-mode (2D)
    c) m-mode
    d) Doppler

107. Which mode allows only echoes from a specific depth to be displayed? (PW is the most common application of this mode.)
    a) A-mode
    b) B-mode
    c) C-mode – constant depth mode
    d) Nyquist mode

108. In-vivo means
    a) within living tissue
    b) within a test tube
    c) within a plant
    d) not living

109. In-vitro means
   a) within living tissue
   b) within a test tube
   c) within vitamins
   d) within a thermal mass

110. An empirical approach to bioeffects
   a) involves determining specific mechanisms causing bioeffects
   b) involves testing on plant and animal cells
   c) involves theoretical approximation of potential damage
   d) involves correlating patient outcomes with large number of studies

111. Which of the following parameters under control of the sonographer can affect the probability of bioeffects?
   a) receiver gain
   b) exposure time
   c) transmit power
   d) more than one of the above choices

112. Cavitation during diagnostic ultrasound is
   a) very unlikely
   b) more likely to be transient than stable
   c) more likely to be stable than transient
   d) dangerous to the sonographer

113. The value of an in-vitro study is
   a) the results are directly applicable to a clinical environment
   b) the results are useful to design in-vivo studies
   c) the results don't need to be further tested since the test is completely independent of patient to patient variability
   d) the results are generally the most accurate

114. Causes of artifacts can be
   a) sonographer error
   b) physics related
   c) poor system design
   d) all of the above

115. System A detects two side-by-side cysts separated by 0.1 cm. System B using the same frequency transducer and similar settings displays only one large cyst. The problem with system B is poor _____, related to the _____.
   a) longitudinal resolution, beamwidth
   b) longitudinal resolution, spatial pulse duration
   c) lateral resolution, beamwidth
   d) temporal resolution, beamwidth

116. Acoustic speckle is caused by _____ and creates a pseudo tissue texture.
    a) refraction
    b) very small structures and scintillation
    c) very large structures and diffraction
    ? d) destructive and constructive interference of acoustic echoes

117. Reverberation artifact results in
    a) artifactual structures deeper than the reflecting structure
    b) laterally displaced artifacts
    c) a resonant, low frequency sound in Doppler
    d) all of the above

118. Grating lobes occur with _____ transducers and are beams of energy _____ to the main beam.
    ₂ a) phased, at an angle
    b) mechanical, at an angle
    c) single crystal, in the same direction
    d) all, great angles

119. Shadowing is caused by _____ and is the opposite of the _____ artifact.
    a) low reflection, refraction
    b) low reflection, enhancement
    c) high attenuation, enhancement
    d) high attenuation, range

120. The most likely artifact to result from a propagation velocity differing from the assumed 1540 m/sec is
    a) longitudinal resolution
    b) speed error
    c) range ambiguity
    d) comet tail

Appendix F • Hemodynamics Exam

Answers: Pg. 955-957

C 1. In Poiseuille's law, the dominant factor affecting resistance is
    a. viscosity.
    b. vessel length.
    c. vessel diameter.
    d. Reynold's number.

A 2. Acceleration, as occurs at the entrance to a vessel or stenosis, generally results in a
    _____ velocity profile.
    a. flattened
    b. parabolic
    c. turbulent
    d. disturbed

C 3. With respect to a stenosis, where is turbulent flow most likely?
    a. just proximal to the stenosis
    b. in the middle of the stenosis
    c. just distal to the stenosis
    d. distal to the stenosis

D 4. Laminar flow is best described as flow which is
    a. completely chaotic.
    b. somewhat irregular.
    c. low in velocity.
    d. regular and moves in layers.

C 5. Flow occurs from a region of _____ pressure to a region of _____
    pressure.
    a. low, low
    b. low, high
    c. high, low
    d. high, higher

A 6. A good reason why the systemic side of the heart is more muscular and the arterial vascular
    walls thicker is
    a. the systemic side is higher pressure.
    b. the systemic side is lower pressure.
    c. the systemic side must overcome gravitational potential energy.
    d. the systemic side is more prone to stenosis and occlusions.

A 7. A vessel which is stenosed such that the diameter is 50% the original diameter is equivalent to
    which of the following?
    a. 50% reduction in radius and 75% reduction in area
    b. 25% reduction in radius and 50% reduction in area
    c. 75% reduction in radius and 50% reduction in area
    d. 50% reduction in radius and 25% reduction in area

8. If a vessel is stenosed such that the radius is 50% reduced, the resistance of the vessel will
   a. increase by a factor of 2.
   b. increase by a factor of 4.
   c. increase by a factor of 16.
   d. decrease by a factor of 16.

9. The calf muscle pump is largely responsible for venous return from the legs when
   a. the patient is standing.
   b. the patient is recumbent.
   c. the patient's legs are elevated above the heart.
   d. never

10. When a person is recumbent, venous return from the legs is aided by
    a. gravitational potential energy.
    b. pressure changes with respiration.
    c. hydrostatic pressure.
    d. the calf muscle pump.

11. Flow is related to the mean velocity by which equation?
    a. simplified law of hemodynamics
    b. continuity equation
    c. resistance equation
    d. Bernoulli's equation

12. In a functioning closed system, if the velocity increases in a specific segment then the flow must have
    a. increased.
    b. decreased.
    c. unable to determine.
    d. remain unchanged.

13. The most likely cause of an increase in velocity in a closed system is
    a. a decreased resistance
    b. a decrease in area
    c. a large capacitance
    d. none of the above

14. In a closed system, the velocity increase which occurs at a narrowed area of increased resistance is a means by which to maintain _____.
    a. turbulence
    b. pressure
    c. flow
    d. kinetic energy

15. The greatest energy loss in the circulatory system occurs in the
    a. arteries.
    b. veins.
    c. arterioles.
    d. aorta.

C

16. A person suffering from severe anemia would be more likely to have cardiac murmur because
    a. the blood viscosity increased with increased blood hematocrit.
    b. the blood viscosity increased with decreased blood hematocrit.
    c. the blood viscosity decreased with decreased blood hematocrit.
    d. of other underlying causes.

A

17. Reynold's number is a dimensionless number which relates above what point flow will gener
    ally become
    a. turbulent.
    b. laminar.
    c. plug.
    d. parabolic.

B

18. Inertial energy losses are the same as
    a. potential energy losses.
    b. kinetic energy losses.
    c. hydrostatic energy losses.
    d. gravitational energy losses.

A

19. Which of the following situations will create the greatest inertial energy loss?
    a. a stenosed carotid
    b. a healthy femoral artery
    c. an obstructed vena cava
    d. an arterial aneurysm

B

20. Turbulence generally occurs for a Reynold's number
    a. above 20,000.
    b. above 2,000.
    c. below 2,000.
    d. below 20,000.

A

21. We know that turbulence is likely to occur just distal to a stenosis. We also know that the
    velocity at a stenosis increases to maintain flow across an increased resistance. A logical
    conclusion is that
    a. $R_E \propto$ velocity.
    b. $R_E \propto$ 1/velocity.
    c. R_E is unrelated to velocity.
    d. R_E is only dependent on viscosity.

C

22. Bernoulli's equation is often simplified to the form $p_1 - p_2 = 4v_2^2$. The reason why v_1 can often
    be ignored is
    a. $v_2 = v_1$ at a stenosis.
    b. $v_2 \ll v_1$ at a stenosis.
    c. $v_2 \gg v_1$ at a stenosis.
    d. $v_2 = 4v_1$ at a stenosis.

23. The driving force for venous flow is principally muscular pumping and respiration resulting in a very small acceleration component relative to arterial flow. As a result, venous flow velocities relative to arterial flow velocities appear
    a. more parabolic.
    b. more plug.
    c. more disturbed.
    d. more turbulent.

24. With pulmonary hypertension, the pulmonic artery flow profile looks more like an aortic wave form because
    a. pulmonary pressure has decreased.
    b. pulmonary resistance has decreased.
    c. right ventricular pressure increases to overcome increased pulmonary resistance.
    d. right ventricular pressure decreases to overcome increased pulmonary resistance.

25. Which of the following organs or systems usually contains approximately 60-70% of the total blood volume?
    a. heart
    b. kidneys
    c. arterial system
    d. venous system

26. All of the following conditions will result in a distension of the veins EXCEPT
    a. high transmural pressure.
    b. high intravascular pressure.
    c. high tissue pressure.
    d. increased flow.

27. A low transmural pressure is given by which of the following situations?
    a. veins distended, intravascular pressure > tissue pressure
    b. veins collapsed, intravascular pressure > tissue pressure
    c. veins distended, intravascular pressure < tissue pressure
    d. veins collapsed, intravascular pressure < tissue pressure

28. For an upright person the hydrostatic pressure will
    a. increase with decreasing blood density.
    b. increase with increasing height.
    c. decrease with increasing height.
    d. none of the above.

29. Hydrostatic pressure within the body is referenced to the _____ and is considered _____ in the head and _____ in the feet.
    a. carotids, positive, negative
    b. ankle, negative, positive
    c. right atrium, positive, positive
    d. right atrium, negative, positive

30. For cuff occlusion studies, Korotokov sounds are heard when systolic _____ and disappear when diastolic _____ .
    a. arterial pressure exceeds cuff pressure, arterial pressure drops below cuff pressure.
    b. arterial pressure drops below cuff pressure, venous pressure exceeds cuff pressure.
    c. arterial pressure exceeds cuff pressure, venous pressure exceeds cuff pressure.
    d. arterial pressure exceeds cuff pressure, arterial pressure exceeds cuff pressure.

31. The AHA recommends all of the following regarding cuff size EXCEPT
    a. the width should be 20% greater than segment diameter.
    b. the length should be at least twice the width.
    c. overestimation of pressure can occur from too narrow a cuff.
    d. overestimation of pressure can occur from two wide a cuff.

32. DC coupling should be used to record
    a. quickly varying large signals.
    b. quickly varying small signals.
    c. slowly varying signals.
    d. none of the above.

33. Arterial flow is generally recorded with
    a. resistive coupling.
    b. AC coupling.
    c. DC coupling.
    d. friendly coupling.

34. The principal reason for using a four-wire measuring technique over a two-wire measuring technique is
    a. stronger signals.
    b. quicker measurements.
    c. less risk to patient.
    d. the ability to calibrate the system.

35. Photoplethysmography would most likely be used for measuring which type of flow?
    a. cutaneous
    b. carotid
    c. aortic
    d. venous

36. Displacement (pneumatic cuff) plethysmography detects changes in blood _____ within the segment under test.
    a. volume
    b. velocity
    c. hematocrit
    d. oxygen levels

37. Displacement plethysmography is often used for arterial testing with an inflated pressure of approximately
    a. 10 mmHg.
    b. 65 mmHg.
    c. 150 mmHg.
    d. 200 mmHg.

38. OPG is used to directly measure what pressure?
    a. ICA
    b. ophthalmic artery
    c. PCA
    d. brachial

39. The transducer or sensor of a four wire system has a high impedance so that
    a. the signals will be very large.
    b. the signals won't vary with time.
    c. there is minimal risk of shock to the patient.
    d. the transducer or sensor itself does not alter the measurement.

40. Within a closed system, a fluid flows at a velocity of 10 m/sec through a pipe of area 2 m^2. What is the flow?
    a. 5 m/sec
    b. 5 m^3/sec
    c. 20 m^3/sec
    d. 10 m^3/sec

41. Within a closed system, measurements of fluid velocities are measured at two different points. Point A has an area of 1 m^2 and a velocity of 8 m/sec. Point B has an area of 2 m^2. What is the velocity of Point B?
    a. 16 m/sec
    b. 8 m/sec
    c. 4 m/sec
    d. 2 m/sec

42. A patient is brought into the emergency room with a bad gun shot wound and severe bleeding. Cardiac output is measured at the aorta as 4.2 l/min. What would you expect the flow rate to be coming back into the right atrium (through inferior and superior vena cavae)?
    a. 4.2 l/min
    b. 4.1 l/min
    c. 6.0 l/min
    d. 1.0 l/min

43. Exercise _____ the _____ of peripheral vessels by increasing the diameter of the _____.
    a. increases, resistance, venules
    b. decreases, resistance, arterioles
    c. increases, velocity, arterioles
    d. decreases, flow, capillaries.

44. The principal reason for the body's reaction to exercise in question #53 is to
    a. decrease blood velocity to maximize time for metabolic transfer
    b. increase blood velocity to meet higher metabolic demands
    c. decrease blood flow to minimize cellular damage
    d. increase blood flow to maintain adequate metabolic transfer

45. A plausible explanation of why a patient's ankle/brachial index might drop after exercise is
    a. a greater energy gradient across the stenotic lesion as a result of decreased velocity from increased peripheral resistance.
    b. a greater energy gradient across the stenotic lesion as a result of increased velocity across the lesion.
    c. a greater energy gradient as a result of increased capacitance of the capillaries.
    d. a decreased energy gradient across the stenotic lesion as a result of increased velocity from decreased peripheral resistance.

46. Pulse Wave Doppler is used for transcranial imaging instead of Continuous Wave Doppler because
    a. PW can detect higher velocities.
    b. PW is safer in the head.
    c. PW gates out the strong returning echoes from the temporal bone.
    d. CW will not penetrate as well as PW.

47. An increase in vessel diameter causes a _____ in peripheral resistance, the result will be a _____ in blood pressure.
    a. decrease, increase
    b. decrease, decrease
    c. increase, increase
    d. increase, instability

48. Inspiration causes all of the following EXCEPT
    a. a decrease in intrathoracic pressure
    b. an increase in venous return from the upper extremities
    c. an increase in intra-abdominal pressure
    d. an increase in venous return from the lower extremities

49. Expiration causes which of the following?
    a. an increase in abdominal pressure from the diaphragm movement
    b. an increase in intrathoracic pressure
    c. a reduction in venous blood return from the legs
    d. an increase in return from the abdominal cavity to the thorax

50. Blood ejected from the heart towards the peripheral vessels decreases in velocity. Blood returning from the heart increases in velocity. The best explanation of why the velocity increases returning to the heart is
    a. the velocity increases with the increasing pressure.
    b. although the individual major vessels have a much larger cross-sectional area than the individual minor vessels, the total cross-sectional area is significantly smaller such that the velocity must increase to maintain constant flow.
    c. there is an increase in flow with the decrease in pressure from peripherals to heart.
    d. more frictional losses in larger vessels requires higher velocities to maintain volumetric flow.

Pg. 917-933

1. c   Ultrasound is defined as frequencies greater than 20 kHz.

2. c   Ultrasound waves are sound waves, just above human hearing.

3. b   The effects of ultrasound on live tissue are called biological effects.

4. d   Diagnostic frequencies are from 2 MHz - 10 MHz.
   (2,000,000 Hz = 2 MHz)

5. d   The speed of sound in soft tissue is 1540 m/sec = 154,000 cm/sec.

6. d   Frequency implies a rate of occurrence - 3 days is a unit of time, not frequency.

7. c   Diagnostic frequencies are from 2 MHz - 10 MHz.

   The period equals the reciprocal of the frequency, or:

   $$period = \frac{1}{frequency}$$

   $$\frac{1}{2 \text{ MHz}} = 0.5 \text{ } \mu sec$$

   $$\frac{1}{10 \text{ MHz}} = 0.1 \text{ } \mu sec$$

8. d   distance = rate time
   rate   = 331 m/sec (Speed of sound in air)
   time   = 5 seconds
   so distance   = (331 m/sec) (5 sec)
                    = 1,655 meters = approximately 1 mile.

9. 1) d $G = 10^9$ = Giga
   2) a $c = 10^{-2}$ = centi
   3) b $da = 10^1$ = deca
   4) f $k = 10^3$ = kilo
   5) e $m = 10^{-3}$ = milli
   6) h $M = 10^6$ = Mega
   7) g $n = 10^{-9}$ = nano
   8) c $\mu = 10^{-6}$ = micro

10. c   Recall that the equation for the area of a circle is: $area = \pi r^2 = \pi \dfrac{d^2}{4}$

So the area is proportional to the radius squared, or, equivalently, the diameter squared. Doubling the diameter increases the area by the square of the change factor, or $2^2 = 4$.

11.   1)   c, f
     2)   d
     3)   a, b, e, g

12. a   Perimeter is the <u>distance</u> around an object.

13. b   Period = 1/frequency so period = $\dfrac{1}{5\ MHz}$ = 0.2 μsec

14. c   A period of 0.5 μsec is the same as a frequency of 2 MHz since $2\ MHz = \dfrac{1}{0.5\mu sec}$

Therefore, both transducers are operating at the same frequency. Since the wavelength depends on both the frequency and the speed of sound, and since both transducers are being used on the same patient, the situation is identical for both transducers and the wavelengths are the same.

15. a $f \bullet \lambda = c$
        $(2.5 \times 10^6\ Hz)\ (1.6 \times 10^{-3}\ m) = 4{,}000$ m/sec

16. b   Propagation velocity increases with increasing stiffness and decreases with increasing density. Since the propagation velocity for sound in soft tissue is 1540 m/sec, a material with a propagation velocity of 3000 m/sec is most likely stiffer than soft tissue. Note that the propagation velocity depends on the properties of the medium - not frequency, so choice d is also incorrect.

17.   1)   b   frequency has units of 1/time
     2)   a   period has units of time
     3)   c   wavelength has units of distance
     4)   d   amplitude has the units of any magnitude

18.

		CW	PW
1)	d	frequency	frequency and PRF
2)	b	period	period and pulse duration
3)	c	wavelength	wavelength and spatial pulse length
4)	a	amplitude	amplitude

19. c   Pulse duration = (period) • (# of cycles per pulse)

20. c   The spatial pulse length depends on the wavelength. Since the wavelength depends on both the frequency and the propagation velocity, the SPL also depends on the fre quency and the propagation velocity for continuous wave and is dependent on both frequency and propagation velocity. Recall that frequency and period give the same information, so choice 'd' is really the same as choice 'a'.

21. b

$$\text{The Duty Factor} = \frac{PD}{PRP}$$

$$\text{The PRP} = \frac{1}{PRF}$$

$so:$

$$\frac{1}{PRF} so \frac{1}{10\ kHz} = 0.1\ msec = 100\ \mu sec$$

$$DF = \frac{2\ \mu sec}{100\ \mu sec} = 2\%$$

22. b   Sound is a longitudinal, mechanical wave.

23. a   Not all waves need a medium to propagate. Electromagnetic waves do not need a medium.

24. a   Infrasound is a sound wave and sound is a longitudinal wave, so particles move "along" the direction of wave propagation. Particles are compressed and rarefied from left to right and right to left.

25. a   In a transverse wave, the particles move across or "trans" the wave propagation direction. Since the wave is traveling East to West, the particles are displaced both North and South.

26. a   The principal difference between electromagnetic waves and mechanical waves is electromagnetic waves do not need a medium to propagate or, equivalently, will work in a vacuum.

27. b   Increasing the frequency is the same as decreasing the period. For a specific speed of sound, increasing the frequency decreases the wavelength.

28. d   Frame rate affects temporal resolution, not detail resolution.

29. c   Temporal resolution depends on how fast images can be created and does not depend on swept gain (which compensates for increasing attenuation with depth).

30. b The four acoustic variables are:
      pressure
      distance
      temperature
      density

31. c Amplitude = max - mean
              = 10 - 3 = 7

32. d Amplitude = max - mean
              = 17 - 3 = 14
      Since intensity (Amplitude)^2
      doubling the amplitude quadruples the intensity.

33. a $\text{Amplitude} = \dfrac{\text{max} - \text{min}}{2} = \dfrac{6\ \text{nm} - (-6\ \text{nm})}{2} = \dfrac{12\ \text{nm}}{2} = 6\ \text{nm}$

34. d The frequency of ultrasound is determined by the pulser and/or the transducer.

35. d Since the frequency and period give the exact some information, this problem is identical to #34.

36. a The wavelength depends on both frequency and the propagation velocity. Since the propagation velocity changes with changes in the medium, the wavelength also changes with changes in the medium.

37. c Attenuation in soft tissue is approximately 0.5 dB/(cm – MHz)
      so (0.5 dB) / (cm - MHz)) • (10 MHz) • (6 cm) = 30 dB

38. b Attenuation in muscle tissue is approximately 1 dB/(cm – MHz)
      so (1 dB) / (cm – MHz)) • (10 MHz) · (6 cm) = 60 dB

39. a
      $\text{Intensity} = \dfrac{\text{power}}{\text{beam area}}$

      and

      $\text{power} \propto (\text{amplitude})^2$

      so only frequency is unrelated

40. b Refraction is governed by Snell's Law and is dependent on propagation velocities and angle of incidence.

41. b The amount of reflection and transmission for normal incidence is determined by the acoustic impedance mismatch. Since $Z = \rho * c$, where ρ is the density and c is the propagation velocity, the answer is b.

42. b Attenuation increases with increasing frequency.

43. a Spectral analysis is the process of separating a signal into its frequency components for quantification.

44. d The axial resolution is equal to one half the spatial pulse length.

45. d Radial resolution is another name for axial resolution and is equal to SPL/2.

46. c Lateral, azimuthal, or transverse resolution is equal to the beamwidth.

47. c Amplitude dB definition => $dB = 20 \log (A_f/A_i)$

$$\frac{A_f}{A_i} = 10$$
$$20*log(10) = 20*1 = 20 \ dB$$

48. a Power definition of dB => $dB = 10 \log (P_f/P_i)$

$$\frac{P_f}{P_i} = 10$$
$$10*log(10) = 10*1 = 10 \ dB$$

49. b Intensity $\propto$ power. From #48, we know that an increase in power by a factor of 10 is equivalent to +10 dB. Therefore, a decrease in power by a factor of 10 is equivalent to -10 dB.

50. d The amount of reflection and transmission is determined by the acoustic impedance mismatch. Since we do not know the acoustic impedance mismatch, there is no way to answer this question.

51. b

$$\% \ reflection = \left[\frac{Z_2 - Z_1}{Z_2 + Z_1}\right]^2 \bullet 100\%$$

since $Z_2 = 2Z_1$

$$\% \ reflection = \left[\frac{2Z_1 - Z_1}{2Z_1 + Z_1}\right]^2 \bullet 100\%$$

$$= \left[\frac{1Z_1}{3Z_1}\right]^2 \bullet 100\%$$

$$= \left(\frac{1}{3}\right) \bullet 100\%$$

$$= \frac{1}{9} \bullet 100\% \approx 11\%$$

52. c $\text{intensity} = \dfrac{\text{power}}{\text{area}}$

If the power is decreased by a factor of 2, the intensity is decreased by a factor of 2. Using the power definition of dB, a decrease by a factor of 2 is equivalent to -3 dB.

53. a   Logarithms convert multiplication into addition, so $100 \cdot 13.7 = 137$ is the same as 40 dB + 22.7 dB = 62.7 dB.

54. c   1 m/sec (towards) + 1 m/sec (towards) = 2 m/sec (towards). Movement towards the transducer produces a positive Doppler shift.

55. e   1 m/sec (towards) - 1 m/sec (towards) = 0 m/sec

56. a

$$\text{recall } f_{Dop} = \frac{2f_0 v}{c} * cos(\theta)$$

so $f_{Dop} \propto f_o$ and if f_o increases, f_{Dop} increases

57. c   Wall filters are <u>high pass</u> filters (allows high frequencies through) which reduce the <u>amplitude</u> of the <u>low</u> frequency signals.

58. a   Again recall

$$f_{Dop} = \frac{2f_0 v}{c} \bullet cos(\theta)$$

$f_{Dop} \propto \dfrac{1}{c}$ so an increase in c will decrease f_{Dop}

59. b

$$PRP = 4 \ cm \bullet \frac{13 \ \mu sec}{cm} = 52 \ \mu sec$$

$$PRF = \frac{1}{PRP} = \frac{1}{52 \ \mu sec} = .02 \ MHz$$

$.02 \ MHz = 20 \ kHz$

by Nyquist:

$$f_{Dop}(max) = \frac{PRF}{2} = \frac{20 \ kHz}{2} = 10 \ kHz$$

60. c

$$\text{Frame time} = \left(\frac{10\ cm}{line}\right)\left(\frac{13\ \mu sec}{cm}\right) \bullet \left(\frac{8\ lines}{packet}\right)\left(\frac{100\ packets}{frame}\right) = 104{,}000\ \frac{\mu sec}{frame}$$

$$= 104\ \frac{msec}{frame}$$

$$\text{Frame rate} = \frac{1}{\text{Frame time}} = \frac{1}{104\ \dfrac{msec}{frame}} = .01\ kHz = 10\ Hz$$

61. b

2^4	2^3	2^2	2^1	2^0
1	0	0	1	0

16 + 0 + 0 + 2 + 0 = 18

62. c   A digital scan converter is effectively a computer memory.

63. d

$$NZL \approx \frac{D^2 f}{6},$$

Which implies: NZL $\propto$ D^2 and NZL $\propto$ f
The smallest diameter, D, and the lowest operating frequency, f, will result in the smallest Near Zone Length.

64. d $intensity = \dfrac{power}{beam\ area}$

If both the power and the area are increased by 10% there is no change in intensity.

65. a

$$intensity = \frac{Power}{area} \propto \frac{(amplitude)^2}{area} = \frac{(2 \bullet amplitude)^2}{\dfrac{area}{2}} = 8 \bullet intensity$$

66. b

$$\text{recall } f_{Dop} = \frac{2f_o v}{c} \bullet cos(\theta)$$

since $cos(90^o) = 0$, $f_{Dop} = 0$ when $\theta = 90^o$

67. b   The source determines the initial intensity of an ultrasound beam.

68. d   Propagation velocity decreases with density and increases with stiffness, or, equivalently, decreases with compressibility.

69. b $2^6 = 2 \cdot 2 \cdot 2 \cdot 2 \cdot 2 \cdot 2 = 64$

70. c   Compensation is used for normalizing gain differences due to attenuation.

71. d   A standard for U.S. television has been a 30 Hz frame rate and 525 lines per frame. The U.S. format is in process of changing such that the frame rate is 60 Hz (non-interlaced video) and more than 525 lines per frame (high definition television).

72. a)   4080 m/sec = bone (2)
    b)   1560 m/sec = blood (6)
    c)   1540 m/sec = soft tissue (7)
    d)   1495 m/sec = water (4)
    e)   1440 m/sec = fat (5)
    f)   500 m/sec = lung (3)
    g)   331 m/sec = air (1)

73. c   As the **frequency** increases the **wavelength** decreases, making the surface of most structures within the body appear rougher, thereby increasing the amount of **scattering**.

74. d   There is no refraction with normal incidence.

75. a   Within the same medium, a shorter wavelength corresponds to a higher frequency. The sky appears blue because blue is scattered more than red, proving that scattering increases with higher frequencies.

76. a

$$Z = \rho \times c$$
$$so: Z_1 = \rho_1 \times c_1 \ and \ Z_2 = \rho_2 \times c_2$$
Given that:
$$\rho_2 = 10 \times \rho_1 \ and \ c_2 = 10 \times c$$
$$Z_2 = 10 \times \rho_1 \times 10 \times c_1$$
$$Z_2 = 100 \times \rho_1 \times c_1$$
$$Z_2 = 100 \times Z_1$$

$$\% \text{ reflection} = \left[\frac{Z_2 - Z_1}{Z_2 + Z_1} \right]^2 \bullet 100 \%$$

$$= \left[\frac{100 \, Z_1 - Z_1}{100 \, Z_1 + Z_1} \right]^2 \bullet 100 \%$$

$$= \left[\frac{99}{101} \right]^2 \bullet 100 \%$$

$$\approx 96 \%$$

77. d   Diagnostic ultrasound is operated over the range from 2 MHz - 12 MHz. Below 2 MHz, the **resolution** is not good enough for small structures within the body and above 12 MHz, there is usually not adequate **penetration**.

78. c   The **piezoelectric** effect is used by the transducer to convert **electropotential** energy into **acoustic** energy and **acoustic** energy into **electropotential** energy.

79. a   A matching layer or layers in transducer construction is used to **lessen impedance mismatch** while a backing material is used to **dampen the spatial pulse length.**

80. d   In CW mode, the operating frequency is determined by the frequency of the drive voltage - <u>not</u> the crystal thickness.

81. d   Be careful! The question states the crystal "diameter", not the "thickness"!! Beamwidth changes with crystal diameter, frequency changes with thickness.

82. c   In pulsed mode, doubling the crystal thickness will halve the operating frequency.

$$f_o = \frac{\text{propagation velocity}}{2 \bullet \text{thickness}} \quad \text{so} \quad f_o \propto \frac{1}{\text{thickness}}$$

83. d   Using a backing material shortens the spatial pulse length and increases transducer bandwidth and decreases sensitivity

84. a   For the unfocused transducer, the best approximation of the beamwidth at a distance twice the near zone length from the transducer face is equal to the aperture. Recall also that at a distance of one near zone length, the beamwidth is approximately one half the aperture.

85. b   Huygen's principle states that all points on a wavefront can be treated as point sources producing spherical secondary waves whose tangential surface predicts the new position of the wavelength over time. From this principle, the laws of reflection and refraction can be determined.

86. e   Focusing effects can only be achieved in the near field. Note that all choices are acceptable focusing techniques in the near field.

87. e   Spatial pulse length determines axial, not lateral resolution. The lateral resolution is approximately equal to the beamwidth.

88. c   The axial resolution $= \dfrac{SPL}{2} = \dfrac{5\ mm}{2} = 2.5$ mm

89. a   A shorter pulse duration increases the bandwidth of a transducer.

90. e   An annular array can change focus in both the lateral and elevation

91. b   To have multiple transmit focuses, a system must shoot **multiple** transmit lines to create a single **display line, decreasing** the frame rate, but possibly improving **lateral** resolution.

92.   (I_{SPTP} is always the biggest)

I_{SPTP}	(c)	Temporal peak is greater than pulse average.
I_{SPPA}	(d)	Pulse average is greater temporal average.
I_{SPTA}	(a)	Spatial peak is greater than spatial average.
I_{SATA}	(b)	(I_{SATA} is always smallest).

93. b   Dynamic range means the ratio of the maximum to the minimum of a quantity.

94. d   M-mode has time on the horizontal axis and depth on the vertical axis.

95. c   The PRF is determined by the time it takes ultrasound to travel through the tissue being imaged, which cannot be changed by phasing.

96. b   To evaluate rapidly moving structures, good **temporal** resolution is necessary.

97. b   Depending on the imaging modality, intensity (SPTA) usually ranges from approximately 100 mW/cm^2 to 800 mW/cm^2. In ophthalmic and transorbital imaging, the intensity is often on the order of 17-30 mW/cm^2.

98. b   Color Doppler provides a mean velocity estimator.

99. b   Regarding thermal bioeffects, the AIUM has determined that a maximum temperature rise of **1°C** above normal physiological levels may be used in clinical examinations without reservation.

100. c   The AIUM's conclusion involving in vivo bioeffects states that there have been "no independently confirmed significant biological effects in mammalian tissues exposed in vivo to unfocused ultrasound with intensities below **100 mW/cm^2** or to focused ultra sound with intensities below **1 W/cm^2.**

101. c   A hydrophone is used to measure acoustic energy in a water bath.

102. a   Nylon lines within a test object are used to test detail resolution.

103. d   Attenuation over depth is corrected by compensation.

104. d   Consider the cosine of each angle. The cosine of 180° is -1, which means a 100% shift <u>away</u> from the transducer. For all of the other angles given, the Doppler shift is less than 100%.

105. a   B-scanning has the worst temporal resolution since the image is built up over time by movements of an articulated arm.

106. a   Since color flow requires multiple acoustic lines per packet, it requires the most time to create an image and therefore, has the worst temporal resolution of the choices given.

107. c   C-mode is constant depth mode.

108. a   In-vivo means within living tissue.

109. b   In-vitro means within a test tube.

110. d   An empirical approach to bioeffects involves correlating patient outcomes with a large number of studies.

111. d   Both the exposure time and the transmit power can effect the probability of bioeffects, receiver gain does not.

112. c   Cavitation during diagnostic ultrasound is more likely to be stable than transient. Note that transient cavitation is a violent collapse of microbubbles.

113. b   The value of an in-vitro study is that the results are useful to sign in-vivo studies.

114. d   Causes of artifacts can be related to sonographer error, physics, system design and system performance.

115. c   System A detects two side-by-side cysts separated by 0.1 cm. System B using the same frequency transducer and similar settings displays only one large cyst. The problem with system B is poor **lateral resolution** , related to the **beamwidth**.

116. d   Acoustic speckle is caused by **destructive and constructive interference of acoustic echoes** and creates a pseudo tissue texture.

117. a   Reverberation results in artifactual structures deeper than the reflecting structure. In the simplest manifestation, reverberation artifact results in multiple, equidistant, artifacts.

118. a   Grating lobes occur with **phased** transducers and are beams of energy **at an angle** to the main beam.

119. c   Shadowing is caused by **high attenuation** and is the opposite of the **enhancement** artifact.

120. b   The most likely artifact to result from a propagation velocity differing from the assumed 1540 m/sec is **speed error**.

(Pg. 935-941)

1. c

2. a

3. c

4. d

5. c

6. a

7. a   diameter = 2 • radius
        so d ∝ r, or 0.5 d ⇒ 0.5 r
        $area = \pi r^2$
        so area ∝ r^2 or area ∝ $(0.5\ r)^2 = 0.25\ r$
        so new area is only 0.25 of original area or 75% reduced.

8. c   Resistance ∝ $\dfrac{1}{r^4}$

9. a

10. b

11. b

12. c   Since we know nothing about the area, we can say nothing about the flow. This is a very tough question.

13. b

14. c   In a closed system, flow must be conserved or the system will cease functioning. As a result, when a pathway narrows becoming more resistive, the velocity must increase to maintain flow.

15. c   The arterioles are known as the resistive element of the vascular system.
        Energy is lost trying to maintain flow across a resistive pathway.

16. c   Recall that for a given velocity, turbulence is more likely to occur with lower viscosity fluids. As the blood hematocrit drops, so does the "apparent" viscosity, increasing the likelihood of turbulence and murmurs.

17. a

18. b

19. a

20. b

21. a $R_E = \dfrac{\rho \, d \, v}{\mu}$, as the velocity increases, so does Reynold's number, increasing the likelihood of turbulence.

22. c

23. a Recall that acceleration tends to flatten a profile. Since arterial flow generally experiences more acceleration than venous, venous flows tend to be more parabolic than arterial flows.

24. c

25. d 60-70% of blood volume is normally contained in the highly capacitive venous system.

26. c Transmural pressure is the difference between intravascular pressure and tissue pressure. A high tissue pressure creates a low transmural pressure, exerting a force on the elastic veins, limiting distension.

27. d Low transmural pressure means tissue pressure is greater than intravascular pressure, collapsing the veins. Remember that transmural pressure is always referenced from the inside of the vessel to outside the vessel.

28. b Hydrostatic pressure is the resulting pressure from the force of the fluid above in a column. The force will increase with both increasing density and height.

29. d Hydrostatic pressure within the body is referenced to the **right atrium** and is considered **negative** in the head and **positive** in the feet.

30. d In cuff occlusion studies, the cuff pressure is brought to supra-systolic pressures. As the pressure is released, the systolic arterial pressure eventually exceeds the cuff pressure at which time Korotokov sounds are heard. As the cuff pressure continues to drop, Korotokov sounds continue until ultimately even the diastolic arterial pressure exceeds cuff pressure and there is no longer any vessel occlusion.

31. d Too wide a cuff can result in underestimation.

32. c DC coupling is needed to look at slowly varying signals.

33. b Rapidly varying signals, such as pulsatile arterial flow, is recorded using AC coupling.

34. d Four-wire systems can be easily calibrated.

35. a   Photoplethysmography uses red or infrared light which cannot penetrate very deep.

36. a   Displacement plethysmography records pressure changes within the cuff as the blood **volume** changes within the limb segment or digit under test.

37. b

38. b   Oculoplethysmography (OPG) is used to directly measure the pressure in the ophthalmic artery from which distal ICA pressures can be inferred.

39. d

40. c $Q = \bar{v} * area = 10 \ \dfrac{m}{sec} * 2 \ m^2 = 20 \ \dfrac{m^3}{sec}$

41. c   In a closed system, the flow at Point A must equal the flow at Point B. At Point A, the flow is $(1m^2) * (8m/sec) = 8 \ m^3/sec$. At Point B the flow must also be $8 \ m^3/sec$, so $8 \ m^3/sec = (2m^2) * (velocity \ at \ pt \ B) = 4 \ m/sec$.

42. b   Normally, for a closed system, venous return flow must match cardiac output. Since this patient is hemorrhaging from the gun shot wound, the system is no longer closed and you would expect lower return than output. Choice d is incorrect since at 1 liter/min return the patient would probably already be dead.

43. b

44. d

45. b

46. c   If CW were used, the small returning echoes from the blood flow would be masked by the enormous echoes present from the temporal bone. PW turns the receivers off when the echoes from the bone arrive.

47. b

48. d

49. b

50. b   Recall that flow is conserved in a closed system, and that $Q = \bar{v} * area$

So $Q_{peripheral} = Q_{right \ atrium}$ and the product of the average velocity and areas must be equal. The total cross-sectional area of the peripheral vessels is significantly greater than the cross-sectional area of the inferior and superior vena cava. Therefore, the velocity must increase to maintain the same volumetric flow.

Appendix H • Answers to Chapter Exercises

Chapter 7 Doppler

Section 1.8 Exercises (Pg. 524-525)

1. **a,b,c** All three choices would yield the same Doppler shift since all three scenarios result in a 60 mph rate.

2. **a,b** Both choices "a" and "b" would have the same frequency shift, even though choice "a" would result in a positive shift and choice "b" would result in a negative shift. Choice "c" would result in no shift since relatively speaking there is no change in distance between the police car and the "perp."

3. **a** Choice "a" is a positive shift. Choices "b" and "c" represent negative shifts. Therefore, the greatest positive shift must be "a."

4. **c** Choice "a" is a positive shift. Both choices "b" and "c" are negative shifts. Choice "c" represents a relative velocity away of 65 mph whereas choice "b" is only 60 mph. Therefore, choice "c" represents a greater negative shift.

5. **b** If the velocity of a train doubles, the frequency shift doubles. (Note that the presumption must be that the direction of the train did not change – just the speed.)

6. **c** If the velocity of a train doubles, the positive frequency shift cannot be determined since direction is not known. (Since there is no way of knowing direction, the shift could have increased in the negative direction or the positive direction. Since the question states "the positive shift," there is no way to answer the question.)

7. **b** -3 kHz represents a greater frequency shift than +2 kHz. Remember a greater shift does not have to be positive.

8. **a** Since the receive signal has a lower frequency than the transmitted frequency, the movement must be "away", not "toward". The shift is 2 kHz "away" or -2 kHz.

Section 5. Conceptual Questions (Pg. 531)

1. The **Doppler Effect** is a shift in frequency caused by relative motion between observer and target.

2. A positive shift is caused by motion **towards** the observer.

3. A **negative** shift is caused by motion away from the observer.

4. A Doppler shift will **increase** if both the target and observer are moving away from each other faster.

5.   A Doppler shift will **increase** if both the target and observer are moving towards each other faster.

6.   In comparison to a target and an observer moving in opposite directions, a Doppler shift will **decrease** if both the target and observer are moving in the same direction.

7.   The **faster** the target moves, the higher the Doppler shift.

8.   The Doppler shifted frequency is **proportional** to the target velocity.

9.   The Doppler shifted frequency is **proportional** to the operating frequency.

10.   The Doppler shifted frequency is **inversely** **proportional** to the propagation velocity.

Section 9. Exercises (Pg. 539)

1.   **4 kHz**
You can solve the entire equation, or you can realize that since $f_{Dop} \propto f_o$, if you double f_o, you double f_{Dop}, − or 2 • (2 kHz) = 4 kHz

2. $\cos(60°) = 0.5$

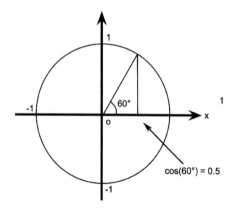

since $f_{dop} \propto \cos(\theta°)$
(2 kHz) (0.5) = **1 kHz**

3.   Since the Doppler shift is proportional to the blood velocity, v, doubling the blood velocity doubles the Doppler shifted frequency.

2 • 2 kHz = **4 kHz**

4.   Since $f_{Dop} \propto v$, if f_{Dop} increases by a factor of 3, the velocity must have increased by a factor of 3, so $3(1.54 \text{ m/sec}) \approx 4.6 \text{ m/sec}$. Solved formally:

$$f_{Dop} = \frac{2f_o v}{c} \cos(\theta) \Rightarrow \frac{f_{Dop} \bullet c}{2f_O \cos(\theta)} = v$$

$$f_o = 1 \, MHz$$
$$f_{Dop} = 6 \, kHz$$
$$\cos(0^0) = 1$$
$$c = 1540 \frac{m}{\sec}$$

so

$$v = \frac{\left(6 \bullet 10^3 \, \frac{1}{\sec}\right)\left(1540 \, \frac{m}{\sec}\right)}{2 \bullet \left(1 \bullet 10^6 \, \frac{1}{\sec}\right) \bullet (1)} = \left(3 \bullet 10^{-3}\right) \bullet \left(1540 \, \frac{m}{\sec}\right) = \underline{\underline{4.6 \, \frac{m}{\sec}}}$$

Section 32. Conceptual Questions (Pg. 589)

1.   The **cosine** term in the Doppler equation corrects for the decrease in the detected shift due to the insonification angle.

2.   A **wall** filter is used to decrease the signal dynamic range by attenuating (lessening) high amplitude, low frequency signals.

3.   A wall filter is a **high** pass filter, allowing higher frequency signals to pass and eliminating lower frequency signals.

4.   A **Fast Fourier Transform (FFT)** is used to separate the spectrum of signals into its individual frequency components.

5.   A typical Doppler frequency shift is within the range of plus or minus **10 kHz,** but can be much higher.

6.   Since the typical Doppler frequency shift is approximately plus or minus 10 kHz, the Doppler shift is within the **audible** range.

7.   The amplitude of a Doppler signal is displayed by the **brightness** of the spectrum.

8.   The horizontal axis of a Doppler display corresponds to **time.**

9.   Range resolution is an advantage of **PW** Doppler.

10.   Aliasing is a disadvantage of **PW** Doppler.

11.   Aliasing occurs when the **Nyquist** limit is violated.

12. The **Nyquist** **limit** requires a sampling rate twice as fast as the highest frequency.

13. **Color** Doppler provides flow information over two dimensions.

14. Color Doppler uses a **correlation** technique to estimate the mean velocity of blood flow.

15. To determine a peak **velocity** spectral Doppler must be used.

16. If a color scale goes from blue below the baseline to red above the baseline, non-aliased flow towards the transducer will be encoded as **red.**

17. If a color scale goes from blue below the baseline to red above the baseline, non-aliased flow away from the transducer will be encoded as **blue.**

18. The use of persistence with color flow will lower **temporal** resolution.

Section 6. Conceptual Questions (Pg. 617-618)

1.	Refraction, which is governed by **Snell's** law, results in objects appearing **laterally** displaced from their true position.

2.	Simple **reverberation** results in the appearance of strongly reflecting structures multiple times at constant depth increments.

3.	Two specular reflectors are located in the same vicinity. If the first reflector is insonified at an oblique angle and the second reflector is off-axis, a **multi-**path artifact will most likely result.

4.	The multi-**path** artifact causes a strongly reflecting structure to appear too deep.

5.	Off-axis beams which result from single element transducers are called **side lobes.**

6.	Off-axis beams created by multi-element transducers are called **grating lobes.**

7.	The general effect of **side lobes** and **grating** lobes is a creation of a spurious lateral structure or a clouding or haze over the image.

8.	**Speed** error results in a mis-registration of a structure because the actual propagation velocity is not the assumed propagation velocity of 1540 m/s.

9.	If the propagation velocity is **greater** than 1540 m/sec an ultrasound system will represent a structure shallower than reality.

10.	If the propagation velocity is **less** than 1540 m/sec an ultrasound, system will represent a structure deeper than reality.

11.	**Range ambiguity** occurs in shallow depth settings in PW Doppler. The result is an echo from a deeper depth registers as if from the shallower depth setting.

12.	The PW Doppler gate is placed in myocardium and mitral flow from a depth of approximately twice the Doppler gate depth is registered. The most likely explanation is **range ambiguity**.

13.	High PRF Doppler utilizes **range** ambiguity to achieve a higher Nyquist **limit**.

14.	**Mirror** image is an artifact similar to multi-path, however, as the name suggests, with **mirror** image, one structure is spuriously displayed twice — once at its correct position and once at its mirrored position.

15.	**Shadowing** is the reduction or absence of echo below a highly **attenuative** structure.

16.	**Enhancement** is the opposite of shadowing.

17. **Enhancement** is a brighter than normal echo below a structure which is less **attenuative** than normal.

18. **Aliasing** results when the Nyquist criterion is violated.

19. The Nyquist limit dictates that to detect a frequency of "f" you must sample at a frequency of at least **"2f"**.

20. Spectral mirroring is evident as a mirrored spectrum in the **reverse** direction of strong flow.

21. **Spectral broadening** is an artifactual smearing of the Doppler spectrum resulting in peak velocity overestimation and possibly the diminishing of the spectral window .

22. Spectral broadening generally becomes a significant concern when using large **linear** arrays and as insonification angles become **larger**.

Section 7. Exercises (Pg. 633)

1. **a)** $I_{SPTP:}$ **Spatial Peak Temporal Peak**
    b) $I_{SPTA:}$ **Spatial Peak Temporal Average**
    c) $I_{SATP:}$ **Spatial Average Temporal Peak**
    d) $I_{SPPA:}$ **Spatial Peak Pulse Average**
    e) $I_{SAPA:}$ **Spatial Average Pulse Average**
    f) $I_{SATA:}$ **Spatial Average Temporal Average**
    g) $I_{m:}$ **Maximum Intensity**

2. **The I_{SPTP} must be the greatest**   (Spatial <u>Peak</u> Temporal <u>Peak</u>)

    The I_{SATA} must be the smallest   (Spatial <u>Average</u> Temporal <u>Average</u>)

3. "Pulse" refers to the energy only during the "pulse on" time or the Pulse Duration (PD). Temporal refers to the energy distribution over the entire **time** or **the PRP.**

4. The "BUF" beam uniformity coefficient is defined as:
$$BUF = \frac{SP}{SA}$$

5. To convert an SP value to an SA value you need to know the **BUF**
$$since \;\; BUF = \frac{SP}{SA} \Rightarrow SA \bullet BUF = SP$$
$$or \;\; \Rightarrow SA \bullet \left(\frac{SP}{SA}\right) = SP$$

6. The peak is always **greater** than or equal to the average.

7. A spatial peak is always **greater** than or equal to a spatial average.

8. A temporal peak is always greater than or equal to a **temporal average.**

9. Spatial refers to the energy distribution over physical space whereas **temporal** refers to a beam's energy distribution over time.

10. The pulse average must be **less** than the pulse peak.

11. The **beam uniformity** factor equals the spatial peak divided by the spatial average, and is a measure of how uniform a beam is spatially.

Section 14. Conceptual Questions (Pg. 651-652)

1. There have been no recorded biological effects observed due to temperatures less than or equal to **2° C** above normal for exposure duration up to 50 hours.

2. The **Mechanical Index (MI)** assists the user in evaluating the likelihood of cavitation-related adverse biological effects.

3. **Transient cavitation** is the violent collapse of microbubbles caused by the energy of the wave.

4. Transient cavitation is known to occur at pressures exceeding **10 MPa (Mega Pascals)**.

5. **Stable cavitation** occurs at energy levels lower than transient cavitation and is basically when bubbles begin to expand and oscillate.

6. The threshold for fetal anomalies over extended periods of time is **41°C.**

7. No significant biological effects in mammalian tissues exposed in vivo have been confirmed for unfocused ultrasound with intensities below 100 mW/cm², or for focused ultrasound with intensities below **1 W/cm².**

8. The **AIUM's** official statement on clinical **safety** basically states no confirmed biological effects have ever been reported on patients or instrument operators caused by exposure at intensities typical of present diagnostic ultrasound instruments. In addition, although future risks may be found, prudent use of diagnostic ultrasound outweighs the risks, if any, that may be present.

9. Tissue heating is caused by absorption. the most important common intensity which predicts thermal effects is the I_{SPTA}.

10. **In vitro** studies are studies done in a "test tube".

11. **In vivo** studies are studies done within living tissue.

12. The AIUM's position on **in vitro** studies is that it is difficult to make conclusions about **biological** effects; however, in vitro studies are valuable for designing appropriate in **vivo** studies.

13. The AIUM's position on diagnostic ultrasound safety, training and research is
    a) don't perform **studies** without reason
    b) don't prolong studies without **reason**
    c) use the minimum output **power** and maximum receiver gain to optimize image quality

14. The AIUM's position on the electrical and mechanical hazards of ultrasound are as follows
    a) use proper **grounding** to avoid electrical shock
    b) routinely **check** equipment for proper condition
    c) ultrasound presents no special electrical **hazards**
    d) since the **transducer** comes in direct contact with the patient, the transducer is most likely to pose a threat, albeit small, to a patient's safety.

15. The **Mechanical Index** (MI) is a better indicator of cavitation-related adverse biological effects than the derated spatial peak, pulse average intensity I_{SPPA}.

Section 7. Conceptual Questions (Pg. 720)

1.   A string phantom is useful for measuring the following parameters: peak **velocity**, spectral **broadening**, depth **accuracy**, and gate size in PW **Doppler**.

2.   A **string** phantom is not useful for determining Doppler sensitivity since the string target is such a strong reflector.

3.   If a tissue mimicking phantom has multiple gray scale targets of varying contrasts, **contrast resolution** can be tested.

4.   If a tissue mimicking phantom has multiple gray scale targets of +15, +10, +2, -3, -6, and -14 dB, which two targets would most likely blend into the surrounding tissue mimicking material and not be visualized?
   +2 dB and -3 dB

5.   A tissue equivalent phantom attempts to mimic tissue's **attenuation** and scattering characteristics.

6.   The **dead zone** is the area at the top of the image which can not produce an accurate image due to the ring down effect.

7.   **Ring** down is when the transmit pulses in a **pulsed** mode feeds back into the receiver causing bright ringing echoes obscuring the near **field** image.

Section 12. Exercises (Pg. 726)

Use the general table /reference to answer the following questions. Be sure that you can answer these questions since these concepts are commonly covered on credentialing exams.

1.   The total number of tests performed is the sum of all of the numbers in the table:
$$\text{Total tests} = TP + FP + TN + FN$$

2. Remember that the golden rule says we always believe the gold standard, so every time the gold standard is positive, the patient really has disease. Therefore, everyone in the column below the plus sign of the gold standard really has disease:

$$\text{Have disease} = TP + FN$$

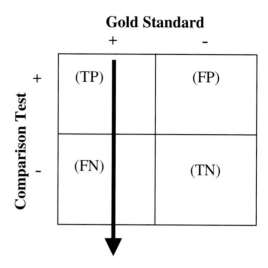

3. Again we believe the gold standard so everyone below the negative sign truly does not have disease.

$$\text{No disease} = FP + TN$$

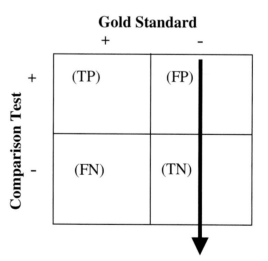

4.   The row next to the plus sign indicates that the test was positive for disease:
Test positive for disease = *TP* + *FP*

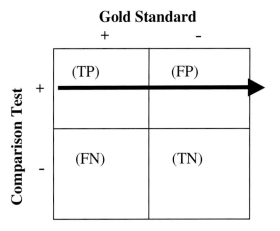

5.   The test correctly predicted disease when the test was both positive and true:
Test correctly predicted disease = *TP*

6.   The row next to the minus sign indicates that the test was negative for disease
Test negative for disease = *TN* + *FN*

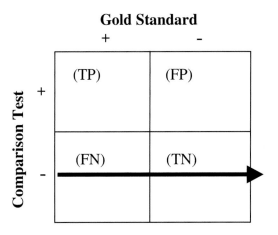

7.   The test correctly predicted the absence of disease when the test was both negative and true:
Test correctly predicted no disease = *TN*

8.   Every time the test was "True" it was correct
Test is correct = *TP* + *TN*

9.   Every time the test was "False" it was incorrect
Test is incorrect = *FP* + *FN*

10.

$$\frac{\# \; True}{total \; tested} = \frac{TP + TN}{TP + FP + TN + FN} \times 100\%$$

11. $$\frac{\# False}{total\ tested} = \frac{FP + FN}{TP + FP + TN + FN} \times 100\%$$

12. $$\frac{\# with\ disease}{total\ tested} = \frac{TP + FN}{TP + FP + TN + FN} \times 100\%$$

13. $$\frac{\# without\ disease}{total\ tested} = \frac{FP + TN}{TP + FP + TN + FN} \times 100\%$$

14. A perfect test (relative to the gold standard would have zeroes for when the test would be false or **FP and FN**.

Section 16. Exercises (Pg. 730)

Of the 24 positive tests, the test matched the gold standard 20 times, so the TP = 20, and the FP = 4. Since the test matched the gold standard 94 times when negative for disease, the TN = 94. This leaves only one parameter of the table to determine, the false negatives (FN). Since the total number of tests performed was 120, the FN is easily calculated by subtracting all of the other test already specified, or $120 - (20 + 4 + 94) = 2$

Putting the data into the "standard" table format, the table becomes:

Gold Standard

	+	−
Test +	(TP) 20	(FP) 4
Test −	(FN) 2	(TN) 94

Now recall that the sensitivity refers to how many times the test correctly predicted disease divided by all the times there truly is disease:

$$Sensitivity = \frac{TP}{TP + FN} = \frac{20}{20 + 2} = \frac{20}{22} = \frac{10}{11} = 91\%.$$

Now recall that specificity refers to how many times the test correctly predicted the absence of disease divided by the total number of times there was no disease:

$$Specificity = \frac{TN}{TN + FP} = \frac{94}{94 + 4} = \frac{94}{98} = 96\%.$$

Now recall that the accuracy is the total number of times the test was correct divided by the total number of tests:

$$\text{Accuracy} = \frac{TP + TN}{TP + FN + TN + FP} = \frac{20 + 94}{20 + 2 + 94 + 4} = \frac{114}{120} = 95\%.$$

Now recall that the positive predictive value is the number of time the test correctly predicted disease divided by the total number of positive predictions:

$$\text{Positive Predictive Value} = \frac{TP}{TP + FP} = \frac{20}{20 + 4} = \frac{20}{24} - \frac{5}{6} = 83\%.$$

Now recall that the negative predictive value is the number of time the test correctly predicted no disease divided by the total number of negative predictions:

$$\text{Negative Predictive Value} = \frac{TN}{TN + FN} = \frac{94}{94 + 2} = \frac{94}{96} = 98\%.$$

Note that the accuracy is between the sensitivity and the specificity, but not necessarily the average of these two values. You should also notice that the accuracy is between the positive and negative predictive value, but not necessarily the mean of those two values.

2.   Of the 45 positive tests, the test did not match the gold standard 14 times, so the FP = 14. The number of correct positive tests must therefore be the difference between the total number of positive tests and the number of incorrect positive tests, or TP = 45 – 14 = 31. The number of negative test was 220 of which 14 tests did not match the gold standard. Therefore, FN = 14, and the TN is the difference, or TN = 220 – 14 = 206.

Putting the data into the "standard" table format, the table becomes:

Gold Standard

		+	-
Test	**+**	(TP) 31	(FP) 14
	-	(FN) 14	(TN) 206

Now recall that the sensitivity refers to how many times the test correctly predicted disease divided by all the times there truly is disease:

$$Sensitivity = \frac{TP}{TP + FN} = \frac{31}{31 + 14} = \frac{31}{45} = 69\%$$

Now recall that specificity refers to how many times the test correctly predicted the absence of disease divided by the total number of times there was no disease:

$$Specificity = \frac{TN}{TN + FP} = \frac{206}{206 + 14} = \frac{206}{220} = 94\%$$

Now recall that the accuracy is the total number of times the test was correct divided by the total number of tests:

$$Accuracy = \frac{TP + TN}{TP + FN + TN + FP} = \frac{31 + 206}{31 + 14 + 206 + 14} = \frac{237}{265} = 89\%$$

Now recall that the positive predictive value is the number of time the test correctly predicted disease divided by the total number of positive predictions:

$$Positive\ Predictive\ Value = \frac{TP}{TP + FP} = \frac{31}{31 + 4} = \frac{31}{45} = 69\%$$

Now recall that the negative predictive value is the number of time the test correctly predicted no disease divided by the total number of negative predictions:

$$Negative\ Predictive\ Value = \frac{TN}{TN + FN} = \frac{206}{206 + 14} = \frac{206}{220} = 94\%$$

Section 1.3 Exercises (Pg. 734)

1. **c** The bully acts like the heart, creating the pressure necessary for the flow to overcome the resistance in the vascular tree.

2. a) The bully = the heart
    b) The tunnel = blood vessels
    c) You and your friends = the blood
    d) Narrowing of the tunnel = a stenosis

3. **d** Flow is represented by the number of children per time who went down the tunnel. (The speed with which the children traveled down the tunnel is velocity - not flow.)

4. **c** Flow (better termed volumetric flow) is represented by volume per time. More children per the same amount of time represents a higher volumetric flow.

5. **b** (choices a & d) $$\frac{2 \bullet (\# \, children)}{2 \bullet time} = \frac{\frac{1}{2} \bullet (\# \, children)}{\frac{1}{2} \bullet (time)}$$

6. **a** The tunnel is best described as the vessel or flow path. (Note: for electricity - the analogous parameter to the flow path is the electrical wire which conducts the current.)

7. **a** The bully at the entrance of the tunnel creates the pressure difference to cause the children flow.

8. **b** The reason you overcame your resistance to go down the tunnel was because the bully created enough pressure to overcome that resistance.

9. **a** The rate at which you traveled down the tunnel is the velocity.

10. **d** This question demonstrates that resistance increases with increasing length.

$$R \propto L \;\; \text{(where } L \text{ represents the length of the vessel)}$$

11. **c** This question demonstrates that resistance increases with decreasing radius. In fact,

$$R \propto \frac{1}{(radius)^4} \;\; \text{(where r represents the radius of the vessel)}$$

Pegasus Lectures, Inc.

12.   **d**   Imagine how difficult it would be to squeeze four people at a time through a tunnel only two feet wide. Clearly, as the tunnel diameter (or radius) decreases, the resistance increases dramatically, which demonstrates that the resistance changes faster with changes in radius than with changes in length.

13.   **c**   At the narrowing of the tunnel, the velocity increases to maintain a constant flow through an increase in resistance. Recall that you personally moved fastest as you were pushed through the narrowing of the tunnel. Since only one at a time could fit through the opening, you had to increase your velocity to keep the same "volumetric" flow.

14.   **b**   Your velocity would be the fastest just as you are exiting the narrowing in the tunnel.

15.   **a**   Flow at the exit of a stenosis is generally turbulent.

16.   **c**   The difference in pressure which results in flow represents **energy** and is called a pressure **gradient (change)**.

17.   **a**   You spent energy to travel through the tunnel, which is why you feel tired. The more resistance you overcome, the more energy you will have to spend. Some of this energy is converted to heat, which is why you feel hot and sweaty.

Section 2.12 Exercises (Pg. 746-747)

1.   In a closed system, an increase in flow velocity results in an increase in **kinetic** energy.

2.   In a closed system, an increase in flow velocity results in a decrease in **potential** energy.

3.   Assuming a closed system with no energy losses to heat, a positive change in potential energy must equal the negative change in **kinetic** energy.

4.   The units for choice c, $\dfrac{m}{\sec}$, is the unit for velocity, not volumetric flow. All of the other choices given have volume per time and are acceptable.

5.   Work is the total energy that is expended. Since system B pumped out more total liters, **system B performed more work**. If the question had asked which system had a greater power, then the answer would be system A, which pumped at a higher flow rate.

6.   Recall that the kinetic energy is proportional to the velocity squared. Therefore, doubling the velocity **quadruples** the kinetic energy.

7.   A change in volume per pressure is a measure of the compliance.

8.   A change in volume per time is a measure of the capacitance.

9.   System A has a capacitance of (10 liters per minute) whereas system B has a capacitance of 0.2 liters per minute. Therefore, system A has a higher capacitance.

10. **a** If energy can be lost to heat, then a distal fluid will have **less** energy than a proximal fluid, presuming that no new energy sources have been added (i.e. a closed system).

Section 7. Exercises (Pg. 770-772)

1. $\Delta P = Q \bullet R$ which implies $\Delta P \propto Q$.
   If Q doubles, ΔP doubles.

2.

$$Q_A = Q_B$$

$$V_A \times Area_A = V_B \times Area_B$$

Solving for V_B yields:

$$V_B = \frac{V_A \times Area_A}{Area_B} = \frac{1\frac{m}{sec} \times 2\ cm^2}{0.5\ cm^2}$$

$$\mathbf{V_B = 4\frac{m}{sec}}$$

3. $R = \dfrac{8\ell\eta}{\pi r^4}$ so $R \propto \dfrac{1}{r^4}$ Doubling the radius decreases the resistance by a factor of 2^4 or 16.

4. How much will the velocity have to increase to maintain the volumetric flow if the cross-sectional area is reduced by 50%?

   A 50% reduction in the cross-sectional area is the same as a decrease by a factor of 2. Since $Q = \overline{V} \bullet area$, if the area decreases by a factor of 2, the velocity must increase by a factor of 2 to maintain the same volumetric flow.

5. What is the hydrostatic pressure for a fluid similar to blood at the bottom of a 2 foot column?

$$hydrostatic\ pressure \approx \frac{2\ mmHg}{inch}$$

$$2\ feet \bullet \frac{12\ inches}{foot} = 24\ inches$$

$$so\ the\ total\ pressure \approx \frac{2\ mmHg}{inch} \bullet 24\ inches$$

$$= 48\ mmHg$$

6.   The pressure is associated with the difference in heights between the two columns. In the reference figure, the difference is 50 cm.

   a)   For figure a, the difference between the columns is 100 cm, or twice the difference in the reference image. Since $\Delta P \propto Q$, doubling the pressure doubles the flow. Since the flow is "Q" in the reference image, the flow for figure a is "2Q".

   b)   The column difference is 50 cm, so the flow is Q for figure b.

7.   For figures c,d, and e, the resistance is different than the reference figure. Since the length of the connecting conduit is twice as long, the resistance is doubled ($R \propto \ell$).

   To answer the question for problem 7, we must now consider that the flow is related to both the pressure and the resistance

$$\left(\Delta P = Q \bullet R \Rightarrow Q = \frac{\Delta P}{R} \right)$$

   a)   For figure c the column height is 50 cm and the resistance is doubled so the flow is $\frac{Q}{2}$.

   b)   For figure d the column height is 100 cm, so the pressure is doubled and the resistance is doubled . Therefore the factor of 2 in the numerator and denominator cancel, and the flow is the same as the reference figure, or Q.

   c)   For the figure e, the column height is 50 cm and the resistance is doubled. Therefore the flow is the same as for figure c, or $\frac{Q}{2}$.

8.   The resistance is proportional to the length and inversely related to the radius to the fourth power.

   a)   Relative to the reference figure, the radius is doubled so the resistance is decreased by a factor of 16.

   b)   For figure f, the column height difference is the same as the reference figure, but the resistance is lower by a factor of 16. Therefore the flow is 16Q.

   c)   For figure g, the height difference is twice the reference figure and the resistance is decreased by a factor of 16. Therefore, the flow is increased by a factor of 32, or 32Q.

   d)   For figure h, the height difference is the same as the reference figure, but the resistance is decreased by a factor of 16. Therefore, the flow is 16Q.

9.   For figure d, since the length is doubled, the resistance is doubled, or 2R.

Appendix I • Answers to Supplemental Exercises

Chapter 7 Doppler (Pg. 897-901)

1. Give the Doppler equation. Define each term.

$$f_{Dop} = \frac{2f_0 v}{c} \cos(\theta)$$

   where:

   f_{Dop} = *Doppler shifted frequency*

   f_0 = *transmit frequency*

   v = *velocity of target through medium*

   c = *speed of interrogating beam through medium (c = 1540 m/sec for sound in tissue)*

   $\cos(\theta)$ = *mathematical correction for angle effect*

   θ = *insonification angle (or angle to flow)*

2. From the equation determine all possible changes which would increase the detected Doppler shift (ex. if v increases, f_{dop} increases).
   if f_o increases, f_{dop} increases
   if v increases, f_{dop} increases
   if θ decreases between 90° and 0°, the cos(θ) increases, so f_{dop} increases
   if c decreases, f_{dop} increases

3. Rewrite the Doppler equation as v = $f_{Dop} = \frac{2f_0 v}{c} \cos(\theta)$

$$\frac{c}{2f_0 \cos(\theta)} * f_{Dop} = \frac{\cancel{c}}{2f_0 \cancel{\cos(\theta)}} = \frac{2f_0 v}{\cancel{c}} \cancel{\cos(\theta)}$$

$$v = \frac{c * f_{Dop}}{2f_0 \cos(\theta)}$$

4. For a fixed blood velocity, if you increase the transmit frequency, what happens to the Doppler shift?
   Since the Doppler shift is proportional to the transmit frequency (operating frequency), if you increase the operating frequency, the Doppler shift will increase proportionally.

5. In the Doppler equation which factors are known, which are assumed, which are detected, and which term is calculated?
   f_{Dop} =   *detected*

$$
\begin{aligned}
f_0 &= && \textit{chosen by user} \\
v &= && \textit{calculated} \\
c &= && \textit{assumed} \\
cos(\theta) &= && \textit{determined by the angle} \\
\theta &= && \textit{indicated by user (assumed to be } 0° \textit{ or } 180° \textit{ in cardiac)}
\end{aligned}
$$

6.   If the target is moving towards the detector, the wavefronts are _____ yielding a _____ Doppler shift.
      a)   decompressed, positive
      b)   compressed, negative
      c)   decompressed, negative
      d)   compressed, positive

7.   In color flow Doppler flash artifact can be caused by
      a)   high amplitude, low velocity changes such as motion of the transducer and motion from breathing
      b)   low amplitude, high velocity changes such as motion of the transducer and motion from breathing
      c)   thermal changes in the transducer
      d)   cavitation of tissue and gel.

8.   If for a specific blood velocity the Doppler shift is 2 kHz, what would the Doppler shift be if you doubled the transmit frequency?
      Recall that the Doppler shift is proportional to the transmit frequency. If you double the transmit frequency, the Doppler shift will double. Therefore the Doppler frequency shift would be 4 kHz.

9.   A negative Doppler shift means
      a)   a negative blood flow velocity
      b)   relative flow away from the transducer
      c)   a decrease in amplitude
      d)   aliasing

10.   What percentage of the Doppler shift is detected at an insonification angle of
      a) $0°$ $\Rightarrow$ **100%**
      b) $30°$ $\Rightarrow$ **86%**
      c) $45°$ $\Rightarrow$ **71%**
      d) $60°$ $\Rightarrow$ **50%**
      e) $90°$ $\Rightarrow$ **0%**
      f) $180°$ $\Rightarrow$ **100% in the opposite direction**

11.   The typical range for Doppler shifts is +10 kHz to -10 kHz, however, it is very common to far exceed these frequencies. Which scenario below would most likely demonstrate much higher frequency shifts?
      a) $90°$ angle to flow, just distal to a severe stenosis, 5 MHz transducer
      b) $90°$ angle to flow, just distal to a severe stenosis, 10 MHz transducer
      c) $0°$ angle to flow, just proximal to a severe stenosis, 10 MHz transducer
      d) $0°$ angle to flow, just distal to a severe stenosis, 10 MHz transducer

You should realize that the greatest frequency shift occurs at the angles of 0 degrees and 180 degrees for a given blood velocity. You should also realize that using a higher frequency transducer results in a greater frequency shift. The highest velocity flow should be just distal to a stenosis.

12. For superficial imaging, high frequency Doppler yields higher amplitude signals. As the depth increases, lower frequency Doppler yields higher amplitude signals. Explain this phenomenon. (Make sure to include Rayleigh scattering and frequency effects in your explanation.)
Recall that red blood cells are generally small with respect to the wavelength of ultrasound, resulting in a weak form of reflection called Rayleigh scattering. As the frequency increases, the wavelength decreases, making the red blood cells look larger thereby increasing the amount of scattering. Since there is very little attenuation with superficial Doppler, using a higher frequency for superficial Doppler results in larger signals because of the increased reflection from the smaller wavelength. As the imaging depth increases, attenuation through absorption dominates, making lower frequencies more efficient than higher frequencies.

13. Knowing the blood velocity is useful since, from **Bernoulli's** equation, a pressure gradient can be determined.

14. Assume that the lowest wall filter setting on an ultrasound machine is 60 Hz. If, for a given transducer, the blood velocity you desire to quantify is below this cutoff, what can you do?
In addition to augmenting the flow by limb compression, using a higher frequency transducer will result in a greater Doppler frequency shift for the same velocity blood. Let's say that the Doppler shift was originally 40 Hz. With the given wall filter of 60 Hz, the signal would be filtered out. Now let's say that the operating frequency is doubled. The frequency shift would be 80 Hz instead of 40 Hz. Since 80 Hz is higher than the wall filter of 60 Hz, the signal can now be detected.

15. Explain what purpose wall filters serve.
Wall filters are designed to discriminate signals based on frequency. Wall filters are high pass filters which pass the higher frequency signals and reject the lower frequency signals. Wall filters are critical to limit the dynamic range. Large "clutter" signals are produced by slowly moving specular reflectors such as valves, heart walls, vessel walls, patient respiration, transducer movement, etc. In contrast, the signals from the blood are extremely small. In order to visualize the smaller signals, the stronger signals need to be rejected to limit the signal dynamic range.

16. Which mode must support the greatest signal dynamic range
    a) B-mode (2D)
    b) color Doppler
    c) PW spectral Doppler
    d) CW spectral Doppler

17. The Nyquist criterion states that to detect a frequency of 2 kHz you must sample at a frequency of at least **4 kHz.**

18. The resulting artifact from violating Nyquist is called **aliasing.**

19. For PW (and color Doppler), Nyquist dictates that to detect a Doppler shift of 3 kHz the **PRF** must

be at least 6 kHz.

20.   Since continuous wave Doppler effectively has an infinite PRF (transmitting continuously), the maximum detectable velocity is much **greater than** for PW and is only restricted by the A/D sample rate.

21.   The analog Doppler signal is analog to digital converted to allow for
    a)   **spectral analysis**
    b)   wall filtering
    c)   amplification and compression
    d)   demodulation

22.   Spectral analysis is most generally performed by a mathematical function called an **FFT** or **Fast Fourier Transform**, which separates the composite frequency shifts into frequency bins for measurement.

23.   Give the major advantage of PW and the major advantage of CW.
    PW has good range specificity but has a potential for aliasing. CW has no range specificity but does not have the problem with aliasing.

24.   It is impossible to do CW Doppler with one crystal so "single crystal" transducers are actually split into two half segments which can either be run as two separate crystals or one whole crystal. Explain why it is not possible to do CW Doppler with only one crystal.
    The reason it take two crystals to perform CW is one crystal must transmit while the other crystal receives. Attempting to receive with the same crystal which transmits is very inefficient since the weak blood signals would be dwarfed by the vibrations of the transmit signal. This situation is tantamount to trying to listen to a whisper while a jet engine is roaring.

25.   As you image deeper the maximum PRF decreases restricting the maximum unaliased velocities detectable. Explain why the PRF decreases with depth.
    The PRF is the reciprocal of the PRP. The PRP is the time is takes for the sound to propagate from the transducer to the depth of interest and back to the transducer. The deeper the depth, the longer the PRP. The longer the PRP, the lower the PRF.

26.   What is the blood velocity if the detected Doppler shift is 2 kHz, the insonification angle is 60°, the transmit frequency is 3.08 MHz, and soft tissue is assumed.

$$f_{Dop} \qquad = 2\ kHz$$
$$f_0 \qquad = 3.08\ MHz$$
$$c \qquad = 1540\ m/sec$$
$$cos(60°) \qquad = 0.5$$
$$v \qquad = ?$$

$$f_{Dop} = \frac{2f_0 v}{c}\cos(\theta) \Rightarrow v = \frac{cf_{Dop}}{2f_0\cos(\theta)} = \frac{1540\ \frac{m}{sec} * 2\ kHz}{2 * 3.08\ MHz * 0.5} = \frac{3080\ \frac{m}{sec} * 10^3}{3.08 * 10^6} = 1000\ \frac{m}{sec} * 10^{-3} = 1\frac{m}{sec}$$

27.   What do the three axes of a Doppler spectrum display?
    a)   **horizontal = time**
    b)   **vertical = Doppler frequency shift or velocity**
    c)   **imaginary = signal intensity**

28. Most color flow techniques use the Doppler effect, however, no FFT is performed since color sectors use multiple lines requiring too much calculation time and no convenient way of displaying the data. Instead of spectral analysis, color Doppler uses a correlation algorithm which yields
   a) a maximum velocity estimator
   b) **a mean velocity estimator**
   c) a modal velocity estimator
   d) a completely unrelated velocity but pretty colors

29. As you increase the sample volume size in PW Doppler, you will most likely see
   a) **more spectral spread**
   b) a major change in the mean velocity
   c) less spectral spread
   d) a lower amplitude Doppler signal.

30. A good approach to minimizing the artifact of spectral broadening is to
   a) always use insonification angles of 60^0 or less
   b) always use insonification angles of 60^0 or more
   c) always make sure that the display is not overgained
   d) **a and c**
   e) b and c

1.　For the figure below, draw the sound paths which create each of the artifactual structures labeled "A", "B", "C", and "D".

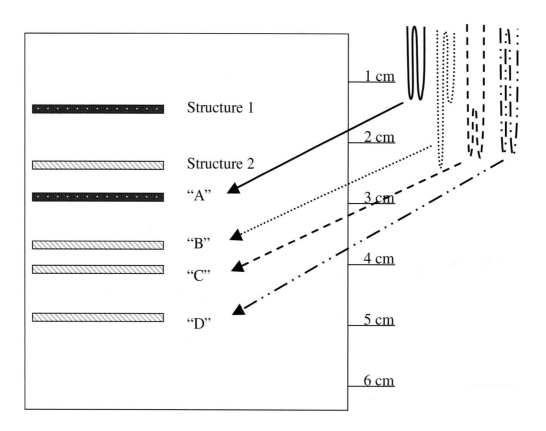

2.　Most imaging artifacts are caused by **specular** reflection. Since this type of reflection is highly **angularly** dependent, using a different imaging window or changing the steering is a good way of identifying whether there is an aspect of an image which is artifactual.

3.　Multi-path artifact results in an artifactual structure appearing **deeper** than reality.

4.　If the propagation speed through a structure is 1100 m/sec, distal to that structure, other structures will appear too deep.

5.　"Ghost" arteries often appear when imaging an artery relatively superficial and just anterior to a strong **specular** reflector. The "ghost" arteries are often classified as an example of **mirroring** artifact although in reality they are caused by reverberation artifact.

6.　**Mirroring** artifact causes an artificial image symmetric about the "mirroring" surface.

7.　**Shadowing** results posterior to a region where there is greater than normal attenuation.

8.   **Shadowing** often occurs from the edges of cysts, blood vessels, and bones because of **refraction**.

9.   Total internal reflection occurs at the **critical** angle.

10.   The reciprocal artifact of shadowing is called **enhancement**.

11.   All of the following will decrease the likelihood of aliasing in spectral Doppler EXCEPT:

        a)   decreasing the Doppler gate depth
        b)   using CW Doppler
        c)   using a lower operating frequency
        d)   shifting the Doppler baseline
        e)   increasing the Doppler scale

        Recall that aliasing occurs when there is a violation of the Nyquist criterion. For Doppler, the maximum detectable frequency shift is equal to the PRF/2. Having a shallower Doppler gate depth decreases the PRP, thereby increasing the PRF and the maximum detectable frequency shift, which decreases the likelihood of aliasing. CW is continuously sampling and hence with the scales set appropriately, has no risk of aliasing. Using a lower operating frequency causes a lower frequency shift for the same velocity of the blood (recall the Doppler equation) and hence, less risk of aliasing. Increasing the Doppler scales increases the PRF and hence decreases the likelihood of aliasing. Shifting the baseline does not change the maximum detectable frequency shift, it only changes how much of the signal range is presented as forward flow and how much is presented as reverse flow.

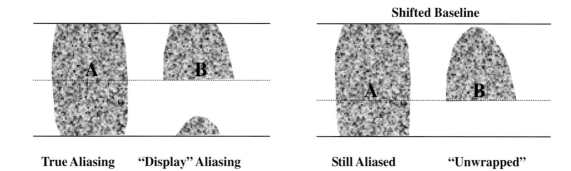

        True Aliasing   "Display" Aliasing   Still Aliased   "Unwrapped"

12.   Which of the following Doppler scenarios would have the greatest risk of exhibiting range ambiguity artifact?

        a)   PW sample volume at 3 cm deep, phased array
        b)   PW sample volume at 3 cm deep, mechanical
        c)   PW sample volume at 6 cm deep, phased array
        d)   PW sample volume at 6 cm deep, mechanical

Recall that the range ambiguity artifact is more likely to occur with shallow depth settings than deep depth settings. This artifact is also more likely to occur with mechanical transducers than with phased array transducers. Simple mechanical transducers have a fixed focus. By design, the fixed focus is usually set as deep as possible (the natural focal depth). Since the focus is fixed, when imaging a superficial structure, the focus is deeper than the desired depth. The result is a greater sensitivity to range ambiguous gates than when the focus is placed at the desired imaging depth.

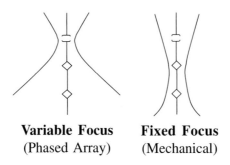

Variable Focus   **Fixed Focus**
(Phased Array)   (Mechanical)

13.   Spectral **mirroring** is caused by poor I and Q channel separation and is exacerbated by high **transmit** power and high receiver gain.

14.   The law which governs the amount of refraction is called **Snell's** law.

15.   Which of the following Doppler changes would decrease the amount of spectral spread in a Doppler spectrum?

     a)   **using a smaller insonification angle**
     b)   using a large linear transducer
     c)   imaging at a shallower depth
     d)   using a higher transmit power
     e)   using a higher receiver gain

Spectral spread is affected by signal strength as well as the geometric aspects of the Doppler angle formed between the beam and the blood flow. Using smaller insonification angles decreases the spread of angles and hence decreases the amount of spectral spread.

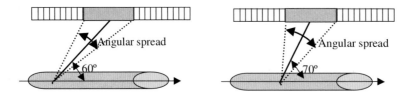

Chapter 9 Bioeffects (Pg. 904-905)

1.   The two principle mechanisms for creating bioeffects are **thermal** and **mechanical**.

2.   Thermal bioeffects are highly dependent on the <u>duty</u> factor as well as whether or not the modality is **scanned** or non-**scanned**.

3.   Mechanical bioeffects are dominated by the peak **rarefactional** pressure.

4.   **Thermal** bioeffects dictate that scan times should be minimized so that heat does not "build up."

5.   The modality which generally has the greatest risk of thermal bioeffects is **CW**, since the **duty** factor is 1.

6.   The intensity measurement which best indicates the risk of thermal bioeffects is the I_{SPTA}.

7.   The modality which generally has the lowest risk of thermal bioeffects is **B-mode**.

8.   The modality which generally has the greatest risk of mechanical bioeffects is **B-mode**.

9.   Transient **cavitation** is the form of "mechanical damage" which occurs when the mechanical index is too high.

10. The risk of mechanical bioeffects dictates that the minimum **transmit (acoustic output)** power necessary to achieve good clinical results should be used.

11. The AIUM fundamental statement about the safety of diagnostic ultrasound states that "ultrasound is a very safe modality and to date there have been no confirmed **biological effects** by exposure to intensities typical of present ultrasound equipment."

12. There have been no confirmed bioeffects for unfocused-beam intensities below **100 mW/cm²**, for focused-beam intensities below **1 W/cm²**, or when the thermal index value is below **2**.

13. For common intensities what does each of the following abbreviations stand for:

     a)   SP: **Spatial Peak**
     b)   SA: **Spatial Average**
     c)   TP: **Temporal Peak**
     d)   TA: **Temporal Average**
     e)   PA: **Pulse Average**
     f) I_m: **Maximum Intensity**

14. The pulse average (PA) $= \dfrac{\text{total energy in pulse}}{\text{pulse time (duration)}}$

The Duty Cycle $= \dfrac{\text{pulse duration}}{\text{total time (PRP)}}$

So if you multiply the PA by the duty cycle, which intensity do you get?

$$\frac{\text{total energy in pulse}}{\text{pulse time (duration)}} * \frac{\text{pulse duration}}{\text{total time (PRP)}} = \frac{\text{total energy in pulse}}{\text{total time (PRP)}} = TA$$

15. Beam uniformity coefficient $= \dfrac{\text{spatial peak}}{\text{spatial average}}$

so SA $\cdot$ (beam uniformity coefficient) $=$ SP

since: spatial average $* \dfrac{\text{spatial peak}}{\text{spatial average}} =$ spatial peak

16. What is the beam uniformity coefficient if the I_{SPTA} is 100 mW/cm² and the I_{SATA} is 25 mW/cm²?

$$BUF = \frac{\text{spatial peak}}{\text{spatial average}} = \frac{100\,\dfrac{mW}{cm^2}}{25\,\dfrac{mW}{cm^2}} = 4$$

Notice that both intensity measurements in this exercise are temporal averages so no conversion is necessary in terms of the temporal distribution of the energy.

17. What is the I_{SATA} given an I_{SPTA} of 100 mW/cm² and a beam uniformity coefficient of 2?

$$BUF = \frac{\text{spatial peak}}{\text{spatial average}} \Rightarrow BUF * \text{spatial average} = \text{spatial peak} \Rightarrow \text{spatial average} = \frac{\text{spatial peak}}{BUF}$$

$$I_{SATA} = \frac{I_{SPTA}}{BUF} = \frac{100\,\dfrac{mW}{cm^2}}{2} = 50\,\frac{mW}{cm^2}$$

18. Given an I_{SATA} of 20 mW/cm², what is the I_{SAPA} if duty factor is 10 % ?

$$Duty\ Factor = \frac{TA}{PA} = \frac{I_{SATA}}{I_{SAPA}} \Rightarrow Duty\ Factor * I_{SAPA} = I_{SATA} \Rightarrow I_{SAPA} = \frac{I_{SATA}}{Duty\ Factor}$$

$$I_{SAPA} = \frac{20\,\dfrac{mW}{cm^2}}{0.1} = 200\,\frac{mW}{cm^2}$$

Notice that both intensity measurements in this exercise are spatial averages so no conversion is necessary in terms of the spatial distribution of the energy.

Chapter 11 Quality Assurance (Pg. 906-907)

1. A Doppler string phantom can be used to test all of the following EXCEPT:
   a) peak velocity
   b) gate registration accuracy
   c) Doppler sensitivity
   d) spectral characteristics

   With a string phantom, the Doppler signal is created by registering frequency shifts which result form the motion of the string. The amplitude of reflections from a string in a water bath is significantly larger than the amplitude of the reflections from blood cells, especially with all of the attenuation through tissue. Since the signals from the string are so strong, a string phantom is generally not very useful for testing sensitivity.

2. **Flow phantoms** use complex fluids to mimic the properties of **blood**. Since, over time, the concentration of the particles in the fluid changes, there is difficulty in making repeatable measurements.

3. The string of a Doppler flow phantom creates a very strong specular reflection that generally causes the artifact of **blossoming**. The result is that the peak velocities are generally significantly overestimated, unless the transmit power and receiver gain are significantly reduced.

4. For the multi-purpose phantom, the monofilament line targets are used for **distance measurements**.

5. Which one of the test objects within a tissue mimicking phantom would most likely be indistinguishable from the background?
   a) -6 dB
   b) -3 dB
   c) +2 dB
   d) +6 dB
   e) +15 dB

6. The pin group very close to the surface of the imaging phantom can be used to test the **dead zone**, or ring down distance.

7. The AIUM standard 100 mm test object does not have **tissue** mimicking properties.

8. Viewing a group of pins which vary in separation distance in depth can be used to test **axial (longitudinal, depth, radial, range)** resolution.

9. The **accuracy** is a percentage which must be between the sensitivity and the specificity.

10. In comparison with a gold standard test, a testing procedure produces the following results: fifty-three patients have disease when the gold standard also found disease. Four patients are found with disease when the gold standard found no disease. One hundred and thirty patients are found with no disease when the gold standard also found no disease. Thirteen patients are found without disease when the gold standard found disease. Calculate the sensitivity, specificity, accuracy, positive predictive value, and the negative predictive value.

TP = 53
FP = 4
TN = 130
FN = 13

Gold Standard

	+	-
+	53	4
-	13	130

Test

$$\text{Sensitivity} = \frac{TP}{TP+FN} = \frac{53}{53+13} = \frac{53}{66} \approx 80\%$$

$$\text{Specificity} = \frac{TN}{TN+FP} = \frac{130}{130+4} = \frac{130}{134} \approx 97\%$$

$$\text{Accuracy} = \frac{TP+TN}{TP+TN+FP+FN} = \frac{53+130}{53+130+4+13} = \frac{183}{200} \approx 92\%$$

$$\text{Negative Predictive Value} = \frac{TN}{TN+FN} = \frac{130}{130+13} = \frac{130}{143} \approx 91\%$$

$$\text{Positive Predictive Value} = \frac{TP}{TP+FP} = \frac{53}{53+4} = \frac{53}{57} \approx 93\%$$

Chapter 12 Fluid Dynamics (Pg. 908-909)

1. Power has units of **Watts** which is the same as energy per **time**, or Joules per **seconds**.

2. **Potential** energy is proportional to height.

3. **Kinetic** energy is proportional to the velocity squared.

4. Doubling the velocity of the flow results in a change in the kinetic energy by a factor of **four**.

$$KE \propto v^2$$

$$\left(v_{new}\right)^2 = \left(2 * v_{old}\right)^2 = 4 * \left(v_{new}\right)^2$$

5. The unit for volumetric flow is $\dfrac{m^3}{sec}$.

6. The equation for volumetric flow is: **Q = v*area**.

7. If a vessel radius triples, the resistance **decreases** by a factor of 81.

$$R \propto \frac{1}{r^4} \Rightarrow \frac{1}{3^4} = \frac{1}{81}$$

8. Calculate the average spatial velocity at point B for the diagram below.

$$Q_A = Q_B$$
$$v_A * Area_A = v_B * Area_B$$
$$\frac{v_A * Area_A}{Area_B} = \frac{v_B * Area_B}{Area_B}$$
$$v_B = \frac{v_A * Area_A}{Area_B} = \frac{4\dfrac{m}{sec} * 4\ cm^2}{1\ cm^2} = 16\ \frac{m}{sec}$$

Point A

Point B

Area$_B$= 4 cm²

V$_B$= ?

Area$_A$= 4 cm²

V$_A$= 4 $\frac{m}{sec}$

9. If a vessel is stenosed such that the residual diameter is 25%, the resistance will increase by a factor of **256**.

$$25\% = \frac{1}{4}$$

$$R \propto \frac{1}{r^4} \Rightarrow \frac{1}{\left(\dfrac{1}{4}\right)^4} = \frac{1}{\dfrac{1}{256}} = 256$$

10. If the viscosity of the blood were to double, the resistance would **double**.

11. The parameter which dominates the resistance is the vessel **radius (diameter)**.

12. For a fixed resistance, doubling the flow will have what effect on the pressure gradient?
$$\Delta P = Q \bullet R$$
Doubling the volumetric flow (Q) results in a doubling of the pressure gradient?

13. If a vessel vasodilates such that the new radius is twice the original radius, how much more blood volume can be supplied for the same pressure gradient?

$$\Delta P = Q \times R \Rightarrow \frac{\Delta P}{R} = Q$$

$$R \propto \frac{1}{r^4} \Rightarrow \text{so if } r \text{ doubles, } R \text{ decreases by a factor of 16.}$$

Therefore, Q can increase by a factor of 16.

14. With an **increase** in distal resistance, the **end-diastolic** flow component decreases.

15. After temporary ischemia, there is a short-term increase in **flow** to re-perfuse the tissue. This response is called **reactive hyperemia**. (Although reactive hypermia is not discussed in this chapter, again it is good to see how resourceful a person will be.)

16. Starting with the simplified law of hemodynamics, develop Poiseuille's law.

$$\Delta P = Q * R$$

$$R = \frac{8l\,\eta}{\pi r^4}$$

$$\Delta P = Q * \frac{8l\,\eta}{\pi r^4}$$

$$Q = \frac{\Delta P \pi r^4}{8l\,\eta}$$

17. As the cross-sectional area of a flow path decreases, the likelihood of turbulence within that region **decreases**.

18. **Acceleration** causes a "plug", or "blunt" flow profile.

19. When the Reynold's number is greater than **2,000**, turbulence typically results.

20. A 25% radius reduction is equivalent to a **44%** reduction in area.

$$r_{new} = 75\% * r_{old} = 0.75 * r_{old}$$

$$= \frac{3}{4} * r_{old}$$

$$\text{Area}_{new} \propto r_{new}^{\,2} \Rightarrow \left(\frac{3}{4} * r_{old}\right)^2 = \frac{9}{16} * r_{old}^{\,2} = 56.25\% * \text{Area}_{old}$$

Area reduction $= 100\% - 56.25\% = 43.75\%$

21.   A 10% reduction in radius is equivalent to a **90%** residual diameter.

   A 10% reduction in radius is equivalent to a 10% reduction in diameter since the diameter and the radius are directly proportional. A 10% reduction in diameter is equivalent to a 90% residual diameter.

22.   A 50% reduction in radius is equivalent to a **25%** residual lumen area.

$$r_{new} = 50\% * r_{old} = 0.5 * r_{old}$$

$$= \frac{1}{2} * r_{old}$$

$$Area_{new} \propto r_{new}{}^2 \Rightarrow \left(\frac{1}{2} * r_{old}\right)^2 = \frac{1}{4} * r_{old}{}^2 = 25\% * Area_{old}$$

23.   A 10% reduction in diameter results in an increase in resistance of **52%**.

$$d_{new} = 90\% * d_{old} \Rightarrow r_{new} = 90\% * r_{old} = 0.9 * r_{old}$$

$$= \frac{9}{10} * r_{old}$$

$$Resistance_{new} \propto \frac{1}{r_{new}{}^4} \Rightarrow \frac{1}{\left(\frac{9}{10} * r_{old}\right)^4} = \left(\frac{10}{9}\right)^4 * \frac{1}{r_{old}{}^4} = \frac{10,000}{6561} * Resistance_{old}$$

$$\frac{10,000}{6561} * Resistance_{old} = 1.52 * Resistance_{old}$$

$$1.52 * Resistance_{old} = 152\% * Resistance_{old} \Rightarrow 52\% \text{ increase}$$

Note: For questions 20-23, it may prove helpful to review pages 48-50 of Chapter 1.

Chapter 13 Hemodynamics (Pg. 910)

1.   The venous system is highly **capacitive**.

2.   **Transmural pressure** is the measure of the difference between the intravascular pressure and the tissue pressure.

3.   When the intravascular pressure within a vein is greater than the surrounding tissue pressure, there is high **transmural** pressure and the veins will be distended.

4.   A blood pressure measurement is made from the radial artery during a surgery. The patient is lying such that the radial artery is below the right atrium by about 10 inches. The measured blood pressure should be **higher**/lower due to **higher** pressure by about **20** mmHg than if the radial artery were at the level of the right atrium.

5.   **Hydrostatic** pressure increases with increasing height.

6.   When recumbent, venous return is aided by **respiratory** effects.

7.   In the standing position, venous return is aided by the **calf muscle pump**.

8.   Hydrostatic pressure is referenced to the **right atrium** and, in the standing position, is considered **negative** in the head and positive in the feet.

9.   In the supine position, the dynamic pressure at the level of the ankle is about **15** mmHg.

10.   With **inspiration** the diaphragm descends increasing intra-abdominal pressure, **decreasing** venous flow from the legs to the abdomen but **increasing** venous return from the abdomen to the right atrium.

11.   The viscosity of normal blood is $\mathbf{10^{-2}}$ pascals.

12.   The **arterioles** are the resistive component of the arterial system.

Appendix A: Vascular Principles (Pg. 911-912)

1. **Energy** equals the average power per time multiplied by time.

2. Using 120 Volts with a resistance of 1kW, what would be the current?

$$\Delta V = I * R$$

$$\frac{\Delta V}{R} = \frac{I * R}{R} \Rightarrow \frac{\Delta V}{R} = I$$

$$\frac{120 \text{ Volts}}{1 \text{ k}\Omega} = 120 \text{ mAmps}$$

3. The output of a stripchart recorder can be calibrated and should be **proportional** to the input signal.

4. **Direct Current** *(DC)* comes from a battery, **alternating** *(AC)* current comes from wall outlets.

5. **Four-wire** measurement devices are preferable to two-wire devices since a **four-wire** device can be calibrated and affects the signal less.

6. Using **AC** coupling for a slowly varying signal may result in no signal detected.

7. If a signal "pegs" the display, the reason may be that **DC** coupling was used when **AC** coupling should have been used.

8. For a normal venous outflow study, the waveform tracing should fall back to baseline within **3** seconds of cuff deflation.

9. In photoplethysmography a slightly slower upstroke, disappearance of the dichroitic notch, and a slight bowing of the downslope away from the baseline would be classified as **mild obstruction**.

10. For OPG, a difference between the two ophthalmic systolic pressures of more than **5** mmHg is considered abnormal.

11. Making a pressure measurement using a Doppler flow meter, the pressure measured is at the level of the **cuff**, not at the level of the Doppler signal insonation.

12. If the diameter of an arm is 10 cm, the appropriate cuff width should be at least **12** cm.

width = 1.2 x segment diameter

13. An ABI greater than **1.0** is considered normal.

14. With significant disease in the legs, the ankle pressure should **decrease**, **decreasing** the ABI.

15. Calculate the right and left ABI given the following pressure measurements:

Right DP = 90 mmHg   Left DP = 120 mmHg
Right PT = 86 mmHg   Left PT = 118 mmHg
Right brachial = 120 mmHg   Left brachial = 110 mmHg

Right ABI =   Left ABI =
Right ABI = 90/120 = 3/4 = 0.75   **Left ABI = 120/120 = 1.0**

16. What is the appropriate cuff occlusion pressure range for the deep venous system?

To occlude the deep venous system, pressures of 40 mmHg – 70 mmHg are typically necessary. Note that it takes greater pressure to occlude the deep system than the superficial system. This greater pressure is needed since it takes some pressure to overcome the compliance of the tissue before the vessels are compressed.

17. Transcranial Doppler should be performed using which of the following conditions?

a) PW, 4 MHz, gate size = 1 mm
b) CW, 2 MHz
c) PW, 2 MHz, gate size = 4 mm
d) CW, 4 MHz
e) PW, 2 MHz, gate size = 12 mm

18. Using a trans-temporal window, if the transcranial spectrum from a depth of 70 mm is away from the transducer, the vessel insonated is either the **ACA (A1)** or the **PCA (P2)** .

19. Doppler signals from transcranial Doppler through a trans-temporal window are often very weak. The primary reason that these signals are generally weak is that the attenuation through bone is greater than **17** dB one-way.

20. A normal HTI is greater than **1.2**.

21. If the current through a 12 Volt device is 0.5 Amps, what is the resistance?

$$\Delta V = I * R$$

$$\frac{\Delta V}{I} = \frac{I * R}{I} \Rightarrow \frac{\Delta V}{I} = R$$

$$\frac{12\ Volts}{0.5\ Amps} = 24\ \Omega$$

Appendix B: Cardiovascular Principles (Pg. 913-915)

1. Sodium ions are **positively** charged.

2. When there is a greater concentration of sodium ions external to the cell membrane there is a **negative** potential.

3. At rest, the "resting potential" is typically **-90** mV.

4. By pumping some of the sodium ions into the cell through the cell membrane, the potential changes. When the potential surpasses a **threshold**, the process becomes self-generating and there is a rush of ions into the cell.

5. The rapid change in polarization which occurs with the "rush" of sodium ions into the cell is called an **action potential** and typically peaks at a voltage of **+40** mV.

6. During the process of **repolarization**, the cell rapidly pumps sodium ions out of the muscle cells until the "resting" potential is again reached.

7. The period of time during which a cell cannot be stimulated by another stimulus is called the **refractory period**.

8. During the **relative refractory** period, a greater stimulus is needed to depolarize a cell than when a cell is at its resting potential.

9. Cardiac muscle has three unique characteristics relative to skeletal muscle:

   a) long refractory period
   b) automaticity
   c) high speed electrical pathways

10. Calculate how many times per minute skeletal muscle can contract given that the refractory period is approximately 3 msec.

    To convert a time into a frequency, take the reciprocal :

    $$\frac{1}{3\,m\sec} = 0.333\ kHz = 333\frac{contractions}{sec}$$

    But the question asked how many beats per minute so we must convert the units from contractions per second to contractions per minute.

    $$\frac{60\ seconds}{1\ minute} * \frac{333\ contractions}{sec\,ond} = \frac{19,980\ contractions}{minute}$$

11. What is the refractory period for cardiac muscle?

    250 msec

12.   Using the refractory period for cardiac muscle, determine the maximum number of cardiac muscle cell contractions per minute.

$$\frac{1}{250 \text{ msec}} = 0.004 \text{ kHz} = 4 \ \frac{\text{contractions}}{\text{sec}}$$

$$4 \ \frac{\text{contractions}}{\text{sec}} * \frac{60 \text{ seconds}}{\text{minute}} = 240 \ \frac{\text{contractions}}{\text{minute}}$$

13.   Explain why it is so important that the refractory period for cardiac muscle is so much longer than the refractory period for skeletal muscle.

Each cardiac muscle contraction represents one heart beat. As the heart rate increases, there is less filling time, making the heart a very inefficient pump. A longer refractory period restricts the maximum heart rate, keeping the heart rate in a reasonable range for efficient pumping. Clearly a heart rate of almost 20,000 beats per minute would not make much sense.

14.   The natural pacing rate of the AV-node is around **60** BPM.

15.   The **Purkinje Fibers** have a natural pacing rate of 40-45 BPM.

16.   Draw and label an EKG tracing over a cardiac cycle making sure to label and describe the electrical event responsible for each wave characteristic.

1	P - Wave	Atrial Depolarization
2	P-R Segment	Delay of depolarizing wave in AV Node
3	QRS Complex	Ventricular Depolarization
4	S-T Segment	Refractory Period
5	T - Wave	Ventricular Repolarization

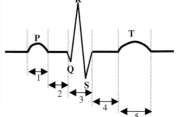

17.   EKG's are plotted such that each minor division is **0.04** seconds and every major division represents five times the minor division, or **0.2** seconds.

18.   An EKG waveform that repeats every fourth major division has a rate of **75** BPM.

19.   The pulse pressure equals the difference between the **peak systolic** pressure and the **end diastolic** pressure.

20.   Calculate the MAP if the peak systolic pressure is 130 mmHg and the end diastolic pressure is 100 mmHg.

$$MAP = ED + \frac{1}{3} * PP$$
$$PP = 130 \text{ mmHg} - 100 \text{ mmHg} = 30 \text{ mmHg}$$
$$MAP = 100 \text{ mmHg} + \frac{1}{3} * 30 \text{mmHg} = 110 \text{ mmHg}$$

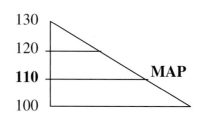

21. The pressure in the ventricle rises dramatically during the phase called **isovolumic contraction**. During this phase, the ventricle is contracting and all valves are **closed** so that the volume remains **constant** but the pressure increases.

22. The **dicrotic notch** occurs when the pressure in the aorta exceeds the pressure in the left ventricle causing a flow **reversal** which causes the **aortic** valve to close.

23. Peak systolic pressure on the right side of the heart is typically **25** mmHg.

24. Give the equation for the cardiac output in terms of the stroke volume:

$$\text{cardiac output}\left(\frac{\text{liters}}{\text{minute}}\right) = \text{stroke volume}\left(\frac{\text{liters}}{\text{beat}}\right) * \text{heart rate}\left(\frac{\text{beats}}{\text{minute}}\right)$$

You should note the units. Knowing the units makes it easy to write this equation.

25. To calculate the cardiac index, what other information is necessary in addition to the cardiac output?

Body Surface Area (BSA)

26. With respect to cardiac loading, an increase in **preload** can result in an increased stroke volume.

27. With respect to cardiac loading, an increase in **afterload** can result in an increased peak systolic pressure.

28. Aortic stenosis can cause pressure **overload**.

29. Most VSD's and ASD's shunt left to right and cause right ventricle and right atrium **enlargement** and may result in pulmonary **hypertension**.

30. For normal patients, the pressure in the left ventricle during passive filling increases within the range of:

a) **0 – 10 mmHg**
b) 0 – 100 mmHg
c) 20 – 100 mmHg
d) 80 – 100 mmHg
e) 20 – 30 mmHg

Remember that the ventricles have extremely high capacitances. After systole, a percentage of the volume has been ejected. During the passive filling phase, even with a significant increase in volume, there is little change in pressure since the chamber can hold so much volume. Therefore the pressure starts out very low and increases only slightly (a few mmHg) during the passive filling phase. The major pressure increase occurs during the isovolumic contraction phase.

Appendix J • Resources

ACCREDITATION AND CREDENTIALING RESOURCES

INDIVIDUAL

American Registry of Diagnostic Medical Sonographers (ARDMS)   www.ardms.org
51 Monroe Street
Plaza East One
Rockville, Maryland 20850-2400
Telephone 1.301.738-8401
Fax 1.301.738-0312

American Registry of Radiologic Technologists (ARRT)   www.arrt.org
1255 Northland Drive
St. Paul, Minnesota 55120-1155
Telephone 1.651.687.0048

Cardiovascular Credentialing International (CCI)   www.cci-online.org
1500 Sunday Drive, Suite 102
Raleigh, NC 27607
Telephone 1.800.326.0268 or 919.861.4539
Fax 919.787.4916

ACCREDITATION

American College of Radiology Commission on Standards and Accreditation (ACR)	www.acr.org
American Institute of Ultrasound in Medicine (AIUM)	www.aium.org
Intersocietal Commission for the Accreditation of Echocardiography Laboratories (ICAEL)	www.icael.org
Intersocietal Commission for the Accreditation of Magnetic Resonance Laboratories (ICAMRL)	www.icamrl.org
Intersocietal Commission for the Accreditation of Nuclear Medicine Laboratories (ICANL)	www.icanl.org
Intersocietal Commission for the Accreditation of Vascular Laboratories (ICAVL)	www.icavl.org
Joint Commission on Accreditation of Health Organizations (JCAHO)	www.jcaho.org

Appendix J

EDUCATION

American College of Radiology Programs (ACR)	www.acr.org
Association of Educators in Imaging and Radiologic Sciences (AERS)	www.aers.org
Accreditation Council for Continuing Medical Education (ACCME)	www.accme.org
Accrediting Bureau of Health Education Schools (ABHES)	www.abhes.org
Canadian Medical Association (CMA)	www.cma.ca
Commission on Accreditation of Allied Health Education Programs (CAAHEP)	www.caahep.org
Educational Credential Evaluators, Inc. (ECE)	www.ece.org
Joint Review Committee on Education in Cardiovascular Technology (JRCCVT)	www.jrccvt.org
Joint Review Committee on Education in Diagnostic Medical Sonography (JRCERT)	www.jrcdms.org

OTHER RESOURCES

Accreditation Consultants

Inside Ultrasound, Inc.	www.insideultrasound.com
KRP Accreditation Specialists, Inc.	www.krpaccreditation.com

Industry Resources

Aloka	www.aloka.com
ATS Laboratories	www.atslaboratories.com
Agfa	www.agfa.com/healthcare/us
Advanced Technological Laboratories	www.medical.philips.com/main/products
B-K Medical	www.bkmed.com
Baxter Medical	www.baxter.com
Biomedix	www.biomedix.com
Biosound Esaote	www.biosound.com
Boston Scientific	www.bostonscientific.com
Bracco Diagnostics	www.bdi.bracco.com
CIRS	www.cirsinc.com
Civco Medical Instruments	www.civcomedical.com
Data Star Systems- Datacheck	www.datastarsystems.com
Dynatek Dalta	www.dynatekdalta.com
Fluke Biomedical	www.flukebiomedical.com/rms
Gammex-RMI	www.gammex.com
GE Medical Systems	www.gemedicalsystems.com
Hitachi Medical Systems	www.hitachimed.com
J.R. Associates	www.1jra.com
JJ&A	www.jja-instruments.com
Kodak	www.kodak.com
Medison Medical Systems	www.medisonusa.com
Onda Corporation	www.ondacorp.com

Parker Laboratories	www.parkerlabs.com
Parks Medical Electronics	www.parksmed.com
Philips Medical Systems	www.medical.philips.com
Precision Acoustics, Inc.	www.acoustics.co.uk/
Siemens Medical Systems (Acuson)	www.siemensultrasound.com
Shimadzu Medical Systems	www.shimadzu.com
Sonosite	www.sonosite.com
Sonus Pharmaceuticals	www.sonuspharma.com
Sound Ergonomics	www.soundergonomics.com
Toshiba Ultrasound	www.toshiba.com
Unetixs, Inc.	www.unetixs.com

Organizations

Alliance of Cardiovascular Professionals (ACP)	www.acp-online.org
American Academy of Family Physicians (AAFP)	www.aafp.org
American Academy of Neurology (AAN)	www.aan.com
American Association for Vascular Surgery (AVS)	www.vascularweb.org
American College of Obstetrics and Gynecologist (ACOG)	www.acog.org
American College of Cardiology (ACC)	www.acc.org
American College of Chest Physicians (ACCP)	www.chestnet.org
American College of Emergency Physicians (ACEP)	www.acep.org
American College of Obstetricians and Gynecologists (ACOG)	www.acog.org
American College of Phebology (ACP)	www.phebology.org
American College of Radiology (ACR)	www.acr.org
American Emergency Ultrasonographic Society (AEUS)	www.aeus.org
American Hospital Association (AHA)	www.aha.com
American Institute of Ultrasound in Medicine (AIUM)	www.aium.org
American Medical Association (AMA)	www.ama-assn.org
American Osteopathic College of Radiology (AOCR)	www.aocr.org
American Roentgen Ray Society (ARRS)	www.arrs.org
American Society of Echocardiography (ASE)	www.asecho.org
American Society of Neurology (ASN)	www.aan.com/professionals
American Society of Neuroimaging (ASN)	www.asnweb.org
American Society of Neuroradiology (ASNR)	www.asnr.org
American Society of Opthalmologic Ultrasound (ASOU)	www.asou.us
American Society of Radiologic Technologists (ASRT)	www.asrt.org
American Urological Association (AUA)	www.auanet.org
Canadian Society of Diagnostic Medical Sonographers (CSDMS)	www.csdms.org
European Society for Vascular Surgery (ESVS)	www.esvs.org
Health Professions Network	www.healthpronet.org
International Society of Radiographers and Radiologic Technologists	www.isrrt.org
Musculoskeletal Ultrasound Society	www.musoc.com
North American Society of Pacing and Electrophysiology (NASPE)	www.naspe.org
North Carolina Ultrasound Society (NCUS)	www.ncus.org
Peripheral Vascular Surgery Society (PVSS)	www.pvss.org
Radiological Society of North America (RSNA)	www.rsna.org
Society of Breast Imaging (SBI)	www.sbi-online.org
Society of Diagnostic Medical Sonography (SDMS)	www.sdms.org
Society of Interventional Radiology (SIR)	www.sirweb.org
Society of Invasive Cardiovascular Professionals (SICP)	www.sicp.com
Society of Nuclear Medicine (SNM)	www.snm.org
Society of Radiologists in Ultrasound (SRU)	www.sru.org

Appendix J

Society for Vascular Medicine and Biology (SVMB)	www.svmb.org
Society for Vascular Surgery (SVS)	www.vascularweb.org
Society for Vascular Ultrasound (SVU)	www.svunet.org
Society of Pediatric Echocardiography (SOPE)	www.sope-online.com
Society of Pediatric Radiology (SPR)	www.pedrad.org
Society of Radiologists in Ultrasound (SRU)	www.sru.org
Vascular Disease Foundation (VDF)	www.vdf.org
World Federation for Ultrasound in Medicine and Biology (WFUMB)	www.wfumb.org

Government Resources

Agency for Health Care Policy and Research Practice Guidelines (AHCPR)	www.ahcpr.gov
Center for Devices and Radiological Health (CDRH/FDA)	www.fda.gov
ClinicalTrials.gov	www.clinicaltrials.gov
National Council on Radiation Protection and Measurement (NCRP)	www.ncrp.com
National Electrical Manufacturers Association (NEMA)	www.nema.org
National Library of Medicine (NLM)	www.nlm.nih.gov
U.S. Department of Health and Human Services	www.os.dhhs.gov
World Federation for Ultrasound in Medicine and Biology (WFUMB)	www.wfumb.org

Glossary

1.5 D array transducers A transducer which has a multiple elements in the lateral dimension and a few (usually) three elements in the elevation dimension. In addition to the ability to steer laterally like the 1-D arrays, a 1.5-D array is capable of producing two different foci in the elevation plane.

1-D array transducers A transducer which consists of multiple elements in one dimension (the lateral direction). 1-D arrays can be steered and focused electronically in only one plane (laterally).

2-D array transducers A transducer that has multiple elements in both the lateral and elevation direction. 2-D arrays can be both steered and focused in two planes (lateral and elevation) such that 3-D scans can be produced.

3-D imaging Any imaging technique which results in a three dimensional representations of structures and images. 3-D imaging can be produced by manually moving a 1-D array across the patient, by using a motor and mechanically steering a 1-D array, or completely electronically with a 2-D array.

Absolute refractory period The period immediately following the activation of a nerve fiber when it cannot be stimulated no matter how great the action potential applied.

Absorption The conversion of energy from the sound wave into heat within the medium. Absorption depends on properties of the medium as well as the frequency of operation.

Absorption coefficient An acoustic parameter which specifies the rate of absorption of sound within a medium.

Accuracy The overall percentage of times a comparison test is correct when compared with a gold standard test. The accuracy is calculated as the total number of times the test agrees with the gold standard divided by the total number of tests performed.

Acoustic Relating to, involving, or typical of sound, hearing, or the study of sound.

Acoustic impedance (Z) A measure of the resistance to sound traveling within a medium. The acoustic impedance (units of Rayls) is calculated by multiplying the density of the medium by the propagation speed of the medium ($Z = p \times c$). Greater differences in acoustic impedances at an acoustic interface (acoustic impedance mismatch) produce stronger reflections.

Acoustic intensity A measure of the distribution of acoustic power over area. Higher acoustic intensities produce stronger echoes but also increase risk of bioeffects.

Acoustic line A single transmitted sound beam in a specific direction and the associated echoes.

Acoustic power A measure of the rate at which acoustic energy is produced from a transducer or is transferred within a medium.

Acoustic variable The name given to the changes that occur to a medium as a result of mechanical interaction with an acoustic wave. The word variable refers to a changing quantity, and acoustic refers to sound. The four acoustic variables are pressure, density, temperature, and particle motion.

Acoustic zoom (write zoom or write magnification) A method of producing a larger specified region of a reference image by transmitting new acoustic lines so as to improve resolution. Since new data is written to the scan converter memory, this technique is often referred to as a "write zoom".

Afterload The force against which the ventricle must pump related primarily to the vascular resistance.

ALARA principle Stands for "as low as reasonably achievable" and is a guideline to define "prudent" use of diagnostic ultrasound instruments.

Aliasing The effect which occurs when a signal is sampled too slowly to accurately detect the true frequency of the signal (a violation of the Nyquist criterion). Specifically, aliasing occurs if the sample rate is less than twice the frequency of the signal to be detected. For Doppler, aliasing occurs when the PRF is less than twice the Doppler shift.

Alternating current (AC) An electric current that reverses its direction at regularly recurring intervals. In the U.S., the phase reversal occurs at 60 Hz.

Ambient light The background light existing within a room. Ambient light affects the ability to visualize low-level signals on a display monitor.

A-mode (amplitude mode) An early mode of ultrasound which displays the amplitude of the returning echo with respect to the depth along a single line. The amplitude is related to the signal strength (reflected signal). The amplitude was generally displayed on the vertical axis and depth on the horizontal axis. This modality is rarely used except is a few ophthalmic cases.

Amplification Making something larger, greater, or stronger. The term amplification is used synonymously with the term "gain".

Amplitude The amplitude (Amp) of a physical quantity is defined as the strength, volume, or size of that physical quantity. In more formal terms, the amplitude is defined as the maximum variation of a variable from its mean value. The units for the four acoustic variables represent amplitude measurements. For electrical variables, the unit of amplitude measure is Volts.

Analog Refers to any mechanism in which data is represented by continuously variable physical quantities.

Anechoic No echogenicity, no or almost no reflected signal.

Angle of incidence The angle formed between a wavefront and the acoustic interface between two structures. The angle of incidence can also be measured as the angle between the wave direction and the line perpendicular (normal) to the acoustic interface.

Angle of reflection The angle formed between a reflected wavefront and the acoustic interface between two structures. The angle of reflection can also be measured as the angle between the reflected wave direction and the line perpendicular (normal) to the acoustic interface. For specular reflection, the angle of incidence equals the angle of reflection.

Angle of transmission The angle formed between the transmitted wavefront and the acoustic interface between two structures. The angle of transmission can also be measured as the angle between the transmitted wave direction and the line perpendicular (normal) to the acoustic interface. If the transmission angle does not equal the angle of incidence, refraction has occurred.

Annular array A transducer type in which the elements are concentric rings (annuli). These transducers are not very common any more with the advent of phased array transducers. Annular arrays are steered mechanically and have a variable focus both laterally and elevationally.

Aortic stenosis A narrowing or obstruction of the heart's aortic valve or aorta which restricts the flow of blood from the left ventricle to the aorta.

Aperture The portion or "window" of the transducer elements being utilized to transmit (transmit aperture) or receive (receive aperture).

Apodization Refers to a process of varying the sensitivity of some elements relative to other elements so as to affect beam characteristics. For ultrasound, apodization is commonly used with array transducers to decrease the amplitude of the grating lobes.

To reduce grating lobe energy, the center elements of the aperture are excited with higher amplitude voltages than the elements near the edge of the aperture. Apodization can also be applied to the receive beam by varying the amplification applied to varying elements of the receive aperture.

Apparent resolution The appearance of improved resolution related to displaying an image larger or smaller than the original image. An image with very good resolution, but displayed in a small image format, will give the appearance of improved resolution when depicted in a larger format. If an image has poor resolution and the image is displayed in a large format, reducing the image display format often yields the appearance of improved resolution.

Apparent Signal to Noise *See Signal-to-noise ratio.*

Area A two-dimensional physical measurement calculated by multiplying a length and a width. Area can also be determined using the fundamental concept of integration (from calculus) as a summation of small regions bounded by a curve.

Array A collection of transducer crystal elements.

Arterial hemodynamics A branch of physiology that deals with the circulation of the blood in the arteries.

Arteries The branching muscular- and elastic-walled vessels that carry blood from the heart through the body.

Arterioles The small, muscularly banded regulating branch of the arterial system before the capillaries. The arterioles are referred to as the resistive component of the cardiovascular system, and are the principal compensatory control mechanism for regulation of blood volume through vasodilation and vasoconstriction.

Arteriovenous fistula An abnormal communication between the arterial and venous systems.

Artifact A broad category which includes an image feature or characteristic which is not representative of the true anatomical location or characteristic. There are two very distinct sources of artifacts in ultrasound images, physical interaction of the sound beam within the body, and external sources such as radio frequencies and power supply noise. Artifacts related to physical interactions are often instructive in that the artifact mechanism reveals a characteristic of the medium.

Attenuation A decrease in intensity and amplitude due to wave interactions with the medium including absorption, refraction, and reflection. Caution: some texts use the word attenuation synonymously with the term absorption.

Attenuation artifacts Artifacts that result from attenuation such as shadowing, enhancement, or refraction.

Audible sound *See human audible range.*

Average The mean value of a set of numbers computed as the sum of the numbers divided by the number of numbers. (example: the average of 3, 7, and 23 is 33/3 = 11)

Axial resolution The ability to distinguish between two structures in the axial (longitudinal, radial, depth, or range) dimension. The axial resolution equals the spatial pulse length (SPL) divided by 2.

Back scattering A type of reflection which results in energy being redirected back toward the source. This type of reflection occurs from surfaces which are rough with respect to the wavelength. Back-scattering is relatively angle independent. (The term scattering is commonly used synonymously.)

Backend (ultrasound system) Refers to the collection of electronics and functions of an ultrasound system that converts the detected and receiver processed signal into an interpretable, measurable, and storable scan.

Backing material The material used in a transducer construction to decrease the number of cycles a crystal rings. By decreasing the number of cycles in the pulse, the spatial pulse length is shortened improving longitudinal resolution. Additionally, fewer cycles implies that the pulse duration is decreased, increasing the transducer bandwidth. The backing material is also referred to as the damping material.

Banding noise An artifact related to the change in system parameters that occurs at boundaries between focal zones when using multiple transmit foci.

Bandwidth The useful range of frequencies over which a device can operate. The bandwidth is typically defined as the difference between the upper frequency corner and lower frequency corner of the device's frequency response.

Beam steering Any technique which results in a change in primary direction of the ultrasound wave over time.

Beam uniformity coefficient A measure of how beam intensity uniformity over space, defined as the spatial peak intensity divided by the spatial average intensity. (Always greater than or equal to 1.)

Beamplots Data taken while scanning the acoustic field over the imaging scan plans (power testing) that is plotted to help determine power distribution and focusing characteristics of a transducer.

Beamshape The physical dimensions (shape) formed over time as the sound wave passes through the medium.

Bernoulli's equation A restatement of the conservation of energy theorem which can be applied to express changes in pressure with fluid flow related to energy conversion between kinetic and potential energy. The equation is simplified to a form which relates the pressure drop (mmHg) across a flow narrowing to $4v^2$.

Binary/Base 2 Digits are restricted to 0 and 1. Each column represents a power of 2, just as each column in base 10 represents a power of 10. Binary is the basis for virtually all electronic devices. Historically, the digit 0 is represented by 0 volts and the digit 1 is represented by +5 volts.

Bioeffects An undesired biological change to tissues as a result of interaction with the ultrasound beam.

Bit The smallest division of a binary number or the smallest division of the digital output from an A/D converter.

Blind Doppler probe *See Pedof or Pencil.* A simple round crystal.

Blossoming Refers to a transducer signal that is essentially overgained such that the signal "bleeds" into neighboring regions of the spectrum.

B-mode Brightness mode. B-mode is a means of converting signal amplitudes into gray-scaled pixels so that a readily interpretable image can be created. The standard convention of B-mode is to present higher amplitude signals as brighter shades of white.

Brightness mode *See B-mode.*

Bruit An audible sound generally caused by vibration such as occurs with a stenosis or high degree of stenosis.

B-scan An obsolete ultrasound technique in which the sonographer physically moved the transducer over the patient to create a scan over time.

Bulk modulus A physical parameter of a material defined by the percent change in pressure (stress) divided by the fractional change in volume (strain). The bulk modulus is inversely related to the compressibility of a material. The propagation velocity of sound in a medium is directly proportional to the square root of the bulk modulus.

Byte 8 bits comprise one byte. A byte is a natural grouping of bits since 8 is a power of 2.

Capacitance A measure of the ability to hold a change in volume per time. The capacitance is critical in the arterial system as a means of storing energy to drive blood flow in diastole as well as part of a system which dampens the pulsatility into more continuous flow. The venous system is referred to as the capacitive component of the cardiovascular system since at rest approximately 65% of the volume resides in the venous system.

Capillaries The smallest blood vessels connecting arterioles with venules and forming networks throughout the body. Metabolic exchange occurs through diffusion at the level of the capillaries.

Cardiac index A method for normalizing the cardiac output relative to the size of the patient.

Cardiac output A measure of the volumetric flow, or volume of blood per time that the heart pumps usually expressed in liters per minute.

Cardiac reserve The difference between the cardiac output or volume at rest and the maximum cardiac output or volume the heart is capable of pumping during stress (exercise).

Cathode ray tube (CRT) The standard monitor technology for many years in which beams of electrons are scanned across a phosphorescent screen to display an image. For color monitors, three CRTs are used to produce red, green, and blue (RGB).

Cavitation Formally refers to the formation of bubbles within a medium. For ultrasound the terms has also come to refer to the interaction of bubbles with wave energy. There are two types of cavitation - stable and transient. Stable cavitation implies that the bubbles oscillate within the varying pressure field but do not implode. Transient cavitation refers to a violent collapse which occurs during the peak rarefactional pressure of the wave.

Cephalad Toward the head or anterior end of the body.

Cine-loop A bank of digital memory which stores imaging data for replay. The replay can either be in real-time, or played back in "slow time" frame-by-frame. It is referred to as a loop since the oldest data is overwritten when the memory is full so that the data forms a "loop" in time.

Claudication Pain in the calf or thigh muscle that occurs after increased metabolic demand as a result of ischemia.

Clutter signals Large returning echoes from structures, which dominate weaker signals.

C-mode (constant depth mode) Any ultrasound mode which listens to echoes returning only from a specific depth such as PW Doppler.

Collateral flow Circulation of blood through dilated (usually smaller) vessels when a more significant vein or artery is functionally impaired (as by obstruction).

Color Doppler A scanned technique based on Doppler principles which allows for flow assessment over a two-dimensional region of the body. The flow information is encoded using a color scale. The color representation is an estimate of the mean velocity at each location for that instant in time. (Also referred to as color imaging, color Doppler imaging, and color flow.)

Color ensemble *See Color packet.*

Color gain Amplification (multiplication) of the received color signal.

Color packet The number of acoustic lines used to create a single color display line. Multiple acoustic lines (a packet or ensemble of lines) are used to produce an estimate of the mean velocity through correlation. A larger color packet size produces a better estimate, reducing noise within the color, but at the expense of time to create a color line and hence, the time to produce a color frame. Therefore, a large packet size reduces the frame rate, decreasing the temporal resolution.

Color persistence A processing technique which averages frames over time so as to improve the signal-to-noise ratio by constructive interference of the signal (signal coherence) and partially destructive interference of the noise. Caution must be used with too much persistence since short duration events can be "persisted" out, while longer duration events may be persisted artificially in time.

Color priority A threshold technique allowing the user to maximize color filling while minimizing color bleed overlaying tissue. Color priority sets a threshold level to determine whether the 2D signal or the color signal is displayed when both signals exist for the same pixel at the same time.

Comet tail A specific form of reverberation named for the appearance of a flashlight or "tail" produced when sound reverberates within a metallic structure such as surgical clips, needles, and prosthetic valve apparatus.

Compensation The name given for varying amplification with depth to compensate for increased attenuation with depth. Controlled on the system by the TGCs (time gain compensation).

Complex plaque A term used to describe complicated plaque characteristics implying a non-uniform pattern which may include hemorrhage, calcifications and lipid deposits.

Compliance A measure of the change in volume per pressure. The compliance is tightly coupled with the capacitance. Although technically not the same parameter, the two terms are often used interchangeably since a high compliance usually implies high capacitance in the cardiovascular system.

Compound imaging A technique to improve signal-to-noise and reduce artifacts by transmitting multiple frames at slightly varying steer angles and then averaging together to create one image.

Compressibility The inverse of stiffness and proportional to elasticity. As the compressibility of a material increases, the propagation velocity decreases.

Compression (acoustic wave) The state in wave propagation when the particles occupy a smaller region in the medium than normal (higher density).

Compression (signal processing) A technique to reduce dynamic range by mapping the larger range into a smaller range. Because of the extraordinary dynamic range of ultrasound signals from the body, compression occurs in many places in the ultrasound system including the receiver and the scan converter. Compression techniques almost always result in a loss of data.

Conservation of energy One of the fundamental tenets of physics. This theorem states that energy cannot be created or destroyed but is only changed from one form to another form.

Constructive interference When two signals or waves interact so as to produce one larger signal or wave. Constructive interference occurs when the two or more signals have similar phases. The principles of constructive interference are the foundation for phased array operation as well as many averaging based processing techniques.

Continuity equation A conservation of energy expression that states that in a closed fluid flow system, all of the flow through one region must equal all of the flow through another region. The continuity equation states the volumetric flow equals the spatial average velocity times the cross-sectional flow area.

Continuous mode *See CW Doppler.*

Continuous wave (CW) Refers to the fact that the transmit wave is continuous -- in contrast with pulsed wave operation which intermittently turns the transmit wave on and off.

Contrast agents Microbubbles usually consisting of a shell filled with a dense gas used to enhance the reflectivity of blood. The increased reflectivity is the result of an increase in the acoustic impedance mismatch as a result of the low density and high compressibility of the contrast agent.

Contrast imaging Any imaging technique which utilizes contrast agent for signal enhancement.

Contrast resolution Ability to distinguish structures based on variations of brightness.

Converge To narrow such as occurs at the beam focus.

Cosine A trigonometric function that for an acute angle is the ratio between the leg adjacent to the angle and the hypotenuse. On the unit circle, the cosine of an angle is determined by plotting the angle and projecting the intersection of the angle with the unit circle to the x-axis.

Critical angle The incident angle at which total internal reflection occurs.

Cross-section A cut at right angles to an axis.

Curie point The temperature at which a piezoelectric material loses its piezoelectric properties. (300 degrees Celsius for PZT)

Current A stream of electrons which move along a conductor from a high potential to a low potential. Electrical current is measured in amperes (Amps).

Curved linear phased array transducers A family of phased array transducers that have a convex surface so as to produce relatively broad near field images and even broader far field images.

CW Doppler A technique which measures the Doppler shifted frequencies by transmitting and receiving waves continuously and simultaneously. CW has the advantage of virtually unlimited maximum detectable frequency shifts (no aliasing) but suffers from no range specificity.

Cyanosis A dusky bluish discoloration of the skin.

Cyclical Periodic or repetitive.

Decibels (dB) A logarithmic power ratio. Decibels express the relative relationship between two powers or intensities. An amplitude form exists which converts the amplitude ratio into a power ratio. Since decibels are based on logarithms, decibels exhibit the same non-linear benefits and drawbacks of compression as logarithms.

Decimal The counting system based on using ten digits (0 through 9). Each column in a decimal (base 10) number represents a power of 10. Base 10 is the standard counting system used primarily because we are born with 10 fingers and 10 toes.

Delta (Δ) An abbreviation for the word "change" or gradient.

Demodulation The process of recovering a signal from a modulated (varied frequency) carrier wave. Also sometimes referred to as signal detection.

Denominator The part of a fraction below the division line.

Density A measure of how tightly "packed" a material is -- calculated as the mass per unit volume.

Dependent rubor A deep red color occurs on the skin due to blood pooling in the arterioles.

Depth of field (focal region) Refers to the general region above and below the focus where the beam is approximately the same width.

Destructive interference The reduction in overall amplitude when two or more waves or signals interfere with different phases. Complete destructive interference occurs when two waves are completely out of phase (180 degrees apart). Destructive interference is critical to produce narrow beams from phased array transducers.

Detail resolution Ability to distinguish between two objects in any of the three dimensions: axial, lateral, or elevation.

Diagnostic range Refers to the range of frequencies commonly used for conventional, non-invasive ultrasound. (Generally considered to be approximately 2-12 MHz.)

Diastole The low pressure phase of the cardiac cycle in which ventricular filling occurs.

Diastolic pressure The force of blood in the arteries during the diastolic phase.

Dicrotic notch The corresponding bump up in pressure (producing a second peaking in the pressure waveform) that occurs as a result of inertia as the aortic valve closes.

Digital filtering Any signal processing technique which removes signal components mathematically in contrast to analog filtering.

Digital scan converter The name given to the part of the system in which individual scan lines are processed and converted into a format for visualization as an image. The digital scan converter is often referred to as a large block of digital memory and the processing unit responsible for grayscale mapping and scan formatting. In actuality, the scan converter is one functional block of the system referred to as the backend which includes the scan converter, the cineloop memory, storage devices, measurement and analysis software, and video display drivers.

Digital signals Any signal which exists as discrete levels at discrete time intervals (a time series of numbers). Analog signals are often converted into discrete digital signals through electronics called an analog to digital converter (A/D converter).

Direct current (DC) Electrical current that does not change direction or amplitude and so maintains constant voltage. DC is produced by batteries.

Direct non-linear proportionality A mathematical relationship whereby two physical quantities (expressed as variables) are related such that as one quantity increases, the other quantity also increases but at a faster rate.

Direct proportionality A mathematical relationship whereby two physical quantities (expressed as variables) are related such that as one quantity increases, the other quantity also increases at the same rate. Similarly, if one quantity decreases, the other related quantity also decreases at the same rate.

Display alias When a Doppler signal appears aliased on the screen but can be "unwrapped" by shifting the baseline or increasing the scales.

Display dynamic range The ratio of the biggest to the smallest signal that can be displayed on a monitor or other display device.

Display line The data displayed on the screen that corresponds to a single direction within the patient.

Distal flow Flow that occurs downstream.

Distal resistance The resistance associated with the extremity farther down the flow path.

Distance equation The equation which specifies that distance is calculated as the velocity (rate) multiplied by time.

Disturbed flow Any deviation from laminar flow.

Diverge To widen as occurs deeper than the focus of a beam.

Doppler A broad category of techniques based on the Doppler effect which includes spectral Doppler, audio Doppler, and color flow imaging. See Doppler effect.

Doppler angle The angle that is formed between the observer's line of sight and the direction of the target object. The Doppler angle is also referred to as the insonification angle.

Doppler artifacts Artifacts that affect any Doppler based modality. Some examples of Doppler artifacts include aliasing, range ambiguity, spectral broadening, and spectral mirroring.

Doppler effect An apparent shift in frequency of any interrogating wave caused by a change in wavelength from relative motion between the observer and the target. A shorter wavelength implies a higher frequency and indicates relative movement toward the observer. Conversely, a longer wavelength implies a lower frequency and relative movement away from the observer.

Doppler gain Amplification of the Doppler received signal.

Doppler shift The difference in frequency between the transmitted and reflected wave caused by the Doppler effect. A higher reflected signal frequency implies a positive frequency shift (motion towards the observer).

Doppler spectrum The graphical display of the range of Doppler frequency shifts (or velocities) over time.

Duty cycle/Duty factor Refers to the percentage of time the energy is actively being transmitted into the body. The duty factor is calculated as the pulse duration divided by the pulse repetition period. In CW, the duty factor is 1. In PW the duty factor is always less than 1.

Dynamic range The ratio of the maximum to the minimum of any quantity.

Dynamic receive focus A receiver based technique which automatically changes the phase delays to provide optimal focusing for the data being received. Dynamic receive focusing became relatively standard with the introduction of digital beamformers.

Echo A sound wave which has been reflected off a surface and is heard after the original sound. The term "echo" is often used to refer to a cardiac scan.

Echogenicity Refers to the strength and/or type of the signal reflection.

Edema An abnormal excess accumulation of serous fluid in connective tissue or in a serous cavity.

Ejection fraction The percentage of blood ventricular volume ejected per beat.

EKG *See electrocardiogram.*

Elasticity The capability of a strained body to recover its size and shape after deformation.

Electrical interference Caused when transducers or ultrasound machines receive energy emanating from other electrical devices or electromagnetic waves.

Electrocardiogram (ECG) The time display of electrical signals which stimulate myocardial contraction.

Electromagnetic (EM) wave An electromagnetic wave is a transfer of energy through a varying electrical and magnetic field.

Electronic noise Random signals added to a signal during amplification from random excitation of electrons.

Electronic steering The steering achieved by using small time or phase delays between the excitation pulses to each of the transducer elements within the array.

Elevation resolution The ability to resolve structure in the elevation plane (slice thickness for 2D imaging).

Energy The ability to perform work. Energy is power integrated over time.

Energy gradient A difference in energy levels.

Enhancement artifact A brighter than normal echo below a structure which is either a weaker reflector or less absorbing than normal.

Envelope detection Part of the receiver function of signal detection which traces the signal peaks and valleys while simultaneously applying some averaging or smoothing.

Exponential notation A way of expressing numbers in terms of powers of ten.

Factor A number that divides into another number exactly. The word factor implies the mathematical operation of multiplication (or its inverse: division).

False negative (FN) Implies that the test incorrectly predicts there is no disease (the test predicts no disease when the gold standard predicts disease).

False positive (FP) Implies that the test incorrectly predicts there is disease (the test predicts disease when the gold standard does not predict disease).

Far field or Fraunhofer zone The region deeper than the natural focus.

Fast fourier transform (FFT) A mathematical technique for separating a spectrum into its individual frequency components.

Fluid Dynamics The study of fluid flow through a flow system.

Focal region (depth of field) Region over which the transducer beam is most tightly focused.

Focus Where the beam reaches its minimum diameter.

Fraction A numerical representation (as 1/7, 2/9, 7.15) indicating the quotient of two numbers.

Fractional bandwidth A figure of merit for transducers which indicates information about the bandwidth relative to the center frequency. The fractional bandwidth is determined by dividing the operating or center frequency by the bandwidth.

Frame frequency *See frame rate.*

Frame rate The frequency at which frames of data are produced or presented. The acoustic frame rate represents how many frames of data per second are produced during imaging. The display frame rate represents the number of frames per second that appear on the monitor. The frame rate (also referred to as the frame frequency) is the reciprocal of the frame time.

Frame time The amount of time it takes to acquire a frame.

Frank-Starling's Law Describes the relationship between cardiac filling (preload) and force of contraction.

Frequency The number of cycles of a particular event in one second (per time).

Frequency bins Divisions of the frequency spectrum that result from performing a Fast Fourier Transform (FFT). Each bin represents a narrow range of frequencies which can be related to velocity through the Doppler equation.

Friction The force that resists relative motion between two bodies in contact. Friction results in a conversion of kinetic energy into heat.

Front-end The collection of electronics and functions in ultrasound equipment where all of the processing takes place before the signal is sent to the "back-end" for conversion into an interpretable, measurable, and storable scan.

Fundamental frequency The term used to refer to the transmit frequency when performing harmonic imaging.

Gain An increase in signal power, voltage, or current expressed as the ratio of the output to the input. The gain ratio in ultrasound, and most electronics, is often expressed in decibels.

Gain dynamic range The range over which a signal can be amplified. The ratio of the maximum to the minimum amplification possible.

Grating lobes Energy that is produced in undesired directions other than the main beam direction. Grating lobes are exacerbated by using larger elements relative to the wavelength of the frequency being transmitted. Grating lobes generally produce laterally displaced structures or a "haze" that may be misconstrued as thrombus.

Harmonic contrast imaging Uses harmonic imaging in conjunction with a contrast agent. The system transmits at the fundamental frequency and then receives at the second harmonic frequency.

Harmonic imaging The technique of transmitting at a lower frequency (the fundamental frequency) and receiving at a harmonic frequency (currently only second harmonic). The technique yields better penetration than conventional imaging operating purely at the higher frequency and better resolution than conventional imaging operating purely at the lower frequency. One of the biggest advantages to harmonic imaging is the reduction in clutter related artifacts in the relative nearfield.

Haze A gray appearance in the image (usually in the relative nearfield) usually caused by grating lobe artifact or reverberation artifact.

Hemodynamics The laws of fluid dynamics as applied to blood flow and the cardiovascular system.

Hertz The unit for frequency. (cycles/second)

Heterogeneous Implies that there is variation within the signal.

Homogenous Implies that the signal is relatively uniform.

HPRF Doppler High pulse repetition frequency Doppler intentionally utilizes the artifact of range ambiguity to increase the maximum detectable velocity with aliasing, at the expense of some range resolution.

Human audible range Sound within the range of human hearing (purported to be 20 Hz to 20 kHz – although usually lower than 17 kHz for most adults).

Huygen's principle States that all points on a wavefront can be treated as point sources producing spherical secondary wavelets, whose tangential surface predicts the new position of the wavefront over time.

Hydrophone A specialized ultrasound transducer that is designed to measure acoustic pressure fields. Hydrophones are used to make power measurements to verify transducer performance as well as make certain that maximum power levels are not exceeded.

Hydrostatic pressure The pressure which results from the weight of the fluid from above in a column. The hydrostatic pressure is related to both the height of the column, the density of the fluid, and gravity.

Hyperechoic Moderate-to-high echogenicity.

Hyperostosis An increase in skull density and thickness.

Hypertension A situation where blood pressure is persistently higher than normal.

Hypoechoic The area of an ultrasound image in which echoes are weaker than normal or in surrounding regions.

Image persistence A processing technique designed to reduce noise in the image through an "averaging" technique of images over time. Most persistence techniques do not use standard averages, but rather weighted averages so that newer frames are more heavily weighted than older frames.

Imaging depth The setting on the ultrasound system that allows the user to determine the maximum depth of interest to display. The imaging depth basically determines the time required between transmitting the next line of data (the PRP).

Impedance (acoustic) *See Acoustic impedance.*

Impedance (electrical) The resistance to current flow down a pathway. The unit for impedance is Ohms.

Impedance (fluid or hydraulic) The resistance to fluid flow down a pathway. The impedance (also referred to as the resistance) is directly related to the length of the flow path and the viscosity of the fluid. The resistance is inversely related to the radius of the flow path raised to the fourth power.

Impulse Response The response of a transducer crystal to a single, short duration pulse. The impulse response demonstrates the bandwidth of a transducer.

In vitro Studies done in a test tube.

In vivo Studies done within living tissue.

Incident angle (θ_i) The angle formed between the beam direction and the normal at the point of incidence. The incident angle can also be measured as the angle formed between the wavefront and the reflecting interface at the point of reflection.

Inertia Property of matter by which it continues in it's existing state unless changed by external force.

Infrasound Sound below human hearing (below 20 Hz).

Input dynamic range The range of signal amplitudes a system can receive and process without causing harmonic distortion.

Insonification (Doppler) angle The Doppler angle is measured between the beam steering direction and the direction (head) of the flow.

Intensity Equals the concentration of energy or power per unit area. The unit for intensity is Watts per square cm. The intensity is a useful parameter to help predict signal strength as well as the risk of bioeffects.

Inverse proportionality Implies an "opposite" relationship between two variables. If one variable increases, the related variable decreases.

Isovolumic Unchanging volume. *See isovolumic contraction.*

Isovolumic contraction During ventricular contraction, during which both the mitral and aortic valves (for the left side) and the tricuspid and pulmonic valves (for the right side) are closed, the volumes remain unchanged while the pressures increase dramatically.

Isovolumic systolic pressure curve Displays the pressure curve, which results for various volumes of blood under ventricular contraction, with the restriction that no blood is allowed to be ejected.

Joule The unit for work/energy.

Kinetic energy Energy related to motion, proportional to the velocity squared of movement.

Korotokov sounds Circulatory sounds heard through the stethoscope in auscultation of blood pressure with cuff inflation. The Korotokov (heart) sounds are produced when releasing the pressure in the cuff such that the intravascular pressure exceeds the cuff pressure and a volume of blood rams into a static column of blood distal to the cuff location.

Laminar flow When fluid flows smoothly without vortices or other turbulence.

Lateral resolution The ability to resolve two structures in the lateral dimension (side by side), angular, transverse, or azimuthal.

Length Distance or extent in space.

Lens A material used to help to focus the beam. (For 1D arrays, a lens is used to help focus in the elevation plane.)

Lift A net upward force created when there is greater pressure pushing up on the wing than pressure pushing down on the wing, as predicted by Bernoulli's equation.

Linear (proportionality) A relationship between variables where the rate of change is the same for both variables.

Linear phased array transducer A family of phased array transducers that have multiple elements in the lateral dimension. These transducer are frequently physically large and consisting of as many as 200 to 300 elements or more and were produced for vascular applications where contact must be maintained with a relatively flat surface. For unsteered imaging, the image is produced by sequencing. For steered imaging the image is produced by both sequencing and phasing.

Linear switched array transducer An obsolete transducer design that used a large group of elements in the linear dimension that could be turned either on or off through electronic switches. The linear switched array is the grandfather to current phased linear array transducers.

Locational artifacts Artifacts that result in structures appearing either displaced in an image from the true location or the presence of a structure or signal which does not even exist.

Logarithms The power to which a base must be raised to get the desired number. Logarithms inherently serve as a non-linear compression scheme.

Longitudinal (beam dimension) The dimension along the axis of the beam corresponding to depth into the patient. Other terms commonly used are axial, radial, depth, and range.

Longitudinal resolution The ability to resolve structures separated in depth. The longitudinal resolution equals the spatial pulse length divided by 2.

Longitudinal wave A wave which propagates through a series of compressions and rarefactions along (in the same direction) as the wave direction.

Lossless compression Any scheme which reduces dynamic range without loss of data.

Low echogenicity Low level reflected signals.

Manual steering Physically moving a transducer over the scan region of interest.

Matching layer A thin layer of material attached to the crystal of the transducer to reduce the acoustic impedance mismatch between the high impedance of the crystal and the low impedance of the tissue. The ideal thickness for a matching layer is quarter wavelength.

Maximum venous capacitance (MVC) The ability of the veins to fill with blood during a period in which the venous outflow is halted.

Maximum venous outflow (MVO) The amount of venous emptying that occurs when the occluding cuff is deflated.

Mean velocity The average velocity. The mean velocity can be calculated relative to time, relative to space (cross-sectional area) or both.

Mechanical annular array transducer A nearly obsolete transducer design which uses multiple rings (annuli) to allow for a varying focus both laterally and elevationally. By turning on or off rings, the transducer aperture is changed, changing the focus. These transducers were usually steered by a motor (mechanical steering).

Mechanical bioeffects Bioeffects that are caused by the physical interaction between the wave and the tissues in the body related to cavitation. Mechanical bioeffects generally occur during the peak rarefactional phase of the wave cycle.

Mechanical index (MI) A parameter that indicates the likelihood of mechanical bioeffects (cavitation) occurring. The MI is calculated by dividing the peak rarefactional pressure by the square root of the operating frequency.

Mechanical steering Refers to changing the ultrasound beam direction through a mechanical means (such as attaching a crystal to a motor) which physically points the crystal in different directions.

Mechanical wave A wave which requires a medium.

Medium The material through which a mechanical wave propagates. During imaging, the medium is the part of the patient being scanned.

Metric system Measurement system based on the decimal form (multiples of 10).

Mirror image artifact An artifact produced when a structure is located in front of a specular reflector which results in the structure being displayed twice: once in the correct location, and once distal to, and symmetric about, the specular reflecting surface.

Mismatch Difference, or having disparate properties. See acoustic impedance.

Mitral regurgitant fraction The difference in the left ventricular inflow and outflow volume normalized by the inflow volume.

M-mode (motion mode) An ultrasound mode commonly used for cardiac and fetal cardiac studies. A single acoustic line is repeatedly transmitted in the same direction such that depth is displayed on the vertical axis and time is displayed on the horizontal axis. The signal amplitude is represented using gray-scale (shades of gray). Since time is plotted on the horizontal axis, motion is detected by changes in depth along the horizontal axis.

Modal velocity The most commonly occurring velocity.

Modulation To change or modify. As a mechanical wave propagates through the body, the interaction modulates the wave. Demodulation is therefore the process of removing the modulation from the initial wave.

Momentum The mass of an object multiplied by its velocity.

Moore's law Expresses the rate of growth of technology.

Motion mode *See M-mode.*

Multi-path artifact An artifact that results in a structure being displayed artificially deeper than reality because the beam does not propagate in a straight line to and from the object. Like must imaging artifacts, multi-path artifact occurs generally in the presence of specular reflectors.

Native or "Tissue" harmonics The production of harmonic energy from non-linear wave propagation through tissue. The harmonic energy results from changes in the propagation velocity which occur with compression and rarefaction. The general term of "harmonic imaging" is now commonly used to refer to "native" or "tissue" harmonics. The terms native harmonics was created to distinguish between harmonics produced from tissue as opposed to harmonics produced by contrast agent.

Natural focus The depth at which a transducer crystal will naturally focus without any application of any focusing techniques.

Natural rate of the cell The rate at which a cell depolarizes without an "external" stimulus.

Near field or Fresnel zone The area between the face of the transducer and the beam focus (also referred to as the near zone).

Near zone length (NZL) The distance from the surface of the transducer to the natural focus (also referred to as the focal depth).

Negative predictive value The percentage of time a test correctly predicted the absence of disease relative to the total number of times the test predicted no disease.

Newtonian fluid A fluid whose viscosity is variable only with changes in temperature.

Noise Any unwanted signal or signals which mask or obscure desired signals.

Noise floor The signal level below which no signals are visible because of the presence of noise.

Non-acoustic zoom (Read zoom) A magnification of a specified region into a larger display region. Non-acoustic zooms do not change the true resolution but may improve the apparent resolution.

Non-scanned modality Any modality which repeatedly transmits in the same direction (such as PW Doppler, CW Doppler, A-mode, and M-mode). Non-scanned modalities generally have greater risks of thermal bioeffects than scanned modalities.

Normal incidence Implies that the wave propagation direction is perpendicular to the interface (or that the wavefront is parallel to the interface). For normal incidence there is no refraction.

Numerator The part of a fraction that is above the division line.

Nyquist criterion States that the sampling frequency must be at least twice the highest frequency in the signal to be detected. Violation of the Nyquist criterion results in incorrect frequency estimation (aliasing).

Nyquist limit Related to the Nyquist criterion. The Nyquist limit refers to the highest detectable Doppler frequency shift without aliasing. The Nyquist limited is determined by the PRF divided by two. If the Doppler shift is less than half of the PRF, then there is no aliasing. If the Doppler shift is greater than half the PRF, aliasing will occur.

Oblique Non-perpendicular and non-parallel.

Oculoplethysmography (OPG) Indirect method used to measure the systolic pressure in the ophthalmic artery by obtaining an indirect measurement of the pulse delay within the opthalmic artery.

OHM's Law The analogous law to the simplified law of hemodynamics for electrical current. Ohm's law dictates that the change in voltage equals the electrical current multiplied by the electrical resistance.

Operating frequency The center frequency of the transmit bandwidth for transducers.

Orthogonal *See perpendicular.*

Out of phase When the peaks (maxima) and troughs (minima) of two waves occur at different times. Waves are purely out of phase when the phase difference is 180 degrees.

Parabolic flow A special type of laminar flow in which the velocity profile is shaped like a parabola across the vessel. The flow in the center of the vessel has a higher velocity than flow along the vessel walls which loses more energy through friction and viscous effects.

Parallel processing A processing technique generally used to improve temporal resolution. Parallel processing is generally performed by transmitting a wider beam than normal and then dividing the transducer elements and receiver channels into two or more parallel groups. Each receiver group processes a receive beam allowing for twice as many (or more) receive beams to be generated in the time required to transmit a single acoustic beam. Almost all digital systems now use parallel processing for color and 2D. Some systems are now performing quad parallel processing.

Parasympathetic nervous system Plays a minor role in regulation of circulation and can affect the heart rate via the parasympathetic fibers carried to the heart in the vagus nerve.

Partially constructive interference When two waves add so that the new wave is not as "big" as when the two waves were in phase and not as small as when the two waves were completely out of phase.

Particle motion One of the four acoustic variables. Occurs when particles oscillate back and forth about their original location, allowing the concentration of energy to propagate along the wave path.

Pedof *See Pencil probe.*

Pencil probe A simple transducer designed to perform only Doppler and no imaging. The pencil probe consists of a single round crystal for PW and a split round crystal for CW Doppler. These transducers are often the most sensitive for Doppler since no tradeoffs are made to accommodate imaging. Since no image is possible these transducers are commonly referred to as a "blind" or "Doppler blind" transducer. Another name for this transducer type is a "pedof".

Percentage A part of a whole expressed in hundredths- a specific way of expressing the ratio of two numbers in terms of hundredths.

Pericardium The thin sac (membrane) that surrounds the heart and the roots of the great blood vessels.

Perimeter The distance around a structure or shape. A perimeter is a one-dimensional measure and has units of distance such as meters or centimeters.

Period The reciprocal of the frequency representing the amount of time it takes for one full cycle to occur.

Peripheral resistance A measure of the resistance of the entire vascular system to flow.

Perpendicular Meeting at a right angle (90 degrees).

Persistence *See image persistence or color persistence.*

Phantoms An object used to perform equipment quality assurance testing. These object usually use materials which mimic properties of tissue in terms of propagation velocity, absorption, and reflection.

Phase A term used to determine a time reference. For cyclical phenomena such as waves, phase is often specified in degrees instead of time.

Phase delay A time delay which results in a waves reaching maxima at different times. Phase delays are used with multiple elements to produce electronic steering and focusing,

Phase difference *See phase delay.*

Phased array sector transducer A family of phase array transducers that produce a sector formatted image. The sector image format is produced by phasing. The sector transducer type was designed with rib access in mind.

Photoplethysmography Light produced from an infrared light-emitting diode and a photosensor to detect changes in blood volume.

Piezoelectric crystals A material which converts electropotential (voltage) into acoustic waves and acoustic waves back into voltage.

Piezoelectric effect The phenomenon of mechanical deformation, which results when an electric field (voltage) is applied to certain crystal materials.

Pixel The smallest division of a display.

Plethysmography A category of methods which records changes in volume.

Plug flow A special type of laminar flow in which the velocity profile is relatively constant across the entire vessel. Plug flow occurs as an entrance effect as the result of acceleration.

Poiseuille's (Equation) law Expresses the relationship between volumetric flow and the pressure gradient, the radius of the flow conduit, the length of the flow conduit, and the viscosity of the fluid.

Poiseuille's law assumes a Newtonian fluid and that there is no energy lost to friction. Poiseuille's law was derived empirically.

Polarization The process of displacing electrical charges such that positive charges exist on one side and negative charges exist on the other side.

Poling A process used to polarize a crystal material so as to enhance the piezoelectric properties. Poling involves heating a crystal to high temperatures and then applying a powerful electromagnetic field.

Popliteal fossa An anatomical region behind the knee.

Positive predictive value The percentage of times a test correctly predicted the presence of disease relative to the total number of times the test predicted disease.

Post-processing Any processing which can be changed post data acquisition such as data compression, colorization, and reject. Post-processing techniques are applied in the backend (scan converter) of the ultrasound system.

Potential energy Stored energy which can be converted to other forms of energy such as kinetic. Pressure across vessel walls represents potential energy.

Power The rate at which work is being performed. The unit for power is Watts.

Power ratio The same as the power gain factor. The power ratio is the final power divided by the initial power, where the final represents the power after a change (such as increasing the transmit power) and the initial power represents the power before the change. The power ratio is used to convert the relative change into decibels.

Preload The stretched condition of the heart muscle related to the volume within the ventricle at the end of diastolic filling just before contraction.

Pre-processing Signal conditioning that occurs in real time and cannot be removed from an image once acquired. Pre-processing occurs before the signal is stored in the backend (scan converter).

Pressure A measure of force per area.

Pressure gradient The change is pressure that occurs as a result of energy conversion with flow. Measuring the pressure at the site of a stenosis, the pressure is decreased relative to proximal to the stenosis since some of the potential energy is converted to kinetic energy within the narrowed region. The difference between the proximal pressure and the lower pressure within the stenosis is referred to as a pressure gradient.

Processing Any condition of a signal in an attempt to interpret or improve the display of that signal.

Propagation A means of transmission from one location to another location through interaction. Sound propagates through a medium by interacting with particles within the medium.

Propagation velocity The rate at which a wave travels through a medium. The propagation velocity is related to the bulk modulus and density of a material. As the bulk modulus increases (assuming no change in density), the propagation velocity increases. As the density increases (assuming no change in bulk modulus), the propagation velocity decreases. In biological materials, an increase in density usually indicates a significant increase in the bulk modulus such that more dense materials have higher propagation velocities than lower density materials.

Proportionality Describes a relative relationship between two variables. See also linear proportionality, direct non-linear proportionality, inverse proportionality, and direct proportional.

PRP (Pulse repetition period) The time between transmit events. The PRP is limited primarily by the imaging depth.

Pseudoaneurysm A false aneurysm created by the perforation of the intima and media, it is contained by a thin layer of adventitia or thrombus.

Pulmonic stenosis An abnormal narrowing of the orifice between the right ventricle and the pulmonary artery which leads to an increase in resistance to blood flow into the pulmonary artery. (Also referred to as pulmonary stenosis.)

Pulsatile flow Flow that dynamically varies cyclically with time. The variation of flow that occurs from the peak of systole to the end of diastole.

Pulse duration The amount of time for which a pulse lasts. The pulse duration equals the period multiplied by the number of cycles within the pulse.

Pulse length *See spatial pulse length.*

Pulse pressure The difference between the peak systolic and end diastolic pressures.

Pulse Repetition Frequency (PRF) The number of pulses that occur in one second and equal to the reciprocal of the PRP.

Pulse Repetition Period (PRP) The time between the start of one transmit pulse until the start of the next transmit pulse. Primarily determined by the imaging depth.

Pulsed mode *See pulsed wave.*

Pulsed wave To transmit and receive intermittently, alternatively.

Pulsed wave Doppler (PW) A Doppler technique which uses pulses to achieve range specificity. The Doppler gate size and depth is set by the user. The system produces a pulse which matches the gate size, and waits the appropriate time for the sound wave to travel to the desired gate depth and return. Unlike continuous wave operation, by restricting the pulse length, signals are primarily received from the depth of interest.

Pulsed wave range ambiguity *See range ambiguity artifact.*

Pulser The part of the front end of the system responsible for creating the transmit pulses to drive the transducer elements.

Quadrant One quarter of the circumference of a circle equivalent to 90 degrees.

Quadrature detection Signifies that the information is detected at two different phases, 90° apart. Quadrature detection is used in Doppler so as to distinguish forward flow from reverse flow.

Quality assurance The combination of steps taken by a lab to guarantee accuracy in testing. Some aspects of quality assurance include routine testing of equipment, having well defined lab protocols, holding regular review meetings, lab accreditation, and individual certification.

Quality factor The reciprocal of the fractional bandwidth.

Radius (r) A line segment extending from the center of a circle or sphere to the circumference or bounding surface.

Range ambiguity artifact An undesirable result of the fact that sound continues to travel and reflect back from depths deeper than the Doppler gate depth. As a result, signals from multiples of the PRP return and are added with signals from the desired gate depth. All pulsed modes suffer from range ambiguity. This phenomenon is generally not a major problem unless the Doppler sample volume (gate) is shallow.

Range resolution *See longitudinal resolution .*

Rarefaction The state of wave propagation in which the particles of the medium are stretched farther apart than normal (lower density).

Rayleigh scattering Frequency dependent scattering. This type of reflection occurs from structures which are small relative to the wavelength.

Rayls The unit for acoustic impedance $[kg/(m^2 \cdot sec)]$.

Reactive hyperemia A condition of temporary ischemia which results in increased blood flow.

Read zoom See non-acoustic zoom.

Real time imaging Implies that all the ultrasound lines are being transmitted, recorded, processed and displayed so as to appear instant and continuous in time.

Receive line The returning echoes registered by the system from a single direction over the time between the transmit event and the time until the next transmit occurs as dictated by the imaging depth.

Receiver The front end of the system which registers and processes the echoes that are detected by the transducer elements.

Receiver gain Amplification of the signal after it has already returned from the patient.

Reciprocal The absolute inverse of a quantity. The product of reciprocals is 1.

Rectification The process of inverting the negative component of a signal. To make (an alternating current) unidirectional. The process of rectification is applied in signal detection.

Reflection The phenomenon of causing a propagating wave to change direction such that some of the wave does not continue to propagate forward.

Reflective mode One form of medical imaging (like diagnostic ultrasound) where a form of energy is transmitted into the patient and the reflected component is used to create the image. (In contrast with transmission modes such as X-ray which process the transmitting energy.)

Refraction The bending of a beam at an interface of two media. For refraction to occur, there must be a change in propagation speed and a an incident angle other than 0 degrees (other than normal).

Refraction artifacts Artifacts that result from refraction which results in lateral displacement of a structure in the image.

Refractive shadowing A drop out or decrease in intensity which results from refraction. Refractive shadowing generally occurs from the edges of specular reflectors, hence, refractive shadowing is often commonly referred to as edge shadowing.

Regurgitation The backward flow of blood through a valve.

Reject A means by which to ignore any signal or noise below a certain amplitude.

Relative refractory period The period shortly after the activation of a nerve fiber when partial repolarization has occurred and only a greater than normal stimulus can stimulate a second response.

Resistance *See impedance.*

Resolution The ability to discern a difference between structures spatially separated, temporally separated, or separated by contrast level. *See longitudinal resolution, lateral resolution, elevation resolution, temporal resolution, and contrast resolution.*

Reverberation An artifact caused by sound bouncing between multiple structures.

Reynold's number The ratio between the inertial forces and the viscous forces. The predictor of turbulence. A higher Reynold's predicts an increased probability of turbulence occurring.

Ring down When sound reverberates within an air sac the boundaries of the air sac are redrawn repeatedly creating a bright tail or "ring down." The term ring down also refers to the reverberation which commonly occurs at the surface of a transducer.

Ring time Another term for the pulse duration – the time for which the transducer rings.

Round-trip effect The fact that sound travels twice as far as the distance to the structure (down and back).

Sampling rate The frequency at which signals are "viewed". From the Nyquist criterion, the highest frequency detectable equals half the sample rate.

Saturation The non-linear state of electronics when the signals being processed become larger than the voltage rails of the electronics.

Scan conversion The process of taking data from the receiver and converting into data which can be displayed as an image. Essentially, the data from the receivers is in A-mode format. The scan converter converts the amplitudes into grayscale levels and then formats each successive line to create an image.

Scanned modality Modalities which transmit acoustic lines in different directions over time so as the present a scan (such as 2-D and color Doppler). Scanned modalities have lower risks of thermal bioeffects but are more likely to suffer mechanical bioeffects.

Sensitivity A measure of the ability to detect small signals. Sensitivity improves with better transducer designs, better electronic design, and using higher transmit power.

Sensitivity (statistical) The ability of a test to detect the presence of disease. Calculated as the true positives (TP) divided by the (TP) plus the false negatives (FN).

Sequencing Exciting groups of elements in a specific pattern to create a desired scan "pattern" or "shape."

Shadowing Caused by any form of attenuation stronger than the attenuation of the surrounding area.

Shock wave A wave from the result of a sudden impact or pulse of energy.

Side lobes The existence of lower pressure or weaker beams pointing off-axis that occur with single element transducers.

Signal Any phenomenon desired to be measured.

Signal-to-noise ratio The amplitude of the signal divided by the amplitude of the noise. A poor signal-to-noise ratio indicates that the image may not be of adequate quality for diagnosis. Methods of improving the signal-to-noise ratio include, using a lower transducer frequency, increasing the transmit power, appropriate setting of the transmit focus, use of different imaging planes, etc.

Simplified Law of Hemodynamics Expresses the fact that the pressure gradient is proportional to the volumetric flow and the resistance to flow.

Sine The trigonometric function for an acute angle is the ratio between the leg opposite the angle and the hypotenuse. On the unit circle, the sine is determined by drawing the angle and projecting the intersection of the angle and the unit circle onto the y-axis.

Snell's law The rule which predicts how much refraction occurs. When the incident angle does not equal the transmitted angle, refraction has occurred. The greater the difference between the incident angle and the transmit angle, the more refraction that has occurred.

Sound A mechanical, longitudinal wave which propagates through a series of compressions and rarefactions. A physical phenomenon that stimulates the sense of hearing.

Spatial Used as a modifier to refer to physical dimensions such as the spatial pulse length or the spatial average intensity.

Spatial average Determining the mean value over a cross-sectional area (in contrast with a temporal average which determines a mean over time).

Spatial averaging (processing) A processing technique which attempts to reduce random noise by subdividing an image into small local regions and averaging.

Spatial pulse length (SPL) The physical length a pulse occupies in a medium. The spatial pulse length equals the wavelength multiplied by the number of cycles in the pulse. Since the wavelength is medium dependent, the SPL is medium dependent.

Specificity The ability of a test to detect the absence of disease. The specificity is calculated as the true negatives (TN) divided by the TN plus the false positives (FP).

Speckle The appearance as tissue texture of random variations in signal strength that results from con-structive and destructive interference as tissue texture.

Spectral broadening The term generally used to refer to the broadened appearance of a spectrum. A spectrum may appear "broadened" because of varying velocities within the Doppler sample volume (also referred to as "spectral spread"), or as an artifact associated with varying angles between the flow and each of the transducer elements. As an artifact, spectral broadening can also be caused by excessive Doppler gain (sometimes referred to as blossoming artifact).

Spectral Doppler A subcategory of Doppler techniques which includes PW Doppler, CW Doppler, and HPRF Doppler which displays a range of frequency shifts (related to a range of velocities through the Doppler equation) on the vertical axis, and time on the horizontal axis. Unlike waveform Doppler systems, variations is flow characteristics are visualized such as spectral broadening, turbulence, and laminar flow.

Spectral mirroring A Doppler artifact which results from one of two sources: imperfect separation between the forward and reverse flow channels (In phase (I) and quadrature (Q) channels), or from an insonification angle close to 90 degrees such that the elements on one side of the center of the aperture are seeing flow at an angle less than 90 degrees while elements on the other side of the center line of the aperture are seeing flow at angles greater than 90 degrees. Since performing Doppler at 90 degrees is highly discouraged, most spectral mirroring is the results of signal bleeding across channels. This bleeding is the result of either poorly designed electronics or extraordinarily strong signals. The former cannot be compensated whereas the latter can be ameliorated by decreasing the transmit power.

Spectral window The open area between the spectrum and the baseline which indicates the presence of laminar flow at the location of the Doppler sample volume. The absence of a spectral window may or may not be an indication of turbulence.

Specular reflection Strong angularly dependent reflection in which the angle of incidence equals the angle of reflection. Mirror-like reflection.

Speed error artifacts The presentation of structures at incorrect depths as a result of a propagation velocity other than the presumed propagation velocity of 1540 m/sec.

Sphygmomanometer An instrument used to measure blood pressure.

Stable cavitation Occurs at energy levels lower than transient cavitation, when bubbles begin to expand and oscillate.

Steady flow Constant volumetric flow.

Stenosis A narrowing of a vessel or flow path that results in increased resistance to flow.

Stiffness Is a property of a material which indicates a lack of compressibility. As the stiffness of a material increases, the propagation velocity through the material increases.

Strip chart recorder A device used for recording measured electrical signals or biologically related electrical signals versus time.

Stroke volume (SV) The stroke volume is the amount of blood ejected from the heart on a beat-by-beat basis.

Supine Lying on one's back.

Sympathetic nervous system The part of the autonomic nervous system that exerts influence over the heart through catecholamines, adrenaline, and noradrenaline circulating in the blood.

Systole The phase of the cardiac cycle during which myocardial contraction occurs increasing circulatory pressure.

Systolic flow Blood flow that occurs during the systolic phase of the cardiac cycle.

Tamponade A condition involving compression of the heart caused by blood or fluid accumulation in the sac around the heart (pericardium).

Tangent One of the acute (less than 90°) angles of a right triangle that is found by dividing the length of the side opposite the angle by the length of the shorter of the two sides adjacent to the angle. The tangent of an angle is also equal to the sine of the angle divided by the cosine of the angle.

Temperature Degree of hot and coldness measured on a definite scale such as Celsius, Fahrenheit, or Kelvin.

Temporal distortion Any process which results in a change in the temporal accuracy of a signal such as time based "averaging" techniques to improve the signal-to-noise ratio. Temporal distortion also occurs naturally when the frame rate is inadequate relative to the dynamics of the structures or hemodynamics.

Temporal resolution The ability to distinguish dynamics, or changes, over time. Inadequate temporal resolution results in temporal distortion. The temporal resolution is commonly limited by the frame rate.

Thermal bioeffects Bioeffects caused by high temperature in a region causing metabolic breakdown and cellular damage.

Thermal index A predictive value which estimates the "maximum" temperature rise expected for the current imaging situation. See thermal indices.

Thermal indices Collective title for three different indices: Thermal Index in Soft Tissue (TIS,) Thermal Index in Bone (TIB,) and Thermal Index in Cranial Bone (TIC). The thermal indices are produced by mathematical models which take into account imaging and system parameters such as the transmit power, the focal depth, the imaging depth, the region of the body being scanned, etc. A thermal index of 1 implies that the model predicts a highest temperature rise expected to be 1 degree Celsius. It is possible for the thermal indices to underestimate the true temperature rise.

Threshold effect Implies that there is a limit or boundary above which a specific outcome is achieved, and below which a different outcome occurs.

Time The measured or measurable period during which an action, process, or condition exists or continues. (An ineffable parameter that we squander frequently and never have enough of.)

Tissue colorization The use of colorization maps to improve visualization when significant dynamic range must be preserved.

Total internal reflection The result of dramatic refraction at an interface between two structures such that no energy is transmitted across the interface, and all of the energy is reflected internally. The incident angle at which total internal reflection occurs is called the critical angle.

Transcranial Doppler A non-invasive Doppler technique to assess the major cerebral arteries through natural cranial windows.

Transcutaneous oxygen tension measurements (toPo2) These are used to measure the metabolic demand of the tissue. The values are a function of cutaneous blood flow, metabolic activity, oxyhemoglobin and oxygen diffusion of the tissue.

Transducer Anything which converts one form of energy to another form of energy. Ultrasound transducers use the piezoelectric effect to convert electropotential energy to mechanical energy and mechanical energy back to electropotential energy.

Transient cavitation The violent collapse of bubbles which generally occurs in the peak rarefactional phase of a sound wave. Transient cavitation generally results in extreme localized effects such as extraordinarily high temperatures.

Transmission mode One form of medical imaging (like x-ray) where the x-rays are transmitted through a patient and the change in transmission properties are used to produce an image. (In contrast to reflective modes like ultrasound which utilize the reflected energy instead of the transmitted energy.)

Transmit Refers to the process of driving a transducer with an electropotential (voltage) to produce energy to propagate into the patient. The transmit is the active phase of imaging which has the most direct consequence on signal strength as well as a significant impact on the risk of bioeffects.

Transmit frequency The frequency of operation. The transmit frequency is the frequency of the wave that is being produced to travel into the patient.

Transmit gain One of many terms which refers to the transmit power.

Transmit power On the electrical side of the transducer, the transmit power refers to the rate of delivering electrical energy to excite the transducer crystals (related to the voltage squared). On the acoustic side of the transducer the transmit power refers to rate of delivering acoustic energy to the patient.

Transmitter The part of the ultrasound system responsible for creating the transmit voltage and communicating the transmit energy to the transducer elements. The transmitter is also sometimes referred to as the pulser.

Transmural pressure The difference between the intravascular pressure and the surrounding tissue pressure. The transmural pressure is always reference from the inside of the vessel to the outside of the vessel. Therefore, when the intravascular pressure is higher than the surrounding tissue pressure, the vessel dilates the transmural pressure is said to be high. Conversely, when the intravascular pressure is lower than the surrounding tissue pressure, the vessel tends to collapse and the transmural pressure is referred to as low.

Transorbital Through the eye.

Transtemporal Through the temporal bone. One of the "windows" used for transcranial Doppler and transcranial imaging.

Transverse wave A wave which propagates by particle motion perpendicular to the wave propagation direction. A sine wave is a depiction of a transverse wave. Although sound is a longitudinal wave, in drawings sound is often depicted as a transverse wave because of the ease of drawing in contrast to a longitudinal wave.

Trigonometry A mathematical discipline that deals with the physical relationship between angles and dimensions of triangles.

Trophic Relating to nutrition.

True negative (TN) Implies that the test correctly predicts that there is no disease (the test predicts no disease when the gold standard predicts no disease).

True positive (TP) Implies that the test correctly predicts that there is disease (the test predicts disease when the gold standard predicts disease).

Turbulence A disturbed state of flow in which flow is virtually random in all directions. Turbulence occurs when conditions are high as dictated by the parameters that define the Reynold's number. Turbulence occurs primarily as an exit effect transitioning from a narrowed region of high kinetic energy to a broader region.

Turbulent flow When a fluid does not move in a "well behaved" manner nor in a uniform direction. When turbulence exists.

Ultrasound Any sound with frequencies above human hearing. (Typically referred to as above 20 kHz.)

Ultrasound transducer Converts electropotential energy (voltage) into mechanical vibration and mechanical vibrations into voltages through the piezoelectric effect. Ultrasound transducers act as both a transmitter and a receiver for sound waves.

Unit Reference for how a measurement of a physical quantity is made.

Unit circle A circle where the radius has a length of one or one unit.

Vacuum The absence of a medium.

Variable Mathematical or physical quantity that does not have a fixed numerical value. A physical parameter that can have a varying value.

Variable gain The ability to change the amount of amplification. User controllable gain as opposed to a fixed gain.

Vasoconstrict The decrease in diameter of a blood vessel, such as an arteriole, resulting in an increase in resistance and restricted blood flow to an organ or portion of the body.

Vasodilate The increase in diameter of a blood vessel, such as an arteriole, resulting in a decrease in resistance and an increase in blood flow to an organ or portion of the body.

Vector A quantity determined by magnitude and direction such as velocity.

Veins Any of the tubular branching vessels that carry blood from the capillaries toward the heart. Veins generally have valves to help prevent reflux of blood in the presence of gravity as well as thinner walls than the arteries.

Velocity A vector quantity which implies both the rate and direction of movement. For ultrasound, we generally presume straight travel such that the scalar quantity of speed can be used. As a result, the term velocity is commonly used to refer to speed. However, with respect to Doppler, since the flow direction is known, the value measured is truly velocity when direction is stated.

Venous capacitance A measure of the ability of the venous system to hold a change in volume per time. The venous system is highly capacitive, and is referred to as the capacitive component of the cardiovascular system.

Venous outflow *See maximum venous outflow.*

Venous refill time (VRT) Method using photophlethysmography to evaluate the presence and severity of venous insufficiency. Dorsiflexion maneuvers empty the cutaneous circulation and the recovery time is measured. Periods below 20 seconds indicate venous reflux.

Venous reflux testing Evaluates the presence and severity of venous insufficiency.

Venous resistance A measure of the resistivity to flow in the venous system.

Vertebral artery A large branch of the subclavian artery that ascends through the foramina in the transverse processes of each of the cervical vertebrae. The right and left vertebral arteries enter the cranium through the foramen magnum, and unite to form the basilar artery.

Viscosity The ratio of the shear stress to the shear rate of a fluid, or more simply stated: a measure of the resistance of a fluid to flow due to attraction of the molecules.

Voltage The difference in electrical potential that drives an electric current to flow from a high potential to a low potential.

Volume The amount of space occupied by a three-dimensional object as measured in cubic units.

Volumetric flow (Q) The amount or quantity which moves past a point per unit time. Volumetric flow is a volume per time such as liters per minute. The simplified law of hemodynamics and Poiseuille's law express the volumetric flow in terms of the pressure gradient and the resistance to flow. The continuity equation expresses the volumetric flow in terms of the average spatial velocity and the flow cross-sectional area.

Wall filter artifacts Artifacts that result from when the "clutter" signals are not adequately attenuated and the signal dynamic range becomes too large causing circuit saturation.

Wall filters A circuit or mathematical process that eliminates signals based on their frequency. For Doppler based techniques, wall filters are high pass filters which "pass" higher frequency signals and filter out lower frequency signals. Wall filters are critical to reduce the enormous dynamic range that exists with Doppler signals. Setting a wall filter too low results in circuit saturation. Setting wall filters too high can result in elimination of actual low velocity signals leading to incorrect hemodynamic conclusions.

Watts The unit for power.

Wavefront The front surface of the wave.

Wavelength The physical distance between cyclical wave peaks within a medium. The wavelength is determined by the propagation velocity divided by the operating frequency. The wavelength is one of the most critical parameters in ultrasound since the wavelength partially determines the axially resolution as well as affects the type of reflection that occurs.

Wavelength equation $\lambda = c / f$.

Waves Mechanism by which energy is conveyed from one place to another. For mechanically propagated waves this energy transfer occurs without the transference of matter.

Write zoom *See Acoustic zoom.*

Zoom *See acoustic and non-acoustic zoom.*

Index

Appendix M • Study Suggestions and CME Materials

STUDY SUGGESTIONS

For the physicians, sonographers, and technologists using this text as an independent learning program to prepare for credentialing and board exams, we have included study suggestions and an outline to help structure your studying. Please proceed at a pace that is comfortable for you. In order to receive continuing medical education credits (CME's), you must complete the conceptual questions, practice exams and the final exam. Mail or fax the final exam answer sheet with a completed evaluation to:

Pegasus Lectures, Inc.
PO Box 157   Forney, TX 75126
Tel: 972-564-3056   Fax: 972-552-9186

1. First read the section in Volume II: Appendix C entitled "Developing a Test Taking Strategy."

2. Take the Ultrasound Physics Practice Exam in Appendix E. (We suggest that you write the answers for the practice exam in a notebook or on scrap paper so that the exam can be re-taken after studying.)

3. Take the Hemodynamics Practice Exam in Appendix F. Vascular physics students should complete the entire exam. Ultrasound students and cardiovascular students should complete questions 1-30.

4. Take the exam as an actual exam.
   - Leave notes closed.
   - Make intelligent guesses on questions you don't know. Indicate with asterisks those questions on which you guessed.
   - Give yourself two uninterrupted hours, (one minute per question). Concentration plays a big role in exam success.
   - After correcting the exam, review all questions, not just the ones you answered incorrectly. Make certain you understand what you did wrong.

5. Pace yourself for the study materials. If you try to read all of the material in one day, you will most likely feel as if you are drowning in information.
   - Focus on the central concepts of each section.
   - Study the examples. Try to do all the examples yourself.
   - Complete the exercises on the same day that you read the associated section.
   - Write down any unresolved questions.
   - Treat the exercises as mini exams. Do not refer to your notes until after correcting your work. Then review every question, not just those done incorrectly.
   - Close your notes and answer the conceptual questions at the end of each chapter. Review those areas on which you had difficulty.

6. Don't worry! You will not understand everything the first time through. Try to review specific areas of weakness every few days.

7. After finishing the study material, take the exam again. This time try to get into the mind of the person who wrote the questions. "Why is this question being asked? What concept is being tested?" After correcting the exam, again review all questions with extra focus on those questions answered incorrectly.

ULTRASOUND PHYSICS CHECKLIST

This checklist is designed to provide a systematic method of preparing for your credentialing exam. Feel free to shorten or lengthen the schedule as necessary to fit your personal time frame for exam preparation.

WEEK	◆	**PREPARATION**	✓
WEEK 1	◆	Read "Developing a Test Taking Strategy"- Volume II: Appendix C	☐
	◆	Take Ultrasound Physics Practice Exam - Volume II: Appendix E	☐
	◆	Review Ultrasound Physics Exam questions	☐
	◆	Begin Chapter 1 (Mathematics)	☐
WEEK 2	◆	Complete Chapter 1	☐
	◆	Begin Chapter 2 (Waves)	☐
	◆	Take Hemodynamics Practice Exam - Volume II: Appendix F (Questions 1-30)	☐
	◆	Review all Hemodynamics Practice Exam questions	☐
WEEK 3	◆	Review Chapter 1	☐
	◆	Complete Chapter 2	☐
	◆	Complete Chapter 3 (Attenuation)	☐
	◆	Complete Chapter 12 (Fluid Dynamics)	☐
WEEK 4	◆	Review Chapters 1, 2, 3 & 12	☐
	◆	Complete Chapter 4 (Pulsed Wave)	☐
	◆	Complete Chapter 5 (Transducers)	☐
	◆	Complete Chapter 13 (Hemodynamics)	☐
WEEK 5	◆	Review Chapters 1-5 & 12-13	☐
	◆	Complete Chapter 6 (System Operation)	☐
	◆	Complete Chapter 7 (Doppler)	☐
	◆	Complete Chapter 8 (Artifacts)	☐
WEEK 6	◆	Review Chapters 1-8 & 12-13	☐
	◆	Complete Chapter 9 (Bioeffects)	☐
	◆	Complete Chapter 10 (Contrast and Harmonics)	☐
	◆	Complete Chapter 11 (Quality Assurance)	☐
WEEK 7	◆	Review Chapters 1-13	☐
	◆	Re-take the Ultrasound Physics Practice Exam	☐
	◆	Re-take Hemodynamics Practice Exam (Questions 1-30)	☐
	◆	Get some well-deserved rest	☐

VASCULAR PHYSICS CHECKLIST

This checklist is designed to provide a systematic method of preparing for your credentialing exam. Feel free to shorten or lengthen the schedule as necessary to fit your personal time frame for exam preparation.

WEEK	◆	**PREPARATION**	✓
WEEK 1	◆	Read "Developing a Test Taking Strategy"- Volume II: Appendix C	☐
	◆	Take Ultrasound Physics Practice Exam - Volume II: Appendix E	☐
	◆	Review Ultrasound Physics Practice Exam questions	☐
	◆	Begin Chapter 1 (Mathematics)	☐
WEEK 2	◆	Complete Chapter 1	☐
	◆	Begin Chapter 2 (Waves)	☐
	◆	Take Hemodynamics Practice Exam - Volume II: Appendix F	☐
	◆	Review all Hemodynamics Practice Exam questions	☐
WEEK 3	◆	Review Chapter 1	☐
	◆	Complete Chapter 2	☐
	◆	Complete Chapter 3 (Attenuation)	☐
	◆	Complete Chapter 12 (Fluid Dynamics)	☐
WEEK 4	◆	Review Chapters 1, 2, 3 & 12	☐
	◆	Complete Chapter 4 (Pulsed Wave)	☐
	◆	Complete Chapter 5 (Transducers)	☐
	◆	Complete Chapter 13 (Hemodynamics)	☐
WEEK 5	◆	Review Chapters 1-5 & 12-13	☐
	◆	Complete Chapter 6 (System Operation)	☐
	◆	Complete Chapter 7 (Doppler)	☐
	◆	Complete Chapter 8 (Artifacts)	☐
WEEK 6	◆	Review Chapters 1-8 & 12-13	☐
	◆	Complete Chapter 9 (Bioeffects)	☐
	◆	Complete Chapter 10 (Contrast and Harmonics)	☐
	◆	Complete Chapter 11 (Quality Assurance)	☐
	◆	Complete Vascular Principles: Volume II, Appendix A	☐
WEEK 7	◆	Review Chapters 1-13 and Appendix A: Vascular Principles	☐
	◆	Re-take the Ultrasound Physics Practice Exam	☐
	◆	Re-take Hemodynamics Practice Exam	☐
	◆	Get some well-deserved rest	☐

CARDIOVASCULAR PHYSICS CHECKLIST

This checklist is designed to provide a systematic method of preparing for your credentialing exam. Feel free to shorten or lengthen the schedule as necessary to fit your personal time frame for exam preparation.

WEEK	◆	**PREPARATION**	✓
WEEK 1	◆	Read "Developing a Test Taking Strategy"- Volume II: Appendix C	☐
	◆	Take Ultrasound Physics Practice Exam - Volume II: Appendix E	☐
	◆	Review Ultrasound Physics Practice Exam questions	☐
	◆	Begin Chapter 1 (Mathematics)	☐
WEEK 2	◆	Complete Chapter 1	☐
	◆	Begin Chapter 2 (Waves)	☐
	◆	Take Hemodynamics Practice Exam - Volume II: Appendix F (Questions 1-30)	☐
	◆	Review all Hemodynamics Practice Exam questions	☐
WEEK 3	◆	Review Chapter 1	☐
	◆	Complete Chapter 2	☐
	◆	Complete Chapter 3 (Attenuation)	☐
	◆	Complete Chapter 12 (Fluid Dynamics)	☐
WEEK 4	◆	Review Chapters 1, 2, 3 & 12	☐
	◆	Complete Chapter 4 (Pulsed Wave)	☐
	◆	Complete Chapter 5 (Transducers)	☐
	◆	Complete Chapter 13 (Hemodynamics)	☐
WEEK 5	◆	Review Chapters 1-5 & 12-13	☐
	◆	Complete Chapter 6 (System Operation)	☐
	◆	Complete Chapter 7 (Doppler)	☐
	◆	Complete Chapter 8 (Artifacts)	☐
WEEK 6	◆	Review Chapters 1-8 & 12-13	☐
	◆	Complete Chapter 9 (Bioeffects)	☐
	◆	Complete Chapter 10 (Contrast and Harmonics)	☐
	◆	Complete Chapter 11 (Quality Assurance)	☐
	◆	Complete Cardiovascular Principles: Volume II, Appendix B	☐
WEEK 7	◆	Review Chapters 1-13 and Appendix B: Cardiovascular Principles	☐
	◆	Re-take the Ultrasound Physics Practice Exam	☐
	◆	Re-take Hemodynamics Practice Exam (Questions 1-30)	☐
	◆	Get some well-deserved rest	☐

**Pegasus Lectures Physics and Instrumentation
Independent Learning Program**

*Jointly Sponsored by A. Webb Roberts Center for Continuing Medical Education of
Baylor Health Care System, Dallas
and Pegasus Lectures, Inc.*

CME ENDURING MATERIAL INFORMATION

Faculty

Frank Miele, MSEE
President, Pegasus Lectures, Inc.

Frank graduated cum laude from Dartmouth College with a triple major in physics, mathematics, and engineering. While at Dartmouth, he was a Proctor Scholar and received citations for academic excellence in comparative literature, atomic physics and quantum mechanics, and real analysis. After completing his graduate work, Frank was awarded the Ruth Goodrich Prize for Academic Excellence. After co-teaching a course in digital electronics at Dartmouth, Frank was a research and design engineer and project leader, designing ultrasound equipment and electronics for more than ten years. In that role, Frank designed the hardware for the first parallel processing color Doppler system, created a Doppler system platform, designed HPRF Doppler, created the first released adaptive ultrasound processing technique, designed transcranial Doppler and transcranial imaging, worked on multiple transducer project teams, and performed extensive clinical trial testing and research.

Frank has been the vice president of Research & Development and chief scientist for a medical device company investigating ultrasound related hemodynamic based measurements. As a researcher and designer of ultrasound, he has lectured across the country to sonographers, physicians, engineers, and students on myriad topics. Frank has authored the Ultrasound & Physics Instrumentation Independent Learning Program, produced multiple educational videos, created exam simulation programs, as well as created the analysis algorithm method and apparatus for evaluating educational performance (patent pending). Frank has served as an author and Co-Chief editor for the ASCeXAM Simulation Review CD in conjunction with the American Society of Echocardiography. He has also served on the faculty for the Society of Vascular Ultrasound and Society of Vascular Surgery and is credited with several ultrasound and medical device patents, trade secrets, and publications.

Purpose and Target Audience

This activity is designed to familiarize physicians and sonographers with the physics and instrumentation concepts employed in diagnostic ultrasound and provide a method to prepare for ultrasound physics credentialing exams and/or accreditation. It will be of interest to, but not limited to, radiologists, cardiologists, neurologists, vascular surgeons, cardiovascular surgeons, anesthesiologists, and/or physicians providing interpretation of diagnostic ultrasound, preparing for accreditation, and/or desiring to improve their understanding of ultrasound physics.

Medium

Printed text
CD

Objectives

Upon completion of the activity, the participant should be able to:

- Define areas of strengths and weaknesses in their understanding of ultrasound physics.
- Comprehend the effect of system controls and transducer parameters on the diagnostic quality of an ultrasound image.
- Demonstrate improved understanding of ultrasound physics and how physics can affect the integrity of a diagnostic image.
- Demonstrate improved interpretative skills for diagnostic ultrasound, Doppler and hemodynamic variables.
- Demonstrate improved preparation for the ultrasound physics credentialing exam.

CME Credit

This activity has been planned an implemented in accordance with the Essential Areas and policies of the Accreditation Council for Continuing Medical Education (ACCME) through the joint sponsorship of the A. Webb Roberts Center for Continuing Medical Education of the Baylor Health Care System, Dallas and Pegasus Lectures, Inc.

The A. Webb Roberts Center for Continuing Medical Education of Baylor Health Care System, Dallas designates this educational activity for a maximum of 35 category 1 credits toward the AMA Physician's Recognition Award. Each physician should claim only those credits that he/she actually spent in the activity.

The A. Webb Roberts Center for Continuing Education of Baylor Health Care System, Dallas is accredited by the ACCME to provide continuing medical education for physicians.

Faculty Disclosure

Frank Miele is the president of Pegasus Lectures, Inc. and owner of Miele Enterprises, LLC.

No unlabeled or investigational uses of a product or medical device are addressed in this CME activity.

Instructions

Participants must:
1. Read Volumes I & II of Ultrasound Physics and Instrumentation
2. Complete conceptual questions and exercises within Volumes I & II
   (Refer to study suggestions in Vol. II, Appendix M)
3. Complete the final exam and evaluation

Final Exam, Evaluation and Processing Fee

At the conclusion of this activity, participants must complete the final exam and the evaluation. A completed evaluation form must accompany the final exam. Please indicate on the evaluation form if you are applying for AMA/PRA Category 1 credit or SDMS CME credit and if you are a licensed physician or not. There is a $30 processing fee for AMA/PRA category 1 credit. **The check for AMA/PRA credit should be made payable to: A. Webb Roberts Center.** Participants should send the original (no copies accepted) final exam for scoring, the processing fee, the evaluation and any correspondence to:

Pegasus Lectures, Inc.
PO Box 157
Forney, TX 75126

Tel: 972.564.3056
Fax: 972.552.9186

NOTE: Participants must achieve a **75% pass rate** on the final exam to be awarded AMA/PRA CME credit. Feedback on exam scores will be provided. A CME certificate will be mailed directly to the participant from the **A. Webb Roberts Center** for Continuing Medical Education of Baylor Health Care System, Dallas.

Date of Original Release: May 2001
Date of Most Recent Update: July 2007
Date of Expiration: July 2010

Estimated time to complete the educational activity: 35 hours

This independent learning educational activity has been approved for 35.0 hours of SDMS CME credit. Each participant should claim only those hours of credit that he/she actually spent in the educational activity.

At the conclusion of this activity participants should complete the final exam and evaluation. A completed evaluation form must accompany the final exam. *Please indicate on the evaluation form if you are applying for AMA/PRA Category 1 credit or SDMS CME credit.* Participants should send the final exam, evaluation and any correspondence to:

Pegasus Lectures, Inc.
PO Box 157
Forney, TX 75126

Tel: 972-564-3056
Fax: 972-552-9186

Participants must achieve a 75% pass rate on the final exam to be awarded CME credit. A CME certificate will be mailed directly to the participant from Pegasus Lectures, Inc.

EVALUATION
Pegasus Lectures:
Ultrasound Physics and Instrumentation Independent Learning Program - Enduring Material

NAME: (PRINT) _____

Please evaluate the following on a scale of A to C: *A = Excellent*   *B = Average*   *C = Poor*

1.   A   B   C   The need for the activity was met.
2.   A   B   C   The overall activity met the stated objectives.
3.   A   B   C   Objectives were relevant to the overall purpose of the program:
to familiarize physicians and sonographers with the physics and instrumentation concepts employed in diagnostic ultrasound and provide a method to prepare for the ultrasound physics certification exam.
4.   A   B   C   The teaching methods utilized were effective in facilitated learning.
5.   A   B   C   I would recommend this program to colleagues.
6.   A   B   C   The material will be of direct value in my practice.

Indicate extent to which the author manifested knowledge of the subject.
7.   A   B   C   Frank Miele

Indicate extent to which the author demonstrated effective teaching ability.
8.   A   B   C   Frank Miele

Please circle Yes or No:
9.   Yes   No   The activity was free from commercial bias.
If not, please explain:

10.   Yes   No   All recommendations involving clinical medicine are based on evidence that is accepted within the profession of medicine as adequate justification for their indications and contraindications in the care of patients.

11.   Yes   No   All scientific research referred to, reported or used in support or justification of patient care recommendation conforms to the generally accepted standards for experimental design, data collection and analysis.

12.   Yes   No   Content of presentations was scientifically rigorous, balanced and unbiased.
If not, please explain:

13.   Yes   No   This activity has enhanced my professional effectiveness.

14.   Yes   No   I will apply the knowledge/skills I learned.

Indicate whether you were able to achieve the course objective by marking: **True** or **False**

15.   T   F   Define areas of strengths and weaknesses in your understanding of ultrasound physics.

16.   T   F   Demonstrate improved understanding of ultrasound physics and how physics affects the integrity of a diagnostic image.

17.   T   F   Comprehend the effect of system controls and transducer parameters on the diagnostic quality of an ultrasound image.

18.   T   F   Demonstrate improved interpretive skills for diagnostic ultrasound, Doppler, and hemodynamic variables.

19.　T　　F　　　　Demonstrate improved preparation for the ultrasound physics credentialing examination.

20.　T　　F　　　　Do you believe that any of these presentations were promotional and not educational? If yes, please explain.

21. How could this program be improved?

22. What are your professional continuing educational needs/wants?

23. Suggestions for future programs:

24. General comments:

In order to receive your continuing education credit, you must return this completed form.

Please indicate which type of CME you wish to receive:

❑　　SDMS CME
❑　　AMA PRA Category 1 CME credit

To receive an AMA/PRA certificate, you must check the following options:

❑　I am a US licensed physician:　　❑ MD　❑ DO　　(You will receive a CME certificate.)
❑　I am not a US licensed physician.　　　　　　　(You will receive a verification of participation certificate.)

There is a processing fee of $30 for AMA PRA Category 1 credit. *Make your check payable to A. Webb Roberts Center.*

Mail this evaluation and applicable fees to:　　*Pegasus Lectures, Inc., PO Box 157, Forney, TX 75126*
　　　　　　　　　　　　　　　　　　　　　　　Tel: 972 564 3056　　　　　　Fax: 972 552 9186

Instructions:
1. Select the best answer and record your choice on the answer sheet.
2. Mail or fax the <u>original</u> answer sheet (no copies accepted) to:

> Pegasus Lectures, Inc.
> PO Box 157
> Forney, TX 75126
> Tel: 972.564.3056
> Fax: 972.552.9186

1)   What is the propagation speed of sound in soft tissue?
   - a)   1.560 m/sec
   - b)   1.540 km/sec
   - c)   15.60 m/sec
   - d)   1540 cm/sec
   - e)   1560 cm/sec

2)   A factor of 2 in amplitude and a factor of 2 in power are equivalent to how many dB, respectively?
   - a)   2 dB, 4 dB
   - b)   3 dB, 6 dB
   - c)   6 dB, 12 dB
   - d)   6 dB, 3 dB
   - e)   4 dB, 2 dB

3)   The cosine and the sine of what angle are equal?
   - a)   0°
   - b)   30°
   - c)   45°
   - d)   60°
   - e)   90°

4)   How much time does it take to image a structure at 1 cm deep?
   - a)   13 μsec
   - b)   13 msec
   - c)   6.5 μsec
   - d)   6.5 msec
   - e)   65 μsec

5)   What is the binary representation of the number 17?
   - a)   0010000
   - b)   0001000
   - c)   0001101
   - d)   0010001
   - e)   0001110

6) **The criterion which states that to accurately reconstruct the frequency content of a signal, you must sample at least twice as fast as the highest frequency content of that signal is called**
   a)   constructive Interference.
   b)   frequency interference.
   c)   Nyquist .
   d)   Snell's law.
   e)   analog to digital conversion rule.

7) **Sound is a**
   a)   longitudinal, mechanical wave.
   b)   longitudinal, transverse wave.
   c)   transverse, mechanical.
   d)   electromagnetic, longitudinal.
   e)   transverse, electromagnetic.

8) **Which is the correct definition and units for density?**
   a)   mass/volume, kg/m^3
   b)   volume/mass, m^3/kg
   c)   mass * volume, kg/m
   d)   volume/mass, kg/ m^3
   e)   mass/volume, m$^{3/}$kg

9) **What is the period for a 2 MHz wave?**
   a)   0.5 μsec
   b)   0.5 msec
   c)   2 μsec
   d)   2 msec
   e)   0.05 μsec

10) **The relationship between the wavelength, the frequency, and the propagation velocity is**
   a) λ is proportional to c, and inversely proportional to f.
   b) λ is proportional to f, and inversely proportional to c.
   c) λ is proportional to c, and proportional to f.
   d) λ is inversely proportional to c, and inversely proportional to f.
   e) λ is proportional to c, and proportional to f^2.

11) **Which of the following statements is true?**
   a)   Frequency and amplitude are disjoint. The frequency corresponds to pitch, whereas the amplitude corresponds to volume.
   b)   Frequency and amplitude are completely equivalent. The frequency corresponds to pitch, whereas the amplitude corresponds to volume.
   c)   Frequency and amplitude are similar. High frequencies generally have high amplitudes.
   d)   Frequency and amplitude are similar. High frequencies generally have low amplitudes.
   e)   Frequency and amplitude are completely disjoint. The frequency corresponds to volume, whereas the amplitude corresponds to pitch.

12) **Which of the following relational statements is true?**
   a)   Intensity $\propto$ power $\propto$ amplitude.
   b)   Intensity $\propto$ power $\propto$ 1/amplitude.
   c)   Intensity $\propto$ power^2 $\propto$ amplitude.
   d)   Intensity $\propto$ power^2 $\propto$ amplitude^2.
   e)   Intensity $\propto$ power $\propto$ amplitude^2.

13) **Which of the following statements about absorption is true?**
   a)   Absorption is the dominant factor of attenuation in bone.
   b)   Absorption decreases with increasing frequency.
   c)   Absorption increase with decreasing frequency.
   d)   Absorption increases exponentially with increasing frequency.
   e)   Absorption principally occurs only at deeper depths.

14) **Snell's law implies that refraction**
   a)   occurs at any incident angle.
   b)   occurs mostly at larger incident angles.
   c)   occurs mostly at smaller incident angles.
   d)   only occurs at normal incident angles.
   e)   occurs only when the incident angle is $0°$.

15) **The amount of reflection is at an interface of two mediums is determined by**
   a)   Snell's law.
   b)   the change in propagation velocities.
   c)   the change in densities.
   d)   the acoustic impedance of the first medium.
   e)   the acoustic impedance mismatch between the two mediums.

16) **The type of reflection which occurs at an interface at which the surface is large and smooth relative to the wavelength is called**
   a)   scattering.
   b)   specular.
   c)   Rayleigh.
   d)   normal.
   e)   refraction.

17) **The approximate attenuation rate for sound in soft tissue is**
   a)   1 dB/cm-MHz.
   b)   0.5 dB/cm.
   c)   0.5 dB/cm-MHz.
   d)   1 dB/cm.
   e)   1 dB/MHz.

18) **The pulse duration is the time for a pulse to occur and equals the**
   a)   (period) * (wavelength).
   b)   (wavelength) * (# of cycles per pulse).
   c)   (period) * (# of cycles per pulse).
   d)   (frequency) * (wavelength).
   e)   (period) * (frequency).

19) One way of decreasing the pulse duration, thereby decreasing the spatial pulse length, improving longitudinal resolution is by
   a) using a thicker crystal.
   b) using a matching layer.
   c) using a larger diameter crystal.
   d) using a backing material.
   e) all of the above.

20) The PRF is the reciprocal of the
   a) PD.
   b) SPL.
   c) frequency.
   d) PRP.
   e) frame rate.

21) Which of the following parameters does not affect the frame rate?
   a) depth
   b) propagation speed of sound in tissue
   c) number of lines per frame
   d) transmit frequency
   e) PRF

22) The duty factor ratio is defined as
   a) PD/PRP.
   b) PRF/PRP.
   c) PRP/PRF.
   d) PRF/PD.
   e) PD/PRF.

23) Which of the following is the correct definition of the I_{SPTA}?
   a) spectral, pulse, temporal, acoustic
   b) spatial pulse, thermal average
   c) safety peak, thermal, acoustic
   d) spatial peak, temporal average
   e) spatial pulse, thermal average

24) The quality factor of a transducer is defined as
   a) 1/fractional bandwidth.
   b) 1/operating frequency.
   c) 1/bandwidth.
   d) 1/period.
   e) 1/center frequency.

25) The point at which piezoelectric materials lose piezoelectric properties is called
   a) the dielectric breakdown point.
   b) the Curie temperature.
   c) poling.
   d) mechanical deformation.
   e) destructive interference.

26) **The transducer type which has a variable focus for both the lateral and elevation planes is**
   a)   pedof (Doppler only).
   b)   linear phased array.
   c)   curved-linear array.
   d)   sector phased array.
   e)   annular array.

27) **The Near Zone Length (NZL) is**
   a)   proportional to the crystal diameter squared.
   b)   inversely proportional to the crystal diameter squared.
   c)   proportional to the operating frequency squared.
   d)   inversely proportional to the operating frequency.
   e)   proportional to the crystal diameter.

28) **Doubling the diameter causes**
   a)   the operating frequency to double.
   b)   the operating frequency to halve.
   c)   the focal depth to increase by a factor of two.
   d)   the focal depth to decrease by a factor of two.
   e)   the focal depth to increase by a factor of four.

29) **Lateral resolution is determined by the _____ , and is best at _____ .**
   a)   SPL, twice the NZL.
   b)   beamwidth, the focus.
   c)   SPL, the focus.
   d)   beamwidth, twice the NZL.
   e)   SPL, in the near-field.

30) **Which of the following is not a standard receiver function of an ultrasound system?**
   a)   amplification
   b)   demodulation
   c)   Fast Fourier Transform (FFT)
   d)   rejection
   e)   compensation

31) **Dynamic range refers to**
   a)   the range of frequency over which a transducer can operate
   b)   the range of times over which a system can respond to signal
   c)   the ratio of the maximum to the minimum of any quantity
   d)   the temporal resolution
   e)   the rate at which images can be acquired

32) **Any unwanted signal is classified as**
   a)   clutter
   b)   noise
   c)   signal to noise ratio
   d)   rejection
   e)   artifact

33) **The principle which helps predict how a series of spherical wavefronts will construct to predict the wavefronts position over time is called**
    a)   Snell's law.
    b)   Huygen's principle.
    c)   Doppler principle.
    d)   the law of superposition.
    e)   spherical wavefront theory.

34) **Which resolution determines the ability to distinguish dynamics or changes over time?**
    a)   temporal
    b)   lateral
    c)   detail
    d)   dynamic
    e)   contract

35) **The Doppler shift increases with all of the following except**
    a)   decreasing propagation speed.
    b)   increasing transmit frequency.
    c)   increasing blood velocity.
    d)   increasing transmit amplitude.
    e)   decreasing insonification angle relative to $90°$.

36) **The wall filters are used to eliminate**
    a)   the high frequency high amplitude signals.
    b)   all high frequency signals.
    c)   the low frequency signals.
    d)   the low amplitude signals.
    e)   the Doppler shifted signals.

37) **The mathematical technique for separating a spectrum into its individual frequency components is called**
    a)   spectral regression.
    b)   separation anxiety transform.
    c)   an FFT.
    d)   a PRF
    e)   spectral integral.

38) **One advantage of CW over PW Doppler is**
    a)   higher detectable velocities.
    b)   better range specificity.
    c)   better sensitivity.
    d)   more accurate peak velocity measurements.
    e)   less risk of thermal bioeffects.

39) **Color Doppler yields**
    a)   peak velocity estimates.
    b)   peak flow estimates.
    c)   mean flow estimates.
    d)   mean velocity estimates.
    e)   median velocity estimates.

40) **The artifact which can result in the appearance of a strongly reflecting structure repeating multiple times at uniform increments of depth is called**

    a)   axial resolution
    b)   mirror image
    c)   multi-path
    d)   reverberation
    e)   dead zone

41) **If the actual propagation speed through a medium is 2,050 m/sec, and the system assumes soft tissue**

    a)   the returning echoes will be brighter than normal
    b)   the returning echoes will be weaker than normal
    c)   structures will appear incorrectly too deep
    d)   structures will appear incorrectly too shallow
    e)   structures will appear brighter and incorrectly too deep

42) **Shadowing is caused by**

    a)   strong reflectors
    b)   weak absorbers
    c)   high transmission
    d)   weak reflectors
    e)   too low transmit power

43) **Aliasing occurs**

    a)   when the Doppler signals are too weak
    b)   with very high PRF's
    c)   most often in CW
    d)   when the Nyquist criterion is violated
    e)   when the wall filters are set too low

44) **The violent collapse of cells and bubbles caused by the energy of the wave is called**

    a)   stable cavitation
    b)   thermal breakdown
    c)   transient cavitation
    d)   mechanical cavitation
    e)   thermal cavitation

45) **The _____ is a better indicator of cavitation related adverse effects than the derated spatial peak pulse average intensity, I_{SPTA}.**

    a) I_{SPTP}
    b)   MI
    c) I_{SATA}
    d) I_{SATP}
    e) I_{m}

46) **There have been no recorded biological effects observed due to temperatures less than or equal to _____ above normal for exposure duration up to 50 hours.**
   a) $1° C$
   b) $1° F$
   c) $2° C$
   d) $2° F$
   e) $10° F$

47) **Regarding in-vitro studies, the AIUM's position is that in-vitro studies**
   a)   are valuable for designing appropriate in vivo studies.
   b)   are relatively useless.
   c)   present great risk to the patient.
   d)   is a good correlation between in vitro studies and bioeffects.
   e)   are directly applicable to human tissue.

48) **The area at the top of an image which cannot be reproduced accurately due to ring down is called**
   a)   grating lobes.
   b)   sidelobes.
   c)   the dead zone.
   d)   near field.
   e)   acoustic mismatch zone.

49) **A string phantom is useful for measuring all of the following parameters except**
   a)   peak velocity.
   b)   spectral broadening.
   c)   accurate PW gate depth accuracy.
   d)   Doppler sensitivity.
   e)   accurate PW gate size.

50) **If the accuracy of a test is 84%, which of the following scenarios is statistically possible?**
   a)   Sensitivity = 82%, Specificity = 85%, PPV = 80%, NPV = 86%
   b)   Sensitivity = 92%, Specificity = 84%, PPV = 84%, NPV = 82%
   c)   Sensitivity = 81%, Specificity = 82%, PPV = 82%, NPV = 99%
   d)   Sensitivity = 81%, Specificity = 83%, PPV = 86%, NPV = 99%
   e)   Sensitivity = 86%, Specificity = 82%, PPV = 83%, NPV = 87%

Mail or fax the <u>original</u> final exam answer sheet (no copies accepted)
with a completed evaluation form to:

Pegasus Lectures, Inc.
PO Box 157
Forney, Texas 75126
Tel: 972.564.3056
Fax: 972.552.9186

PHYSICS INDEPENDENT LEARNING PROGRAM
ANSWER SHEET

1. A ○   B ○   C ○   D ○   E ○
2. A ○   B ○   C ○   D ○   E ○
3. A ○   B ○   C ○   D ○   E ○
4. A ○   B ○   C ○   D ○   E ○
5. A ○   B ○   C ○   D ○   E ○
6. A ○   B ○   C ○   D ○   E ○
7. A ○   B ○   C ○   D ○   E ○
8. A ○   B ○   C ○   D ○   E ○
9. A ○   B ○   C ○   D ○   E ○
10. A ○   B ○   C ○   D ○   E ○
11. A ○   B ○   C ○   D ○   E ○
12. A ○   B ○   C ○   D ○   E ○
13. A ○   B ○   C ○   D ○   E ○
14. A ○   B ○   C ○   D ○   E ○
15. A ○   B ○   C ○   D ○   E ○
16. A ○   B ○   C ○   D ○   E ○
17. A ○   B ○   C ○   D ○   E ○
18. A ○   B ○   C ○   D ○   E ○
19. A ○   B ○   C ○   D ○   E ○
20. A ○   B ○   C ○   D ○   E ○
21. A ○   B ○   C ○   D ○   E ○
22. A ○   B ○   C ○   D ○   E ○
23. A ○   B ○   C ○   D ○   E ○
24. A ○   B ○   C ○   D ○   E ○
25. A ○   B ○   C ○   D ○   E ○

Name _____

Address _____

City _____ St _____ Zip _____

Daytime telephone _____

Evening telephone _____

Fax number _____

Last Four Digits of SS# _____

Total hours to complete workbook _____

Office Use Only

Date Received _____

Date
Graded _____

Score _____ / 50 _____ % ____

Certificate Mailed _____

26. A ○   B ○   C ○   D ○   E ○

27. A ○   B ○   C ○   D ○   E ○

28. A ○   B ○   C ○   D ○   E ○

29. A ○   B ○   C ○   D ○   E ○

30. A ○   B ○   C ○   D ○   E ○

31. A ○   B ○   C ○   D ○   E ○

32. A ○   B ○   C ○   D ○   E ○

33. A ○   B ○   C ○   D ○   E ○

34. A ○   B ○   C ○   D ○   E ○

35. A ○   B ○   C ○   D ○   E ○

36. A ○   B ○   C ○   D ○   E ○

37. A ○   B ○   C ○   D ○   E ○

38. A ○   B ○   C ○   D ○   E ○

39. A ○   B ○   C ○   D ○   E ○

40. A ○   B ○   C ○   D ○   E ○

41. A ○   B ○   C ○   D ○   E ○

42. A ○   B ○   C ○   D ○   E ○

43. A ○   B ○   C ○   D ○   E ○

44. A ○   B ○   C ○   D ○   E ○

45. A ○   B ○   C ○   D ○   E ○

46. A ○   B ○   C ○   D ○   E ○

47. A ○   B ○   C ○   D ○   E ○

Name (Print) _____

48. A ○   B ○   C ○   D ○   E ○

Signature _____

49. A ○   B ○   C ○   D ○   E ○

Date exam
completed _____

50. A ○   B ○   C ○   D ○   E ○

Abbreviations: Physical Units

Related to time:

P or T	Period (seconds)
PD	Pulse duration (the time for which the transmit pulse lasts)
PRP	Pulse repetition period (the time to transmit and receive an acoustic line of data)
Frame time	The time required to build up a frame = the time per acoustic line multiplied the total number of lines in the frame.

Related to frequency:

f	Frequency (Hz)
f₀	Operating or transmit frequency of a transducer (for diagnostic ultrasound 2-12 MHz common)
PRF	Pulse repetition frequency = 1/PRP (typically less than 10 kHz)
Frame rate	The reciprocal of the frame time (typically less than 100 Hz)
Hz	Hertz = 1 cycle/second

Various parameters that have units of amplitude:

V	Volts: unit of electromotive force
m	Meters: unit of distance (metric system)
Z	Rayls: unit of acoustic impedance
R	Resistance, either electrical or to fluid flow
P	Pressure: mmHg, atm, dynes/cm^2, kg/m^2, etc.,: unit of pressure (*not to be confused with P for period or P for power)

Related to power:

P	Power: units of Watts (*not to be confused with P for period or P for pressure)
W	Watts
I	Intensity = power/area: units of W/m^2
dB	Decibels: a logarithmic power ratio

Related to distance:

d	Distance (*not to be confused with D or d for diameter)
λ	Lambda: wavelength which has units of distance
SPL	Spatial Pulse Length
NZL	The distance from the transducer face to the focus of the transducer

Related to measure and circular dimensions:

ρ	Density = mass/volume = kg/ m^3
r	Radius of a circle: units of distance
d	Diameter of a circle = 2 • radius: units of distance
A	Area: units of m^2
Vol	Volume: units of m^3
Q	Volumetric flow: volume per time, or m^3/sec

Related to motion:

      r   The general term usually used in the distance equation for the velocity. (*not to be confused with r for radius)

      v   Velocity of blood: units of m/sec

      c   Propagation speed of sound: units of m/sec

Related to hemodynamics:

      P   Pressure: mmHg, atm, dynes/cm^2, kg/m^2, etc.,: units of pressure (*not to be confused with P for period or P for power)

      ΔP   Pressure gradient (change in pressure = $P_2 - P_1$ where P_2 is the distal pressure and P_1 is the proximal pressure): units as above

      Q   Volumetric flow: volume per time, or m^3/sec

      R   Resistance: either electrical or to fluid flow

Note: Caution must be used since many letters can stand for more than one physical quantity. Also pay attention as to whether the letter is uppercase or lower case, since in some cases a capitalized letter indicates a different parameter than a lower case letter.

Appendix O • Equations

Related to Time and Frequency:

1. $Period\ (P)\ =\ \dfrac{1}{frequency\ (f)}$

2. $PD = P*(\#of\ cycles\ in\ pulse)$

3. $PRP\ =\ \dfrac{13\ \mu\sec}{cm}*imaging\ depth\ (cm) = \dfrac{1}{PRF}$

4. $Frame\ time\ =\ PRP\ *\ \dfrac{\#\ lines}{frame} = \dfrac{1}{frame\ rate}$

5. $Duty\ Factor\ =\ \dfrac{PD}{PRP}*100\% = \dfrac{Temporal\ Average\ Intensity\ (TA)}{Pulse\ Average\ Intensity\ (PA)}*100\%$

Related to Amplitude and Power:

1. $Amplitude\ =\ max-mean = mean-min = \dfrac{max-min}{2}$

2. $Power\ \propto\ \left(Amplitude\right)^2$

3. $Intensity = \dfrac{Power}{Beam\ area}$

4.   a) $dB \triangleq 10*\log\left(\dfrac{P_f}{P_i}\right)\ where\ \left(\dfrac{P_f}{P_i}\right)is\ the\ power\ ratio\ (power\ gain\ factor)$

      b) $dB \triangleq 20*\log\left(\dfrac{A_f}{A_i}\right)\ where\ \left(\dfrac{A_f}{A_i}\right)is\ the\ amplitude\ ratio\ (amplitude\ gain\ factor)$

Related to Distance (Physical Dimension):

1. $d = r*t$

2. $\lambda = \dfrac{c}{f}$

3. $SPL = \lambda *\left(\#\ cycles\ in\ pulse\right)$

Related to Circular Dimensional Measurement:

1. $Circle\ circumference = 2\pi r = \pi d$

2. $Circle\ area = \pi r^2$

3. $Circle\ volume = \dfrac{4\pi r^3}{3}$

Related to Resolution:

1. $Axial\ Resolution = \dfrac{SPL}{2}$

2. $Lateral\ Resolution = lateral\ beamwidth$

3. $Elevation\ Resolution = elevation\ beamwidth$

4. $Temporal\ Resolution$ is determined by the acoustic frame rate and the monitor frame rate

5. $Nyquist\ Limit:\ Maximum\ detectable\ frequency\ = \dfrac{Sample\ frequency}{2}$

6. $Contrast\ resolution\ of\ a\ monitor\ =\ 2^n:$

   $Where\ n\ =\ number\ of\ bits\ assigned\ to\ greyscale\ of\ monitor$

Related to Transducers:

1. $NZL = \dfrac{D^2}{4\lambda} \approx \dfrac{D^2 f}{6}$ $\left(D\ must\ be\ in\ mm\ and\ f\ must\ be\ in\ MHz\ to\ use\ the\ approximate\ form\right)$

2. $Beamwidth \approx \dfrac{D}{2}$ (at the focal depth, the beam is approximately half the crystal diameter)

3. $Beamwidth \approx D$ (at twice the focal depth, or $2*NZL$)

4. a) $f_0 = \left(frequency\ of\ the\ drive\ Voltage\ for\ CW\right)$

   b) $f_0 = \dfrac{C_{crytsal}}{2*thickness_{crystal}} \left(for\ PW\right)$

5. $Bandwidth\ (BW)\ =\ upper\ frequency\ corner\ -\ lower\ frequency\ corner$

6. $FBW\ \% = \dfrac{BW}{f_o} * 100\%$

7. $Quality\ (Q)\ factor\ =\ \dfrac{1}{FBW}$

8. $BUF\ (beam\ uniformity\ factor)\ =\ \dfrac{Spatial\ Peak\ Intensity\ (SP)}{Spatial\ Average\ Intensity\ (SA)}$

Related to Properties of Material and Attenuation:

1. $\rho = \dfrac{mass}{volume}$

2. $Z = \rho * c$

3. $\% \ reflection + \% \ transmission = 100\%$

4. $\% \ reflection = \left[\dfrac{Z_2 - Z_1}{Z_2 + Z_1} \right]^2$

5. $R = \dfrac{8\ell\,\eta}{\pi r^4}$

6. $c_i * \sin\left(\theta_t\right) = c_t * \sin\left(\theta_i\right)$

7. $Attenuation\ rate: \approx \dfrac{0.5\ dB}{cm \times MHz} \ \left(soft\ tissue\right)$

$\approx \dfrac{1\ dB}{cm \times MHz} \ \left(muscle\right)$

Related to Hemodynamics and Doppler:

1. $f_{Dop} = \dfrac{2 f_o v \cos\left(\theta\right)}{c}$

2. $f_{Dop}(max) = \dfrac{PRF}{2} \ (without\ aliasing\ by\ Nyquist)$

3. $\Delta P = Q * R \ \ (simplified\ law\ of\ hemodynamics)$

4. $Q = \bar{v} * area \ (continuity\ equation)$

5. $R = \dfrac{8\ell\,\eta}{\pi r^4}$

6. $Q = \dfrac{\Delta P \pi r^4}{8\ell\,\eta} \ \ (Poisieulle's\ law)$

7. $K.E. = \dfrac{1}{2}\rho v^2 \Rightarrow \Delta P \approx 4\left(v_2^2 - v_1^2\right) \approx 4\left(v_2^2\right) \ if \ v_2 \gg v_1$

8. $Hydrostatic\ pressure = mgh \approx 2 \ \dfrac{mmHg}{inch}$

Pegasus Lectures, Inc.

Pegasus Lectures, Inc.

Your resource for a lifetime of learning.

Pegasus Lectures offers a wide array of educational materials:

<u>Exam Sim Suite CD-ROMs</u>

<u>Case Study CD-ROMs</u>

<u>Tutorial CD-ROMs</u>

<u>Videos</u>

<u>Texts</u>

<u>Seminars</u>

- Ultrasound Physics and Instrumentation
- Vascular Physics and Instrumentation
- Cardiovascular Physics and Instrumentation
- Abdomen
- Adult Echocardiography

- Breast Ultrasound
- Musculoskeletal Imaging
- Obstetrics and Gynecology
- Pediatric Echocardiography
- Vascular Technology

For additional information regarding Pegasus Lectures, Inc., please visit our website at:

www.PegasusLectures.com

or call/write us at:

Pegasus Lectures, Inc.
P.O. Box 157
Forney, Texas 75126
PegasusLectures@aol.com

Tel: 972.564.3056
Fax: 972.552.9186